*Mathematics
for Scientists*

Thor A. Bak

University of Copenhagen

Jonas Lichtenberg

Royal Danish College of Education

Mathematics for Scientists

W. A. Benjamin, Inc.

New York   *Amsterdam*

1966

93203

510
B166

Mathematics for Scientists

Copyright © 1966 by W. A. Benjamin, Inc.
All rights reserved
Library of Congress Catalog Card Number 66-12698
Manufactured in the United States of America
The manuscript was put into production on June 1, 1965;
this volume was published on July 22, 1966

W. A. BENJAMIN, INC.
New York, New York 10016

Preface

This book is a revised and somewhat expanded edition of *Videregående Matematik*, the first edition of which appeared in 1960. The Danish book was originally written for a one-year course given by the authors for chemists, biochemists, and M.D.'s doing basic research.

The course for which the book was originally designed had the specific purpose of providing the necessary mathematical background for further studies and research in physical chemistry and biophysics. Since the book has in fact also been used in other courses, we have now added material which we believe will make it more generally useful.

To write a book on mathematics for scientists always presents the problem of finding a reasonable balance between rigor and fundamental understanding on one side, and immediate usability and a sufficient coverage of material on the other. We have attempted to solve this problem by the following procedure: Throughout the book we formulate rather precisely the results which have been obtained even in the cases where the proofs have to be omitted. The way we formulate the results changes somewhat, however, from the beginning of the book, where we use a more rigorous mathematical formulation, to the last part, where to a large extent we use the somewhat looser formulation which has become standard practice in many textbooks of physics and chemistry.

Part 1 contains the material on vectors, tensors, and groups and can be read without any knowledge of calculus. Our experience is that it can be read in a one-semester course meeting two hours a week. Part 2 contains the material on functions of one and several real variables. In this part the concept of a vector is used quite often, and at the end of Chapter 4 matrices and the concept of a tensor are used. Apart from this the volume can be read independently of Part 1, and, combined with a small amount of material from Part 3, it could form the basis of a one-semester course in calculus meeting four hours a week. Part 3 contains the material normally included in books on advanced calculus: series, differential equations, functions of a complex variable, and numerical methods. This part is written so that to a large measure it is independent of the specific formulations given in the other parts, but it does require a knowledge of matrices up to eigenvalue problems and to functions of one and several variables. In our original one-year course which met four hours a week, we read Chapters 1, 3, 4, and 5 and parts of Chapters 6 and 8.

Answers are given to the exercises marked with a star. The book also contains a fair number of worked-out examples, which have been set in the same type as the rest of the book to indicate that we believe they form an essential part of the book. We use the symbol □ to show when an example ends and the main text continues. At the end of each part we give a short list of books which we believe one could profitably read simultaneously with or after this one. Of course, these references by no means form a complete list of books about the subjects discussed.

We are indebted to Drs. Brian Phillips and Peeter Kruus, who initially translated a large part of the book, and to Professor H. Rosenberg, who gave good advice when the manuscript was finally completed and who should not be blamed for remaining errors or obscurities. We are also indebted to Barbara Zeiders for almost unlimited amounts of patience and valuable suggestions on preparation of the manuscript. Finally, we should like to record our gratitude to Mrs. Lise Seifert, who typed the first draft, and to Miss Emmy Christiansen, who typed the final manuscript, and who both did much to keep our spirits up during the process.

Thor A. Bak
Jonas Lichtenberg

Copenhagen, Denmark
January 1966

Contents

Part I

Vectors, Tensors, and Groups

1

Vectors and Tensors

1-1. THE PLANE

Two-Dimensional Vectors

In this section we shall consider some geometric notions in relation
to the plane.   Later on we shall extend these to space.

We define a *proper two-dimensional vector* as a directed line segment
belonging to the given plane.   A vector is determined by its *initial
point* and its *terminal point*.   If those are A and B, respectively, then
the vector is denoted **AB**, while its *length* measured in chosen units is
written $|\mathbf{AB}|$ or just AB.   Often a vector is represented by a single
lower-case letter, such as **p**, in which case the length is written $|\mathbf{p}|$,
or p.   In a diagram the *direction* of a vector is indicated by an arrow-
head at the terminal point.

Two vectors are said to be *equivalent* when one of them can be moved
to coincide with the other by a translation, i.e., when the two vectors
have the same direction and the same length.   In this way the set of
all vectors in the plane is separated into classes of mutually equivalent
vectors.   We will consider equivalent vectors as being equal—as representing the same *free vector*.   Given a vector **a** and a point P, obviously
there will be exactly one vector **PQ**, with its initial point in P, such that

1

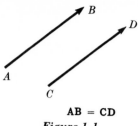

AB = CD

Figure 1-1

$\mathbf{PQ} = \mathbf{a}$. The vector $\mathbf{PQ}$ is said to be the result of *drawing* the vector $\mathbf{a}$ from the point P (Fig. 1-1).

An arbitrary point A is considered a *degenerate vector* $\mathbf{AA}$. A is both the initial and the terminal point of the vector, its length is 0, and it has no direction. All degenerate vectors are considered as being equivalent—as representing the so-called *zero vector* (or *null vector*), which is also denoted $\mathbf{0}$. A *unit vector* is just a vector of length 1. Thus there exists an infinity of different unit vectors.

Multiplication by a Real Number, Addition, and Subtraction

Three mathematical operations will now be defined for (free) vectors: multiplication of a vector by a real number, addition of two vectors, and subtraction of two vectors.

If k is an arbitrary real number and $\mathbf{a}$ an arbitrary vector, then the *product* $k\mathbf{a}$ or $\mathbf{a}k$ is defined to be the zero vector if $k = 0$ or $\mathbf{a} = \mathbf{0}$; in all other cases it is a proper vector with length $|k|\,|\mathbf{a}|$ in the same or opposite direction as $\mathbf{a}$, depending on whether $k > 0$ or $k < 0$. The vector $(-1)\mathbf{a}$ is written simply $-\mathbf{a}$ and is called $\mathbf{a}$'s opposite vector (Fig. 1-2).

If $\mathbf{a}$ and $\mathbf{b}$ are two arbitrary vectors, then the *vector sum* $\mathbf{a} + \mathbf{b}$ is defined in the following manner: $\mathbf{a}$ is drawn from an arbitrary point

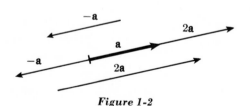

Figure 1-2

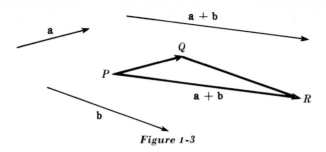

Figure 1-3

P as **PQ**; **b** is then drawn from Q as **QR**. The vector sum **a** + **b** is then **PR** (Fig. 1-3).

With the above-defined mathematical operations, it is easy to see that the same rules hold as those used in calculations with real numbers:

commutative laws: $k\mathbf{a} = \mathbf{a}k$; $\mathbf{a} + \mathbf{b} = \mathbf{b} + \mathbf{a}$.
associative laws: $(kl)\mathbf{a} = k(l\mathbf{a})$; $(\mathbf{a} + \mathbf{b}) + \mathbf{c} = \mathbf{a} + (\mathbf{b} + \mathbf{c})$.
distributive laws: $(k + l)\mathbf{a} = k\mathbf{a} + l\mathbf{a}$; $k(\mathbf{a} + \mathbf{b}) = k\mathbf{a} + k\mathbf{b}$.

Let two given vectors **a** and **b** be drawn from an arbitrary point P such that **PQ** = **a** and **PS** = **b**. The parallelogram $PQRS$ is said to be *spanned* by the vectors **a** and **b**. The diagonal vector **PR** is the sum of the given vectors, while the diagonal vector **QS** is seen to be the unique solution of the vector equation $\mathbf{a} + \mathbf{x} = \mathbf{b}$. This solution is denoted $\mathbf{b} - \mathbf{a} (= \mathbf{b} + (-\mathbf{a}))$ and is called the *difference* between the vectors **b** and **a** (Fig. 1-4).

It follows from the above that it is possible to reduce more complicated vector expressions, just as in calculations with real numbers. There is, however, one marked difference from operations with real

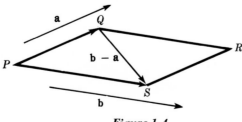

Figure 1-4

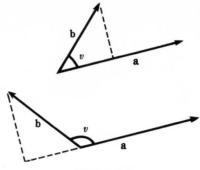

Figure 1-5

numbers.   When multiplying, only one of the factors is of the specified type, i.e., a vector—the other factor is a real number.   The product is still a vector.

Scalar Product

When $\mathbf{a}$ and $\mathbf{b}$ are two arbitrary vectors in the plane, their *scalar product* (*dot product* or *inner product*), $\mathbf{a} \cdot \mathbf{b}$ is defined as a number, which is 0 if one of the vectors is the zero vector; otherwise it is the product of the lengths of the two vectors and the cosine of the angle v between them: $\mathbf{a} \cdot \mathbf{b} = |\mathbf{a}| \, |\mathbf{b}| \cos v$.   The scalar product $\mathbf{a} \cdot \mathbf{a}$ is shortened to $\mathbf{a}^2$; $\mathbf{a}^2 = |\mathbf{a}|^2 = a^2$.   The two vectors $\mathbf{a}$ and $\mathbf{b}$ are said to be *orthogonal* in case $\mathbf{a} \cdot \mathbf{b} = 0$.   If they are both proper vectors, this means that they are at right angles to each other.

The scalar product of two proper vectors $\mathbf{a}$ and $\mathbf{b}$ is seen to be positive when their angle is acute, negative when it is obtuse.   In any case, the absolute value of $\mathbf{a} \cdot \mathbf{b}$ is then equal to the product of $|\mathbf{a}|$ and the length of the projection of $\mathbf{b}$ on $\mathbf{a}$, or the product of $|\mathbf{b}|$ and the length of the projection of $\mathbf{a}$ on $\mathbf{b}$ (Fig. 1-5).

It can be seen easily that the following basic rules apply to the scalar product: $\mathbf{a} \cdot \mathbf{b} = \mathbf{b} \cdot \mathbf{a}$, $(k\mathbf{a}) \cdot \mathbf{b} = k(\mathbf{a} \cdot \mathbf{b})$.   The pure scalar form of

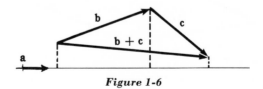

Figure 1-6

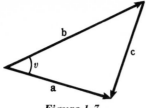

Figure 1-7

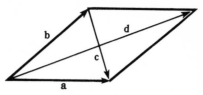

Figure 1-8

the associative law is without meaning, as we have here to consider an expression such as $(\mathbf{a} \cdot \mathbf{b}) \cdot \mathbf{c}$, i.e., the scalar product of a number $(\mathbf{a} \cdot \mathbf{b})$ and a vector. This can be adapted to give two meaningful expressions: $(\mathbf{a} \cdot \mathbf{b})\mathbf{c}$ and $\mathbf{a}(\mathbf{b} \cdot \mathbf{c})$. These are generally different from each other, as they are vectors parallel to $\mathbf{c}$ and $\mathbf{a}$, respectively. However, the distributive law holds: $\mathbf{a} \cdot (\mathbf{b} + \mathbf{c}) = \mathbf{a} \cdot \mathbf{b} + \mathbf{a} \cdot \mathbf{c}$. For $\mathbf{a} = \mathbf{0}$, 0 is obtained on both sides of the equals sign. For $\mathbf{a} \neq \mathbf{0}$ it follows from the fact that the projection of vector $\mathbf{b} + \mathbf{c}$ on $\mathbf{a}$ is equal to the sum of the projections of vectors $\mathbf{b}$ and $\mathbf{c}$ on $\mathbf{a}$ (Fig. 1-6).

Example 1-1. $\mathbf{c}^2 = (\mathbf{a} - \mathbf{b}) \cdot (\mathbf{a} - \mathbf{b}) = \mathbf{a}^2 + \mathbf{b}^2 - 2\mathbf{a} \cdot \mathbf{b}$, or $c^2 = a^2 + b^2 - 2ab \cos v$, which is the law of cosines (Fig. 1-7). $\square$

Example 1-2. $\mathbf{c} \cdot \mathbf{d} = (\mathbf{a} - \mathbf{b}) \cdot (\mathbf{a} + \mathbf{b}) = \mathbf{a}^2 - \mathbf{b}^2$. When $|\mathbf{a}| = |\mathbf{b}|$ the parallelogram is a rhombus, and we obtain $\mathbf{c} \cdot \mathbf{d} = 0$, or the known fact that the diagonals in a rhombus are perpendicular to each other (Fig. 1-8). $\square$

Coordinate Systems

A coordinate system is now introduced in the plane. We shall first consider a *general parallel coordinate system.* Thus we choose as the so-called *base vectors* two arbitrary proper vectors $\mathbf{i}$ and $\mathbf{j}$ which do not lie on the same line. Drawn from a chosen point O, called the *origin* of the coordinate system, they determine the directed *axes* of the coordinate system. These will be called the X-*axis* and the Y-*axis*, respectively. At the same time, a positive sense of rotation in the plane is defined as being from the X-axis to the Y-axis (counterclockwise in Fig. 1-9).

An arbitrary (free) vector $\mathbf{PQ}$ is now uniquely determined by an ordered pair of real numbers (x,y), which gives the *coordinates of the vector:* As $\mathbf{P_1Q_1}$ is the projection parallel to the Y-axis of $\mathbf{PQ}$ on the

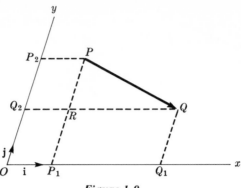

Figure 1-9

X-axis, then the X-*coordinate* (the *abscissa*) of the given vector can be determined from the equation $\mathbf{P}_1\mathbf{Q}_1 = x\mathbf{i}$. In an analogous manner, $\mathbf{P}_2\mathbf{Q}_2$ is drawn as the projection of $\mathbf{PQ}$ parallel to the X-axis on the Y-axis. The Y-*coordinate* (the *ordinate*) of the given vector can then be determined from the equation $\mathbf{P}_2\mathbf{Q}_2 = y\mathbf{j}$; thus we have $\mathbf{PQ} = \mathbf{PR} + \mathbf{RQ} = \mathbf{RQ} + \mathbf{PR} = \mathbf{P}_1\mathbf{Q}_1 + \mathbf{P}_2\mathbf{Q}_2 = x\mathbf{i} + y\mathbf{j}$. The vector $\mathbf{PQ} = (x,y)$ appears therefore as a *linear combination* of the base vectors with the magnitudes of the coefficients determined by the coordinates. $\mathbf{PQ}$ is said to be *resolved* into components along the directions $\mathbf{i}$ and $\mathbf{j}$.

In this book, with a few exceptions, *usual right-angled coordinate systems* will be used. This means that we choose as base vectors unit vectors which are at right angles: $\mathbf{i}^2 = \mathbf{j}^2 = 1$ and $\mathbf{i} \cdot \mathbf{j} = 0$.

It is now easy to express in coordinates the vector operations introduced previously. For $\mathbf{a} = (a_1,a_2)$ and $\mathbf{b} = (b_1,b_2)$, we obtain

$$k\mathbf{a} = k(a_1\mathbf{i} + a_2\mathbf{j}) = (ka_1)\mathbf{i} + (ka_2)\mathbf{j} = (ka_1,ka_2),$$
$$\mathbf{a} \pm \mathbf{b} = (a_1\mathbf{i} + a_2\mathbf{j}) \pm (b_1\mathbf{i} + b_2\mathbf{j}) = (a_1 \pm b_1)\mathbf{i} + (a_2 \pm b_2)\mathbf{j}$$
$$= (a_1 \pm b_1, a_2 \pm b_2),$$
$$\mathbf{a} \cdot \mathbf{b} = (a_1\mathbf{i} + a_2\mathbf{j}) \cdot (b_1\mathbf{i} + b_2\mathbf{j}) = a_1b_1\mathbf{i}^2 + a_2b_2\mathbf{j}^2 + (a_1b_2 + a_2b_1)\mathbf{i} \cdot \mathbf{j}$$
$$= a_1b_1 + a_2b_2.$$

The length of a vector $\mathbf{a} = (a_1,a_2)$ is found from $a = \sqrt{a^2} = \sqrt{\mathbf{a}^2} = \sqrt{a_1^2 + a_2^2}$, and the angle v between vectors $\mathbf{a}$ and $\mathbf{b}$ is found from

$$\cos v = \frac{\mathbf{a} \cdot \mathbf{b}}{|\mathbf{a}|\,|\mathbf{b}|} = \frac{a_1b_1 + a_2b_2}{\sqrt{a_1^2 + a_2^2}\,\sqrt{b_1^2 + b_2^2}}.$$

Finally we have $\mathbf{a} = (\mathbf{a} \cdot \mathbf{i})\mathbf{i} + (\mathbf{a} \cdot \mathbf{j})\mathbf{j}$, as is easily seen from the equation $\mathbf{a} = a_1\mathbf{i} + a_2\mathbf{j}$ by scalar multiplication with $\mathbf{i}$ and $\mathbf{j}$. It is seen here that the special assumption regarding the type of coordinate system is used only in connection with the scalar product.

The coordinates of a point P in the plane can now be defined as the coordinates of the *position vector* $\mathbf{OP}$ from the origin O to the point P. Let the coordinates of two points P and Q be $P = (x_1,y_1)$ and $Q = (x_2,y_2)$; then the coordinates of the vector $\mathbf{PQ}$ are found as the difference between the coordinates of the terminal and initial points of the vector: $\mathbf{PQ} = \mathbf{OQ} - \mathbf{OP} = (x_2,y_2) - (x_1,y_1) = (x_2 - x_1, y_2 - y_1)$. The distance between P and Q is then $PQ = |\mathbf{PQ}| = \sqrt{(x_2 - x_1)^2 + (y_2 - y_1)^2}$ (Fig. 1-10).

Analytic Geometry

Let us consider a straight line l, which contains a point $P_0 = (x_0,y_0)$ and has a normal vector $\mathbf{v} = (a_1,b_1)$. The points $P = (x,y)$ lying on l may be characterized as those for which the scalar product of the vectors $\mathbf{P_0P}$ and $\mathbf{v}$ is 0; $\mathbf{P_0P} \cdot \mathbf{v} = (x - x_0, y - y_0) \cdot (a,b) = a(x - x_0) + b(y - y_0) = 0$, or $ax + by + c = 0$, where $c = -ax_0 - by_0$ (Fig. 1-11). This equation is thus satisfied by the coordinates of all the points on l and by no other points. It is therefore an *equation* of the straight line, while l is the *graph* of the equation. More generally, the graph of an arbitrary equation in x and y, $F(x,y) = 0$, is composed of all the points $P = (x,y)$, the coordinates of which satisfy the equation. If $b \neq 0$ and the line is therefore not parallel to the Y-axis, the equation can be brought into the form $y = ax + q$, where α denotes the *slope* of the line. $(1,\alpha)$ is then a vector parallel to the line.

If a unit vector $\mathbf{n} = (\alpha,\beta)$, $\alpha^2 + \beta^2 = 1$, is used to determine the

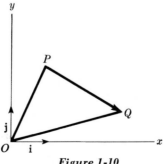

Figure 1-10

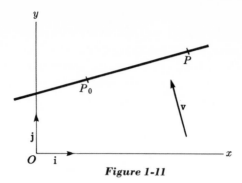

Figure 1-11

equation for l, and if all the terms are gathered on the left side of the equals sign, then the equation is said to be *normalized:* $\alpha x + \beta y + \gamma = 0$. In this case, the distance p from the line to an arbitrary point $P_1 = (x_1, y_1)$ in the plane can be obtained by substituting the coordinates of the point into the left side of the equation: $p = \mathbf{n} \cdot \mathbf{P_0 P_1} = \alpha(x_1 - x_0) + \beta(y_1 - y_0) = \alpha x_1 + \beta y_1 + \gamma$, since (x_0, y_0) satisfies the equation. The distance is thus seen to be determined with a sign corresponding to the direction of $\mathbf{n}$ (Fig. 1-12).

When the straight line l contains a point $P_0 = (x_0, y_0)$ and the vector $\mathbf{u} = (h, k)$, the line can be represented in *parametric form* as follows: $\mathbf{OP} = \mathbf{OP_0} + t\mathbf{u}$, or in the coordinates

$$x = x_0 + ht,$$
$$y = y_0 + kt,$$

where the *parameter* t varies through all real numbers. When in a special case the so-called *slope vector* $\mathbf{u}$ is a unit vector, then t gives the distance on the line from P_0 to the point P. With the elimination of

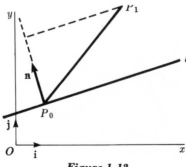

Figure 1-12

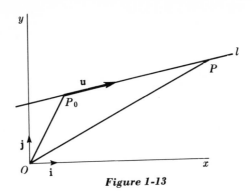

Figure 1-13

the parameter, an equation of the line is obtained in any case (Fig. 1-13).

For $\mathbf{a} = (a_1, a_2)$, an arbitrary vector in the plane, the so-called *cross vector* of $\mathbf{a}$, $\hat{\mathbf{a}}$, is obtained by rotation of $\mathbf{a}$ through $+90°$ in the plane. Expressed in coordinates, $\hat{\mathbf{a}} = (-a_2, a_1)$. The area T of the parallelogram spanned by vectors $\mathbf{a}$ and $\mathbf{b}$ is found as the scalar product of $\hat{\mathbf{a}}$ and $\mathbf{b}$:

$$T = \hat{\mathbf{a}} \cdot \mathbf{b} = -a_2 b_1 + a_1 b_2 = \begin{vmatrix} a_1 & b_1 \\ a_2 & b_2 \end{vmatrix}.$$

The area thus found is positive or negative according as the sense of rotation in the parallelogram determined by the first-mentioned vector is positive or negative (Fig. 1-14).

Changing System of Coordinates

It will often prove advantageous to be able to work in a problem with more than one coordinate system at the same time. One of the

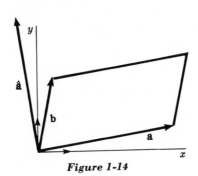

Figure 1-14

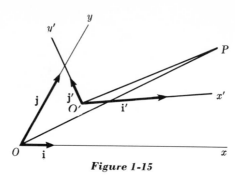

Figure 1-15

first tasks will then be to determine the formulas necessary to change from the "old" to the "new" coordinates, both of which uniquely determine given points and vectors.

We shall first consider two general parallel coordinate systems XY and $X'Y'$, where the origin and base vectors in the *old* (unprimed) *system* are O, $\mathbf{i}$, and $\mathbf{j}$, and in the *new* (primed) *system* are O', $\mathbf{i}'$, and $\mathbf{j}'$. For a vector $\mathbf{v}$ with old coordinates (v_1,v_2) and new ones (v_1',v_2') we have $\mathbf{v} = v_1\mathbf{i} + v_2\mathbf{j} = v_1'\mathbf{i}' + v_2'\mathbf{j}'$.

Now let the coordinates of the new origin and the new base vectors in the old system be $O' = (x_0,y_0)$, $\mathbf{i}' = (a_1,a_2)$, and $\mathbf{j}' = (b_1,b_2)$, respectively. If the vector equation is expressed in old coordinates, then $v_1(1,0) + v_2(0,1) = v_1'(a_1,a_2) + v_2'(b_1,b_2)$, or

$$v_1 = a_1v_1' + b_1v_2',$$
$$v_2 = a_2v_1' + b_2v_2'.$$

These expressions are the desired equations for changing from the new to the old coordinates for vectors. If the opposite is required, then the equations can be solved for v_1' and v_2'.

For the point P with old coordinates (x,y) and new coordinates (x',y'), the equations for changing the coordinates can be found from the vector equation $\mathbf{OP} = \mathbf{OO'} + \mathbf{O'P}$ or $x\mathbf{i} + y\mathbf{j} = \mathbf{OO'} + x'\mathbf{i}' + y'\mathbf{j}'$, which expressed in old coordinates gives (Fig. 1-15)

$$x = x_0 + a_1x' + b_1y',$$
$$y = y_0 + a_2x' + b_2y'.$$

We next consider the special case where both coordinate systems are usual right-angled systems, with the origin and the positive sense of rotation being the same in the two systems. In this case the new system $X'Y'$ is obtained upon rotating the old system XY by an angle θ about O.

The coordinates of the new base vectors in the old system are then $\mathbf{i}' = (\cos \theta, \sin \theta)$ and $\mathbf{j}' = (- \sin \theta, \cos \theta)$. As we have here $(x_0, y_0) = (0,0)$ the same formulas are obtained for changing the coordinates of a vector and of a point (Fig. 1-16):

$$x = x' \cos \theta - y' \sin \theta,$$
$$y = x' \sin \theta + y' \cos \theta.$$

On solving these equations with respect to x' and y', we obtain

$$x' = x \cos \theta + y \sin \theta,$$
$$y' = -x \sin \theta + y \cos \theta.$$

This is obvious, as the unprimed system can equally well be considered as being derived from the primed system by a rotation of $-\theta$, in which case θ is replaced by $-\theta$ in the original formulas, and at the same time the primes are transferred.

Example 1-3. Determine the curve which in a given usual right-angled coordinate system XY has the equation

$$5x^2 + 7y^2 - 2\sqrt{3}\,xy - 32 = 0.$$

In order to remove the "cross" term, $-2\sqrt{3}\,xy$, a new system of coordinates $X'Y'$ is introduced. It is rotated through an angle θ (as yet undetermined) in relation to the given system XY:

$$x = x' \cos \theta - y' \sin \theta,$$
$$y = x' \sin \theta + y' \cos \theta.$$

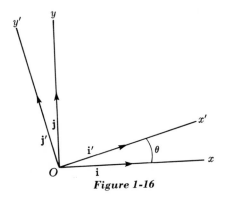

Figure 1-16

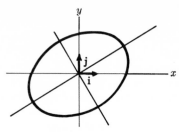

Figure 1-17

Introducing this we find the equation of the given curve in the new coordinate system:

$$5(x' \cos \theta - y' \sin \theta)^2 + 7(x' \sin \theta + y' \cos \theta)^2$$
$$- 2\sqrt{3}(x' \cos \theta - y' \sin \theta)(x' \sin \theta + y' \cos \theta) - 32 = 0,$$

or

$$x'^2(5 \cos^2 \theta + 7 \sin^2 \theta - 2\sqrt{3} \cos \theta \sin \theta)$$
$$+ y'^2(5 \sin^2 \theta + 7 \cos^2 \theta + 2\sqrt{3} \cos \theta \sin \theta)$$
$$+ x'y'(4 \sin \theta \cos \theta - 2\sqrt{3} \cos^2 \theta + 2\sqrt{3} \sin^2 \theta) - 32 = 0.$$

We then choose θ such that

$$2\sqrt{3} \sin^2 \theta + 4 \sin \theta \cos \theta - 2\sqrt{3} \cos^2 \theta = 0,$$

or

$$2 \sin 2\theta - 2\sqrt{3} \cos 2\theta = 0, \qquad \tan 2\theta = \sqrt{3}, \qquad \theta = 30° + p \cdot 90°.$$

With $\theta = 30°$ we obtain the equation $4x'^2 + 8y'^2 - 32 = 0$ or $(x'^2/8) + (y'^2/4) = 1$; this is an ellipse with semiaxes $2\sqrt{2}$ and 2.

The curve under consideration is thus an ellipse with center $(0,0)$, whose major axis makes an angle of $30°$ with the X-axis and has a length of $4\sqrt{2}$, and whose minor axis is 4 (Fig. 1-17).

If we choose $\theta = 120°$ we obtain the equation $8x'^2 + 4y'^2 - 32 = 0$, or $(x'^2/4) + (y'^2/8) = 1$; this represents an ellipse with semiaxes 2 and $2\sqrt{2}$. In the coordinate system the major axis lies on the Y'-axis. This is in complete agreement with the previous case, as the coordinate system now has been rotated $90°$ more than it was previously.

The given curve must of course be situated in the same way in relation to the given coordinate system, no matter how the new system is chosen. $\square$

Exercises

*1. Reduce the following two vector expressions, where A, B, and C are given points in the plane:

(a) $\mathbf{BA} + 2(\mathbf{AB} + \mathbf{CA}) + \mathbf{BC}$.

(b) $3(\mathbf{BC} - \mathbf{BA}) + 2\mathbf{CA} - \mathbf{BC}$.

*2. In the triangle ABC the intersection of the medians is M. O is an arbitrary point in the plane. Express $\mathbf{OM}$ by means of $\mathbf{OA}$, $\mathbf{OB}$, and $\mathbf{OC}$.

*3. O, A, and B are given points in the plane. Describe the set of points P for which it is true that $\mathbf{OP} = x\mathbf{OA} + y\mathbf{OB}$, where x and y are nonnegative real numbers with the sum 1.

4. Show that $\mathbf{AD} \cdot \mathbf{BC} + \mathbf{BD} \cdot \mathbf{CA} + \mathbf{CD} \cdot \mathbf{AB} = 0$ when A, B, C, and D are arbitrary points in the plane. Use this formula to show that the three altitudes of any triangle pass through the same point.

5. O and A are given points in the plane with the distance 3. Describe the following two point sets:

(a) The set of points X in the plane for which it is true that $\mathbf{OX} \cdot \mathbf{OA} = 6$.

(b) The set of points X in the plane for which it is true that $\mathbf{OX} \cdot (\mathbf{OX} - 2\mathbf{OA}) = 7$.

6. In a coordinate system with base vectors $\mathbf{i}$ and $\mathbf{j}$ are given the points $A = (-1,2)$, $B = (4,-1)$, and $C = (2,3)$. Determine the coordinates of vectors $\mathbf{AB}$ and $\mathbf{AC}$, the lengths of these vectors, and the angle between them in each of the two cases given below. Also, find parametric equations of the line AB and—by elimination of the parameter—a usual equation of this line:

(a) $|\mathbf{i}| = |\mathbf{j}| = 1, \mathbf{i} \cdot \mathbf{j} = 0$.

(b) $|\mathbf{i}| = 1, |\mathbf{j}| = 2, \mathbf{i} \cdot \mathbf{j} = 1$.

*7. In a usual right-angled coordinate system are given the points $A = (-1,9)$, $B = (4,-1)$, and $C = (-3,3)$. Find an equation for the circle having C as its center and AB as a tangent.

*8. Given a usual right-angled coordinate system XY, show that the graph of $x^2 + y^2 - 2x - 6y + 1 = 0$ is a circle. Find equations for the tangents from the point $(4,7)$ to this circle.

*9. Find the area of the region which in a usual right-angled coordinate system XY is given by the inequalities $4x + y \geq 13$, $3x - 4y \leq 5$ and $x + 5y \leq 46$.

10. Sketch the graph of the equation

$$(y + 2x + 5 - 3|x + 2| + |x - 3|)(x^2 + y^2 - 16x - 12y + 96) = 0$$

in a usual right-angled coordinate system.

*11. Given a coordinate system $X'Y'$, where $|\mathbf{i}'| = 1$, $|\mathbf{j}'| = 2$, and $\mathbf{i}' \cdot \mathbf{j}' = 1$, find an equation for the straight line passing through the points $(2,1)$ and $(3,2)$ and an equation for the circle with center at $(0,0)$ and radius 1. Also, find the coordinates of the points of intersection between the straight line and the circle.

A usual right-angled coordinate system XY is next introduced, having the same origin and the same sense of rotation as the system $X'Y'$ and with X and X' coinciding. Find equations for the same straight line and the same circle as before, and find the coordinates of their points of intersection. Finally, check the results regarding the points of interesction by means of the transformation formulas.

12. Graph the curve which in a usual right-angled coordinate system XY has the equation $6x^2 + 10y^2 + 4\sqrt{3}\,xy = 48$.

Answers

1. (a) **CA**. (b) **AB**.
2. $\frac{1}{3}(\mathbf{OA} + \mathbf{OB} + \mathbf{OC})$.
3. The line segment AB.
7. $x^2 + y^2 + 6x - 6y - 2 = 0$.
8. $x = 4$ and $7x - 24y + 140 = 0$.
9. 38.
11. $y' = x' - 1$; $x'^2 + 4y'^2 + 2x'y' - 1 = 0$; $(1,0)$ and $(\frac{3}{7}, -\frac{4}{7})$.
    $y = (\sqrt{3}/2)$.
    $(x - 1)$; $x^2 + y^2 = 1$; $(1,0)$ and $(-\frac{1}{7}, -4\sqrt{3}/7)$.

1-2. THE SPACE OF THREE DIMENSIONS

Three-Dimensional Vectors

A three-dimensional vector is defined as a directed line segment in space, i.e., just as a two-dimensional vector, only now we may consider at the same time segments lying in different planes of the three-dimensional space.

The nomenclature for vectors in space is the same as that introduced for vectors in a plane. Also, two equivalent vectors in space, i.e., vectors having the same length and the same direction, are considered as being equal—as representing the same free vector, and a point is still considered as representing the zero vector.

Multiplication of a vector by a real number, addition and subtraction of two vectors, and scalar multiplication of two vectors are defined exactly as before. Thus the basic rules of operation are seen to maintain their validity.

Vector Product

In addition to the scalar product of two (free) vectors, another product is defined for spatial vectors; this is the *vector product* (*cross product* or *outer product*). The scalar product is a number, but the vector product is itself a (free) vector.

Let the two vectors be **a** and **b**. The vector product is then written **a** ✕ **b**. It is equal to the zero vector if either **a** or **b** is equal to the zero vector or if the given vectors are parallel (either in the same or in

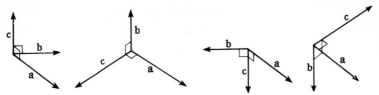

Figure 1-18

opposite directions). In all other cases it is a proper vector with length $|\mathbf{a}|\ |\mathbf{b}|\sin v$, where v is the angle between $\mathbf{a}$ and $\mathbf{b}$. The vector product is also at right angles to both $\mathbf{a}$ and $\mathbf{b}$, in such a manner that the three vectors $\mathbf{a}$, $\mathbf{b}$, and $\mathbf{a}\times\mathbf{b}$ in this order are related by the *right-hand rule* (form a *positive triple*). This means that when drawn from the same point, they lie as the first three fingers on the right hand (Fig. 1-18). In the figure $\mathbf{b}$ describes in all four cases a vector in the plane of the paper, while $\mathbf{a}$ is imagined to point obliquely out toward the reader. The length of the vector product gives the area of the parallelogram spanned by $\mathbf{a}$ and $\mathbf{b}$.

The following basic rules of operation can easily be seen to hold for the vector product $\mathbf{a}\times\mathbf{b}=-\mathbf{b}\times\mathbf{a}$; $(k\mathbf{a})\times\mathbf{b}=k(\mathbf{a}\times\mathbf{b})$. The pure vector form of the associative law is not valid. Let, for example, $\mathbf{a}$ and $\mathbf{b}$ be two unit vectors perpendicular to each other. In this case $(\mathbf{a}\times\mathbf{a})\times\mathbf{b}=0\times\mathbf{b}=0$, but $\mathbf{a}\times(\mathbf{a}\times\mathbf{b})=-\mathbf{b}$ (Fig. 1-19).

The distributive laws, however, can be shown to apply: $\mathbf{a}\times(\mathbf{b}+\mathbf{c})=\mathbf{a}\times\mathbf{b}+\mathbf{a}\times\mathbf{c}$. With the use of the modified commutative law, it then follows immediately that $(\mathbf{b}+\mathbf{c})\times\mathbf{a}=\mathbf{b}\times\mathbf{a}+\mathbf{c}\times\mathbf{a}$. Using the distributive laws, it is seen that vector expressions of more than one term are multiplied vectorially in the usual way; only now it is necessary to ensure that the given order of the factors is maintained, as a change in the order of the two factors necessitates a change of sign.

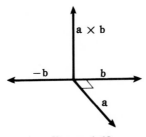

Figure 1-19

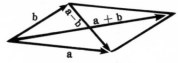

Figure 1-20

Example 1-4. (a − b) ✕ (a − b) = a ✕ a − a ✕ b − b ✕ a + b ✕ b = 0 − a ✕ b + a ✕ b + 0 = 0. This is evident, as the two factors are parallel vectors (or **0**). ☐

Example 1-5. (a − b) ✕ (a + b) = a ✕ a + a ✕ b − b ✕ a − b ✕ b = 2a ✕ b. The length of the given vector product represents the area of the parallelogram spanned by vectors (a − b) and (a + b) and is thus double the area of the parallelogram spanned by a and b (Fig. 1-20). ☐

Coordinate Systems

A coordinate system is now introduced in space. Here we shall also first consider a *general parallel coordinate system;* i.e., we shall choose as base vectors three proper vectors **i, j,** and **k**, which may not, however, lie in the same plane. The base vectors are drawn from an arbitrarily chosen origin O; they thus define the directed axes X, Y, and Z of the coordinate system. An arbitrary vector **PQ** is now uniquely determined by its coordinates (x,y,z) as **PQ** = x**i** + y**j** + z**k** (Fig. 1-21).

We shall in the following description restrict ourselves to considering *usual right-angled right-handed coordinate systems*, or, briefly, orthogonal right-handed coordinate systems. This means that **i, j,** and **k**

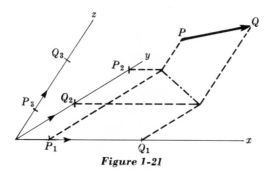

Figure 1-21

will be unit vectors perpendicular to each other, and in the above-mentioned order form a positive triple. In this case we have $\mathbf{i} \times \mathbf{j} = \mathbf{k}$, $\mathbf{j} \times \mathbf{k} = \mathbf{i}$, and $\mathbf{k} \times \mathbf{i} = \mathbf{j}$.

The mathematical operations introduced can now be easily expressed in the coordinate system. When $\mathbf{a} = (a_1, a_2, a_3)$ and $\mathbf{b} = (b_1, b_2, b_3)$, then:

$$ka = k(a_1\mathbf{i} + a_2\mathbf{j} + a_3\mathbf{k}) = ka_1\mathbf{i} + ka_2\mathbf{j} + ka_3\mathbf{k} = (ka_1, ka_2, ka_3),$$

$$\begin{aligned}
\mathbf{a} \pm \mathbf{b} &= (a_1\mathbf{i} + a_2\mathbf{j} + a_3\mathbf{k}) \pm (b_1\mathbf{i} + b_2\mathbf{j} + b_3\mathbf{k}) \\
&= (a_1 \pm b_1)\mathbf{i} + (a_2 \pm b_2)\mathbf{j} + (a_3 \pm b_3)\mathbf{k} \\
&= (a_1 \pm b_1, a_2 \pm b_2, a_3 \pm b_3),
\end{aligned}$$

$$\begin{aligned}
\mathbf{a} \cdot \mathbf{b} &= (a_1\mathbf{i} + a_2\mathbf{j} + a_3\mathbf{k}) \cdot (b_1\mathbf{i} + b_2\mathbf{j} + b_3\mathbf{k}) \\
&= a_1b_1\mathbf{i}^2 + a_1b_2\mathbf{i} \cdot \mathbf{j} + a_1b_3\mathbf{i} \cdot \mathbf{k} + \cdots = a_1b_1 + a_2b_2 + a_3b_3,
\end{aligned}$$

$$\begin{aligned}
\mathbf{a} \times \mathbf{b} &= (a_1\mathbf{i} + a_2\mathbf{j} + a_3\mathbf{k}) \times (b_1\mathbf{i} + b_2\mathbf{j} + b_3\mathbf{k}) \\
&= a_1b_1\mathbf{i} \times \mathbf{i} + a_1b_2\mathbf{i} \times \mathbf{j} + a_1b_3\mathbf{i} \times \mathbf{k} + a_2b_1\mathbf{j} \times \mathbf{i} + a_2b_2\mathbf{j} \times \mathbf{j} \\
&\quad + a_2b_3\mathbf{j} \times \mathbf{k} + a_3b_1\mathbf{k} \times \mathbf{i} + a_3b_2\mathbf{k} \times \mathbf{j} + a_3b_3\mathbf{k} \times \mathbf{k} \\
&= (a_2b_3 - a_3b_2)\mathbf{i} + (a_3b_1 - a_1b_3)\mathbf{j} + (a_1b_2 - a_2b_1)\mathbf{k} \\
&= \left(\begin{vmatrix} a_2 & a_3 \\ b_2 & b_3 \end{vmatrix}, \begin{vmatrix} a_3 & a_1 \\ b_3 & b_1 \end{vmatrix}, \begin{vmatrix} a_1 & a_2 \\ b_1 & b_2 \end{vmatrix} \right).
\end{aligned}$$

The length a of vector $\mathbf{a}$ is obtained from $a = |\mathbf{a}| = \sqrt{\mathbf{a} \cdot \mathbf{a}} = \sqrt{a_1{}^2 + a_2{}^2 + a_3{}^2}$. The angle v between vectors $\mathbf{a}$ and $\mathbf{b}$ is obtained from

$$\cos v = \frac{\mathbf{a} \cdot \mathbf{b}}{|\mathbf{a}| \, |\mathbf{b}|} = \frac{a_1b_1 + a_2b_2 + a_3b_3}{\sqrt{a_1{}^2 + a_2{}^2 + a_3{}^2} \sqrt{b_1{}^2 + b_2{}^2 + b_3{}^2}}.$$

Finally we have $\mathbf{a} = (\mathbf{a} \cdot \mathbf{i})\mathbf{i} + (\mathbf{a} \cdot \mathbf{j})\mathbf{j} + (\mathbf{a} \cdot \mathbf{k})\mathbf{k}$, as is easily seen from the equation $\mathbf{a} = a_1\mathbf{i} + a_2\mathbf{j} + a_3\mathbf{k}$ by scalar multiplication with $\mathbf{i}$, $\mathbf{j}$, and $\mathbf{k}$.

It is seen here that the special assumption about the type of coordinate system (usual right-angled right-handed system) is used only in connection with the scalar and the vector products, and that the right-handed nature of the system only has significance for the vector product.

The coordinates of a point P in space may now be defined as the coordinates of the position vector $\mathbf{OP}$ of the point P. If $P = (x_1, y_1, z_1)$ and $Q = (x_2, y_2, z_2)$, then $\mathbf{PQ} = (x_2 - x_1, y_2 - y_1, z_2 - z_1)$, and therefore the distance between the two points is

$$PQ = |\mathbf{PQ}| = \sqrt{(x_2 - x_1)^2 + (y_2 - y_1)^2 + (z_2 - z_1)^2}.$$

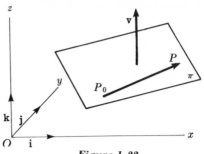

Figure 1-22

Analytic Geometry

Consider a plane π which contains the point $P_0 = (x_0, y_0, z_0)$ and has a normal vector $\mathbf{v} = (a, b, c)$ (Fig. 1-22). Then it is a characteristic property of those points $P = (x, y, z)$ which lie in π that the scalar product of the vectors $\mathbf{P_0 P}$ and $\mathbf{v}$ is 0:

$$\mathbf{P_0 P} \cdot \mathbf{v} = (x - x_0)a + (y - y_0)b + (z - z_0)c = 0,$$

or $ax + by + cz + d = 0$, where $d = -ax_0 - by_0 - cz_0$. The equation obtained is satisfied only by the coordinates of the points lying in π. It is therefore called an *equation* of this plane, while conversely π is the *graph* of the equation. More generally, the graph of an arbitrary equation in x, y, and z, $F(x, y, z) = 0$, is composed of all the points P in space the coordinates of which, (x, y, z), satisfy the equation considered.

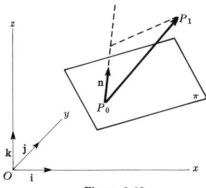

Figure 1-23

When a unit vector $\mathbf{n} = (\alpha, \beta, \gamma)$, $\alpha^2 + \beta^2 + \gamma^2 = 1$, is used as a normal vector for determination of the equation for π, and when all the terms are gathered on the left side of the equals sign, the equation is said to be *normalized*: $\alpha x + \beta y + \gamma z + \delta = 0$ (Fig. 1-23). In this case, the distance p from the plane to an arbitrary point $P_1 = (x_1, y_1, z_1)$ in space is obtained by substituting the coordinates of the point in the left side of the equation:

$$p = \mathbf{n} \cdot \mathbf{P_0 P_1} = \alpha(x_1 - x_0) + \beta(y_1 - y_0) + \gamma(z_1 - z_0)$$
$$= \alpha x_1 + \beta y_1 + \gamma z_1 + \delta.$$

The distance is obtained with a sign corresponding to the direction of $\mathbf{n}$.

When the plane π is considered to be determined by containing the point $P_0 = (x_0, y_0, z_0)$ and the two proper vectors $\mathbf{v}_1 = (h_1, k_1, j_1)$ and $\mathbf{v}_2 = (h_2, k_2, j_2)$, which do not lie on the same line, then a *parametric equation* of the plane is obtained in the following manner: $\mathbf{OP} = \mathbf{OP_0} + t_1 \mathbf{v}_1 + t_2 \mathbf{v}_2$, or, in coordinates,

$$x = x_0 + t_1 h_1 + t_2 h_2,$$
$$y = y_0 + t_1 k_1 + t_2 k_2,$$
$$z = z_0 + t_1 j_1 + t_2 j_2,$$

where the *parameters* t_1 and t_2 vary through all the real numbers independent of each other. (t_1, t_2) gives the coordinates of the point P in π in a plane system of coordinates with origin P_0 and base vectors $\mathbf{v}_1$ and $\mathbf{v}_2$. Upon elimination of the parameters, an equation of the plane is obtained. It can, of course, be found directly, if the vector $\mathbf{v}_1 \times \mathbf{v}_2$ is used as a normal vector (Fig. 1-24).

A *parametric equation* of a straight line l which passes through the

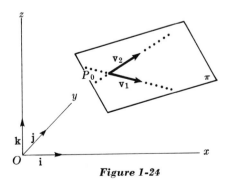

Figure 1-24

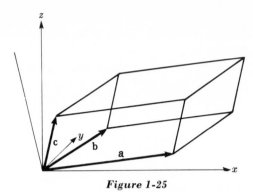

Figure 1-25

point $P_0 = (x_0, y_0, z_0)$ and contains the proper vector $\mathbf{u} = (h, k, j)$ is obtained as $\mathbf{OP} = \mathbf{OP_0} + t\mathbf{u}$, or, in coordinates,

$$x = x_0 + th,$$
$$y = y_0 + tk,$$
$$z = z_0 + tj,$$

where the parameter t varies through all the real numbers. On elimination of the parameter, no matter how this is done, two equations are obtained, each of which represents a plane perpendicular to one of the coordinate planes. The intersection of the two planes is then the given straight line l.

Some Vector Identities

Let us consider three vectors $\mathbf{a}$, $\mathbf{b}$, and $\mathbf{c}$, which do not lie in the same plane, and which are drawn from the origin O of the coordinate system. We then wish to find the volume V of the parallelepiped spanned by these vectors.

The area of the base spanned by $\mathbf{a}$ and $\mathbf{b}$ is $|\mathbf{a} \times \mathbf{b}|$. The corresponding altitude is then the projection of $\mathbf{c}$ on the normal of the base. As the vector $\mathbf{a} \times \mathbf{b}$ has exactly this direction, then $V = (\mathbf{a} \times \mathbf{b}) \cdot \mathbf{c}$. In this way the volume is automatically obtained with a sign, which is seen to be positive only when the vectors $\mathbf{a}$, $\mathbf{b}$, and $\mathbf{c}$ form a positive triple (Fig. 1-25).

From these observations the following rules are deduced:

$$(\mathbf{a} \times \mathbf{b}) \cdot \mathbf{c} = (\mathbf{b} \times \mathbf{c}) \cdot \mathbf{a} = (\mathbf{c} \times \mathbf{a}) \cdot \mathbf{b} = -(\mathbf{c} \times \mathbf{b}) \cdot \mathbf{a}$$
$$= -(\mathbf{b} \times \mathbf{a}) \cdot \mathbf{c} = -(\mathbf{a} \times \mathbf{c}) \cdot \mathbf{b}.$$

We obtain especially, $(\mathbf{a} \times \mathbf{b}) \cdot \mathbf{c} = (\mathbf{b} \times \mathbf{c}) \cdot \mathbf{a} = \mathbf{a} \cdot (\mathbf{b} \times \mathbf{c})$, which is written [abc] and is called the *scalar triple product* (or *box product*) of vectors $\mathbf{a}$, $\mathbf{b}$, and $\mathbf{c}$.

In connection with this, two more formulas are presented:

$$\mathbf{a} \times (\mathbf{b} \times \mathbf{c}) = (\mathbf{a} \cdot \mathbf{c})\mathbf{b} - (\mathbf{a} \cdot \mathbf{b})\mathbf{c},$$
$$(\mathbf{a} \times \mathbf{b}) \times \mathbf{c} = -(\mathbf{b} \cdot \mathbf{c})\mathbf{a} + (\mathbf{a} \cdot \mathbf{c})\mathbf{b}.$$

The proofs can be easily obtained by introducing coordinates. Incidentally, it is immediately clear that the vector $\mathbf{a} \times (\mathbf{b} \times \mathbf{c})$ may be written as a linear combination of vectors $\mathbf{b}$ and $\mathbf{c}$; if $\mathbf{b}$ and $\mathbf{c}$ are parallel or if only one of them is $\mathbf{0}$, then $\mathbf{0}$ is obtained on both sides of the equals sign. In all other cases, $(\mathbf{b} \times \mathbf{c})$ will be perpendicular to the plane containing $\mathbf{b}$ and $\mathbf{c}$; hence $\mathbf{a} \times (\mathbf{b} \times \mathbf{c})$ must be a vector in this plane. The second formula is derived from the first using the modified commutative law.

Changing System of Coordinates

Just as in the plane, it will also often be practical in space to be able to work at the same time with several coordinate systems in a given problem.

Here we shall also first consider two general parallel coordinate systems XYZ and $X'Y'Z'$, called, respectively, the "old" and the "new" system. They have the origin and the base vectors O, $\mathbf{i}$, $\mathbf{j}$, $\mathbf{k}$ and O', $\mathbf{i}'$, $\mathbf{j}'$, $\mathbf{k}'$, respectively.

Let the coordinates of O', $\mathbf{i}'$, $\mathbf{j}'$, and $\mathbf{k}'$ in the old system be $O' = (x_0, y_0, z_0)$, $\mathbf{i}' = (a_1, a_2, a_3)$, $\mathbf{j}' = (b_1, b_2, b_3)$, and $\mathbf{k}' = (c_1, c_2, c_3)$. Then vector $\mathbf{v}$ with old coordinates (v_1, v_2, v_3) and new coordinates (v'_1, v'_2, v'_3) will have the transformation formulas

$$v_1 = a_1 v'_1 + b_1 v'_2 + c_1 v'_3,$$
$$v_2 = a_2 v'_1 + b_2 v'_2 + c_2 v'_3,$$
$$v_3 = a_3 v'_1 + b_3 v'_2 + c_3 v'_3.$$

Similarly, for the point P with old coordinates (x,y,z) and new coordinates (x',y',z'), these will be (Fig. 1-26)

$$x = x_0 + a_1 x' + b_1 y' + c_1 z',$$
$$y = y_0 + a_2 x' + b_2 y' + c_2 z',$$
$$z = z_0 + a_3 x' + b_3 y' + c_3 z'.$$

In the special case when both systems are usual right-angled coordinate systems with a common origin O, the new system $X'Y'Z'$ can be

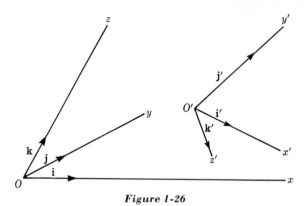

Figure 1-26

obtained entirely by rotation of the old system XYZ about O, combined with a reflection in a plane through O in the case when the one system is right- and the other left-handed (Fig. 1-27).

If we designate the old coordinates of the new base vectors $\mathbf{i}' = (\alpha_1,\alpha_2,\alpha_3)$, $\mathbf{j}' = (\beta_1,\beta_2,\beta_3)$, and $\mathbf{k}' = (\gamma_1,\gamma_2,\gamma_3)$, then we have, for example, $\alpha_1{}^2 + \alpha_2{}^2 + \alpha_3{}^2 = 1$; $\alpha_1\beta_1 + \alpha_2\beta_2 + \alpha_3\beta_3 = 0$, and $\alpha_1\gamma_1 + \alpha_2\gamma_2 + \alpha_3\gamma_3 = 0$. As $(x_0,y_0,z_0) = (0,0,0)$, the same transformation formulas will be obtained for both vector and point coordinates:

$$x = \alpha_1 x' + \beta_1 y' + \gamma_1 z',$$
$$y = \alpha_2 x' + \beta_2 y' + \gamma_2 z',$$
$$z = \alpha_3 x' + \beta_3 y' + \gamma_3 z'.$$

The solution of these equations with respect to x', y', z' can be obtained very easily. On multiplying the three equations by α_1, α_2, α_3, respectively, and then adding, we obtain, after using the above-mentioned equations:

$$x' = \alpha_1 x + \alpha_2 y + \alpha_3 z;$$

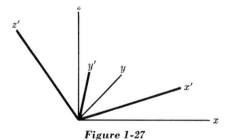

Figure 1-27

analogously we find

$$y' = \beta_1 x + \beta_2 y + \beta_3 z,$$
$$z' = \gamma_1 x + \gamma_2 y + \gamma_3 z.$$

Example 1-6. Determine the surface which in an orthogonal right-handed coordinate system XYZ has the equation

$$5x^2 + 2y^2 + 2z^2 - 2xy + 4yz - 2zx - 6 = 0.$$

This problem is solved in analogy with the previously considered plane problem; thus the cross terms are removed by introduction of a new coordinate system $X'Y'Z'$, which is rotated in a suitable manner relative to the given coordinate system. As we shall later give a systematic treatment of this problem, we shall omit here the rather long calculations which the direct method leads to, and content ourselves with discussing the solution.

The new base vectors introduced are $\mathbf{i}' = (1/\sqrt{3}, 1/\sqrt{3}, 1/\sqrt{3})$, $\mathbf{j}' = (2/\sqrt{6}, -1/\sqrt{6}, -1/\sqrt{6})$, and $\mathbf{k}' = \mathbf{i}' \times \mathbf{j}' = (0, 1/\sqrt{2}, -1/\sqrt{2})$. These determine the new coordinate system. The expressions

$$x = \frac{1}{\sqrt{3}} x' + \frac{2}{\sqrt{6}} y' + 0z',$$

$$y = \frac{1}{\sqrt{3}} x' - \frac{1}{\sqrt{6}} y' + \frac{1}{\sqrt{2}} z',$$

$$z = \frac{1}{\sqrt{3}} x' - \frac{1}{\sqrt{6}} y' - \frac{1}{\sqrt{2}} z'$$

are next introduced into the given equation, whereby the equation of the surface in the new system is obtained. Upon reduction this becomes $3x'^2 + 6y'^2 + 0z'^2 - 6 = 0$, or $(x'^2/2) + (y'^2/1) = 1$. In the $X'Y'$-plane this equation represents an ellipse with center at the origin, major axis on the X'-axis, and semiaxes $\sqrt{2}$ and 1. As the equation does not contain the Z'-coordinate, it will be satisfied by all points in space which after projection in the direction of the Z'-axis on the $X'Y'$-plane fall on this ellipse. The equation therefore represents an elliptic cylinder, with the ellipse obtained as directrix and with generators parallel to the Z'-axis.

In the original coordinate system, the generators have the direction given by the vector $(0, 1/\sqrt{2}, -1/\sqrt{2})$. The plane of the directrix is perpendicular to this, with its center at O and its major axis containing the vector $(1/\sqrt{3}, 1/\sqrt{3}, 1/\sqrt{3})$. $\square$

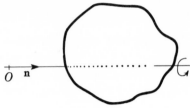

Figure 1-28

Exercises

1. Given an arbitrary tetrahedron $ABCD$ and some point O, show by calculations with the four space vectors **OA**, **OB**, **OC**, and **OD** that all the three line segments joining the midpoints of two opposite edges of the tetrahedron bisect each other.

2. Given an arbitrary tetrahedron $ABCD$ and some point O, show by calculations with the four space vectors **OA**, **OB**, **OC**, and **OD** that if it is true that two pairs of opposite edges are at right angles to each other, it is also true for the third pair.

*3. A rigid body rotates with angular velocity ω around a fixed axis through the point O. **n** is a unit vector on the axis directed so that it determines a right-hand screw together with the sense of rotation (Fig. 1-28). Find a vector expression for the velocity of an arbitrary point P of the rotating body.

*4. Find the volume of the polyhedron determined by the inequalities $0 \le x$, $0 \le y \le 5$, $0 \le z$, $x + z \le 8$, and $x + 2y + 3z \ge 6$.

*5. Given the points $A = (4,3,5)$, $B = (6,0,0)$, $C = (0,4,0)$, and $D = (0,0,2)$, find the distance between A and the plane BCD. Also find the projection of A into the plane.

*6. Find the distance between the point $(3,4,4)$ and the line $(x,y,z) = (4 - 3t, 1 + 2t, 2t)$.

*7. Given the points $A = (6,0,3)$, $B = (10,-1,2)$, $C = (7,-10,8)$, and $D = (5,-7,6)$, find the shortest distance between the lines AB and CD.

*8. Determine the angle between the planes $x - y + z = 1$ and $2x - y - 2z = 4$. Also find parametric equations for the intersection of the two planes.

9. Prove the validity of the formula

$$(\mathbf{a} \times \mathbf{b}) \cdot (\mathbf{c} \times \mathbf{d}) = \begin{vmatrix} \mathbf{a} \cdot \mathbf{c} & \mathbf{b} \cdot \mathbf{c} \\ \mathbf{a} \cdot \mathbf{d} & \mathbf{b} \cdot \mathbf{d} \end{vmatrix}.$$

10. Find an equation of the cylindrical surface of rotation which has radius 1 and axis $(x,y,z) = (t,2t,2t)$.

Answers

3. $\omega \mathbf{n} \times \mathbf{OP}$.

4. 154.

5. $5; (\frac{18}{7}, \frac{6}{7}, \frac{5}{7})$.

6. 3.

7. 3.

8. $78.9°; (x,y,z) = (3 + 3t, 2 + 4t, t)$, for example.

1-3. VECTORS AND SCALARS

Plane Geometry as a Special Case of Solid Geometry

After this short treatment of some important concepts in plane and solid geometry, we shall now try to extend even further the concept of a vector.

However, it must first be pointed out that the whole topic of plane analytic geometry can be considered as a special case of solid geometry in which we deal with quantities that are never outside the XY-plane. The coordinates of vectors and points are then all of the form $(a_1,a_2,0)$. The scalar product of two vectors is therefore calculated (in a usual right-angled system) as a sum of only two terms. The vector product of two vectors never comes into consideration, as this requires operating outside the XY-plane. The equation $ax + by + c = 0$ still represents a plane. But as long as we limit ourselves to considering points in the XY-plane only, the equation represents a straight line, namely, the intersection between the plane under consideration and the XY-plane.

The following considerations formulated for space may in an analogous way be applied to the plane.

Representation of Vectors

A vector in space was defined as a directed line segment. On introduction of a coordinate system it was represented by an ordered triple of real numbers, and in such a way that equivalent (equal) vectors were represented by the same ordered triple, while nonequivalent vectors were represented by different ordered triples. We may also say that by introducing a coordinate system we established a one-to-one correspondence between the set of free vectors in space and the set of ordered triples of real numbers.

The same vector will, however, generally be represented by different ordered triples in different coordinate systems. The relation between these is given by the transformation formulas derived earlier.

An ordered triple (a_1,a_2,a_3) without specification of a system of coordinates therefore does not represent any definite vector. The triple will certainly give a vector in each system of coordinates, but it will not be the same vector in different coordinate systems: The vectors considered all have the same coordinates in their respective systems and will therefore have different directions and lengths corresponding to the different base vectors.

In a system of coordinates which has been defined in advance, however, (a_1, a_2, a_3) represents a definite vector. Only in other systems will this vector "dress" in other triples.

Scalars. The Scalar Product

The scalar product of two vectors was defined as the product of the lengths of the two vectors and the cosine of the angle between them. It is immediately clear that this quantity (a so-called *scalar*) is independent of the system of coordinates in which the vectors are described.

If on the other hand, we had defined relative to each system of coordinates the scalar product of two given vectors as the sum of the products of the corresponding coordinates of the given vectors, then it would have been necessary to ascertain if the number so obtained for the two given vectors was independent of the system of coordinates in which the vectors were described—in other words, whether it really was a scalar, and thus invariant under arbitrary (linear) transformation of coordinates.

As the expression used for the calculation of the scalar product, as mentioned before, generally is valid only for usual right-angled systems of coordinates, the product sum will in fact only be invariant as long as we limit ourselves to such systems. When we define the scalar product analytically, we can thus only allow rotations and translations of an originally given usual right-angled system, possibly combined with a reflection, which is equivalent to a shift from a right-handed to a left-handed system or vice versa.

The proof for the invariance can in this case be obtained by direct calculation, in which the "orthonormality" of the new base vectors is of course made use of but which is not affected by whether the base vectors form a positive triple or do not. With the use of the transformation formulas derived earlier, we obtain, as desired, $a_1 b_1 + a_2 b_2 + a_3 b_3 = a_1' b_1' + a_2' b_2' + a_3' b_3'$.

As a special result we obtain $a_1^2 + a_2^2 + a_3^2 = a_1'^2 + a_2'^2 + a_3'^2$, which is geometrically quite clear, as the number so obtained simply gives the square of the length of the vector concerned. But although the sum of the squares of the coordinates of a vector is invariant under rigid movements and reflections of the usual right-angled system, this is not true, for example, for the sum of the coordinates themselves. If we thus consider the vector which in a given coordinate system has coordinates (1,1,0), then with a rotation of 30° of the system about the

Z-axis, it gets the new coordinates

$$\left(\frac{\sqrt{3}}{2} + \frac{1}{2}, \frac{\sqrt{3}}{2} - \frac{1}{2}, 0\right)$$

and

$$1 + 1 + 0 \neq \left(\frac{\sqrt{3}}{2} + \frac{1}{2}\right) + \left(\frac{\sqrt{3}}{2} - \frac{1}{2}\right) + 0$$

(while of course

$$1^2 + 1^2 + 0^2 = \left(\frac{\sqrt{3}}{2} + \frac{1}{2}\right)^2 + \left(\frac{\sqrt{3}}{2} - \frac{1}{2}\right)^2 + 0^2\right).$$

Vectors. The Vector Product

Let us next consider the vector product, limiting ourselves from the outset to consideration of usual right-angled coordinate systems. The length of the vector product is defined geometrically without reference to the arbitrary system of coordinates used, but in determining its direction use is made of the notion of right-handedness, which is a property of the coordinate system.

If we now require that any three proper vectors $\mathbf{a}$, $\mathbf{b}$, and $\mathbf{a} \times \mathbf{b}$ must always form a positive triple, regardless of the type of coordinate system, then the expression for the coordinates of a vector product derived earlier can be valid only for right-handed systems:

$$\mathbf{a} \times \mathbf{b} = (a_1\mathbf{i} + a_2\mathbf{j} + a_3\mathbf{k}) \times (b_1\mathbf{i} + b_2\mathbf{j} + b_3\mathbf{k})$$

$$= \begin{vmatrix} a_2 & a_3 \\ b_2 & b_3 \end{vmatrix} \mathbf{j} \times \mathbf{k} + \begin{vmatrix} a_3 & a_1 \\ b_3 & b_1 \end{vmatrix} \mathbf{k} \times \mathbf{i} + \begin{vmatrix} a_1 & a_2 \\ b_1 & b_2 \end{vmatrix} \mathbf{i} \times \mathbf{j}$$

$$= \pm \left(\begin{vmatrix} a_2 & a_3 \\ b_2 & b_3 \end{vmatrix}, \begin{vmatrix} a_3 & a_1 \\ b_3 & b_1 \end{vmatrix}, \begin{vmatrix} a_1 & a_2 \\ b_1 & b_2 \end{vmatrix} \right),$$

where the sign refers to right- and left-handed systems, respectively.

If, on the other hand, we decide that the formulas for the coordinates with positive sign be the definition of the vector product of $\mathbf{a}$ and $\mathbf{b}$, then this will still give the coordinates of the same vector in the case of all usual right-angled right-handed systems. If we go over to a left-handed system, it will, however, represent the opposite vector. This result is often summarized by saying that the vector product is a *pseudovector*.

These relations are, however, unimportant as long as we limit ourselves to usual right-angled right-handed systems. Using the above-mentioned formula (with positive sign) in different systems, we get triples representing the same vector in the respective systems. The proof of this can of course also be obtained by direct calculation. Using the transformation formulas, we obtain

$$\begin{vmatrix} a_2 & a_3 \\ b_2 & b_3 \end{vmatrix} = \alpha_1 \begin{vmatrix} a_2' & a_3' \\ b_2' & b_3' \end{vmatrix} + \beta_1 \begin{vmatrix} a_3' & a_1' \\ b_3' & b_1' \end{vmatrix} + \gamma_1 \begin{vmatrix} a_1' & a_2' \\ b_1' & b_2' \end{vmatrix},$$

$$\begin{vmatrix} a_3 & a_1 \\ b_3 & b_1 \end{vmatrix} = \alpha_2 \begin{vmatrix} a_2' & a_3' \\ b_2' & b_3' \end{vmatrix} + \beta_2 \begin{vmatrix} a_3' & a_1' \\ b_3' & b_1' \end{vmatrix} + \gamma_2 \begin{vmatrix} a_1' & a_2' \\ b_1' & b_2' \end{vmatrix},$$

$$\begin{vmatrix} a_1 & a_2 \\ b_1 & b_2 \end{vmatrix} = \alpha_3 \begin{vmatrix} a_2' & a_3' \\ b_2' & b_3' \end{vmatrix} + \beta_3 \begin{vmatrix} a_3' & a_1' \\ b_3' & b_1' \end{vmatrix} + \gamma_3 \begin{vmatrix} a_1' & a_2' \\ b_1' & b_2' \end{vmatrix},$$

as desired.

If we now again consider both right- and left-handed systems, we see that the double vector product $(\mathbf{a} \times \mathbf{b}) \times \mathbf{c}$, which is the vector product of a pseudovector and a vector, is a "pseudo-pseudovector," i.e., a usual vector which is in agreement with the formulas developed earlier (p. 21).

The box product $(\mathbf{a} \times \mathbf{b}) \cdot \mathbf{c}$, as the scalar product of a pseudovector and a vector, is a *pseudoscalar*, which retains its value in all right-handed systems but changes sign with transformation to a left-handed system, if we use the coordinate definition of the vector product.

With this, we shall for the present end our study of three-dimensional vectors, in order to consider a generalization of the notion of a vector to an arbitrary number of dimensions.

1-4.   N-DIMENSIONAL VECTORS

Definition of a Vector

As we are now attempting to extend the notion of a vector to an arbitrary number of dimensions, it is clear that a purely geometric definition is impossible.

Instead we shall take as a starting point the previously developed possibility of representing three-dimensional vectors by ordered triples. A *vector in N-dimensional space* is defined as an ordered N-tuple of real numbers. For the N-dimensional vector $\mathbf{a} = (a_1, a_2, \ldots, a_N)$, the real number a_i is called the *ith coordinate* or *component*. Two vectors $\mathbf{a} = (a_1, a_2, \ldots, a_N)$ and $\mathbf{b} = (b_1, b_2, \ldots, b_N)$ are said to be equal only when all corresponding coordinates are equal: $a_1 = b_1, a_2 = b_2, \ldots, a_N = b_N$.

In connection with the above discussion (p. 25) it must be stressed that we are here considering the vectors in relation to a given "coordinate system." Later it will be shown how a given vector's coordinates change when the coordinate system is "rotated."

The words "coordinate system" and "rotate" are here used in the general N-dimensional case, even if they have so far been given a meaning only in the cases $N = 2$ (the plane) and $N = 3$ (the ordinary space). In what follows such *generalizations of the terminology* to N dimensions will be applied without further comment. Many well-known terms used in the plane and in space will be carried over to more dimensions. The basic condition for this procedure will simply be that the expressions concerned in the cases $N = 2$ and $N = 3$ are always in agreement with the usual terminology.

Vector Operations

A series of mathematical operations are introduced for vectors. Let $\mathbf{a}$ and $\mathbf{b}$ be two arbitrary N-dimensional vectors $\mathbf{a} = (a_1, a_2, \ldots, a_N)$, $\mathbf{b} = (b_1, b_2, \ldots, b_N)$, and k an arbitrary real number. The *product* of k and $\mathbf{a}$ is then the vector $k\mathbf{a} = (ka_1, ka_2, \ldots, ka_N)$, the *sum* of $\mathbf{a}$ and $\mathbf{b}$ is the vector $\mathbf{a} + \mathbf{b} = (a_1 + b_1, a_2 + b_2, \ldots, a_N + b_N)$, the *difference* between $\mathbf{a}$ and $\mathbf{b}$, the vector $\mathbf{a} - \mathbf{b} = (a_1 - b_1, a_2 - b_2, \ldots, a_N - b_N)$, and finally, the *scalar product* of $\mathbf{a}$ and $\mathbf{b}$ is the real number $\mathbf{a} \cdot \mathbf{b} = a_1 b_1 + a_2 b_2 + \cdots + a_N b_N$.

The above definition of the scalar product means that the given coordinate system after the above remarks must be described as a usual right-angled system (an orthogonal system). This is because only then will the previously considered scalar product ($N = 2$ and $N = 3$) be determined by the formula given here. The basic rules of operation derived for $N = 2$ and $N = 3$ are all seen to retain their validity.

The *length* of the vector $\mathbf{a}$ is defined as

$$|\mathbf{a}| = \sqrt{\mathbf{a} \cdot \mathbf{a}} = \sqrt{\mathbf{a}^2} = \sqrt{a_1{}^2 + a_2{}^2 + \cdots + a_N{}^2}.$$

The length so defined has, among other things, the following properties: (1) $|\mathbf{a}| > 0$ when $\mathbf{a}$ is a proper vector, while for the zero vector $\mathbf{0} = (0, 0, \ldots, 0)$ we have $|\mathbf{0}| = 0$; (2) $|k\mathbf{a}| = |k|\,|\mathbf{a}|$; (3) $|\mathbf{a} \cdot \mathbf{b}| \leq |\mathbf{a}|\,|\mathbf{b}|$; and (4) $|\mathbf{a} + \mathbf{b}| \leq |\mathbf{a}| + |\mathbf{b}|$ (triangle inequality).

The proof for (1) and (2) automatically follows from the definitions. To prove (3) we construct a real-valued function f defined for all real numbers x: $f(x) = (x\mathbf{a} + \mathbf{b}) \cdot (x\mathbf{a} + \mathbf{b}) = x^2 \mathbf{a} \cdot \mathbf{a} + 2x\mathbf{a} \cdot \mathbf{b} + \mathbf{b} \cdot \mathbf{b}$. Obviously all values of f are nonnegative. Therefore the second-order polynomial in x which appears must have a discriminant which is either negative or 0: $D = 4(\mathbf{a} \cdot \mathbf{b})^2 - 4(\mathbf{a})^2(\mathbf{b})^2 \leq 0$; from this (3) is proved. The equals sign is seen to be valid only when the equation $x\mathbf{a} + \mathbf{b} = \mathbf{0}$ has a solution, i.e., when the given vectors are proportional. The proof for (4) is now readily obtained from (3):

$$|\mathbf{a} + \mathbf{b}|^2 = (\mathbf{a} + \mathbf{b}) \cdot (\mathbf{a} + \mathbf{b}) = \mathbf{a}^2 + 2\mathbf{a} \cdot \mathbf{b} + \mathbf{b}^2$$
$$\leq |\mathbf{a}|^2 + 2|\mathbf{a}| \, |\mathbf{b}| + |\mathbf{b}|^2 = (|\mathbf{a}| + |\mathbf{b}|)^2.$$

A vector is said to be *normalized* when its length is 1, i.e., when it is a *unit vector*. An arbitrary vector $\mathbf{a}$ can be normalized, i.e., changed to a vector with the same or opposite direction and of length 1, by multiplying by $\pm 1/|\mathbf{a}|$. The given coordinate system has N *axes*, numbered $1, 2, \ldots, N$. The unit vector on axis 1 has the coordinates $(1, 0, \ldots, 0)$.

A point P in N-dimensional space is defined by its *position vector* $(x_1, x_2, x_3, \ldots, x_N)$. The *distance* between the points $(a_1, a_2, \ldots, a_N)$ and $(b_1, b_2, \ldots, b_N)$ is defined as

$$|\mathbf{b} - \mathbf{a}| = \sqrt{(b_1 - a_1)^2 + (b_2 - a_2)^2 + \cdots + (b_N - a_N)^2}.$$

The *angle* v between the two proper vectors $\mathbf{a}$ and $\mathbf{b}$ is defined by $\cos v = \mathbf{a} \cdot \mathbf{b}/|\mathbf{a}| \, |\mathbf{b}|$. Owing to property (3) above, this equation has a real solution. The two vectors are said to be *orthogonal* when their scalar product is 0.

Linear Independence

Let us now consider p N-dimensional vectors $\mathbf{a}_1, \mathbf{a}_2, \ldots, \mathbf{a}_p$. These are said to be *linearly independent* if the vector equation

$$c_1 \mathbf{a}_1 + c_2 \mathbf{a}_2 + \cdots + c_p \mathbf{a}_p = \mathbf{0}$$

only has the trivial solution $c_1 = c_2 = c_3 \cdots = c_p = 0$ (the so-called null or zero solution); otherwise the p vectors are said to be *linearly dependent*.

With the introduction of coordinates, the vector equation considered leads to N homogeneous linear equations with p unknowns, $c_1, c_2, \ldots, c_p$:

$$c_1 a_{11} + c_2 a_{12} + \cdots + c_p a_{1p} = 0,$$
$$c_1 a_{21} + c_2 a_{22} + \cdots + c_p a_{2p} = 0,$$
$$\cdot$$
$$\cdot$$
$$\cdot$$
$$c_1 a_{N1} + c_2 a_{N2} + \cdots + c_p a_{Np} = 0,$$

when

$$\mathbf{a}_i = (a_{1i}, a_{2i}, \ldots, a_{Ni}) \quad (i = 1, 2, \ldots, p).$$

If the vector system contains the zero vector, then the p vectors will always be linearly dependent, as then we can choose the coefficient of the zero vector to be different from 0 and the rest of the coefficients equal to 0.

If the system is composed of two proper vectors, then linear dependence means that the vectors are proportional: We have in this case $c_1\mathbf{a}_1 + c_2\mathbf{a}_2 = \mathbf{0}$, where none of the coefficients can be 0, and we obtain, for example, $\mathbf{a}_2 = -(c_1/c_2)\mathbf{a}_1$.

When $p > N$, there is always linear dependence. This is equivalent to saying that N homogeneous linear equations with more than N unknowns always have a nontrivial solution. The proof can be carried out by induction on N.

On the other hand, it can be shown that among all N-dimensional vectors, it is possible in an infinite number of ways to choose up to N vectors which are linearly independent. An especially simple example of this is the N unit vectors $\mathbf{e}_1 = (1,0,\ldots,0)$, $\mathbf{e}_2 = (0,1,\ldots,0),\ldots,$ $\mathbf{e}_N = (0,0,\ldots,1)$.

For $N = 2$, we graph the vectors in a usual right-angled plane coordinate system, drawing them all from the origin. Two proper vectors are then seen to be linearly independent when they do not lie on the same line.

According to the above general theorem, 3 two-dimensional vectors $\mathbf{a}_1$, $\mathbf{a}_2$, and $\mathbf{a}_3$ will always be linearly dependent. The proof for this can be readily obtained. When one of the vectors is the zero vector we already know that the three vectors are linearly dependent. Now let the three vectors all be proper. When two of them are linearly dependent, the three of them are also linearly dependent, as the coefficient of the third can be chosen as 0. The remaining case is when all three vectors are proper and lie on different lines. We resolve $\mathbf{a}_3$ into components along $\mathbf{a}_1$ and $\mathbf{a}_2$: $\mathbf{a}_3 = k_1\mathbf{a}_1 + k_2\mathbf{a}_2$, giving $k_1\mathbf{a}_1 + k_2\mathbf{a}_2 + (-1)\mathbf{a}_3 = \mathbf{0}$ (Fig. 1-29).

More than three vectors in the plane will also be linearly dependent now, as we can choose the coefficients of all vectors except three to be 0; after this the problem reduces to that just treated above.

In an analogous manner, it is seen that linear independence of 3 three-dimensional vectors drawn from the origin of a space-coordinate

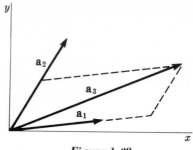

Figure 1-29

system is equivalent to the fact that they do not lie in the same plane. The linear dependence of 4 three-dimensional vectors, of which no three lie in the same plane, is demonstrated by resolving one of them into components along the other three.

Bases of a Vector System

Let us now consider an arbitrary vector system consisting of a (finite or infinite) number of N-dimensional vectors. The *maximum degree* (or *rank*) of the system, ρ, is defined as the greatest number of linearly independent vectors which can be chosen from the system. As more than N vectors of dimension N are always linearly dependent, the maximum degree can never be greater than N. ρ linearly independent vectors in the system are said to constitute a *basis* of the system. Each vector system which contains the N unit vectors $e_1 = (1,0,\ldots,0)$, $e_2 = (0,1,\ldots,0),\ldots,e_N = (0,0,\ldots,1)$ will have the maximum degree N, since these are, as already stated, linearly independent.

Let a given vector system be of maximum degree ρ and let the vectors $m_1, m_2,\ldots,m_\rho$ constitute a basis of the system. We consider an arbitrary vector a belonging to the system.

As the maximum degree is ρ, then the $\rho + 1$ vectors $m_1,m_2,\ldots,m_\rho,a$ will be linearly dependent, which means that there exist numbers $k_1,k_2,\ldots,k_\rho,k$ which are not all 0 such that

$$k_1 m_1 + k_2 m_2 + \cdots + k_\rho m_\rho + ka = 0.$$

k cannot be 0 here, as in this case the m-vectors would be linearly dependent, and this leads to

$$a = -\frac{k_1}{k} m_1 - \frac{k_2}{k} m_2 - \cdots - \frac{k_\rho}{k} m_\rho,$$

which shows that vector $\mathbf{a}$ can be written as a linear combination of the basis vectors.

This representation by the basis vectors is unique. Let $\mathbf{a} = c_1\mathbf{m}_1 + c_2\mathbf{m}_2 + \cdots + c_\rho\mathbf{m}_\rho$ and at the same time $\mathbf{a} = d_1\mathbf{m}_1 + d_2\mathbf{m}_2 + \cdots + d_\rho\mathbf{m}_\rho$; from this it follows on subtraction that $\mathbf{0} = (c_1 - d_1)\mathbf{m}_1 + (c_2 - d_2)\mathbf{m}_2 + \cdots + (c_\rho - d_\rho)\mathbf{m}_\rho$. Because of the linear independence of the m-vectors, we conclude that $c_1 = d_1$, $c_2 = d_2,\ldots,$ $c_\rho = d_\rho$.

We have now shown that an arbitrary vector $\mathbf{a}$ from the system can in one and only one way be represented as a linear combination of the basis vectors.

Linear Vector Spaces

A system of N-dimensional vectors is called a *linear vector space* when it has the following properties:

(1) If the system contains vector $\mathbf{a}$, it also contains the vector $k\mathbf{a}$, where k is an arbitrary real number.

(2) If the system contains vectors $\mathbf{a}$ and $\mathbf{b}$, it also contains the vector $\mathbf{a} + \mathbf{b}$.

Let vectors $\mathbf{a}_1, \mathbf{a}_2,\ldots,\mathbf{a}_\rho$ constitute a basis of a given linear vector space. According to the previous section, any vector in the system can be represented as a linear combination of these basis vectors. Combining conditions (1) and (2), we now conclude that any such vector belongs to the system. We say that the vector space is *spanned* by the vectors $\mathbf{a}_1,\mathbf{a}_2,\ldots,\mathbf{a}_\rho$.

As a special case it is seen that the N linearly independent vectors $\mathbf{e}_1,\mathbf{e}_2,\ldots,\mathbf{e}_N$ span the N-*dimensional Euclidean space*, which consists of all N-dimensional vectors; for the arbitrary vector $\mathbf{x} = (x_1,x_2,\ldots,x_N)$ we have $x = x_1\mathbf{e}_1 + x_2\mathbf{e}_2 + \cdots + x_N\mathbf{e}_N$. In this case the basis vectors are all normalized and orthogonal to each other. The basis is said to be composed of *orthonormal* vectors.

We shall now show that something analogous can be obtained—in an infinite number of different ways—for an arbitrary vector space of maximum degree ρ $(2 \leq \rho \leq N)$. For this purpose let there be given an arbitrary basis of the vector space, say the ρ linearly independent vectors $\mathbf{a}_1,\mathbf{a}_2,\ldots,\mathbf{a}_\rho$. Our problem will then be to construct ρ linearly independent vectors $\mathbf{n}_1,\mathbf{n}_2,\ldots,\mathbf{n}_\rho$, also in the given vector space, which furthermore, are, orthonormal. The main problem will be to ensure the mutual orthogonality of the desired vectors, as it is readily seen that an arbitrary number of mutually orthogonal proper vectors must always be linearly independent. With regard to the restriction regarding the length of the individual vectors, normalizing of the vectors during the derivation will not have any effect on the orthogonality properties already obtained.

As the first vector we choose $\mathbf{n}_1 = \mathbf{a}_1/|\mathbf{a}_1|$. Next a number x_{21} is determined, such that the vector $\mathbf{b}_2 = \mathbf{a}_2 - x_{21}\mathbf{n}_1$ becomes orthogonal to $\mathbf{n}_1$: $0 = \mathbf{b}_2\mathbf{n}_1 = \mathbf{a}_2\mathbf{n}_1 - x_{21}\mathbf{n}_1^2$, or $x_{21} = \mathbf{a}_2\mathbf{n}_1$. On normalizing, $\mathbf{n}_2 = \mathbf{b}_2/|\mathbf{b}_2|$.

Continuing by use of the same method ($\mathbf{b}_3 = \mathbf{a}_3 - x_{31}\mathbf{n}_1 - x_{32}\mathbf{n}_2$, etc.), we find

$$\left.\begin{aligned}
0 = \mathbf{b}_3\mathbf{n}_1 &= \mathbf{a}_3\mathbf{n}_1 - x_{31}\mathbf{n}_1^2 - x_{32}\mathbf{n}_2\mathbf{n}_1 \\
&= \mathbf{a}_3\mathbf{n}_1 - x_{31},\ x_{31} = \mathbf{a}_3\mathbf{n}_1 \\
0 = \mathbf{b}_3\mathbf{n}_2 &= \mathbf{a}_3\mathbf{n}_2 - x_{31}\mathbf{n}_1\mathbf{n}_2 - x_{32}\mathbf{n}_2^2 \\
&= \mathbf{a}_3\mathbf{n}_2 - x_{32},\ x_{32} = \mathbf{a}_3\mathbf{n}_2
\end{aligned}\right\}\ \mathbf{n}_3 = \frac{\mathbf{b}_3}{|\mathbf{b}_3|},$$

$$\cdot$$
$$\cdot$$
$$\cdot$$

$$\mathbf{b}_\rho = \mathbf{a}_\rho - x_{\rho 1}\mathbf{n}_1 - x_{\rho 2}\mathbf{n}_2 - \cdots - x_{\rho,\rho-1}\mathbf{n}_{\rho-1},$$

$$x_{\rho i} = \mathbf{a}_\rho\mathbf{n}_i\ (i = 1,\ldots,\rho - 1);\ \mathbf{n}_\rho = \frac{\mathbf{b}_\rho}{|\mathbf{b}_\rho|}.$$

As this results in vectors which all belong to the given vector space, the problem is solved.

It is further observed that the problem can be solved in an infinite number of ways, as instead of choosing the vectors $\mathbf{a}_1, \mathbf{a}_2, \ldots, \mathbf{a}_\rho$ as a starting point, we could, for example, choose the similarly linearly independent vectors $\mathbf{a}_1 + x\mathbf{a}_2$, $\mathbf{a}_1 - x\mathbf{a}_2$, $\mathbf{a}_3, \ldots, \mathbf{a}_\rho$ ($x \neq 0$), which already give rise to an infinite number of different solutions.

Exercises

*1. $\mathbf{a} = (9, -1, 0, -2)$, $\mathbf{b} = (0, 5, 2, 1)$, and $\mathbf{c} = (3, -1, -4, 2)$. Solve each of the following equations:
    (a) $\mathbf{a} - 2\mathbf{b} + 3\mathbf{x} = \mathbf{c}$.
    (b) $(x\mathbf{a} + 3(\mathbf{b} - \mathbf{c})) \cdot (\mathbf{b} + 2\mathbf{c}) = 0$.

*2. Show that the vectors $\mathbf{a}_1 = (4, 1, -2)$, $\mathbf{a}_2 = (1, -5, 3)$, and $\mathbf{a}_3 = (2, 5, -4)$ are linearly dependent. Solve the equation $x\mathbf{a}_1 + y\mathbf{a}_2 = \mathbf{a}_3$.

3. Show that the vectors $\mathbf{a}_1 = (1, 2, 2)$, $\mathbf{a}_2 = (2, 1, 1)$, and $\mathbf{a}_3 = (0, 1, 3)$ are linearly independent. Find orthonormal vectors $\mathbf{n}_1$, $\mathbf{n}_2$, and $\mathbf{n}_3$ such that $\mathbf{n}_1$ is parallel to $\mathbf{a}_1$ and $\mathbf{n}_2$ lies in the plane of $\mathbf{a}_1$ and $\mathbf{a}_2$. (All vectors are considered as having the same initial point.)

4. Show that if p N-dimensional vectors are proper and mutually orthogonal, they are also linearly independent (cf. p. 34).

*5. A basis of orthonormal vectors n_1, n_2, n_3, and n_4 is given in four-dimensional space. Solve the equation

$$c_1 n_1 + c_2 n_2 + c_3 n_3 + c_4 n_4 = a,$$

where a is a given four-dimensional vector and c_1, c_2, c_3, and c_4 are unknowns.

6. In six-dimensional space are given the vectors $a = (1,1,0,0,0,0)$, $b = (0,1,1,0,0,0)$, $c = (0,0,1,1,0,0)$, $d = (0,0,0,1,1,0)$, $e = (0,0,0,0,1,1)$, and $f = (1,0,0,0,0,1)$. Show that they are linearly dependent. Also, show that a, b, c, d, e are linearly independent. Finally, determine a vector g such that a, b, c, d, e, g are linearly independent.

Answers
1. (a) $x = (-2, \frac{10}{3}, 0, 2)$. (b) $x = 3$.
2. We have (for example) $5a_1 - 6a_2 - 7a_3 = 0$, which shows that a_1, a_2, a_3 are linearly dependent. The equation $x a_1 + y a_2 = a_3$ has the only solution $(x, y) = (\frac{5}{7}, -\frac{6}{7})$.
5. $c_i = a \cdot n_i$ ($i = 1, 2, 3, 4$).

1-5. DETERMINANTS

Definition of a Determinant

In the following, a short presentation of the theory of determinants will be given. To an arbitrary ordered N^2-tuple of real numbers we attach a so-called *determinant of order* N which is a real number. It turns out to be very convenient to represent such a determinant by a square array of the given N^2 numbers (the *elements* of the determinant) enclosed by two vertical lines.

If as a short name of a determinant we use a single capital letter enclosed by vertical lines, then the elements of the determinant will be represented by the corresponding lower-case letter with two indices; the first one determines the *row* number and the second one the *column* number of the element:

$$|A| = \begin{vmatrix} a_{11} & a_{12} & \cdots & a_{1N} \\ a_{21} & a_{22} & \cdots & a_{2N} \\ \cdot & & & \\ \cdot & & & \\ \cdot & & & \\ a_{N1} & a_{N2} & \cdots & a_{NN} \end{vmatrix},$$

or, in short, $|A| = |a_{rs}|$. A determinant $|A|$ may very well be a negative number. The absolute value of the determinant is of course written $\|A\|$. These two different uses of vertical lines should not give rise to any misunderstandings.

As the definition of a determinant is quite complicated in the general case, we shall first consider the simplest cases, $N = 2$ and $N = 3$. For $N = 2$ we have

$$|A| = \begin{vmatrix} a_{11} & a_{12} \\ a_{21} & a_{22} \end{vmatrix} = a_{11}a_{22} - a_{12}a_{21}.$$

For $N = 3$ we have

$$|A| = \begin{vmatrix} a_{11} & a_{12} & a_{13} \\ a_{21} & a_{22} & a_{23} \\ a_{31} & a_{32} & a_{33} \end{vmatrix} = a_{11}a_{22}a_{33} - a_{11}a_{23}a_{32} \\ + a_{12}a_{23}a_{31} - a_{12}a_{21}a_{33} \\ + a_{13}a_{21}a_{32} - a_{13}a_{22}a_{31}.$$

The definition can in this case be represented conveniently by the following:

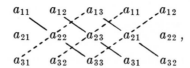

where the solid lines represent a plus and the dashed lines a minus. This practical rule is not, however, extended to determinants of higher order.

The definition of a determinant of arbitrary order N is obtained by the following generalization of the two cases considered:

A determinant appears as an expression containing $N!$ terms, of which half are preceded by a plus and half by a minus. Each term contains N factors, one representative for each row and one for each column. As there are exactly $N!$ such products, all the possibilities are seen to be included. Only the distribution of the signs remains. To determine the sign of a term, the factors are arranged after increasing row number. The column numbers will then form a permutation of the numbers $1, 2, . . ., N$. By a suitable number of exchanges of two elements in this permutation, it will always be possible to rearrange it into the permutation $1, 2, . . ., N$. The number of necessary exchanges may depend on the line of action, but it turns out that this number is either always even or always odd. In the first case, the given permutation is said to be *even,* in the other *odd.* The sign of the term considered is now positive if the permutation is even, negative if it is odd.

It is immediately seen that this general definition is in agreement with what was originally stated for the case $N = 2$. For the case $N = 3$ the general definition gives the following 3! terms:

$$a_{11}a_{22}a_{33} \qquad a_{11}a_{23}a_{32} \qquad a_{12}a_{23}a_{31}$$
$$a_{12}a_{21}a_{33} \qquad a_{13}a_{21}a_{32} \qquad a_{13}a_{22}a_{31}.$$

In each term we have arranged the factors according to increasing row number. Below the corresponding column numbers are treated in accordance with the general directions.

1,2,3	1,3,2	2,3,1	2,1,3	3,1,2	3,2,1
	1,2,3	2,1,3	1,2,3	1,3,2	1,2,3
		1,2,3		1,2,3	
even	*odd*	*even*	*odd*	*even*	*odd*

Hence, as wanted,

$$|A| = a_{11}a_{22}a_{33} - a_{11}a_{23}a_{32} + a_{12}a_{23}a_{31} - a_{12}a_{21}a_{33} + a_{13}a_{21}a_{32}$$
$$- a_{13}a_{22}a_{31}.$$

Let us next consider just one of the 24 terms appearing in the case $N = 4$, for instance, $a_{13}a_{24}a_{32}a_{41}$. The permutation to be treated is then 3,4,2,1:

3,4,2,1		3,4,2,1	
1,4,2,3		3,4,1,2	
1,2,4,3	or (less elegantly)	3,1,4,2	or $\cdots$.
1,2,3,4		1,3,4,2	
		1,3,2,4	
		1,2,3,4	

It follows that the term considered will have a negative sign. It is obvious that the calculation of a determinant of order 4 or higher according to the definition will give rise to much work. As we shall see below, such a calculation can always be reduced to that of calculating a certain number of determinants of lower order.

Cofactor and Complementary Minor

Let us consider an arbitrary determinant of order N:

$$|A| = \begin{vmatrix} a_{11} & a_{12} & \cdots & a_{1s} & \cdots & a_{1N} \\ a_{21} & a_{22} & \cdots & a_{2s} & \cdots & a_{2N} \\ \vdots & & & & & \\ a_{r1} & a_{r2} & \cdots & a_{rs} & \cdots & a_{rN} \\ \vdots & & & & & \\ a_{N1} & a_{N2} & \cdots & a_{Ns} & \cdots & a_{NN} \end{vmatrix}.$$

This consists, as mentioned, of $N!$ terms. Exactly $(N-1)!$ of these will contain the factor a_{rs}. These terms can together be written $a_{rs}A_{rs}$, i.e., as a product of element a_{rs} and the corresponding so-called *cofactor* A_{rs}. This cannot contain elements either from the rth row or the sth column.

As each term in the determinant contains exactly one factor from the rth row, we have

$$|A| = a_{r1}A_{r1} + a_{r2}A_{r2} + \cdots + a_{rs}A_{rs} + \cdots + a_{rN}A_{rN} \\ = \sum_{s=1}^{N} a_{rs}A_{rs},$$

where none of the cofactors which occur contain elements from the rth row. The determinant is said to be *resolved* according to the rth row. In an analogous way, the determinant can be resolved according to the sth column:

$$|A| = a_{1s}A_{1s} + a_{2s}A_{2s} + \cdots + a_{rs}A_{rs} + \cdots + a_{Ns}A_{Ns} \\ = \sum_{r=1}^{N} a_{rs}A_{rs}.$$

The *complementary minor* D_{rs} corresponding to the element a_{rs} in the determinant considered is defined as the determinant of order $(N-1)$ which appears from the given determinant by elimination of the rth row and the sth column.

It follows from the above remarks that the cofactor A_{rs} depends only on the elements of the corresponding complementary minor D_{rs}. Moreover, it can be shown that this dependence is extremely simple, as we have

$$A_{rs} = (-1)^{r+s}D_{rs}.$$

This implies that the calculation of the determinant $|A|$ can be considerably simplified by resolving according to the rth row as

$$|A| = a_{r1}(-1)^{r+1}D_{r1} + a_{r2}(-1)^{r+2}D_{r2} + \cdots + a_{rN}(-1)^{r+N}D_{rN},$$

or, by resolving according to the sth column, as

$$|A| = a_{1s}(-1)^{1+s}D_{1s} + a_{2s}(-1)^{2+s}D_{2s} + \cdots + a_{Ns}(-1)^{N+s}D_{Ns}.$$

When, if necessary, we continue to resolve the complementary minors, then finally the problem can be reduced to that of evaluating determinants of the third or second order.

For $N = 3$ we obtain, for example, on resolving according to the third row,

$$|A| = a_{31}(-1)^{3+1}\begin{vmatrix} a_{12} & a_{13} \\ a_{22} & a_{23} \end{vmatrix} + a_{32}(-1)^{3+2}\begin{vmatrix} a_{11} & a_{13} \\ a_{21} & a_{23} \end{vmatrix}$$

$$+ a_{33}(-1)^{3+3}\begin{vmatrix} a_{11} & a_{12} \\ a_{21} & a_{22} \end{vmatrix}.$$

When further reduced this is seen to be in agreement with the definition originally given.

Symbolically, the vector product of 2 three-dimensional vectors $\mathbf{a}$ and $\mathbf{b}$ can be written as a determinant of the third order; this can be seen on resolving according to the first row:

$$\mathbf{a} \times \mathbf{b} = \begin{vmatrix} \mathbf{i} & \mathbf{j} & \mathbf{k} \\ a_1 & a_2 & a_3 \\ b_1 & b_2 & b_3 \end{vmatrix}.$$

The scalar triple product of vectors $\mathbf{a}$, $\mathbf{b}$, and $\mathbf{c}$ is then obtained as

$$[\mathbf{abc}] = \begin{vmatrix} a_1 & a_2 & a_3 \\ b_1 & b_2 & b_3 \\ c_1 & c_2 & c_3 \end{vmatrix}.$$

Example 1-7.   On resolving according to the first row, we obtain

$$
\begin{vmatrix} 1 & -2 & 3 & 2 \\ 2 & 0 & -1 & -2 \\ -2 & 4 & 1 & 1 \\ 3 & -3 & 2 & 1 \end{vmatrix} = 1 \begin{vmatrix} 0 & -1 & -2 \\ 4 & 1 & 1 \\ -3 & 2 & 1 \end{vmatrix} + 2 \begin{vmatrix} 2 & -1 & -2 \\ -2 & 1 & 1 \\ 3 & 2 & 1 \end{vmatrix}
$$

$$
+ 3 \begin{vmatrix} 2 & 0 & -2 \\ -2 & 4 & 1 \\ 3 & -3 & 1 \end{vmatrix} - 2 \begin{vmatrix} 2 & 0 & -1 \\ -2 & 4 & 1 \\ 3 & -3 & 2 \end{vmatrix}
$$

$$
= 1(0(-1) + 1(7) - 2(11)) + 2(2(-1)
$$
$$
+ 1(-5) - 2(-7)) + 3(2(7) - 0(-5)
$$
$$
- 2(-6)) - 2(2(11) - 0(-7) - 1(-6))
$$
$$
= -15 + 14 + 78 - 56 = 21. \qquad \square
$$

Rules for Determinants

A series of rules regarding determinants will now be given.   Corresponding to an arbitrary determinant $|A|$ we define its *transposed* determinant $|\tilde{A}|$ as the one that is obtained on interchanging rows and columns.   It can be shown that the two determinants are equal: $|\tilde{A}| = |A|$.

On interchanging two rows (or two columns) the determinant changes sign, as each term changes its permutation between even and odd.   From this it follows that a determinant with two identical rows (or two identical columns) must equal 0: On interchanging these rows, the determinant must remain unchanged, but at the same time change its sign.

This leads to an important extension of the previously introduced formula for resolution of a determinant according to a row:

$$
a_{p1}A_{q1} + a_{p2}A_{q2} + \cdots + a_{pN}A_{qN} = \sum_{i=1}^{N} a_{pi}A_{qi} = \delta_{pq}|A|,
$$

where

$$
\delta_{pq} = \begin{cases} 1 & \text{for } p = q, \\ 0 & \text{for } p \neq q. \end{cases}
$$

For $p \neq q$, the left side represents the resolution according to the qth row of a determinant which has elements in the qth row equal to the corresponding elements in the pth row, i.e., a determinant with two identical rows.   Therefore the left side equals zero for $p \neq q$. The formula for resolution according to a column can be extended in an analogous manner:

$$a_{1p}A_{1q} + a_{2p}A_{2q} + \cdots + a_{Np}A_{Nq} = \sum_{i=1}^{N} a_{ip}A_{iq} = \delta_{pq}|A|.$$

On multiplication of all the elements in a row (column) by a number, the value of the determinant will be multiplied by the same number; this can, for example, be seen by resolving according to the row (column) concerned. In the special case when a determinant has a row (column) of zeros, it is equal to zero. This is also obvious from the definition, as each term must contain a factor from the row (column) concerned.

Consider the qth row of the determinant $|A|$ and suppose that its elements $a_{q1}, a_{q2}, \ldots$ are replaced by $a_{q1} + ka_{p1}, a_{q2} + ka_{p2}, \ldots$, respectively, where $k \neq 0$ and $p \neq q$. The result of this procedure, called a *row operation*, is a new determinant which turns out to be equal to the original one:

$$
\begin{vmatrix}
\vdots & & & \\
a_{p1} & a_{p2} & \cdots & a_{pN} \\
\vdots & & & \\
a_{q1}+ka_{p1} & a_{q2}+ka_{p2} & \cdots & a_{qN}+ka_{pN} \\
\vdots & & &
\end{vmatrix}
\begin{aligned}
&= (a_{q1} + ka_{p1})A_{q1} \\
&\quad + (a_{q2} + ka_{p2})A_{q2} \\
&\quad + \cdots + (a_{qN} \\
&\qquad\qquad + ka_{pN})A_{qN} \\
\\
&= (a_{q1}A_{q1} + a_{q2}A_{q2} \\
&\quad + \cdots + a_{qN}A_{qN}) \\
&\quad + k(a_{p1}A_{q1} + a_{p2}A_{q2} \\
&\qquad + \cdots + a_{pN}A_{qN}) \\
&= |A| + k \cdot 0 = |A|.
\end{aligned}
$$

The last set of parentheses is equal to zero, because $p \neq q$. A corresponding theorem is, of course, valid for *column operations*.

Often several row and column operations are used successively in the calculation of a determinant to obtain zeros at all positions except one in a chosen column or row; then resolution according to this becomes particularly simple.

Example 1-8. In the previously considered determinant of order 4, the first row is multiplied by -2, 2, and -3, and then added to the second, third, and fourth rows, respectively:

$$|A| = \begin{vmatrix} 1 & -2 & 3 & 2 \\ 2 & 0 & -1 & -2 \\ -2 & 4 & 1 & 1 \\ 3 & -3 & 2 & 1 \end{vmatrix} = \begin{vmatrix} 1 & -2 & 3 & 2 \\ 0 & 4 & -7 & -6 \\ 0 & 0 & 7 & 5 \\ 0 & 3 & -7 & -5 \end{vmatrix}$$

$$= 1(-1)^{1+1} \begin{vmatrix} 4 & -7 & -6 \\ 0 & 7 & 5 \\ 3 & -7 & -5 \end{vmatrix}.$$

Addition of the second row to the third row gives

$$|A| = \begin{vmatrix} 4 & -7 & -6 \\ 0 & 7 & 5 \\ 3 & 0 & 0 \end{vmatrix} = 3(-1)^{3+1} \begin{vmatrix} -7 & -6 \\ 7 & 5 \end{vmatrix} = 21.$$

Interchanging, for example, the first and second columns in the given determinant would have altered the sign of the determinant. In the above calculations, this would have shown itself on resolution according to the simple column (no. 2) obtained in the analogous manner, as the element different from 0 would then have taken up an "odd" position. □

Exercises

*1. Evaluate the following determinants:

$$\begin{vmatrix} 1 & 2 & 3 \\ 4 & 5 & 6 \\ 7 & 8 & 9 \end{vmatrix}, \begin{vmatrix} 1 & 4 & 7 \\ 2 & 5 & 8 \\ 3 & 6 & 9 \end{vmatrix}, \begin{vmatrix} 1 & 2 & 3 \\ 8 & 9 & 4 \\ 7 & 6 & 5 \end{vmatrix}, \begin{vmatrix} 1 & 0 & -1 & 1 \\ 0 & 2 & -2 & 2 \\ -3 & 6 & 0 & 4 \\ -4 & 2 & 5 & 3 \end{vmatrix}.$$

*2. Solve the following equations:

$$\text{(a)} \quad \begin{vmatrix} 1 & 5 & 3 \\ x & 2 & 0 \\ -4 & -1 & -3 \end{vmatrix} = \begin{vmatrix} 1 & 5 & 3 \\ 6 & 2 & 0 \\ -4 & -1 & -3 \end{vmatrix}.$$

$$\text{(b)} \quad \begin{vmatrix} 1 & 4 & 5 \\ x & 2 & 4 \\ 5 & -4 & -5 \end{vmatrix} = \begin{vmatrix} 1 & 4 & 5 \\ 6 & 2 & 4 \\ 5 & -4 & -5 \end{vmatrix}.$$

3. Solve the equation

$$\begin{vmatrix} 4 & 6 & 1 & 3 \\ 4 & 7 & 6 & 1 \\ 0 & 2 & -5 & 4 \\ 3 & 1 & -1 & 6 \end{vmatrix} = \begin{vmatrix} 1 & 3 & 3 & -3 \\ 4x & 1 & 5 & -2+7x \\ 1 & 5 & -2 & 1 \\ 4 & -2 & 5 & 3 \end{vmatrix}.$$

4. Show that the volume of a tetrahedron with vertices (x_1, y_1, z_1), (x_2, y_2, z_2), (x_3, y_3, z_3), and (x_4, y_4, z_4) in an orthogonal coordinate system is

$$\frac{1}{6} \begin{vmatrix} x_1 & x_2 & x_3 & x_4 \\ y_1 & y_2 & y_3 & y_4 \\ z_1 & z_2 & z_3 & z_4 \\ 1 & 1 & 1 & 1 \end{vmatrix}.$$

5. Show that the determinant $|A|$ of order N with elements $a_{ik} = 1 - \delta_{ik}$ $(i, k = 1, 2, \ldots, N)$ equals $(-1)^{N-1}(N - 1)$.

* 6. Find the value of the determinant $|A|$ of order N in which all elements of the form a_{ii}, $a_{i(i-1)}$ and $a_{i(i+1)}$ are equal to 1 while all other elements are equal to 0.

Answers

1. 0; 0; -48; 24.

2. (a) $x = 6$. (b) Any real number is a solution.

6. The result is given in the following table, which is periodical with a period of 6:

N	2	3	4	5	6	7	8	9	$\ldots$
$|A|$	0	-1	-1	0	1	1	0	-1	$\ldots$

1-6. LINEAR EQUATIONS

Formulations of the Problem

Determinants are of importance in the theory of linear equations. Let us first quite generally consider N linear equations with p unknowns $x_1, x_2, \ldots, x_p$:

$$a_{11}x_1 + a_{12}x_2 + \cdots + a_{1p}x_p = b_1,$$
$$a_{21}x_1 + a_{22}x_2 + \cdots + a_{2p}x_p = b_2,$$
$$\vdots$$
$$a_{N1}x_1 + a_{N2}x_2 + \cdots + a_{Np}x_p = b_N.$$

On introducing the $(p + 1)$ N-dimensional vectors $\mathbf{a}_i = (a_{1i}, a_{2i}, \ldots, a_{Ni})$, $i = 1, 2, \ldots, p$, and $\mathbf{b} = (b_1, b_2, \ldots, b_N)$, the equations are seen to be equivalent to the one vector equation $x_1\mathbf{a}_1 + x_2\mathbf{a}_2 + \cdots + x_p\mathbf{a}_p = \mathbf{b}$. The question of whether the given equations have a solution is now one of whether there exists a linear combination of $\mathbf{a}_1, \mathbf{a}_2, \ldots, \mathbf{a}_p$ which gives vector $\mathbf{b}$; or whether vector $\mathbf{b}$ can be resolved after the $\mathbf{a}$'s.

The general theory will not be considered here, but it is relevant to point out that there will always be either an infinite number of solutions, or a unique solution, or no solution.

Another formulation of the given equations is the following:

$$\begin{Bmatrix} a_{11} & a_{12} & \cdots & a_{1p} \\ a_{21} & a_{22} & \cdots & a_{2p} \\ & & & \\ & & & \\ & & & \\ a_{N1} & a_{N2} & \cdots & a_{Np} \end{Bmatrix} \begin{Bmatrix} x_1 \\ x_2 \\ \cdot \\ \cdot \\ \cdot \\ x_p \end{Bmatrix} = \begin{Bmatrix} b_1 \\ b_2 \\ \cdot \\ \cdot \\ \cdot \\ b_N \end{Bmatrix},$$

or, briefly, $AX = B$. Here the arrays in braces are called *matrices;* the matrix of the coefficients A is a matrix with N *rows* and p *columns*, X is a column matrix with p rows, and B is a column matrix with N rows.

The left side is considered as a product of matrices A and X. As two matrices are only called *equal* when they are composed of an equal number of rows and an equal number of columns, and when all *elements* in the corresponding positions are equal, then the definition of the product is obtained from the given equations. It is seen that the number of columns in the first factor is equal to the number of rows in the second factor, and that the product is a matrix with as many rows as in the first factor and as many columns as in the second (that is, one).

In the special case when $\mathbf{b} = \mathbf{0}$, the given equations are homogeneous; $x_1 = x_2 = \cdots = x_p = 0$ is then always a solution (the zero solution). The question of the existence of another (so-called *proper*) solution is seen in the vector formulation to be the question of whether the $\mathbf{a}$'s are linearly dependent. As mentioned previously (p. 31), this is always the case when $p > N$.

Solutions in a Special Case

In the special case when $N = p$, i.e., when the number of equations and the number of unknowns is the same, the coefficient matrix A is *square*, with N rows and N columns. The matrix is said to be of *order* N. In this case there exists a determinant $|A|$ corresponding to the coefficient matrix A, the so-called *main determinant* of the equations. If $|A| \neq 0$, the system of equations has exactly one solution:

$$a_{11}x_1 + a_{12}x_2 + \cdots + a_{1i}x_i + \cdots + a_{1N}x_N = b_1 \qquad A_{1i},$$
$$a_{21}x_1 + a_{22}x_2 + \cdots + a_{2i}x_i + \cdots + a_{2N}x_N = b_2 \qquad A_{2i},$$
$$\cdot$$
$$\cdot$$
$$\cdot$$
$$a_{N1}x_1 + a_{N2}x_2 + \cdots + a_{Ni}x_i + \cdots + a_{NN}x_N = b_N \qquad A_{Ni}.$$

On multiplying the individual equations by the cofactors to the ith column of the main determinant shown on the right, and then adding the equations, we eliminate all the unknowns except x_i and get (cf. p. 41):

$$(a_{1i}A_{1i} + a_{2i}A_{2i} + \cdots + a_{Ni}A_{Ni})x_i = b_1 A_{1i} + b_2 A_{2i} + \cdots + b_N A_{Ni},$$

or $|A|x_i = |B_i|$, where $|B_i|$ represents the determinant which is obtained from $|A|$ by replacing the elements in the ith column with the corresponding b's. Thus when $|A| \neq 0$, the only possible solution is $x_i = |B_i|/|A|$ $(i = 1,2,\ldots,N)$. By substituting in the given equations this can be shown to be a solution, thus proving the statement.

When $|A| = 0$, there is either an infinity of solutions or no solution.

Example 1-9

$$N = 2: \quad a_{11}x_1 + a_{12}x_2 = b_1,$$
$$a_{21}x_1 + a_{22}x_2 = b_2.$$

Here the following is obtained:

$$|A| \neq 0: \quad (x_1,x_2) = \left(\frac{|B_1|}{|A|}, \frac{|B_2|}{|A|} \right).$$

$|A| = 0$, $|B_1|$ and $|B_2|$ not both zero: There is no solution, as the equations contradict each other.

$|A| = |B_1| = |B_2| = 0$: There is an infinity of solutions, as the equations are equivalent. $\square$

Homogeneous Equations

When $p = N$ and $\mathbf{b} = \mathbf{0}$ there are N homogeneous linear equations with N unknowns. In this case there will, as mentioned, always be at least one solution, the zero solution. When $|A| \neq 0$, this is as we have shown the only solution, and the a-vectors are linearly independent. In the case $|A| = 0$, there is an infinity of solutions, the specification of which requires one or more independent parameters; the a-vectors are here linearly dependent.

When one of the complementary minors of $|A|$ is different from 0 (and $|A| = 0$), then only one parameter is needed to give all the solutions. Let, for example, $D_{NN} \neq 0$. In this case x_N is chosen arbitrarily $(= t)$ and the first $(N - 1)$ equations are solved to obtain the other $(N-1)$ unknowns. As $D_{NN} \neq 0$, exactly one solution is found corresponding to each t. It can be shown that the solutions determined in this way also satisfy the Nth equation.

Example 1-10

$$2x_1 - 3x_2 + 4x_3 = 0, \qquad |A| = \begin{vmatrix} 2 & -3 & 4 \\ -4 & 5 & -3 \\ -2 & 1 & 6 \end{vmatrix} = 0.$$
$$-4x_1 + 5x_2 - 3x_3 = 0,$$
$$-2x_1 + x_2 + 6x_3 = 0,$$

As

$$\begin{vmatrix} 2 & -3 \\ -4 & 5 \end{vmatrix} = -2 \neq 0,$$

then we set $x_3 = t$ and solve the first two equations:

$$2x_1 - 3x_2 = -4t,$$
$$-4x_1 + 5x_2 = 3t, \qquad x_1 = \frac{\begin{vmatrix} -4t & -3 \\ 3t & 5 \end{vmatrix}}{-2} = \frac{11}{2}t,$$

$$x_2 = \frac{\begin{vmatrix} 2 & -4t \\ -4 & 3t \end{vmatrix}}{-2} = 5t.$$

Substituting $(x_1,x_2,x_3) = (\frac{11}{2}t,5t,t)$ we see that the third equation is also satisfied for any value of t.

On multiplying the first two equations by 3 and 2, respectively, and then adding them, the third equation is obtained. This shows in a direct way that every solution of the first two equations must automatically satisfy the third equation. The three equations are not "independent." □

Exercises

*1. Solve each of the following two systems of linear equations:

$$
\begin{array}{ll}
& 9x_1 - 2x_2 + 5x_3 = 0, \\
\text{(a)} & 3x_1 + 2x_2 + 7x_3 = 0, \\
& -5x_1 + 4x_2 + 3x_3 = 0.
\end{array}
\qquad
\begin{array}{ll}
& 9x_1 - 2x_2 + 5x_3 = 0, \\
\text{(b)} & 3x_1 + 2x_2 + 7x_3 = 0, \\
& -5x_1 + 4x_2 + 3x_3 = x_3.
\end{array}
$$

*2. Solve the following system of linear equations:

$$4x_1 + 2x_2 - 3x_3 = 4,$$
$$-x_1 + x_3 + 2x_4 = -1,$$
$$3x_1 + 4x_2 - 4x_3 + x_4 = 0,$$
$$2x_1 - 3x_2 + x_3 + 3x_4 = 1.$$

*3. Discuss the following system of linear equations, where a is the parameter:

$$x - (1 + a)y + z = 1,$$
$$(2 - a)x + 4y + 4z = 4,$$
$$3x + 3y + (5 + a)z = 5.$$

4. Corresponding to a given determinant $|A|$ of order N we consider the following system of $(N - 1)$ linear and homogeneous equations:

$$a_{11}x_1 + a_{12}x_2 + \cdots + a_{1N}x_N = 0$$
$$a_{21}x_1 + a_{22}x_2 + \cdots + a_{2N}x_N = 0$$
$$.$$
$$.$$
$$.$$
$$a_{q1}x_1 + a_{q2}x_2 + \cdots + a_{qN}x_N = 0$$

$(q = N - 1)$. Show that one solution is $(x_1,x_2,\ldots,x_N) = (A_{N1},A_{N2},\ldots,A_{NN})$. Show next that if this is not the zero solution, then the complete set of solutions is the set of all N-tuples proportional to the one given.

5. Show that the vectors $(2,1,-1,1)$, $(1,1,2,-1)$, and $(1,-2,1,1)$ are of the same length and mutually orthogonal. Determine a fourth vector also of that length and orthogonal to the other three.

Answers
1. (a) $(x_1,x_2,x_3) = (t,2t,-t)$.   (b) $(x_1,x_2,x_3) = (0,0,0)$.
2. $(x_1,x_2,x_3,x_4) = (3,2,4,-1)$.
3. $a = 0$: $(x,y,z) = (4t, t, 1 - 3t)$. $a = -2$: no solution. $a \neq 0$ and -2: $(x,y,z) = (-4/(a + 2), -1/(a + 2), 5/(a + 2))$.

1-7. MATRICES

Vectors in Matrix Notation

Above we introduced the notion of a matrix in connection with the presentation of a number of linear equations. We shall now look more closely at some special matrices.

Let the following matrix equation be given:

$$\begin{Bmatrix} y_1 \\ y_2 \\ . \\ . \\ . \\ y_N \end{Bmatrix} = \begin{Bmatrix} a_{11} & a_{12} & \cdots & a_{1N} \\ a_{21} & a_{22} & \cdots & a_{2N} \\ . \\ . \\ . \\ a_{N1} & a_{N2} & \cdots & a_{NN} \end{Bmatrix} \begin{Bmatrix} x_1 \\ x_2 \\ . \\ . \\ . \\ x_N \end{Bmatrix},$$

or $Y = AX$. In the following, a *column matrix* with N rows is regarded as merely another way of representing an N-dimensional vector (in a given coordinate system). The square matrix A of order

N, can then be looked upon as an *operator*, a quantity which by "acting upon" the N-dimensional vector X *maps* (*transforms*) this onto the N-dimensional vector Y. The matrix A thus determines a *vector function* f (a *transformation* or a *mapping*) defined for all N-dimensional vectors, such that X is carried over into $Y = f(X) = AX$. Y is said to be the *image* of X.

When we consider a matrix A with determinant $|A| \neq 0$, we obtain a one-to-one mapping of the set of all N-dimensional vectors onto the set of all N-dimensional vectors: Corresponding to an arbitrary vector Y we find all possible vectors X such that $f(X) = Y$ by solving the N linear equations given by the matrix equation $AX = Y$. As $|A| \neq 0$, exactly one solution is obtained. The given vector function in this case has an *inverse* function, also defined for all N-dimensional vectors.

The following mathematical operations previously defined for N-dimensional vectors are immediately carried over to column matrices: multiplication of a vector by a real number and addition and subtraction of two vectors. Thus when a column matrix is multiplied by a real number, all the elements are multiplied by the number, and when two column matrices (with the same number of rows) are added (subtracted), the corresponding elements are added (subtracted).

Linear Vector Functions

On direct calculation the above-defined vector function is seen to have the following properties: (1) $f(kX) = kf(X)$ and (2) $f(X' + X'') = f(X') + f(X'')$. The vector function is said to be *linear*.

By repeated use of rules (1) and (2), it is seen that the image of an arbitrary linear combination of vectors may be obtained as the same linear combination of the images of the individual vectors:

$$f(k_1X_1 + k_2X_2 + \cdots + k_nX_n) = k_1f(X_1) + k_2f(X_2) + \cdots + k_nf(X_n).$$

Let us now specifically look at the following N unit vectors:

$$E_1 = \begin{Bmatrix} 1 \\ 0 \\ \cdot \\ \cdot \\ \cdot \\ 0 \end{Bmatrix}, E_2 = \begin{Bmatrix} 0 \\ 1 \\ \cdot \\ \cdot \\ \cdot \\ 0 \end{Bmatrix}, \ldots, E_N = \begin{Bmatrix} 0 \\ 0 \\ \cdot \\ \cdot \\ \cdot \\ 1 \end{Bmatrix}.$$

Their images are evidently the column matrices contained in the given square matrix:

$$f(E_1) = A_1 = \begin{Bmatrix} a_{11} \\ a_{21} \\ \cdot \\ \cdot \\ \cdot \\ a_{N1} \end{Bmatrix}, f(E_2) = A_2 = \begin{Bmatrix} a_{12} \\ a_{22} \\ \cdot \\ \cdot \\ \cdot \\ a_{N2} \end{Bmatrix}, \dots,$$

$$f(E_N) = A_N = \begin{Bmatrix} a_{1N} \\ a_{2N} \\ \cdot \\ \cdot \\ \cdot \\ a_{NN} \end{Bmatrix}.$$

Using the linearity of the vector function we obtain

$$f(X) = f(x_1 E_1 + x_2 E_2 + \cdots + x_N E_N)$$
$$= x_1 f(E_1) + x_2 f(E_2) + \cdots + x_N f(E_N)$$
$$= x_1 A_1 + x_2 A_2 + \cdots + x_N A_N.$$

The image of an arbitrary vector X can thus be said to be a vector with the same coordinates in the coordinate system determined by the A's (provided these are linearly independent, i.e., $|A| \neq 0$).

The determinant $|A|$ corresponding to the transformation matrix represents what may be called the *scale of volume* of the transformation: For $N = 2(3)$, $|A|$ is seen to give the area (volume) of the parallelogram (parallelepiped) spanned by the unit vectors.

Example 1-11

$$A = \begin{Bmatrix} 1 & k \\ 0 & 1 \end{Bmatrix},$$

and thus

$$y_1 = x_1 + kx_2,$$
$$y_2 = x_2$$

(Fig. 1-30). □

Example 1-12

$$A = \begin{Bmatrix} 1 & -\sqrt{3} \\ \sqrt{3} & 1 \end{Bmatrix},$$

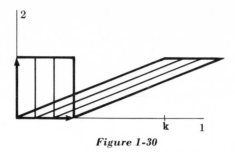

Figure 1-30

and thus

$$y_1 = x_1 - \sqrt{3}\, x_2,$$
$$y_2 = \sqrt{3}\, x_1 + x_2$$

(Fig. 1-31).   □

Because of the generalizations (and contrary to the above) we are here led to represent the two coordinates of a given vector with the same letter (x or y), but with indices 1 and 2, respectively.

Example 1-13. In two-dimensional space a vector function is required which rotates every vector by an angle θ, leaving its length unchanged.

We must then choose

$$A_1 = \begin{Bmatrix} \cos\theta \\ \sin\theta \end{Bmatrix} \quad \text{and} \quad A_2 = \begin{Bmatrix} -\sin\theta \\ \cos\theta \end{Bmatrix}.$$

From this,

$$A = \begin{Bmatrix} \cos\theta & -\sin\theta \\ \sin\theta & \cos\theta \end{Bmatrix},$$

which is really a solution.   □

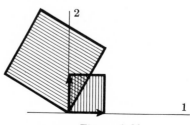

Figure 1-31

Operations with Square Matrices

Some mathematical operations for square matrices shall now be introduced. These give the *product* of a real number and a matrix, and the *sum, difference,* and *product* of two matrices. The previously mentioned principle that two matrices are only considered as being *equal* when they are "completely identical" continues to apply.

As we want definitions such that the operator properties of matrices are stressed, the following is demanded:

$$(kA)X = (Ak)X = k(AX),$$
$$(A \pm B)X = AX \pm BX,$$
$$(AB)X = A(BX).$$

It automatically follows from this that we are forced to the following definition: When a matrix is multiplied by a real number, each matrix element is multiplied by the number; when two matrices are added (subtracted), all corresponding elements are added (subtracted). In a short form, we thus have

$$k\{a_{ik}\} = \{a_{ik}\}k = \{ka_{ik}\} \qquad \text{and} \qquad \{a_{ik}\} \pm \{b_{ik}\} = \{a_{ik} \pm b_{ik}\}.$$

As matrix multiplication leads to a lengthier calculation, we shall first consider the case $N = 2$:

$$
\begin{aligned}
A(BX) &= A\left[\begin{Bmatrix} b_{11} & b_{12} \\ b_{21} & b_{22} \end{Bmatrix} \begin{Bmatrix} x_1 \\ x_2 \end{Bmatrix} \right] = \begin{Bmatrix} a_{11} & a_{12} \\ a_{21} & a_{22} \end{Bmatrix} \begin{Bmatrix} b_{11}x_1 + b_{12}x_2 \\ b_{21}x_1 + b_{22}x_2 \end{Bmatrix} \\
&= \begin{Bmatrix} a_{11}(b_{11}x_1 + b_{12}x_2) + a_{12}(b_{21}x_1 + b_{22}x_2) \\ a_{21}(b_{11}x_1 + b_{12}x_2) + a_{22}(b_{21}x_1 + b_{22}x_2) \end{Bmatrix} \\
&= \begin{Bmatrix} (a_{11}b_{11} + a_{12}b_{21})x_1 + (a_{11}b_{12} + a_{12}b_{22})x_2 \\ (a_{21}b_{11} + a_{22}b_{21})x_1 + (a_{21}b_{12} + a_{22}b_{22})x_2 \end{Bmatrix} \\
&= \begin{Bmatrix} a_{11}b_{11} + a_{12}b_{21} & a_{11}b_{12} + a_{12}b_{22} \\ a_{21}b_{11} + a_{22}b_{21} & a_{21}b_{12} + a_{22}b_{22} \end{Bmatrix} \begin{Bmatrix} x_1 \\ x_2 \end{Bmatrix} = (AB)X.
\end{aligned}
$$

We must therefore define the matrix product C of A and B as follows:

$$
\begin{Bmatrix} c_{11} & c_{12} \\ c_{21} & c_{22} \end{Bmatrix} = \begin{Bmatrix} a_{11} & a_{12} \\ a_{21} & a_{22} \end{Bmatrix} \begin{Bmatrix} b_{11} & b_{12} \\ b_{21} & b_{22} \end{Bmatrix} = \begin{Bmatrix} \sum_{i=1}^{2} a_{1i}b_{i1} & \sum_{i=1}^{2} a_{1i}b_{i2} \\ \sum_{i=1}^{2} a_{2i}b_{i1} & \sum_{i=1}^{2} a_{2i}b_{i2} \end{Bmatrix},
$$

or $c_{rs} = \Sigma_{i=1}^{2} a_{ri}b_{is}$.

With analogous calculation for square matrices of order N, the

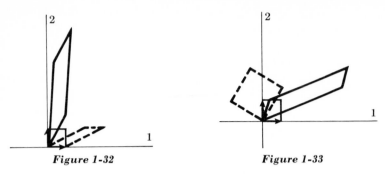

Figure 1-32   Figure 1-33

elements in the product matrix $C = AB$ are seen to be determined by the product sums

$$c_{rs} = \sum_{i=1}^{N} a_{ri} b_{is}.$$

Example 1-14

$$\left\{\begin{matrix} 1 & -\sqrt{3} \\ \sqrt{3} & 1 \end{matrix}\right\} \left\{\begin{matrix} 1 & k \\ 0 & 1 \end{matrix}\right\} = \left\{\begin{matrix} 1 & k-\sqrt{3} \\ \sqrt{3} & k\sqrt{3}+1 \end{matrix}\right\}.$$

(Fig. 1-32). The product matrix is the operator corresponding to the composition of the two previously considered transformations in the order then given (Examples 1-11 and 1-12).   □

Example 1-15

$$\left\{\begin{matrix} 1 & k \\ 0 & 1 \end{matrix}\right\} \left\{\begin{matrix} 1 & -\sqrt{3} \\ \sqrt{3} & 1 \end{matrix}\right\} = \left\{\begin{matrix} 1+k\sqrt{3} & -\sqrt{3}+k \\ \sqrt{3} & 1 \end{matrix}\right\}.$$

(Fig. 1-33). The two single transformations are carried out here in reversed order. The result is different, showing that matrix multiplication is not commutative.   □

Example 1-16

$$\left\{\begin{matrix} 1 & -2 & -1 \\ 0 & 1 & 1 \\ 2 & 1 & 0 \end{matrix}\right\} \left(\begin{matrix} 2 & 0 & -2 \\ 1 & -1 & 0 \\ 1 & 2 & 1 \end{matrix}\right) = \left\{\begin{matrix} -1 & 0 & -3 \\ 2 & 1 & 1 \\ 5 & -1 & -4 \end{matrix}\right\},$$

$$\left\{\begin{matrix} 2 & 0 & -2 \\ 1 & -1 & 0 \\ 1 & 2 & 1 \end{matrix}\right\} \left\{\begin{matrix} 1 & -2 & -1 \\ 0 & 1 & 1 \\ 2 & 1 & 0 \end{matrix}\right\} = \left\{\begin{matrix} -2 & -6 & -2 \\ 1 & -3 & -2 \\ 3 & 1 & 1 \end{matrix}\right\}.$$

The numbers inside the dashed lines concern the calculation of element (2,3) in the two products. These are again seen to be different. $\square$

It is easily seen that the following rules apply: $(k + l)A = kA + lA$, $(kl)A = k(lA)$, $k(A + B) = kA + kB$, $k(AB) = (kA)B = A(kB)$. Also, addition of matrices follows the commutative and associative laws, while the commutative law, as is shown above, is not valid for the multiplication of matrices. In connection with this, the so-called *commutator* of two matrices A and B is introduced as $[A,B] = AB - BA$. When it is the zero matrix (which has only zeros as elements), the two matrices are said to *commute*. Only in this case is the order of the factors of no importance. The associative as well as the distributive laws hold for multiplication, as can be shown from direct calculations: $(AB)C = A(BC)$, $A(B + C) = AB + AC$, and $(A + B)C = AC + BC$.

All the above considered, we may now conclude that calculations with matrices go off similarly to those with numbers, only that the order of given factors must be preserved.

Example 1-17

$$\begin{Bmatrix} 2 & 1 \\ 3 & -1 \end{Bmatrix} \left[2 \begin{Bmatrix} -1 & 1 \\ 1 & 4 \end{Bmatrix} - \begin{Bmatrix} 3 & -1 \\ 2 & 0 \end{Bmatrix} \begin{Bmatrix} 1 & 2 \\ 3 & 4 \end{Bmatrix} \right]$$

$$= \begin{Bmatrix} 2 & 1 \\ 3 & -1 \end{Bmatrix} \left[\begin{Bmatrix} -2 & 2 \\ 2 & 8 \end{Bmatrix} - \begin{Bmatrix} 0 & 2 \\ 2 & 4 \end{Bmatrix} \right]$$

$$= \begin{Bmatrix} 2 & 1 \\ 3 & -1 \end{Bmatrix} \begin{Bmatrix} -2 & 0 \\ 0 & 4 \end{Bmatrix} = \begin{Bmatrix} -4 & 4 \\ -6 & -4 \end{Bmatrix}. \qquad \square$$

In what follows we shall also meet square matrices of the first order. For these the operations are as follows:

$$k\{a_{11}\} = \{ka_{11}\}, \qquad \{a_{11}\} \pm \{b_{11}\} = \{a_{11} \pm b_{11}\},$$
$$\{a_{11}\}\{b_{11}\} = \{a_{11}b_{11}\}.$$

Apart from notation (the braces) the results are exactly as for real numbers, and we will therefore simply identify square matrices of the first order with real numbers.

Operations with Matrices in General

In the above we have only considered operations with square matrices. The definitions introduced can in some cases be extended to other (rectangular) matrices.

The multiplication of a matrix by a real number can always be carried out, but addition (subtraction) of two matrices requires that the two matrices have the same number of rows and the same number of columns. These definitions are in full agreement with the definitions already introduced for column matrices (p. 48). This is, of course, a necessary condition for the above mentioned identification of vectors and column matrices.

In the case of matrix multiplication, the number of columns in the first factor must be equal to the number of rows in the second factor. The product will then be a matrix with as many rows as the first factor and as many columns as the second factor. The previously introduced product of a matrix with N rows and p columns and a column matrix with p rows (p. 44) is thus seen to be in agreement with the general definition.

The basic rules mentioned above are easily seen to be valid in all cases where they have a meaning.

Example 1-18

$$\begin{Bmatrix} 1 & -2 & -1 \\ 0 & 1 & 1 \end{Bmatrix} \begin{pmatrix} 2 & 0 & -2 & -2 \\ 1 & -1 & 0 & 1 \\ 1 & 2 & 1 & -1 \end{pmatrix} = \begin{Bmatrix} -1 & 0 & -3 & -3 \\ 2 & 1 & 1 & 0 \end{Bmatrix},$$

$$\begin{pmatrix} 1 & -2 & -1 \\ 0 & 1 & 1 \\ 2 & 1 & 0 \end{pmatrix} \begin{Bmatrix} 2 \\ 1 \\ 1 \end{Bmatrix} = \begin{Bmatrix} -1 \\ 2 \\ 5 \end{Bmatrix}$$

(cf. Example 1-16).   □

Special Matrices

We will now again limit ourselves to consideration of square matrices, and look at some especially important ones.

We have previously mentioned the *zero matrix* 0 of order N, which has nothing but zeros as elements. It is obvious that $0 + A = A$ and that $0A = A0 = 0$ for every Nth-order matrix A. The *unit matrix* E of order N is defined as the matrix which is composed of ones in the *main diagonal* and zeros elsewhere: $E = \{\delta_{ik}\}$. The unit matrix commutes with every matrix of the same order, as $EA = AE = A$. More generally, a matrix which has zeros everywhere outside the main diagonal is called a *diagonal matrix*. Any two diagonal matrices of the same order commute.

Corresponding to an arbitrary matrix A, there is a *transpose* $\tilde{A}$ with rows and columns interchanged. With

$$A = \begin{Bmatrix} a_{11} & a_{12} & \cdots & a_{1N} \\ a_{21} & a_{22} & \cdots & a_{2N} \\ & \cdot & & \\ & \cdot & & \\ & \cdot & & \\ a_{N1} & a_{N2} & \cdots & a_{NN} \end{Bmatrix},$$

we get

$$\tilde{A} = \begin{Bmatrix} a_{11} & a_{21} & \cdots & a_{N1} \\ a_{12} & a_{22} & \cdots & a_{N2} \\ & \cdot & & \\ & \cdot & & \\ & \cdot & & \\ a_{1N} & a_{2N} & \cdots & a_{NN} \end{Bmatrix}.$$

When $\tilde{A} = A$, A is said to be *symmetric*. When $\tilde{A} = -A$, A is said to be *skew-symmetric (antisymmetric)*; the diagonal elements must in this case all be 0. Every matrix may be written as the sum of a symmetric and a skew-symmetric matrix, as $A = \frac{1}{2}(A + \tilde{A}) + \frac{1}{2}(A - \tilde{A})$.

Example 1-19

$$\begin{Bmatrix} 2 & 1 & 6 \\ -1 & 5 & 0 \\ 2 & 2 & 1 \end{Bmatrix} = \begin{Bmatrix} 2 & 0 & 4 \\ 0 & 5 & 1 \\ 4 & 1 & 1 \end{Bmatrix} + \begin{Bmatrix} 0 & 1 & 2 \\ -1 & 0 & -1 \\ -2 & 1 & 0 \end{Bmatrix}. \qquad \square$$

On consideration of an arbitrary element it is seen that the transpose of a product of two matrices equals the product of the two transposes in the reversed order: $(\widetilde{AB}) = \tilde{B}\tilde{A}$.

Example 1-20

$$\begin{Bmatrix} 1 & 2 \\ 3 & 4 \end{Bmatrix} \begin{Bmatrix} 5 & 6 \\ 7 & 8 \end{Bmatrix} = \begin{Bmatrix} 19 & 22 \\ 43 & 50 \end{Bmatrix},$$

$$\begin{Bmatrix} 5 & 7 \\ 6 & 8 \end{Bmatrix} \begin{Bmatrix} 1 & 3 \\ 2 & 4 \end{Bmatrix} = \begin{Bmatrix} 19 & 43 \\ 22 & 50 \end{Bmatrix}. \qquad \square$$

Although symmetry and antisymmetry can, of course, only have meaning in connection with square matrices, the process of transposing can be used in a completely arbitrary matrix. The product rule mentioned retains its validity in this case.

Given two column matrices A and B, we obtain

$$\tilde{A}B = \{a_1 \quad a_2 \cdots a_N\} \begin{Bmatrix} b_1 \\ b_2 \\ \cdot \\ \cdot \\ \cdot \\ b_N \end{Bmatrix} = \{a_1 b_1 + a_2 b_2 + \cdots + a_N b_N\}.$$

The result is a square matrix of the first order that is a number, namely, the scalar product of the two vectors $\mathbf{a} = (a_1, a_2, \ldots, a_N)$ and $\mathbf{b} = (b_1, b_2, \ldots, b_N)$. This can in matrix language be expressed as the one vector written as a transposed column matrix, i.e., as a *row matrix*, multiplied by the other vector as a column matrix. If the order of the factors is changed, a square matrix of order N is obtained.

The following rules apply to the determinants which correspond to square matrices: $|kA| = k^n |A|$, $|\tilde{A}| = |A|$, and $|AB| = |A| \, |B|$. The first two rules follow immediately from previous considerations. The third rule is seen in the cases when $N = 2$ and $N = 3$ to be a consequence of the previously mentioned interpretation of the determinant as a scale of volume, but it also holds for matrices of higher order. There is no similarly simple connection between the determinants corresponding to two matrices and their sum or difference.

Inverse Matrices

Corresponding to the square matrix A we will now consider the simple matrix equation $AX = E$. The determinant $|X|$ of a possible solution must necessarily satisfy the equation $|A| \, |X| = |E|$, or $|A| \, |X| = 1$; from this it follows that no solution exists when $|A| = 0$. In the case $|A| \neq 0$, at least one solution can be given at once:

$$X = A^{-1} = \begin{Bmatrix} \dfrac{A_{11}}{|A|} & \dfrac{A_{21}}{|A|} & \cdots & \dfrac{A_{N1}}{|A|} \\[2mm] \dfrac{A_{12}}{|A|} & \dfrac{A_{22}}{|A|} & \cdots & \dfrac{A_{N2}}{|A|} \\[2mm] \cdot \\ \cdot \\ \cdot \\ \dfrac{A_{1N}}{|A|} & \dfrac{A_{2N}}{|A|} & \cdots & \dfrac{A_{NN}}{|A|} \end{Bmatrix},$$

or, in short, $\{x_{ik}\} = \{A_{ki}/|A|\}$. On substituting this matrix into the given equation, we obtain for the element rs on the left side (see p. 40),

$$\sum_{i=1}^{N} a_{ri}x_{is} = \sum_{i=1}^{N} a_{ri}\frac{A_{si}}{|A|} = \frac{1}{|A|}\sum_{i=1}^{N} a_{ri}A_{si} = \frac{1}{|A|}(\delta_{rs}|A|) = \delta_{rs},$$

or exactly the corresponding element on the right side. The same matrix also satisfies the equation $XA = E$:

$$\sum_{i=1}^{N} x_{ri}a_{is} = \sum_{i=1}^{N} \frac{A_{ir}}{|A|}a_{is} = \frac{1}{|A|}\sum_{i=1}^{N} A_{ir}a_{is} = \frac{1}{|A|}(\delta_{rs}|A|) = \delta_{rs}.$$

The matrix A^{-1}, called the *inverse matrix* of A, thus has the following properties: $AA^{-1} = A^{-1}A = E$. It is formed by replacing the elements in A by their cofactors divided by the determinant of A, and then transposing the matrix so obtained.

It can also now be seen that each of the two equations has only the one solution. On multiplication from the left of $AX = E$ by A^{-1} we obtain $A^{-1}(AX) = A^{-1}E$, or $(A^{-1}A)X = A^{-1}$, or $EX = A^{-1}$, or $X = A^{-1}$; and by analogy, multiplication from the right of $XA = E$ by A^{-1} gives $(XA)A^{-1} = EA^{-1}$, or $X(AA^{-1}) = A^{-1}$, or $XE = A^{-1}$, or $X = A^{-1}$.

Now we are in a position to consider the more general matrix equation $AX = B(|A| \neq 0)$. On multiplication from the left by A^{-1} we obtain $X = A^{-1}B$, which thus represents the only possible solution of the equation. Substitution shows that it really satisfies the equation

$$A(A^{-1}B) = (AA^{-1})B = EB = B.$$

In an analogous manner, the unique solution $X = BA^{-1}$ is obtained for the equation $XA = B(|A| \neq 0)$. As the matrices A^{-1} and B do not generally commute, the two "quotients" $A^{-1}B$ and BA^{-1} are usually different; hence a symbol, such as B/A will not be introduced.

Example 1-21. Solve the equations $AX_1 = B$ and $X_2A = B$, where

$$A = \{a_{ik}\} = \begin{Bmatrix} 2 & 1 & 2 \\ 1 & 3 & 2 \\ -1 & 1 & 0 \end{Bmatrix} \quad \text{and} \quad B = \begin{Bmatrix} 1 & 3 & 2 \\ -1 & -2 & 0 \\ 1 & 4 & -2 \end{Bmatrix}.$$

$$\{A_{ik}\} = \begin{Bmatrix} -2 & -2 & 4 \\ 2 & 2 & -3 \\ -4 & -2 & 5 \end{Bmatrix}, \quad |A| = 2, \quad A^{-1} = \begin{Bmatrix} -1 & 1 & -2 \\ -1 & 1 & -1 \\ 2 & -\frac{3}{2} & \frac{5}{2} \end{Bmatrix}.$$

$$X_1 = A^{-1}B = \begin{Bmatrix} -1 & 1 & -2 \\ -1 & 1 & -1 \\ 2 & -\frac{3}{2} & \frac{5}{2} \end{Bmatrix} \begin{Bmatrix} 1 & 3 & 2 \\ -1 & -2 & 0 \\ 1 & 4 & -2 \end{Bmatrix}$$

$$= \begin{Bmatrix} -4 & -13 & 2 \\ -3 & -9 & 0 \\ 6 & 19 & -1 \end{Bmatrix},$$

$$X_2 = BA^{-1} = \begin{Bmatrix} 1 & 3 & 2 \\ -1 & -2 & 0 \\ 1 & 4 & -2 \end{Bmatrix} \begin{Bmatrix} -1 & 1 & -2 \\ -1 & 1 & -1 \\ 2 & -\frac{3}{2} & \frac{5}{2} \end{Bmatrix}$$

$$= \begin{Bmatrix} 0 & 1 & 0 \\ 3 & -3 & 4 \\ -9 & 8 & -11 \end{Bmatrix}.$$

The two solutions, as expected, are different. They do, however, have the same determinant (of course):

$$|X_1| = |X_2| = |A^{-1}| \, |B| = \frac{1}{|A|} |B| = \frac{1}{2}(-6) = -3.$$

The nine elements in the matrix X_1 (or X_2) could also have been found by solving the nine linear equations which appear when the given matrix equation is written out in its elements. From this, three times three equations are obtained, each of which determines the values of the elements in a single column (row) of the desired matrix. The main determinant in each of the three systems of equations will be the same, namely, $|A|$. ☐

Orthogonal Matrices

Finally, orthogonal matrices will be considered. A square matrix A is said to be *orthogonal* if the column matrices of the matrix $A_1, A_2, \ldots, A_N$ are normalized and orthogonal to each other (orthonormal). As

$$A = \begin{Bmatrix} a_{11} & a_{12} & \cdots & a_{1N} \\ a_{21} & a_{22} & \cdots & a_{2N} \\ \cdot & & & \\ \cdot & & & \\ \cdot & & & \\ a_{N1} & a_{N2} & \cdots & a_{NN} \end{Bmatrix},$$

we have

$$A_1 = \begin{Bmatrix} a_{11} \\ a_{21} \\ \cdot \\ \cdot \\ \cdot \\ a_{N1} \end{Bmatrix}, \qquad A_2 = \begin{Bmatrix} a_{12} \\ a_{22} \\ \cdot \\ \cdot \\ \cdot \\ a_{N2} \end{Bmatrix}, \ldots, \qquad A_N = \begin{Bmatrix} a_{1N} \\ a_{2N} \\ \cdot \\ \cdot \\ \cdot \\ a_{NN} \end{Bmatrix}.$$

In matrix language the condition of normalization can be formulated $\tilde{A}_1 A_1 = \tilde{A}_2 A_2 = \cdots = \tilde{A}_N A_N = 1$, while the condition of orthogonality is $\tilde{A}_1 A_2 = \tilde{A}_1 A_3 = \cdots = \tilde{A}_{N-1} A_N = 0$, or, in all, $\tilde{A}_i A_k = \delta_{ik}$ $(i = 1,2,\ldots,N; k = 1,2,\ldots,N)$.

It follows directly from the definition that an arbitrary orthogonal matrix has the following property:

$$\tilde{A}A = \begin{Bmatrix} a_{11} & a_{21} & \cdots & a_{N1} \\ a_{12} & a_{22} & \cdots & a_{N2} \\ \cdot \\ \cdot \\ \cdot \\ a_{1N} & a_{2N} & \cdots & a_{NN} \end{Bmatrix} \begin{Bmatrix} a_{11} & a_{12} & \cdots & a_{1N} \\ a_{21} & a_{22} & \cdots & a_{2N} \\ \cdot \\ \cdot \\ \cdot \\ a_{N1} & a_{N2} & \cdots & a_{NN} \end{Bmatrix}$$

$$= \begin{Bmatrix} 1 & 0 & \cdots & 0 \\ 0 & 1 & \cdots & 0 \\ \cdot \\ \cdot \\ \cdot \\ 0 & 0 & \cdots & 1 \end{Bmatrix} = E.$$

The corresponding determinant equation gives $|\tilde{A}|\,|A| = 1$, or, as $|\tilde{A}| = |A|$, $|A|^2 = 1$. The determinant of an orthogonal matrix is therefore either $+1$ or -1.

Furthermore, it follows from the matrix equation intself that $\tilde{A}$ is a solution to the equation $XA = E$. But this equation has only one solution, A^{-1}; hence $\tilde{A} = A^{-1}$. This also could have been used as a definition of the orthogonality of a matrix A. As $AA^{-1} = E$, it follows that $A\tilde{A} = E$, or, when written out in elements, that the row vectors of the matrix A are also orthonormal.

Orthogonal Matrices of Orders Two and Three

A closer look will now be taken at orthogonal matrices of the second and third order with special reference to the corresponding vector functions. All vectors considered are supposed to be given in a usual right-angled (in space also right-handed) coordinate system.

As the first column of an orthogonal matrix of second order, we can freely choose a unit vector $\mathbf{a}_1$ which can always be written in the form $\mathbf{a}_1 = (\cos \theta, \sin \theta)$. There are now only two possibilities for the choice of the second column, either $\hat{\mathbf{a}}_1 = (-\sin \theta, \cos \theta)$ or $-\hat{\mathbf{a}}_1 = (\sin \theta, -\cos \theta)$. Collected, the following are the two possibilities:

$$A = \begin{cases} \cos \theta & -\sin \theta \\ \sin \theta & \cos \theta \end{cases} \quad \text{and} \quad A' = \begin{cases} \cos \theta & \sin \theta \\ \sin \theta & -\cos \theta \end{cases}.$$

A is orthogonal with determinant 1 and represents a rotation through an angle θ. A' is orthogonal with determinant -1 and represents a rotation through an angle θ followed by a reflection in the direction defined by $\mathbf{a}_1$.

Example 1-22. $\theta = 60°$.

$$A = \begin{cases} \dfrac{1}{2} & -\dfrac{\sqrt{3}}{2} \\ \dfrac{\sqrt{3}}{2} & \dfrac{1}{2} \end{cases}, \quad A' = \begin{cases} \dfrac{1}{2} & \dfrac{\sqrt{3}}{2} \\ \dfrac{\sqrt{3}}{2} & -\dfrac{1}{2} \end{cases}.$$

See Fig. 1-34.   □

An arbitrary unit vector in space, $\mathbf{a}_1 = (\alpha_1, \alpha_2, \alpha_3)$, can be chosen as the first column in an orthogonal matrix of third order. For the second column we must choose a unit vector $\mathbf{a}_2$ perpendicular to $\mathbf{a}_1$, or, in other words, a unit vector in the plane normal to $\mathbf{a}_1$. There are then two possibilities for the choice of the third column, either $\mathbf{a}_1 \times \mathbf{a}_2$ or $-\mathbf{a}_1 \times \mathbf{a}_2$.

The first choice gives an orthogonal matrix with determinant 1, which represents a rotation, while the second choice gives an orthog-

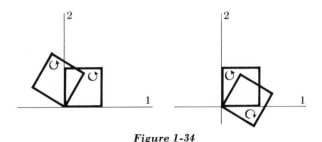

Figure 1-34

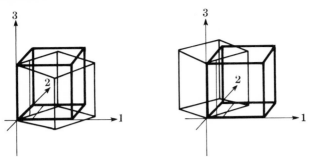

Figure 1-35

onal matrix with determinant -1, which—if a_1 and a_2 are chosen in the same manner in both cases—represents the same rotation followed by a reflection in the plane defined by a_1 and a_2.

Example 1-23. $a_1 = (\frac{1}{2}, \sqrt{3}/2, 0)$, $a_2 = (0,0,1)$, $a_1 \times a_2 = (\sqrt{3}/2, -\frac{1}{2}, 0)$.

$$A = \begin{Bmatrix} \dfrac{1}{2} & 0 & \dfrac{\sqrt{3}}{2} \\ \dfrac{\sqrt{3}}{2} & 0 & -\dfrac{1}{2} \\ 0 & 1 & 0 \end{Bmatrix}, \qquad A' = \begin{Bmatrix} \dfrac{1}{2} & 0 & -\dfrac{\sqrt{3}}{2} \\ \dfrac{\sqrt{3}}{2} & 0 & \dfrac{1}{2} \\ 0 & 1 & 0 \end{Bmatrix}.$$

See Fig. 1-35. □

Exercises

*1. Evaluate the matrices $3A$, $A + B$, $A - B$, and AB and the corresponding determinants when

$$A = \begin{Bmatrix} 1 & 2 & 1 \\ 0 & 2 & 1 \\ 0 & 0 & 2 \end{Bmatrix} \quad \text{and} \quad B = \begin{Bmatrix} 1 & -1 & 1 \\ 2 & 0 & 0 \\ 1 & -1 & 2 \end{Bmatrix}.$$

*2. Evaluate the matrices $[B,A]$, $A^2 - B^2$, and $(A + B)(A - B)$ when

$$A = \begin{Bmatrix} -1 & 0 & 2 \\ 0 & 1 & 1 \\ -2 & 3 & 0 \end{Bmatrix} \quad \text{and} \quad B = \begin{Bmatrix} 0 & 1 & 2 \\ -1 & 1 & 0 \\ 3 & -2 & 1 \end{Bmatrix}.$$

3. Evaluate the squares of the following matrices:

$$\begin{Bmatrix} 1 & 2 \\ 3 & 4 \end{Bmatrix}, \begin{Bmatrix} 1 & 0 & 2 \\ 0 & 3 & 4 \\ 1 & 2 & 3 \end{Bmatrix}, \begin{Bmatrix} 1 & 2 & 0 & 0 & 0 \\ 3 & 4 & 0 & 0 & 0 \\ 0 & 0 & 1 & 0 & 2 \\ 0 & 0 & 0 & 3 & 4 \\ 0 & 0 & 1 & 2 & 3 \end{Bmatrix}.$$

4. Evaluate the matrix $C = AB + (A + B)(2A - B) + BB$ when

$$A = \begin{Bmatrix} -2 & 1 & 3 \\ 2 & 0 & 1 \\ 0 & 4 & -2 \end{Bmatrix} \quad \text{and} \quad B = \begin{Bmatrix} 1 & 2 & 1 \\ 2 & 0 & 1 \\ 3 & 1 & 2 \end{Bmatrix}.$$

*5. Evaluate the matrix

$$\{1 \quad -1 \quad 1 \quad -1\} \begin{Bmatrix} 1 & -2 & 3 \\ 3 & 0 & 1 \\ 0 & 3 & -2 \\ -2 & 1 & 0 \end{Bmatrix} \begin{Bmatrix} 1 & 3 & 2 & 3 & 1 \\ 2 & 1 & 3 & 2 & 1 \\ 3 & 2 & 1 & 2 & 3 \end{Bmatrix} \begin{Bmatrix} 1 \\ 0 \\ 1 \\ 0 \\ 1 \end{Bmatrix}.$$

*6. In an orthogonal right-handed coordinate system is given the vector $\mathbf{a} = (a_1, a_2, a_3)$. Determine a matrix A of order 3 such that the corresponding linear vector function maps the arbitrary vector $\mathbf{x} = (x_1, x_2, x_3)$ onto the vector $\mathbf{a} \times \mathbf{x}$.

*7. Consider the vector function $Y = AX$, where

$$A = \begin{Bmatrix} 1 & -2 \\ -2 & -2 \end{Bmatrix}.$$

Determine the set of vectors X for which it is true that the corresponding vector Y is parallel to X.

*8. Consider the linear vector function which in relation to a given usual right-angled coordinate system S is determined by the equation $Y = AX$, where

$$A = \begin{Bmatrix} 1 & 2 \\ 3 & -1 \end{Bmatrix}.$$

A new coordinate system S' is now introduced by a rotation of S through $45°$ counterclockwise about the origin of S. Find a matrix A' such that the equation $Y' = A'X'$ determines the same vector function in relation to the new system.

9. Consider the linear vector function $Y = AX$, where

$$A = \begin{Bmatrix} 1 & 2 & 3 \\ 0 & 1 & -2 \\ 2 & 7 & 0 \end{Bmatrix}.$$

Show that all vectors Y (drawn as position vectors) lie in the same plane. Find a vector perpendicular to this plane.

10. The following transformation is performed with the position vectors in an orthogonal right-handed coordinate system XYZ: At first they are rotated $30°$ around the Z-axis in the positive direction (Fig. 1-36); then they are rotated $90°$ around (the original position of) the Y-axis, also in the positive direction. Find the matrix corresponding to this. Also, find the matrix corresponding to the transformation which is obtained when the two rotations are performed in the inverse order. Finally, show that the vector $(\sqrt{3} - 2, -1,$

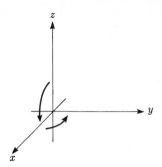

Figure 1-36

$\sqrt{3} - 2$) is mapped onto itself by the first transformation and that the vector $(\sqrt{3} - 2, 1, 2 - \sqrt{3})$ is mapped onto itself by the second transformation.

11. Consider a linear vector function $Y = AX$, where A is skew-symmetric. Show that any vector X is orthogonal to its image Y.

*12. Evaluate the matrices A^{-1}, B^{-1}, $A^{-1}B^{-1}$, BA, and $(BA)^{-1}$ when A and B are as in Exercise 1.

*13. Solve each of the equations

(a) $AX = B + X$, (b) $XA = B + X$,

when

$$A = \begin{Bmatrix} 5 & 2 \\ -2 & 1 \end{Bmatrix} \quad \text{and} \quad B = \begin{Bmatrix} 2 & 0 \\ 4 & 6 \end{Bmatrix}.$$

14. Evaluate the inverse of the matrix

$$A = \begin{Bmatrix} -3 & 2 & 4 & 2 \\ -2 & 5 & 0 & -3 \\ 0 & -4 & 1 & 4 \\ 0 & 2 & 0 & -2 \end{Bmatrix}.$$

15. Consider two square matrices A and B of the same order having nonzero determinants. Show that $(AB)^{-1} = B^{-1}A^{-1}$.

16. Consider a square matrix which has nonzero elements in its main diagonal and zeros under its main diagonal. Show that this matrix has an inverse with the same properties.

17. Show that the product of any two orthogonal matrices of the same order is also an orthogonal matrix. Show that the analogue is not true for the sum.

Answers

1. $\begin{Bmatrix} 3 & 6 & 3 \\ 0 & 6 & 3 \\ 0 & 0 & 6 \end{Bmatrix}, \begin{Bmatrix} 2 & 1 & 2 \\ 2 & 2 & 1 \\ 1 & -1 & 4 \end{Bmatrix}, \begin{Bmatrix} 0 & 3 & 0 \\ -2 & 2 & 1 \\ -1 & 1 & 0 \end{Bmatrix}, \begin{Bmatrix} 6 & -2 & 3 \\ 5 & -1 & 2 \\ 2 & -2 & 4 \end{Bmatrix}.$

2. $\begin{Bmatrix} -10 & 12 & 1 \\ -1 & 2 & -2 \\ -2 & 0 & 8 \end{Bmatrix}, \begin{Bmatrix} -8 & 9 & -4 \\ -1 & 4 & 3 \\ -3 & 4 & -8 \end{Bmatrix}, \begin{Bmatrix} -18 & 21 & -3 \\ -2 & 6 & 1 \\ -5 & 4 & 0 \end{Bmatrix}.$

5. $\{0\}(=0)$.

6. $\left\{\begin{array}{ccc} 0 & -a_3 & a_2 \\ a_3 & 0 & -a_1 \\ -a_2 & a_1 & 0 \end{array}\right\}$.

7. All vectors of the form $X = \left\{\begin{array}{c} t \\ 2t \end{array}\right\}$ or $\left\{\begin{array}{c} -2t \\ t \end{array}\right\}$.

8. $\left\{\begin{array}{cc} \frac{5}{2} & -\frac{3}{2} \\ -\frac{1}{2} & -\frac{5}{2} \end{array}\right\}$.

12. $\left\{\begin{array}{ccc} 1 & -1 & 0 \\ 0 & \frac{1}{2} & -\frac{1}{4} \\ 0 & 0 & \frac{1}{2} \end{array}\right\}$, $\left\{\begin{array}{ccc} 0 & \frac{1}{2} & 0 \\ -2 & \frac{1}{2} & 1 \\ -1 & 0 & 1 \end{array}\right\}$, $\left\{\begin{array}{ccc} 2 & 0 & -1 \\ -\frac{3}{4} & \frac{1}{4} & \frac{1}{4} \\ -\frac{1}{2} & 0 & \frac{1}{2} \end{array}\right\}$,

$\left\{\begin{array}{ccc} 1 & 0 & 2 \\ 2 & 4 & 2 \\ 1 & 0 & 4 \end{array}\right\}$, $\left\{\begin{array}{ccc} 2 & 0 & -1 \\ -\frac{3}{4} & \frac{1}{4} & \frac{1}{4} \\ -\frac{1}{2} & 0 & \frac{1}{2} \end{array}\right\}$.

13. (a) $\left\{\begin{array}{cc} -2 & -3 \\ 5 & 6 \end{array}\right\}$. (b) $\left\{\begin{array}{cc} 0 & -1 \\ 3 & 4 \end{array}\right\}$.

1-8. VECTORS AND TENSORS

Coordinate Transformations in Two and Three Dimensions

It has been shown previously how the coordinates of two- and three-dimensional vectors are changed on introduction of a new coordinate system. We shall now generalize these results to vectors of higher dimensions. Because of the scalar product we limit ourselves to considering usual right-angled coordinate systems.

Thus in the cases $N = 2$ and $N = 3$ we will only consider transformations to new coordinate systems which can be constructed from an originally given usual right-angled one, by a rotation possibly combined with a movement of the origin and a reflection in a line or plane. As to a reflection, this means in the plane a change in the sense of rotation given by the coordinate system and in space a change between right- and left-handed systems.

We again first consider the case when $N = 2$ in order to obtain a new formulation of the results obtained previously. Let (x_1,x_2) be the old coordinates of an arbitrary vector in the plane and (x_1',x_2') the new coordinates of the same vector. When the old coordinates of the new base vectors 1 and 2 are (q_{11},q_{21}) and (q_{12},q_{22}), respectively, the following results are obtained (cf. p. 10):

$$
\begin{array}{c} x_1 = q_{11}x_1' + q_{12}x_2' \\ x_2 = q_{21}x_1' + q_{22}x_2' \end{array} \quad \text{or} \quad \left\{\begin{array}{c} x_1 \\ x_2 \end{array}\right\} = \left\{\begin{array}{cc} q_{11} & q_{12} \\ q_{21} & q_{22} \end{array}\right\} \left\{\begin{array}{c} x_1' \\ x_2' \end{array}\right\}.
$$

The requirement that the new coordinate system be a usual right-angled one is now seen—as expressed in the old (usual right-angled) coordinate system—to be equivalent to requiring that the square matrix Q must be orthogonal, and with a positive determinant if the sense of rotation is to remain the same. If the origin of the coordinate system is not shifted, then the relation between the old and the new point coordinates will be the same.

For $N = 3$ we get corresponding results. The relation between the old coordinates (x_1,x_2,x_3) and the new coordinates (x'_1,x'_2,x'_3) to an arbitrary vector in space is

$$x_1 = q_{11}x'_1 + q_{12}x'_2 + q_{13}x'_3,$$
$$x_2 = q_{21}x'_1 + q_{22}x'_2 + q_{23}x'_3, \quad \text{or}$$
$$x_3 = q_{31}x'_1 + q_{32}x'_2 + q_{33}x'_3,$$

$$\begin{Bmatrix} x_1 \\ x_2 \\ x_3 \end{Bmatrix} = \begin{Bmatrix} q_{11} & q_{12} & q_{13} \\ q_{21} & q_{22} & q_{23} \\ q_{31} & q_{32} & q_{33} \end{Bmatrix} \begin{Bmatrix} x'_1 \\ x'_2 \\ x'_3 \end{Bmatrix}.$$

Here the columns in the resulting square matrix Q give the old coordinates of the new base vectors, and the requirement that the new coordinate system be usual right-angled is expressed by the condition that Q must be an orthogonal matrix, and with a positive determinant if the relative position of the base vectors is to be kept. If the origin of the coordinate system is not moved, then the relation between the old and the new point coordinates will be the same.

Coordinate Transformations in N Dimensions

The relation between what will be called the *old coordinates* $(x_1,x_2,\ldots,x_N)$ and the *new coordinates* $(x'_1,x'_2,\ldots,x'_N)$ of an arbitrary vector in N-dimensional space will now be found. N normalized and mutually orthogonal vectors $\mathbf{q}_1 = (q_{11},q_{21},\ldots,q_{N1})$, $\mathbf{q}_2 = (q_{12},q_{22},\ldots,q_{N2}),\ldots,\mathbf{q}_N = (q_{1N},q_{2N},\ldots,q_{NN})$ are chosen as new *base vectors*. The square matrix

$$Q = \begin{Bmatrix} q_{11} & q_{12} & \cdots & q_{1N} \\ q_{21} & q_{22} & \cdots & q_{2N} \\ \cdot & & & \\ \cdot & & & \\ \cdot & & & \\ q_{N1} & q_{N2} & \cdots & q_{NN} \end{Bmatrix}$$

is orthogonal; its determinant therefore is different from zero, and the N chosen base vectors will be linearly independent (p. 45).

An arbitrary N-dimensional vector $(x_1, x_2, \ldots, x_N)$ can then in a unique way be resolved according to the q-vectors (p. 33)

$$(x_1, x_2, \ldots, x_N) = x_1' \mathbf{q}_1 + x_2' \mathbf{q}_2 + \cdots + x_N' \mathbf{q}_N.$$

The coefficients on the right side are now the new coordinates of the vector considered. Written out in (old) coordinates, we obtain

$$x_1 = q_{11} x_1' + q_{12} x_2' + \cdots + q_{1N} x_N',$$
$$x_2 = q_{21} x_1' + q_{22} x_2' + \cdots + q_{2N} x_N',$$
$$\vdots$$
$$x_N = q_{N1} x_1' + q_{N2} x_2' + \cdots + q_{NN} x_N',$$

or

$$\begin{Bmatrix} x_1 \\ x_2 \\ \cdot \\ \cdot \\ \cdot \\ x_N \end{Bmatrix} = \begin{Bmatrix} q_{11} & q_{12} & \cdots & q_{1N} \\ q_{21} & q_{22} & \cdots & q_{2N} \\ \cdot & & & \\ \cdot & & & \\ \cdot & & & \\ q_{N1} & q_{N2} & \cdots & q_{NN} \end{Bmatrix} \begin{Bmatrix} x_1' \\ x_2' \\ \cdot \\ \cdot \\ \cdot \\ x_N' \end{Bmatrix}.$$

Generally it will be said that the new coordinate system has come from the old by a pure rotation if $|Q| = 1$, while $|Q| = -1$ corresponds to a rotation followed by a reflection.

Vectors

The previous considerations regarding transformation of two- and three-dimensional vectors (p. 25) will now be generalized.

An N-dimensional vector is a "geometric" quantity which in every (usual right-angled) coordinate system is represented by an N-tuple (a column matrix with N rows). The same vector is usually represented by different N-tuples (column matrices) in different systems.

The relation between the N-tuples $\mathbf{x}$ and $\mathbf{x}'$ (the column matrices X and X'), representing a given vector in two different systems S and S', is determined by a square array of numbers (an orthogonal matrix Q of order N), which depends only upon the position of the one system relative to the other and is independent of which vector is considered. In matrix formulation we thus have $X = QX'$, or, as Q is orthogonal, $X' = \tilde{Q}X$. The column matrix X is here said to have undergone an *orthogonal transformation*, giving as a result the column matrix X'.

We have defined previously the product of a real number and an N-dimensional vector and the sum and the difference of two N-dimensional vectors, all in a given coordinate system. In any case, a *vector* is obtained. By this we mean the following: When carried out on the column matrices of the same vectors in different coordinate systems, these operations will give rise to different column matrices, which, however, represent the same vector but expressed in the respective coordinate systems. This is easily seen:

$$(kX') = k\tilde{Q}X = \tilde{Q}(kX) \quad \text{and} \quad X' \pm Y' = \tilde{Q}X \pm \tilde{Q}Y = \tilde{Q}(X \pm Y).$$

For $N = 2$ and $N = 3$, incidentally, these results are immediate consequences of the purely geometric definitions of the operations considered. Similarly, the scalar product of two N-dimensional vectors is really a *scalar* (invariant under an orthogonal transformation of coordinates); i.e., its value is independent of the coordinate system (cf. p. 26). The relation $\tilde{X} = \tilde{X}'\tilde{Q}$ is obtained from $X = QX'$. The scalar product expressed in terms of the system S is then $\tilde{X}Y = \tilde{X}'\tilde{Q}QY' = \tilde{X}'EY' = \tilde{X}'Y'$, which is the scalar product expressed in S'. In the derivation we have used the orthogonality of Q, as this implies $\tilde{Q}Q = E$.

Tensors

In a given coordinate system S, a square matrix A of order N defines a linear vector function $Y = AX$. If we introduce another system S', by means of an orthogonal matrix Q, then in general the same vector function will appear in quite a different form. We now want to find a matrix A' which in the new system represents the same vector function.

We have $Y = AX$, $X = QX'$, and $Y = QY'$. On substituting, we get $QY' = AQX'$, and on multiplying from the left by $\tilde{Q}(= Q^{-1})$, we get $Y' = (\tilde{Q}AQ)X'$, and thus the result $A' = \tilde{Q}AQ$ is obtained. The two matrices A and A' represent the same vector function (operator) in S and S', respectively.

This important result is generally expressed in the following way: A *tensor* (linear vector function) in N-dimensional space is an operator which in every (usual right-angled) coordinate system appears as a square matrix of order N. The relation between the matrices A and A' of a given tensor in two different coordinate systems S and S' is determined by an orthogonal matrix Q of order N. Q depends only on the position of the one system relative to the other, and thus is independent of the tensor considered: $A' = \tilde{Q}AQ$. The square matrix A is said to have undergone an *orthogonal transformation*, giving as a result the square matrix A'.

In order to stress the distinction between a given linear vector function and its numerical representation (different in different systems) in square matrices, the name *tensor* has been introduced to denote the vector function itself. Something analogous could have been considered for vectors by speaking of column matrices only in connection with each fixed coordinate system, reserving the name *vector* for the "geometric" quantity.

It is now easily seen that the operations introduced previously for tensors in a given coordinate system (i.e., for matrices) really do give tensors:

$$kA' = k\tilde{Q}AQ = \tilde{Q}(kA)Q,$$
$$A' \pm B' = \tilde{Q}AQ \pm \tilde{Q}BQ = \tilde{Q}(AQ \pm BQ) = \tilde{Q}(A \pm B)Q,$$
$$A'B' = \tilde{Q}AQ\tilde{Q}BQ = \tilde{Q}AEBQ = \tilde{Q}(AB)Q.$$

The product of a tensor and a vector is also a vector:

$$A'X' = \tilde{Q}AQ\tilde{Q}X = \tilde{Q}AEX = \tilde{Q}(AX).$$

Finally a scalar can be constructed from a tensor and two vectors:

$$\tilde{X}'A'Y' = (\widetilde{\tilde{Q}X})\tilde{Q}AQ\tilde{Q}Y = \tilde{X}\tilde{\tilde{Q}}\tilde{Q}AQ\tilde{Q}Y = \tilde{X}Q\tilde{Q}AQ\tilde{Q}Y = \tilde{X}EAEY$$
$$= \tilde{X}AY.$$

This agrees with what has been previously stated, as the quantity discussed here is the scalar product of two vectors (X and AY).

Example 1-24. Let us consider the tensor f which in a given usual right-angled two-dimensional coordinate system S is represented by the matrix

$$A = \begin{Bmatrix} 3 & 1 \\ 0 & 2 \end{Bmatrix}.$$

The image of vector $\mathbf{a} = (2,1)$ is $f(\mathbf{a}) = (7,2)$, since

$$\begin{Bmatrix} 3 & 1 \\ 0 & 2 \end{Bmatrix} \begin{Bmatrix} 2 \\ 1 \end{Bmatrix} = \begin{Bmatrix} 7 \\ 2 \end{Bmatrix}.$$

We now introduce a new coordinate system S' with the same origin and with base vectors (relative to S) $\mathbf{q}_1 = (\frac{4}{5}, \frac{3}{5})$ and $\mathbf{q}_2 = (-\frac{3}{5}, \frac{4}{5})$, corresponding to the orthogonal matrix

$$Q = \begin{Bmatrix} \frac{4}{5} & -\frac{3}{5} \\ \frac{3}{5} & \frac{4}{5} \end{Bmatrix}.$$

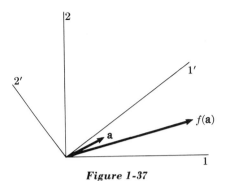

Figure 1-37

The new coordinates of **a** and $f(\mathbf{a})$ are then $\mathbf{a} = (\frac{11}{5}, -\frac{2}{5})$ and $f(\mathbf{a}) = (\frac{34}{5}, -\frac{13}{5})$, since (Fig. 1-37)

$$\begin{Bmatrix} \frac{4}{5} & \frac{3}{5} \\ -\frac{3}{5} & \frac{4}{5} \end{Bmatrix} \begin{Bmatrix} 2 \\ 1 \end{Bmatrix} = \begin{Bmatrix} \frac{11}{5} \\ -\frac{2}{5} \end{Bmatrix}$$

and

$$\begin{Bmatrix} \frac{4}{5} & \frac{3}{5} \\ -\frac{3}{5} & \frac{4}{5} \end{Bmatrix} \begin{Bmatrix} 7 \\ 2 \end{Bmatrix} = \begin{Bmatrix} \frac{34}{5} \\ -\frac{13}{5} \end{Bmatrix}.$$

According to the above theory, we could also have determined the new coordinates of $f(\mathbf{a})$ as follows: In the new system S', the given tensor f is represented by the matrix A', where

$$A' = \tilde{Q}AQ = \begin{Bmatrix} \frac{4}{5} & \frac{3}{5} \\ -\frac{3}{5} & \frac{4}{5} \end{Bmatrix} \begin{Bmatrix} 3 & 1 \\ 0 & 2 \end{Bmatrix} \begin{Bmatrix} \frac{4}{5} & -\frac{3}{5} \\ \frac{3}{5} & \frac{4}{5} \end{Bmatrix}$$

$$= \begin{Bmatrix} \frac{4}{5} & \frac{3}{5} \\ -\frac{3}{5} & \frac{4}{5} \end{Bmatrix} \begin{Bmatrix} 3 & -1 \\ \frac{6}{5} & \frac{8}{5} \end{Bmatrix} = \begin{Bmatrix} \frac{78}{25} & \frac{4}{25} \\ -\frac{21}{25} & \frac{47}{25} \end{Bmatrix}.$$

As the new coordinates of **a** are $(\frac{11}{5}, -\frac{2}{5})$ we may then find the new coordinates of $f(\mathbf{a})$ in this way:

$$\begin{Bmatrix} \frac{78}{25} & \frac{4}{25} \\ -\frac{21}{25} & \frac{47}{25} \end{Bmatrix} \begin{Bmatrix} \frac{11}{5} \\ -\frac{2}{5} \end{Bmatrix} = \begin{Bmatrix} \frac{34}{5} \\ -\frac{13}{5} \end{Bmatrix}. \qquad \square$$

Example 1-25. Let us consider the tensor f, which in a given usual right-angled two-dimensional coordinate system S is represented by the matrix

$$A = \begin{Bmatrix} 5 & -\sqrt{3} \\ -\sqrt{3} & 7 \end{Bmatrix}.$$

We want to determine its matrix A' in the system S' obtained by rotating the original system through an angle of 30° about the origin.

As this corresponds to

$$Q = \begin{Bmatrix} \dfrac{\sqrt{3}}{2} & -\dfrac{1}{2} \\ \dfrac{1}{2} & \dfrac{\sqrt{3}}{2} \end{Bmatrix},$$

we find

$$A' = \tilde{Q}AQ = \begin{Bmatrix} \dfrac{\sqrt{3}}{2} & \dfrac{1}{2} \\ -\dfrac{1}{2} & \dfrac{\sqrt{3}}{2} \end{Bmatrix} \begin{Bmatrix} 5 & -\sqrt{3} \\ -\sqrt{3} & 7 \end{Bmatrix} \begin{Bmatrix} \dfrac{\sqrt{3}}{2} & -\dfrac{1}{2} \\ \dfrac{1}{2} & \dfrac{\sqrt{3}}{2} \end{Bmatrix}$$

$$\begin{Bmatrix} \dfrac{\sqrt{3}}{2} & \dfrac{1}{2} \\ -\dfrac{1}{2} & \dfrac{\sqrt{3}}{2} \end{Bmatrix} \begin{Bmatrix} 2\sqrt{3} & -4 \\ 2 & 4\sqrt{3} \end{Bmatrix} = \begin{Bmatrix} 4 & 0 \\ 0 & 8 \end{Bmatrix}.$$

Thus in the system S' the given tensor is represented by a particularly simple matrix. The image of any vector is here obtained by multiplying the first coordinate by 4 and the second by 8. Especially it is noted that vectors on the axes of the coordinate system S' have images with unchanged directions.

These results are intimately connected with the fact that matrix A is symmetric. We shall return to this later. □

The Two Uses of Square Matrices

Square matrices have now been used in two different ways; first, to determine a linear vector function in a given coordinate system: $Y = AX$, and second, in changing coordinates: $X = QX'$. In the first case, X and Y give the coordinates of two different vectors in the same coordinate system. In the second case, X and X' give the coordinates of the same vector in two different coordinate systems.

To clarify the relation between these two applications of square matrices, we shall now consider in more detail an orthogonal matrix of order 2. The corresponding linear vector function is then

$$\begin{Bmatrix} y_1 \\ y_2 \end{Bmatrix} = \begin{Bmatrix} \cos\theta & -\sin\theta \\ \sin\theta & \cos\theta \end{Bmatrix} \begin{Bmatrix} x_1 \\ x_2 \end{Bmatrix}.$$

The image of the unit vector $e_1 = (1,0)$ is the unit vector $f_1 = (\cos\theta, \sin\theta)$, while the image of the unit vector $e_2 = (0,1)$ is the unit vector $f_2 = (-\sin\theta, \cos\theta)$. In both cases the image is obtained by a rotation of angle θ about the origin of the coordinate system. As shown previously (p. 49), the linearity of the vector function now implies that this is also valid for the image (y_1, y_2) of an arbitrary vector (x_1, x_2):

$$(y_1, y_2) = (x_1 \cos\theta - x_2 \sin\theta, \; x_1 \sin\theta + x_2 \cos\theta)$$
$$= x_1(\cos\theta, \sin\theta) + x_2(-\sin\theta, \cos\theta) = x_1 f_1 + x_2 f_2.$$

We may also say that the image of the vector $(x_1, x_2) = x_1 e_1 + x_2 e_2$ is a vector with the same coordinates, but in the coordinate system spanned by the rotated base vectors f_1 and f_2 (Fig. 1-38). Instead of rotating the vector x through the angle θ, we could of course also have obtained the position of the image vector y relative to the coordinate system by rotating the system through the angle $-\theta$ about the origin.

The last point of view corresponds to what occurs when the given orthogonal matrix is used to define a change of coordinates:

$$\begin{Bmatrix} x_1 \\ x_2 \end{Bmatrix} = \begin{Bmatrix} \cos\theta & -\sin\theta \\ \sin\theta & \cos\theta \end{Bmatrix} \begin{Bmatrix} x_1' \\ x_2' \end{Bmatrix}.$$

As (x_1, x_2) and (x_1', x_2') are now to represent coordinates of the same vector, then the ordered pair (x_1, x_2) must belong to a coordinate system S which is rotated through the angle $-\theta$ relative to the system S' to which the ordered pair (x_1', x_2') belongs (Fig. 1-39).

Inversely we therefore have that the system S' is rotated through

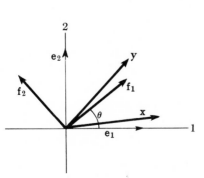

Figure 1-38

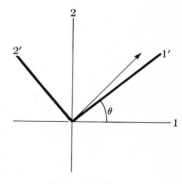

Figure 1-39

the angle $+\theta$ relative to the system S—in exact agreement with earlier results (p. 11).

Some General Remarks

In the preceding sections we have developed a theory of vectors and tensors. At no point, however, have we properly defined an N-dimensional vector. It is true that this was tried on page 28 in terms of ordered N-tuples of real numbers, but it was immediately stressed that this was only the "representation" of an N-dimensional vector in a given "coordinate system." On page 66 we were able to go a little further, even if an N-dimensional vector was described simply as a "geometric" quantity. To get started it was still necessary to know the representation in one coordinate system of the vector to be considered, but it was now shown explicitly how a change of coordinate system influenced the appearance of this vector. However, what an N-dimensional vector *really* is was not explained.

Similar questions may often be posed, also in very elementary and familiar connections. Let us as an example consider the question: What is a positive integer? As is well known, the same integer will appear differently in different systems of enumeration. The integer which in the decimal system appears for instance as 19 will in the binary system, based on two, appear as 10011, in the ternary system, based on three, as 201, etc. What is nineteen then really?

We shall, of course, not consider this problem here. Returning instead to the consideration of N-dimensional vectors, we note first that even if the geometric terminology used is very suggestive, it is only a manner of speaking; and second, the theory developed above at any rate has turned out to have wide applications in many different branches of science. In every particular application, the concept of an N-dimensional vector as well as the concept of changing a system of coordinates is then given a definite *interpretation*. In such an interpretation the above question of what an N-dimensional vector is is easily answered.

Exercises

*1. Consider a tensor which in a given usual right-angled right-handed coordinate system is represented by the matrix

$$\left\{ \begin{array}{rrr} 1 & 1 & 0 \\ 1 & 0 & 1 \\ -2 & -1 & 2 \end{array} \right\}.$$

A new usual right-angled right-handed coordinate system with base vectors $\mathbf{i'}$, $\mathbf{j'}$, and $\mathbf{k'}$ is now introduced. The directions of $\mathbf{i'}$ and $\mathbf{j'}$ are given by the vectors $(1, 2, 2)$ and $(0, -1, 1)$, respectively. Determine the matrix representing the given tensor in the new system.

*2. Show that if a tensor is represented by a symmetric matrix of order N in one orthogonal system, the same will be true in any orthogonal system. Investigate whether an analogous theorem is valid for skew-symmetric matrices.

3. Show that the square of a symmetric matrix is itself a symmetric matrix, while the product of two symmetric matrices need not be symmetric.

4. Show that the product of two symmetric matrices is symmetric if and only if the two matrices commute.

5. Consider the set of all matrices of order N. Let A and B be two such matrices. B is now said to be *conjugate* to A in case there exists a matrix T of order N with determinant different from zero such that $B = T^{-1}AT$. Show that the following is valid for arbitrary matrices A, B, and C of order N. A is conjugate to itself. If A is conjugate to B, then B is to A. If A is conjugate to B, and B is conjugate to C, then A is conjugate to C. Defining the *class* of A to be the set of all matrices conjugate to A, finally show that any matrix of order N belongs to one and only one class. (First show that any matrix belongs to at least one class, and second that if two classes have one matrix in common, they are identical.)

Answers

1.
$$\left\{ \begin{array}{ccc} 1 & \dfrac{7}{3\sqrt{2}} & -\dfrac{1}{\sqrt{2}} \\[2ex] -\dfrac{1}{\sqrt{2}} & 1 & -2 \\[2ex] \dfrac{1}{\sqrt{2}} & -\dfrac{4}{3} & 1 \end{array} \right\}$$

2. From $A = \tilde{A}$ and $A' = \tilde{Q}AQ$ we get $\tilde{A'} = \tilde{Q}\tilde{A}\tilde{\tilde{Q}} = \tilde{Q}AQ = A'$, which shows that A' is also symmetric. Correspondingly, from $A = -\tilde{A}$ and $A' = \tilde{Q}AQ$ we get $\tilde{A'} = \tilde{Q}\tilde{A}\tilde{\tilde{Q}} = \tilde{Q}(-A)Q = -\tilde{Q}AQ = -A'$, which shows that A' is also skew-symmetric.

1-9. DIAGONALIZATION

Formulation of the Problem

Problems in connection with the so-called *diagonalization* of matrices will now be considered. Consider a tensor which in one coordinate system S is represented by a symmetric matrix A. In the coordinate system S' obtained by transformation through an orthogonal matrix Q, the tensor will be represented by the matrix $A' = \tilde{Q}AQ$. This will also be symmetric, as $\tilde{A'} = \tilde{Q}\tilde{A}\tilde{\tilde{Q}} = \tilde{Q}AQ = A'$. For that reason symmetry is said to be a *tensor property*. The problem now is to find possible coordinate systems where the given symmetric tensor is represented by an especially simple symmetric matrix, namely a diagonal matrix, and to find the elements of this. Hence the problem is to solve the matrix equation $\tilde{Q}AQ = D$, where Q and D are unknowns with the condition that Q is orthogonal and D diagonal.

On multiplication from the left by Q we obtain $AQ = QD$:

$$
\begin{pmatrix} a_{11} & a_{12} & \cdots & a_{1N} \\ a_{21} & a_{22} & \cdots & a_{2N} \\ & & & \\ & & & \\ & & & \\ a_{N1} & a_{N2} & \cdots & a_{NN} \end{pmatrix}
\begin{pmatrix} q_{11} & q_{12} & \cdots & q_{1N} \\ q_{21} & q_{22} & \cdots & q_{2N} \\ & & & \\ & & & \\ & & & \\ q_{N1} & q_{N2} & \cdots & q_{NN} \end{pmatrix}
$$

$$
= \begin{pmatrix} q_{11} & q_{12} & \cdots & q_{1N} \\ q_{21} & q_{22} & \cdots & q_{2N} \\ & & & \\ & & & \\ & & & \\ q_{N1} & q_{N2} & \cdots & q_{NN} \end{pmatrix}
\begin{pmatrix} d_{11} & 0 & \cdots & 0 \\ 0 & d_{22} & \cdots & 0 \\ & & & \\ & & & \\ & & & \\ 0 & 0 & \cdots & d_{NN} \end{pmatrix},
$$

or

$$
\begin{pmatrix} a_{11} & a_{12} & \cdots & a_{1N} \\ a_{21} & a_{22} & \cdots & a_{2N} \\ & & & \\ & & & \\ & & & \\ a_{N1} & a_{N2} & \cdots & a_{NN} \end{pmatrix}
\begin{pmatrix} q_{11} & q_{12} & \cdots & q_{1N} \\ q_{21} & q_{22} & \cdots & q_{2N} \\ & & & \\ & & & \\ & & & \\ q_{N1} & q_{N2} & \cdots & q_{NN} \end{pmatrix}
$$

$$
= \begin{pmatrix} d_{11}q_{11} & d_{22}q_{12} & \cdots & d_{NN}q_{1N} \\ d_{11}q_{21} & d_{22}q_{22} & \cdots & d_{NN}q_{2N} \\ & & & \\ & & & \\ & & & \\ d_{11}q_{N1} & d_{22}q_{N2} & \cdots & d_{NN}q_{NN} \end{pmatrix}.
$$

When the corresponding columns on the right and left sides of the equation are identified, N matrix equations are obtained, which together are equivalent to the given equation:

$$AQ_1 = d_{11}Q_1,\ AQ_2 = d_{22}Q_2, \ldots, AQ_N = d_{NN}Q_N.$$

Each of these equations sets a condition on only one of the columns of the unknown matrix Q and the corresponding diagonal element in D.

The Eigenvalue Problem

The above equations are seen to be all of the same form: $AX = \lambda X$, which represents the so-called *eigenvalue problem* for the matrix A. We shall consider this more closely. The problem is to find all possible numbers λ and the corresponding nonzero column matrices X, such that when A operates on X, the result is simply multiplication by the number λ. The usable values of λ are called the *eigenvalues* of the given matrix, while the corresponding column matrices (vectors) are called the *eigenvectors* corresponding to the eigenvalues concerned.

The equation can be rewritten to give

$$AX = \lambda EX \quad \text{or} \quad (A - \lambda E)X = 0.$$

This represents N linear homogeneous equations with N unknowns. Of course these always have the zero solution. As we are looking for nonzero solutions, the main determinant of the equations (cf. p. 45) must be 0: $|A - \lambda E| = 0$.

Thus an equation of the Nth degree in λ is obtained; this is called the *characteristic* or the *secular equation*. Its roots are the only possible eigenvalues for the matrix A. It can now be shown from the symmetry of A that the secular equation has N real roots, when each single root is counted as many times as given by its multiplicity. Let these be $\lambda_1, \lambda_2, . . ., \lambda_N$, where some of the λ's may be equal.

If λ_i is a single root, the system of equations can be shown to have a single infinity of (mutually proportional) solutions; among these there will be exactly two normalized (and opposite) eigenvectors. When λ_k is a root with a multiplicity of p (for example, $\lambda_k = \lambda_{k+1} = \cdots = \lambda_{k+p-1}$), then the system has a pth infinity of solutions, among which it is possible (in an infinity of ways) to choose exactly p normalized mutually orthogonal eigenvectors.

Solution of the Problem

We now return to the N equations

$$AQ_1 = d_{11}Q_1, \; AQ_2 = d_{22}Q_2, . . ., AQ_N = d_{NN}Q_N.$$

We have seen above that the only possible diagonal elements d_{ii} are the roots in the secular equation $|A - \lambda E| = 0$. As the columns $Q_1, Q_2, . . ., Q_N$ in the orthogonal matrix Q must be normalized and mutually orthogonal, we conclude that a single root λ_i in the secular equation can be used only once as a diagonal element, for example $d_{ii} = \lambda_i$, with only two possibilities for the corresponding normalized column matrix Q_i. Furthermore, a root λ_k, which has a multiplicity of p, can be used as a diagonal element at most p times; for example, $d_{kk} = d_{k+1,k+1} = \cdots = d_{k+p-1,k+p-1} = \lambda_k$, with an infinite number of possible ways of choosing the corresponding normalized mutually orthogonal column matrices $Q_k, Q_{k+1}, \ldots, Q_{k+p-1}$.

Using all the roots of the secular equation, a total of exactly N normalized column matrices can thus be obtained, among which two that correspond to the same eigenvalue are mutually orthogonal.

There remains only the question of whether the column matrices corresponding to different eigenvalues are also orthogonal, as required. This condition turns out to be automatically satisfied: Let $AQ_i = \lambda_i Q_i$ and $AQ_k = \lambda_k Q_k$, $\lambda_i \neq \lambda_k$. From this $\tilde{Q}_k A Q_i = \lambda_i \tilde{Q}_k Q_i$ and $\tilde{Q}_i A Q_k = \lambda_k \tilde{Q}_i Q_k$. On transposing the last equation, we obtain $\tilde{Q}_k \tilde{A} \tilde{\tilde{Q}}_i = \lambda_k \tilde{Q}_k \tilde{\tilde{Q}}_i$, or, as A is symmetric, $\tilde{Q}_k A Q_i = \lambda_k \tilde{Q}_k Q_i$. Then by subtracting, $0 = (\lambda_i - \lambda_k)\tilde{Q}_k Q_i$, or $\tilde{Q}_k Q_i = 0$, and orthogonality is proved.

Aside from the distribution of the roots of the secular equation along the main diagonal in D, this matrix is seen to be uniquely determined. This "diagonalized" matrix can thus be found without knowledge of Q.

Corresponding to a definite choice of the diagonal matrix, there will be, for the case when all the roots of the secular equation are different from each other, a total of 2^N solutions for Q, half of these giving orthogonal matrices with determinant $+1$. When the secular equation has two (or more) roots which are equal, then there is an infinity of solutions for Q.

Similar Matrices

Given two arbitrary symmetric matrices A and B of order N. A is then said to be *similar* to B ($A \sim B$) when there exists an orthogonal matrix Q which transforms A onto B ($B = \tilde{Q}AQ$). It is easily seen that (1) $A \sim A$, (2) $A \sim B$ implies $B \sim A$, and (3) $A \sim B$ and $B \sim C$ implies $A \sim C$. As a consequence of property (2), matrices A and B are also said simply to be similar (to each other) if only one of them is similar to the other.

Corresponding to the arbitrary symmetric matrix A, we now define the class K_A as the set of all matrices which are similar to A. In this way a partition of the set of all symmetric matrices is defined, as from properties (1) to (3) we see that each symmetric matrix belongs to one and only one class: The matrix A belongs to its own class, (1), and to no other class, for if A belongs also to K_B, i.e., $A \sim B$, then the classes K_A and K_B are seen to be identical, (2) and (3).

The similarity of two symmetric matrices A and B means that these represent the same tensor in two different coordinate systems. What we have achieved in the above is to have obtained within each class certain especially simple representations—matrices with zeros everywhere outside the main diagonal. As a major result, we found that the diagonal elements were uniquely determined as roots of the characteristic equation.

Two symmetric matrices A and A' belonging to the same class thus have characteristic equations with the same roots. If the equations also have a common coefficient, for example, to λ^N, then the two equations must be identical. By identifying the corresponding coefficients in two such equations we obtain a series of quantities which are invariant under arbitrary orthogonal transformations.

The characteristic equation for A is obtained as

$$\begin{vmatrix} a_{11} - \lambda & a_{12} & \cdots & a_{1N} \\ a_{21} & a_{22} - \lambda & \cdots & a_{2N} \\ \cdot & & & \\ \cdot & & & \\ \cdot & & & \\ a_{N1} & a_{N2} & \cdots & a_{NN} - \lambda \end{vmatrix} = 0,$$

or

$$(-1)^N \lambda^N + (a_{11} + a_{22} + \cdots + a_{NN})(-1)^{N-1}\lambda^{N-1} + \cdots + |A| = 0.$$

From this it is seen that the determinant of the matrix A, and the sum of the diagonal elements of the matrix, the so-called *trace* (Tr A or Sp A), is invariant under an arbitrary orthogonal transformation. In the case of the determinant, this also can be shown from the equation $A' = \tilde{Q}AQ$, as $|A'| = |\tilde{Q}| \, |A| \, |Q| = (\pm 1)|A|(\pm 1) = |A|$.

Upon comparison with a diagonal matrix from the class of A, we find that the determinant $|A| = \lambda_1\lambda_2 \cdots \lambda_N$, and correspondingly that the trace $a_{11} + a_{22} + \cdots + a_{NN} = \lambda_1 + \lambda_2 + \cdots + \lambda_N$, in agreement with well-known rules regarding the roots in an equation of degree N. The invariance of the trace plays an important role in quantum mechanics.

Matrix Functions

Corresponding to a polynomial which for the sake of simplicity is chosen of degree 2, $f(x) = ax^2 + bx + c$, where a, b, and c are real numbers, we consider the matrix function f defined for all symmetric matrices A of order N such that $f(A) = aA^2 + bA + cE$. Here the constant term appears as a product of the number c and the unit matrix E.

If Q is an orthogonal matrix which diagonalizes A, $(\tilde{Q}AQ = D)$, then we obtain

$$\tilde{Q}f(A)Q = \tilde{Q}aAAQ + \tilde{Q}bAQ + \tilde{Q}cEQ = a(\tilde{Q}AQ)(\tilde{Q}AQ)$$
$$+ b(\tilde{Q}AQ) + c(\tilde{Q}EQ)$$
$$= aD^2 + bD + cE.$$

This is also a diagonal matrix. The matrix $f(A)$ is thus diagonalized by the same orthogonal matrix as A. When the eigenvalues of A are λ_i $(i = 1,2,. . .,N)$, the eigenvalues for $f(A)$ are seen to be $f(\lambda_i)$. This result is obviously valid for polynomials of an arbitrarily high degree.

As a continuation of this we shall finally consider the matrix which appears on the left side of the characteristic equation belonging to the symmetric matrix A when we substitute A for λ (and multiply the constant term by E). From the expression $f(\lambda) = (-1)^N\lambda^N + (-1)^{N-1}(\mathrm{Tr}\,A)\lambda^{N-1} + \cdots + |A|$, the matrix function $f(A) = (-1)^N A^N + (-1)^{N-1}(\mathrm{Tr}\,A)A^{N-1} + \cdots + |A|E$ is obtained. Intuitively it would be expected that this matrix function of A is identical with the zero matrix; this will now be shown to be the case.

When the matrix $f(A)$ operates on an eigenvector X of A, then we obtain $f(A)X = f(\lambda)X = 0X = 0$, where the first 0 is the number 0 and the other 0 represents the zero vector. This result is valid for all eigenvectors of A, and from these it will always be possible to choose N linearly independent vectors. Each N-dimensional vector can, however, be resolved according to N linearly independent vectors. Hence the linearity of the vector function shows that $f(A)$ operating on each N-dimensional vector gives the zero vector. $f(A)$ must therefore be the zero matrix.

This result, often called the *Cayley-Hamilton theorem*, states in loose formulation that each square matrix satisfies its own characteristic equation. The validity of the theorem has only been shown in a special case (A symmetric), but it is valid for all square matrices.

Reduction of Quadratic Forms in Two Dimensions

As a simple application of the above theory, the so-called *reduction of quadratic forms* in two (and three) variables will now be discussed.

Let us consider an arbitrary equation of second degree in the two variables x and y:

$$ax^2 + by^2 + 2cxy + dx + ey + f = 0.$$

In a usual right-angled coordinate system S—with the exception of "degenerate" cases—this always represents a conical section when the cross term is missing ($c = 0$). We shall now show that the same is also true in the more general case when $c \neq 0$, as with an appropriate rotation of the coordinate system we can obtain a new system where the equation of the given curve appears without a cross term.

The given equation can be written in matrix language as

$$\{x \quad y\} \begin{Bmatrix} a & c \\ c & b \end{Bmatrix} \begin{Bmatrix} x \\ y \end{Bmatrix} + \{d \quad e\} \begin{Bmatrix} x \\ y \end{Bmatrix} + \{f\} = \{0\},$$

where all the terms are matrices of the first order, i.e., numbers (in part dependent on x and y). The square matrix which appears is chosen to be symmetric and is thus uniquely determined. It is called the *form matrix* corresponding to the *quadratic form* $ax^2 + by^2 + 2cxy$.

We next introduce a new usual right-angled coordinate system S' with the same origin. The connection between the old and new point coordinates (x,y) and (x',y') will then be given by an orthogonal matrix Q, with $|Q| = \pm 1$, according to whether the two systems have the same sense of rotation or not (p. 60). The equation of the given curve in the new system is obtained by introducing $X = QX'$ (and thus $\tilde{X} = \tilde{X}'\tilde{Q}$):

$$\{x' \quad y'\} \begin{Bmatrix} q_{11} & q_{21} \\ q_{12} & q_{22} \end{Bmatrix} \begin{Bmatrix} a & c \\ c & b \end{Bmatrix} \begin{Bmatrix} q_{11} & q_{12} \\ q_{21} & q_{22} \end{Bmatrix} \begin{Bmatrix} x' \\ y' \end{Bmatrix} + \{d \quad e\} \begin{Bmatrix} q_{11} & q_{12} \\ q_{21} & q_{22} \end{Bmatrix} \begin{Bmatrix} x' \\ y' \end{Bmatrix}$$
$$+ \{f\} = \{0\}.$$

In this way a new quadratic form with the form matrix $A' = \tilde{Q}AQ$ is found. The problem will then be to choose the new coordinate system (i.e., Q) such that A' becomes diagonal. The reduction of the given quadratic form thus becomes the problem of diagonalizing the corresponding form matrix.

The eigenvalues of A are obtained from the equation

$$\begin{vmatrix} a - \lambda & c \\ c & b - \lambda \end{vmatrix} = 0.$$

When the roots are a' and b', the equation of the given curve in the new system is

$$\{x' \quad y'\} \begin{Bmatrix} a' & 0 \\ 0 & b' \end{Bmatrix} \begin{Bmatrix} x' \\ y' \end{Bmatrix} + \{d \quad e\} \begin{Bmatrix} q_{11} & q_{12} \\ q_{21} & q_{22} \end{Bmatrix} \begin{Bmatrix} x' \\ y' \end{Bmatrix} + \{f\} = \{0\},$$

or $a'x'^2 + b'y'^2 + d'x' + e'y' + f = 0$.

This can then be rewritten in the usual way to determine fully the type and location of the given curve in the new coordinate system. From Q the new coordinate system is determined, and finally the position of the given curve in the original coordinate system.

Example 1-26. Determine the curve which in a given usual right-angled system has the equation $5x^2 + 7y^2 - 2\sqrt{3}xy - 32 = 0$. In matrix formulation we have

$$\{x \quad y\} \begin{Bmatrix} 5 & -\sqrt{3} \\ -\sqrt{3} & 7 \end{Bmatrix} \begin{Bmatrix} x \\ y \end{Bmatrix} + \{-32\} = \{0\}.$$

The eigenvalues of the form matrix are obtained from the equation

$$\begin{vmatrix} 5 - \lambda & -\sqrt{3} \\ -\sqrt{3} & 7 - \lambda \end{vmatrix} = 0$$

or $\lambda^2 - 12\lambda + 32 = 0$, giving the roots 4 and 8. There are now two possibilities: (1) $a' = 4$, $b' = 8$; and (2) $a' = 8$, $b' = 4$.

(1) As the first-degree terms are missing in the given equation of the curve, the new equation can be written down without a knowledge of the corresponding Q: $4x'^2 + 8y'^2 - 32 = 0$ or $(x'^2/8) + (y'^2/4) = 1$, which is an ellipse.

Determining the first column in Q, we obtain

$$\begin{Bmatrix} 5 - 4 & -\sqrt{3} \\ -\sqrt{3} & 7 - 4 \end{Bmatrix} \begin{Bmatrix} q_{11} \\ q_{21} \end{Bmatrix} = \begin{Bmatrix} 0 \\ 0 \end{Bmatrix} \quad \text{or} \quad \begin{aligned} q_{11} - \sqrt{3}q_{21} &= 0, \\ -\sqrt{3}q_{11} + 3q_{21} &= 0. \end{aligned}$$

All the solutions to this are $(q_{11}, q_{21}) = t(\sqrt{3}, 1)$, where t is a free parameter. Among these are two normalized solutions, $(\sqrt{3}/2, \frac{1}{2})$ and $(-\sqrt{3}/2, -\frac{1}{2})$. The second column in Q is found by solving the equation

$$\begin{Bmatrix} 5 - 8 & -\sqrt{3} \\ -\sqrt{3} & 7 - 8 \end{Bmatrix} \begin{Bmatrix} q_{12} \\ q_{22} \end{Bmatrix} = \begin{Bmatrix} 0 \\ 0 \end{Bmatrix} \quad \text{or} \quad \begin{aligned} -3q_{12} - \sqrt{3}q_{22} &= 0, \\ -\sqrt{3}q_{12} - q_{22} &= 0, \end{aligned}$$

which gives $(q_{12}, q_{22}) = t(-1, \sqrt{3})$, from which the normalized solutions $(-\frac{1}{2}, \sqrt{3}/2)$ and $(\frac{1}{2}, -\sqrt{3}/2)$ are found. In all there are four possibilities for Q:

$$\begin{Bmatrix} \dfrac{\sqrt{3}}{2} & -\dfrac{1}{2} \\[2mm] \dfrac{1}{2} & \dfrac{\sqrt{3}}{2} \end{Bmatrix}, \quad \begin{Bmatrix} -\dfrac{\sqrt{3}}{2} & \dfrac{1}{2} \\[2mm] -\dfrac{1}{2} & -\dfrac{\sqrt{3}}{2} \end{Bmatrix}, \quad \begin{Bmatrix} \dfrac{\sqrt{3}}{2} & \dfrac{1}{2} \\[2mm] \dfrac{1}{2} & -\dfrac{\sqrt{3}}{2} \end{Bmatrix},$$

$$\begin{Bmatrix} -\dfrac{\sqrt{3}}{2} & -\dfrac{1}{2} \\[2mm] -\dfrac{1}{2} & \dfrac{\sqrt{3}}{2} \end{Bmatrix}.$$

Of these, the first two have a positive determinant and the last two have a negative determinant. In the first cases, the second column could immediately have been found as the cross vector of the first column, and in the last two cases as the opposite of this.

(2) Here the equation in the new system is $8x'^2 + 4y'^2 - 32 = 0$ or $(x'^2/4) + (y'^2/8) = 1$.

In obtaining Q it is seen that exchanging the eigenvalues gives rise to an exchange of the columns. We again obtain four solutions, two with $|Q| = 1$ and two with $|Q| = -1$:

$$\begin{Bmatrix} -\dfrac{1}{2} & -\dfrac{\sqrt{3}}{2} \\[2mm] \dfrac{\sqrt{3}}{2} & -\dfrac{1}{2} \end{Bmatrix}, \quad \begin{Bmatrix} \dfrac{1}{2} & \dfrac{\sqrt{3}}{2} \\[2mm] -\dfrac{\sqrt{3}}{2} & \dfrac{1}{2} \end{Bmatrix}, \quad \begin{Bmatrix} \dfrac{1}{2} & -\dfrac{\sqrt{3}}{2} \\[2mm] -\dfrac{\sqrt{3}}{2} & -\dfrac{1}{2} \end{Bmatrix},$$

$$\begin{Bmatrix} -\dfrac{1}{2} & \dfrac{\sqrt{3}}{2} \\[2mm] \dfrac{\sqrt{3}}{2} & \dfrac{1}{2} \end{Bmatrix}.$$

In all eight cases the same curve is of course obtained, this being an ellipse with its center at the origin of the coordinate system (because of the absence of first-order terms), the major axis of which is at an angle of 30° with the X-axis, and which has semiaxes $2\sqrt{2}$ and 2.

The eight possibilities only correspond to different choices for a new coordinate system (Fig. 1-40). □

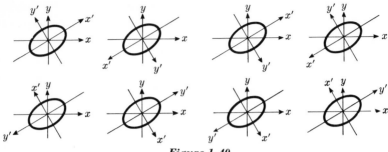

Figure 1-40

The above example is identical with that considered previously (p. 11). It is doubtful whether the method used here is to be preferred in the case of two dimensions. It should rather be looked upon as just an example of a diagonalizing process.

Reduction of Quadratic Forms in Three Dimensions

In the three-dimensional case, the advantages of the matrix methods are easily seen. The problem here is to determine the properties of a surface which has the following equation of the second degree in the three variables x, y, and z in a usual right-angled (and right-handed) coordinate system S:

$$ax^2 + by^2 + cz^2 + 2dxy + 2eyz + 2fzx + gx + hy + kz + l = 0.$$

We again want, by an appropriate rotation of the given coordinate system, to obtain another system S', where cross terms do not appear in the equation. From this, it will be possible to obtain a simple description of the given surface relative to the new system and thus also relative to the old one.

In matrix formulation we have

$$\{x \quad y \quad z\} \begin{Bmatrix} a & d & f \\ d & b & e \\ f & e & c \end{Bmatrix} \begin{Bmatrix} x \\ y \\ z \end{Bmatrix} + \{g \quad h \quad k\} \begin{Bmatrix} x \\ y \\ z \end{Bmatrix} + \{l\} = \{0\},$$

where the form matrix A corresponding to the quadratic form is again seen to be uniquely determined from a condition of symmetry.

With the introduction of a new usual right-angled coordinate system S' having the same origin, the relation between the old and the new point coordinates (x,y,z) and (x',y',z') is of the form $X = QX'$, where Q is an orthogonal matrix of third order. In the new system an equation is now obtained which has a corresponding form matrix $A' = \tilde{Q}AQ$. The problem of reducing the given quadratic form is again one of diagonalizing, this time a symmetric matrix of third order.

Example 1-27. Determine the surface which in a given usual right-angled right-handed coordinate system XYZ has the equation

$$5x^2 + 2y^2 + 2z^2 - 2xy + 4yz - 2zx - 6 = 0.$$

In matrix formulation we have

$$\{x \quad y \quad z\} \begin{pmatrix} 5 & -1 & -1 \\ -1 & 2 & 2 \\ -1 & 2 & 2 \end{pmatrix} \begin{pmatrix} x \\ y \\ z \end{pmatrix} - \{6\} = \{0\}.$$

The eigenvalues of the form matrix are obtained from the equation

$$\begin{vmatrix} 5-\lambda & -1 & -1 \\ -1 & 2-\lambda & 2 \\ -1 & 2 & 2-\lambda \end{vmatrix} = 0 \quad \text{or} \quad -\lambda^3 + 9\lambda^2 - 18\lambda = 0,$$

which has the roots 3, 6, and 0. When the eigenvalues are chosen in the listed order, the equation of the surface in a corresponding new coordinate system $X'Y'Z'$ becomes

$$\{x' \quad y' \quad z'\} \begin{pmatrix} 3 & 0 & 0 \\ 0 & 6 & 0 \\ 0 & 0 & 0 \end{pmatrix} \begin{pmatrix} x' \\ y' \\ z' \end{pmatrix} - \{6\} = \{0\},$$

or

$$3x'^2 + 6y'^2 - 6 = 0.$$

Determining the first column in Q we obtain

$$\begin{pmatrix} 5-3 & -1 & -1 \\ -1 & 2-3 & 2 \\ -1 & 2 & 2-3 \end{pmatrix} \begin{pmatrix} q_{11} \\ q_{21} \\ q_{31} \end{pmatrix} = \begin{pmatrix} 0 \\ 0 \\ 0 \end{pmatrix},$$

or

$$2q_{11} - q_{21} - q_{31} = 0,$$
$$-q_{11} - q_{21} + 2q_{31} = 0,$$
$$-q_{11} + 2q_{21} - q_{31} = 0.$$

The main determinant $|A|$ for these equations is of course 0, and as there are complementary minors of $|A|$ which are different from zero (see p. 45), a single infinity of solutions is obtained: $(q_{11}, q_{21}, q_{31}) = t(1,1,1)$. Of the two normalized solutions,

$$(q_{11}, q_{21}, q_{31}) = \left(\frac{1}{\sqrt{3}}, \frac{1}{\sqrt{3}}, \frac{1}{\sqrt{3}} \right)$$

is selected. Determining the second column, we find

$$\begin{Bmatrix} 5-6 & -1 & -1 \\ -1 & 2-6 & 2 \\ -1 & 2 & 2-6 \end{Bmatrix} \begin{Bmatrix} q_{12} \\ q_{22} \\ q_{32} \end{Bmatrix} = \begin{Bmatrix} 0 \\ 0 \\ 0 \end{Bmatrix},$$

or

$$-q_{12} - q_{22} - q_{32} = 0,$$
$$-q_{12} - 4q_{22} + 2q_{32} = 0,$$
$$-q_{12} + 2q_{22} - 4q_{32} = 0,$$

and thus $(q_{12}, q_{22}, q_{32}) = t(2, -1, -1)$. Of the two normalized solutions, we select

$$(q_{12}, q_{22}, q_{32}) = \left(\frac{2}{\sqrt{6}}, -\frac{1}{\sqrt{6}}, -\frac{1}{\sqrt{6}} \right).$$

The third column is now uniquely determined if we require an orthogonal matrix with positive determinant. Instead of solving the three corresponding equations, we can immediately find the third column vector as the vector product of the first two column vectors,

$$(q_{13}, q_{23}, q_{33}) = \left(\frac{1}{\sqrt{3}}, \frac{1}{\sqrt{3}}, \frac{1}{\sqrt{3}} \right) \times \left(\frac{2}{\sqrt{6}}, -\frac{1}{\sqrt{6}}, -\frac{1}{\sqrt{6}} \right)$$
$$= \left(0, \frac{1}{\sqrt{2}}, -\frac{1}{\sqrt{2}} \right).$$

All together we obtain

$$Q = \begin{Bmatrix} \dfrac{1}{\sqrt{3}} & \dfrac{2}{\sqrt{6}} & 0 \\ \dfrac{1}{\sqrt{3}} & -\dfrac{1}{\sqrt{6}} & \dfrac{1}{\sqrt{2}} \\ \dfrac{1}{\sqrt{3}} & -\dfrac{1}{\sqrt{6}} & -\dfrac{1}{\sqrt{2}} \end{Bmatrix}.$$

The columns of Q give the old coordinates of the new base vectors $\mathbf{i}'$, $\mathbf{j}'$, and $\mathbf{k}'$, respectively. See Example 1-6. $\square$

Example 1-28. Determine the surface which in a given usual right-angled right-handed coordinate system has the equation

$$3x^2 + 3y^2 + 3z^2 - 2xy - 2yz - 2zx - 4 = 0.$$

The eigenvalues are obtained from the equation

$$\begin{vmatrix} 3 - \lambda & -1 & -1 \\ -1 & 3 - \lambda & -1 \\ -1 & -1 & 3 - \lambda \end{vmatrix} = 0 \quad \text{or} \quad -\lambda^3 + 9\lambda^2 - 24\lambda + 16 = 0,$$

which has roots, 1, 4, and 4.

Corresponding to the eigenvalue 1, the first column in Q is obtained from the equations

$$2q_{11} - q_{21} - q_{31} = 0,$$
$$-q_{11} + 2q_{21} - q_{31} = 0,$$
$$-q_{11} - q_{21} + 2q_{31} = 0,$$

from which $(q_{11}, q_{21}, q_{31}) = (1/\sqrt{3}, 1/\sqrt{3}, 1/\sqrt{3})$ (or the opposite vector). The eigenvalue 4 will then give the two other columns in Q:

$$-q_1 - q_2 - q_3 = 0,$$
$$-q_1 - q_2 - q_3 = 0,$$
$$-q_1 - q_2 - q_3 = 0.$$

All the solutions to this are $(q_1, q_2, q_3) = t(1, -1, 0) + s(1, 0, -1)$, where t and s are independent parameters.

As we knew beforehand, there is here a double infinity of solutions, these being all vectors which have coordinates that satisfy the one equation $q_1 + q_2 + q_3 = 0$.

Drawn from the origin of the coordinate system, the end points of these vectors are seen to form the plane $x + y + z = 0$, which of course also contains the origin. All the vectors should be perpendicular to that found for the first column in Q; this is also the case, as the vector $(1/\sqrt{3}, 1/\sqrt{3}, 1/\sqrt{3})$ is a normal to the plane $x + y + z = 0$.

As the second column to Q we can freely choose any unit vector in the plane $x + y + z = 0$, for example $(-1/\sqrt{2}, 1/\sqrt{2}, 0)$; after this the third column is obtained as $(1/\sqrt{3}, 1/\sqrt{3}, 1/\sqrt{3}) \times (-1/\sqrt{2}, 1/\sqrt{2}, 0)$.

In the new coordinate system, the equation of the surface, with the chosen order of eigenvalues, will be

$$x'^2 + 4y'^2 + 4z'^2 = 4 \quad \text{or} \quad \frac{x'^2}{4} + \frac{y'^2}{1} + \frac{z'^2}{1} = 1.$$

This is a so-called *ellipsoid*, in this special case an ellipsoid of revolution, as two of the semiaxes are equal: A plane perpendicular to the X'-axis, $x' = a$ $(-2 < a < 2)$, intersects the surface in a circle $y'^2 + z'^2 = 1 - a^2/4$. The surface can then be formed by revolving about the X'-axis the ellipse $x'^2/4 + y'^2/1 = 1$, which lies in the $X'Y'$-plane. This symmetry may be said to be the reason why the new coordinate system can be so freely chosen.

In the original coordinate system, the axis of rotation has the direction $(1/\sqrt{3},\ 1/\sqrt{3},\ 1/\sqrt{3})$, as determined by the first eigenvector. ☐

Exercises

*1. Find a diagonal matrix D and an orthogonal matrix Q such that $\tilde{Q}AQ = D$ when

$$A = \begin{Bmatrix} \frac{34}{25} & 0 & \frac{12}{25} \\ 0 & 2 & 0 \\ \frac{12}{25} & 0 & \frac{41}{25} \end{Bmatrix}.$$

*2. Find the eigenvalues of the matrix.

$$A = \begin{Bmatrix} 2 & 1 & -1 \\ 1 & 1 & -2 \\ -1 & -2 & 1 \end{Bmatrix}.$$

Also, find an orthogonal matrix Q which transforms A into a diagonal matrix.

*3. Show that the two matrices

$$A = \begin{Bmatrix} 15 & -5 \\ -5 & 15 \end{Bmatrix} \quad \text{and} \quad B = \begin{Bmatrix} 18 & 4 \\ 4 & 12 \end{Bmatrix}$$

are similar, and determine an orthogonal matrix Q which transforms A into B.

4. Show that if two symmetric matrices of order N are similar, their squares are also similar. Use this result to show that the squares of the eigenvalues of a given symmetric matrix are the eigenvalues of the square of this matrix.

5. Show that any matrix A of order 3 which is orthogonal and has a positive determinant must have the eigenvalue 1. Use this result to show that any rigid motion of space with a fixed point is a rotation around an axis through this point (possibly the zero motion which leaves every point fixed).

6. Sketch the following curves in a usual right-angled coordinate system:

(a) $5x^2 + 7y^2 + 2\sqrt{3}xy = 32.$ (c) $x^2 + 3y^2 + 2\sqrt{3}xy - 2x = 0.$
(b) $xy + y^2 + 2x + 3y = 1.$

7. Show that the equation

$$x^2 + 3y^2 + 5z^2 + 8yz + 6zx + 4xy + 16 = 0$$

in an orthogonal coordinate system represents a hyperbolic cylinder, i.e., a cylindrical surface with a hyperbola as directrix and with generators perpendicular to the plane of the hyperbola.

*8. Examine the surface which in an orthogonal coordinate system has the equation

$$8x^2 + 5y^2 + 5z^2 - 4xy - 8yz - 4zx - 36x - 72y - 72z = 0.$$

Answers

1.
$$D = \begin{Bmatrix} 1 & 0 & 0 \\ 0 & 2 & 0 \\ 0 & 0 & 2 \end{Bmatrix}; Q = \left\{ \begin{matrix} \frac{4}{5} & 0 & \frac{3}{5} \\ 0 & 1 & 0 \\ -\frac{3}{5} & 0 & \frac{4}{5} \end{matrix} \right\} \quad \text{(for example).}$$

2. Eigenvalues: -1, 1, and 4.

$$Q = \left\{ \begin{matrix} 0 & \dfrac{2}{\sqrt{6}} & \dfrac{1}{\sqrt{3}} \\[2mm] \dfrac{1}{\sqrt{2}} & -\dfrac{1}{\sqrt{6}} & \dfrac{1}{\sqrt{3}} \\[2mm] \dfrac{1}{\sqrt{2}} & \dfrac{1}{\sqrt{6}} & -\dfrac{1}{\sqrt{3}} \end{matrix} \right\} \quad \text{(for example).}$$

3. A and B are similar, as they have the same characteristic equation.

$$Q = \frac{1}{\sqrt{10}} \begin{Bmatrix} 1 & 3 \\ -3 & 1 \end{Bmatrix} \quad \text{(for example).}$$

8. In an orthogonal system with $\mathbf{i}' = (\frac{1}{3}, \frac{2}{3}, \frac{2}{3})$ the equation of the surface is $y'^2 + z'^2 - 12x' = 0$. Hence it is a paraboloid of revolution with its axis containing $\mathbf{i}'$.

1-10. COMPLEX NUMBERS

Operations with Complex Numbers

As is well known, *complex numbers* can be introduced as quantities of the form $a = [a_1, a_2]$, where a_1 and a_2, the *components* of the complex number, are real numbers.

Two complex numbers $a = [a_1, a_2]$ and $b = [b_1, b_2]$ are said to be *equal* ($a = b$) only if this is the case for the corresponding components: $a_1 = b_1$ and $a_2 = b_2$. Two operations, *addition* and *multiplication*, are now defined for complex numbers:

$$a + b = [a_1 + b_1, a_2 + b_2],$$
$$ab = [a_1 b_1 - a_2 b_2, a_1 b_2 + a_2 b_1].$$

It is easily shown that the basic rules known from calculations with real numbers also are valid for complex numbers.

As in the case of real numbers, the *difference b-a* and the *quotient b/a* of two complex numbers a and b are defined as the uniquely determined solutions to the equations $a + x = b$ and $ax = b$; in the latter case it is assumed that $a \neq [0,0]$. As to the concepts "greater than" and "less than," it proves impossible to introduce an *ordering* of the complex numbers corresponding to that of the real numbers.

If we consider the set of complex numbers with 0 as the second component, then calculations with these will never take us out of this set: $[a_1,0] + [b_1,0] = [a_1 + b_1, 0]$; $[a_1,0][b_1,0] = [a_1b_1,0]$. As the first component of the sum (product) becomes the real sum (product) of the first components of the terms (factors), we can consider these quantities as just another way of writing the corresponding real numbers; i.e., we introduce $a = [a,0]$.

Introducing furthermore the *imaginary unit* $i = [0,1]$, we obtain the following way of writing an arbitrary complex number a:

$$a = [a_1,a_2] = [a_1,0] + [0,a_2] = [a_1,0] + [0,1][a_2,0]$$
$$= a_1 + ia_2.$$

This is the most common way of presenting complex numbers. Calculations with complex numbers are then carried out exactly as with real numbers, except that $i^2 = [0,1][0,1] = [-1,0] = -1$.

In a usual right-angled coordinate system XY, the complex number $a = [a_1,a_2]$ is represented by the point $A = (a_1,a_2)$ in the plane, or by the position vector $\mathbf{OA} = (a_1,a_2)$. The X-axis is then naturally called the *real axis*, and the Y-axis the *imaginary axis*. The sum of two complex numbers is then represented by the sum of the vectors corresponding to the terms. An equivalently simple geometric interpretation of the product is obtained with the help of the notions of modulus and argument. We shall return to this after introducing the polar system of coordinates. Here we just mention that the *absolute value* or *modulus* $|a|$ of the complex number $a = [a_1,a_2]$ is defined to be the nonnegative real number $|a| = \sqrt{a_1{}^2 + a_2{}^2}$.

Corresponding to the complex number $a = [a_1,a_2]$, the (*complex*) *conjugate* a^* is defined as $a^* = [a_1, -a_2]$. Geometrically it is obtained by a reflection of a in the real axis. The following rules are seen to hold: $(a + b)^* = a^* + b^*$, $(a - b)^* = a^* - b^*$, $(a \cdot b)^* = a^*b^*$, and $(a/b)^* = a^*/b^*$. From this it follows that on conjugation of a complex expression made up arbitrarily with the four operations considered, all the numbers concerned must be conjugated (Fig. 1-41).

Complex Roots of Polynomials

The imaginary unit i was originally introduced as an "imaginary" solution of the equation $x^2 + 1 = 0$. Later it turned out that among the set of all complex numbers, any polynomial equation of nth degree

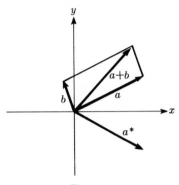

Figure 1-41

with one unknown has exactly n solutions when each individual root is counted as many times as given by its multiplicity, and this even if the coefficients are complex numbers.

If we consider a polynomial equation of nth degree with real coefficients, then all nonreal roots will occur as complex-conjugate pairs. Let $\alpha = \alpha_1 + i\alpha_2$ be a root:

$$a_n(\alpha_1 + i\alpha_2)^n + a_{n-1}(\alpha_1 + i\alpha_2)^{n-1} + \cdots + a_1(\alpha_1 + i\alpha_2) + a_0 = 0.$$

On conjugating we obtain

$$a_n^*(\alpha_1 - i\alpha_2)^n + a_{n-1}^*(\alpha_1 - i\alpha_2)^{n-1} + \cdots$$
$$+ a_1^*(\alpha_1 - i\alpha_2) + a_0^* = 0.$$

As all coefficients (and 0) are real, and hence $a_i = a_i^*$, it is seen that $\alpha^* = \alpha_1 - i\alpha_2$ is also a root of the given equation.

If α is a root with multiplicity p, then this will also be the case for α^*; when α and α^* are roots, then the real factor $(x - \alpha)(x - \alpha^*) = x^2 - 2\alpha_1 x + \alpha_1^2 + \alpha_2^2$ can be removed, and the proof continued with the remaining real polynomial of order $(n - 2)$. It also follows from this that an arbitrary real polynomial of degree n can be factored into real polynomials of the first and second degree: A real root α_0 gives rise to a factor $(x - \alpha_0)$, while a complex root $(\alpha_1 + i\alpha_2)$, together with the complex conjugate $(\alpha_1 - i\alpha_2)$, gives a factor $(x^2 - 2\alpha_1 x + \alpha_1^2 + \alpha_2^2)$. This will be used in connection with the integration of rational functions.

Example 1-29. Solve the equation $x^3 - 5x^2 + 7x + 13 = 0$, and find the ratio of the two complex roots.

The only possible rational roots are ± 1 and ± 13; -1 is readily seen to be a root. The equation can thus be rewritten $(x + 1)(x^2 - 6x + 13) = 0$. The other two roots are then obtained from the equation $x^2 - 6x + 13 = 0$:

$$x = \frac{6 \pm \sqrt{36 - 52}}{2} = \frac{6 \pm 4i}{2} = 3 \pm 2i.$$

As the ratio we get

$$\frac{3 + 2i}{3 - 2i} = \frac{(3 + 2i)^2}{9 + 4} = \frac{5}{13} + \frac{12}{13} i.$$

The inverse ratio is then

$$\frac{3 - 2i}{3 + 2i} = \left(\frac{3 + 2i}{3 - 2i}\right)^* = \frac{5}{13} - \frac{12}{13} i. \qquad \square$$

Complex Matrices

The previously treated theory of (real) vectors, determinants, and matrices can now be generalized by the introduction of arbitrary complex numbers instead of real numbers. As the basic rules of operation for complex numbers are the same as for real numbers, the results must also be expected to be formally the same as before. However, one special circumstance should be noted.

As a real number is not changed on conjugation, we are free to introduce conjugation in certain cases in extending the various definitions to the complex case. This arises in connection with the definition of the transpose corresponding to a given (complex) matrix. We shall not consider the problems arising from this more closely, only remark that the *Hermitian adjoint* matrix $A^\dagger$, corresponding to a given complex matrix A, is defined as the matrix which arises from A on exchanging rows and columns, and at the same time conjugating. For a real matrix A, this process gives the transpose of A.

The *length* of an arbitrary complex N-dimensional vector $\mathbf{a}$ (column matrix A) is a nonnegative real number, the square of the length of the vector being defined as

$$A^\dagger A = \{a_1^* a_2^* \cdots a_N^*\} \begin{pmatrix} a_1 \\ a_2 \\ \cdot \\ \cdot \\ \cdot \\ a_N \end{pmatrix} = a_1^* a_1 + a_2^* a_2 + \cdots + a_N^* a_N$$

$$= |a_1|^2 + |a_2|^2 + \cdots + |a_N|^2.$$

A square matrix A is said to be *Hermitian* if it is equal to its Hermitian adjoint: $A^\dagger = A$. For real matrices, this means that the matrix is symmetric.

A square matrix A is said to be *unitary* when its Hermitian adjoint is equal to its inverse: $A^\dagger = A^{-1}$. For real matrices this means that the matrix is orthogonal.

Matrices with complex numbers are important in calculations in, for example, quantum mechanics. A theorem which is here of fundamental importance is that any Hermitian matrix can be diagonalized by a unitary matrix. The eigenvalues so obtained for a given Hermitian matrix are uniquely determined, and real, even if the original matrix has complex elements. In the case of real matrices, this theorem is seen to summarize the results obtained previously.

Linear Equations with Complex Numbers

The theory for linear equations is unchanged when complex numbers are involved. It is also true here, for instance, that N linear equations with N unknowns have exactly one solution when the main determinant of the equations is different from 0.

Example 1-30

$$(1 + i)x_1 + (2 + 3i)x_2 - (3 + 2i)x_3 = 7 + 5i,$$
$$(1 - 4i)x_2 + (1 + 7i)x_3 = -7 - 5i,$$
$$(2 + 2i)x_1 - (1 + 2i)x_2 + (3 - 4i)x_3 = 0.$$

$$|A| = \begin{vmatrix} 1 + i & 2 + 3i & -3 - 2i \\ 0 & 1 - 4i & 1 + 7i \\ 2 + 2i & -1 - 2i & 3 - 4i \end{vmatrix}$$

$$= \begin{vmatrix} 1 + i & 2 + 3i & -3 - 2i \\ 0 & 1 - 4i & 1 + 7i \\ 0 & -5 - 8i & 9 \end{vmatrix}$$

$$= (1 + i)(-1)^{1+1} \begin{vmatrix} 1 - 4i & 1 + 7i \\ -5 - 8i & 9 \end{vmatrix} = -7(7 + 5i) \neq 0,$$

$$|B_1| = \begin{vmatrix} 7 + 5i & 2 + 3i & -3 - 2i \\ -7 - 5i & 1 - 4i & 1 + 7i \\ 0 & -1 - 2i & 3 - 4i \end{vmatrix}$$

$$= \begin{vmatrix} 7 + 5i & 2 + 3i & -3 - 2i \\ 0 & 3 - i & -2 + 5i \\ 0 & -1 - 2i & 3 - 4i \end{vmatrix}$$

$$= (7 + 5i)(-1)^{1+1} \begin{vmatrix} 3 - i & -2 + 5i \\ -1 - 2i & 3 - 4i \end{vmatrix} = -7(7 + 5i)(1 + 2i).$$

From this, $x_1 = |B_1|/|A| = 1 + 2i$. Correspondingly, we obtain $x_2 = |B_2|/|A| = 3 - i$ and $x_3 = |B_3|/|A| = 1 + i$. $\quad\square$

Exercises

*1. Solve each of the following equations:

(a) $(1 + i)x^2 + (1 - 7i)x - 8 + 6i = 0$.
(b) $(1 - i)x^2 + (1 + 7i)x - 8 - 6i = 0$.

*2. Solve the following system of equations:

$$(2 + 3i)x - (1 + i)y = 3 + 4i,$$
$$(1 - 3i)x - (1 - 2i)y = -2 - 6i.$$

*3. Evaluate the following determinants:

$$\begin{vmatrix} 1+i & 2+i & 4+i \\ 0 & 1 & 2 \\ -i & 0 & i \end{vmatrix}, \qquad \begin{vmatrix} 1-i & 0 & i \\ 2-i & 1 & 0 \\ 4-i & 2 & -i \end{vmatrix}.$$

4. Find the inverse of the complex matrix

$$\begin{Bmatrix} 1+i & 2+i & 4+i \\ 0 & 1 & 2 \\ -i & 0 & i \end{Bmatrix}.$$

*5. Determine the eigenvalues of the Hermitian matrix

$$A = \begin{Bmatrix} 0 & -i \\ i & 0 \end{Bmatrix}.$$

Also, find a unitary matrix Q which transforms A into a diagonal matrix, i.e., such that $Q^\dagger A Q$ is diagonal.

6. Determine the eigenvalues of the Hermitian matrix

$$\begin{Bmatrix} 0 & -\sqrt{3}i & 0 & 0 \\ \sqrt{3}i & 0 & -2i & 0 \\ 0 & 2i & 0 & -\sqrt{3}i \\ 0 & 0 & \sqrt{3}i & 0 \end{Bmatrix}.$$

7. Show that if there exists a unitary matrix Q which diagonalizes the two matrices A and B, then A and B commute.

Answers

1. (a) $x = \begin{cases} 2+i \\ 1+3i \end{cases}$

 (b) $x = \begin{cases} 2-i \\ 1-3i \end{cases}$

2. $(x,y) = (2 + i, 1 + 3i)$
3. $i; -i$
5. Eigenvalues: 1 and -1

$$Q = \frac{1}{\sqrt{2}} \begin{Bmatrix} 1 & i \\ i & 1 \end{Bmatrix} \qquad \text{(for example)}$$

2

Groups and Group Representations

2-1. INTRODUCTION

The Group Concept

In chapter 1 we several times met the concept of a group without explicitly saying so. We shall now give a formal definition of this, and later study the representation of groups by means of matrices.

A set S is said to be *organized* by a (binary) *composition rule* if corresponding to any ordered pair (a,b) of elements from S there exists one and only one element called the composition of a and b. In general we shall write this unique element as ab, and also call it the product of (the factors) a and b. These latter conventions do not necessarily indicate that the elements of S are numbers, or, in case they are, that ab necessarily is the ordinary product of a and b.

A set G organized by some composition rule is now said to form a *group* if the following conditions are satisfied:

(1) The set G is *closed* under the composition rule; i.e., for all a and b in G it is true that ab is also in G.

(2) The composition rule is *associative;* i.e., for all a, b, and c in G it is true that $a(bc) = (ab)c$.

(3) There exists an element e in G such that $ae = ea = a$ for all a in G.

(4) Corresponding to any element a in G there exists an element b also in G such that $ab = ba = e$.

From the above conditions it can be shown that there exists only one element e with the property mentioned in (3); it is called the *unit element* of the group. Also it can be shown that corresponding to any element a there is only one element b with the property mentioned in (4); this element is called the *inverse* element of a and written a^{-1}.

It is an immediate consequence of the group axioms (1) through (4) that any equation of the form $ax = b$ or $xa = b$, where a and b are given elements of the group, has one and only one solution, namely, $a^{-1}b$ and ba^{-1}, respectively. These two solutions need not be equal. Another simple consequence of the group axioms is the following rule valid for arbitrary elements a and b: $(ab)^{-1} = b^{-1}a^{-1}$.

For any element a and any integer n, the *nth power of a*, written a^n, is defined in this way: The product of n factors a if n is positive, the unit element e if n is zero, the product of $-n$ factors a^{-1} if n is negative. It is then easily shown that the following two rules have general validity: $a^n a^m = a^{n+m}$ and $(a^n)^m = a^{nm}$.

Above we have not mentioned the commutative law. If this is also valid for the group considered, i.e., if we have $ab = ba$ for arbitrary elements a and b, the group is said to be *Abelian* or, simply, *commutative*. In that case we have a third power rule, namely, $(ab)^n = a^n b^n$.

Finite Groups

For a *finite group*, i.e., a group with a finite number of elements, the composition rule can be completely defined by means of a so-called *composition table* (see Table 2-1). Here an element listed in the square is the product of the corresponding elements in the left-hand column

Table 2-1

	a	b	c	$\cdots$
a				
b			bc	
c				
.				
.				
.				

and the top row (taken in that order). The number of elements in a finite group is called the *order* of the group.

Example 2-1. Let us consider the set consisting of the two numbers 1 and -1 organized by ordinary multiplication (see Table 2-2). Obviously conditions (1) and (2) are fulfilled. Also (3), as 1 is a unit element. Finally (4), as both 1 and -1 are their own inverse elements. We have thus been considering a group. It is of order 2, and it is Abelian. □

Table 2-2

	1	-1
1	1	-1
-1	-1	1

Example 2-2. We consider the symmetrical figure formed by the vertices of an equilateral triangle PQR (Fig. 2-1). Below we list all the operations which transform this figure onto itself, using one of the standard notations. We want to show that the set of these operations, with a suitable composition rule, forms a non-Abelian group of order 6.

E: The identity operation, which leaves the figure unchanged.
$C_3(1)$: A clockwise rotation through 120° around O, the center of the triangle.
$C_3(2)$: A counterclockwise rotation through 120° around O.
C_2: A reflection in the line l.
C_2': A reflection in the line m.
C_2'': A reflection in the line n.

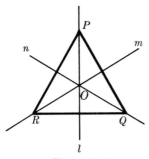

Figure 2-1

The composition of any two of these operations is now defined as the operation which results from using the two given operations consecutively, as indicated below. We have, for instance,

$$C_3(1) \begin{bmatrix} & P & \\ R & & Q \end{bmatrix} = \begin{bmatrix} & R & \\ Q & & P \end{bmatrix},$$

$$C_2 \begin{bmatrix} & R & \\ Q & & P \end{bmatrix} = \begin{bmatrix} & R & \\ P & & Q \end{bmatrix},$$

and, therefore,

$$C_2 C_3(1) \begin{bmatrix} & P & \\ R & & Q \end{bmatrix} = \begin{bmatrix} & R & \\ P & & Q \end{bmatrix} = C_2'' \begin{bmatrix} & P & \\ R & & Q \end{bmatrix},$$

so that

$$C_2 C_3(1) = C_2''.$$

Proceeding in this way we can construct the composition table shown in Table 2-3. It should be noted that the product ab of two arbitrary elements by definition is found by first performing the operation b and then the operation a.

Consider an element $(ab)c$. This is found by first performing c and then ab, i.e., c, then b, and then a. Exactly the same is true about the element $a(bc)$. Hence, the associative law is valid. From Table 2-3 it is now easily verified that the set forms a group with E as its unit element, and also that the group is not Abelian: We have, for instance,

$$C_2 C_2'' = C_3(1),$$
$$C_2'' C_2 = C_3(2).$$

It should be noted that in each column and in each row appear all the elements of the group. This property is common to the composition tables for all groups of finite order. It follows at once from the fact

Table 2-3

	E	$C_3(1)$	$C_3(2)$	C_2	C_2'	C_2''
E	E	$C_3(1)$	$C_3(2)$	C_2	C_2'	C_2''
$C_3(1)$	$C_3(1)$	$C_3(2)$	E	C_2'	C_2''	C_2
$C_3(2)$	$C_3(2)$	E	$C_3(1)$	C_2''	C_2	C_2'
C_2	C_2	C_2''	C_2'	E	$C_3(2)$	$C_3(1)$
C_2'	C_2'	C_2	C_2''	$C_3(1)$	E	$C_3(2)$
C_2''	C_2''	C_2'	C_2	$C_3(2)$	$C_3(1)$	E

that any equation $xa = b$ and any equation $ax = b$ has exactly one solution (p. 94). Finally it is seen that some of the subsets of the given group (when organized by the same composition rule) form a group by themselves, a so-called *subgroup* of the given group. This is the case for the subset consisting of E, $C_3(1)$, and $C_3(2)$, and (in a trivial way) for the subset consisting of the one element E (and for the improper subset consisting of all the elements in the group considered). □

Infinite Groups

As examples of *infinite groups* we mention at random the set of integers organized by addition, the set of real numbers organized by addition, the set of positive real numbers organized by multiplication, the set of N-dimensional vectors organized by (vector) addition, and the set of square matrices of order N with determinant different from zero organized by (matrix) multiplication. These groups are all Abelian except the matrix group mentioned. As subgroups of this we have, for instance, the set of orthogonal matrices of order N (non-Abelian) and the set of diagonal matrices of order N with all diagonal elements different from zero (Abelian).

Let us now consider the set of congruences in the plane, i.e., the set of length-preserving mappings of the plane onto itself. As members of this set we have, for instance, the translations, the rotations, and the reflections. Let a and b be any two congruences in the plane; we then define the product ab as the mapping which is obtained by first performing b and then a. Obviously ab is also a congruence. Therefore our set is closed under the composition rule just defined. The validity of the associative law follows from the fact that $(ab)c$ as well as $a(bc)$ may be obtained by first performing c, then b, and then a. The identity congruence which leaves every point unchanged is a unit element. Finally, any congruence has an inverse element, the one that corresponds to "undoing" all that was done. It follows that the set considered, organized as explained, is a group. This group is not Abelian. Let a and b be reflections in two parallel lines, for example; both ab and ba are then translations, but in opposite directions.

Consider now the set of all congruences mapping a given figure onto itself. By mapping the given figure onto itself we only mean that every point of the figure is mapped onto some point of the figure, not necessarily onto itself. It follows easily that this set when organized as above constitutes a subgroup of the original one. The finite group considered in Example 2-2 may be looked upon as an example of this kind, the invariant figure being the triangle PQR. Many important groups are conveniently defined correspondingly.

Subgroups

Above we have introduced the concept of a subgroup. We shall now prove that the order of a subgroup of a given finite group G is always a divisor of the order of G.

Let the subset $\{a_1, a_2, \ldots, a_p\}$ of the group G form a subgroup H of order p. We choose an element x of G and consider the elements $a_1 x, a_2 x, \ldots, a_p x$. These elements are all different, as they all belong to the same column in the composition table of G. If x belongs to H, they are simply all the elements of H. If x does not belong to H, none of the elements listed above can be elements of H either: Assume, for instance, $a_i x = a_k$. We then have $x = a_i^{-1} a_k$, in contradiction to the assumption that x was not an element of the subgroup. We therefore have that $\{a_1 x, a_2 x, \ldots, a_p x\}$, which is called a *right coset* of H, is either identical with H or has no element in common with it.

We now choose another element y of G and consider the set $\{a_1 y, a_2 y, \ldots, a_p y\}$. According to the above this set has p elements and is either identical with H or has no element in common with H. We shall now show that the two right cosets considered also are either identical or have no element in common. Assume that they have one element in common: $a_i x = a_k y$. Then we have $(a_k^{-1} a_i) x = y$.

Introducing $c = a_k^{-1} a_i$ we obtain $cx = y$, where c is an element of H. But this implies that the y-coset can be written $\{(a_1 c)x, (a_2 c)x, \ldots, (a_p c)x\}$, which shows that the y-coset is identical with the x-coset. Therefore, if the two cosets are to be different, they cannot have a single element in common. From this follows finally that we can exhaust the group G by taking out first the elements of H, then the elements of all the different (right) cosets. Since all the cosets have the same number of elements as H, it follows that the number of elements in G must be an integer times the number of elements in H.

Isomorphism. Abstract Groups

Example 2-3. Consider the set e of even numbers and the set o of odd numbers. We shall now investigate whether the set $\{e, o\}$ forms a group when we choose ordinary multiplication and ordinary addition, respectively, as composition rules. We form the composition tables of Table 2-4. It is seen that in the table on the left there is no unit

Table 2-4

	even	odd		even	odd
even	even	even	even	even	odd
odd	even	odd	odd	odd	even

multiplication	*addition*

element and therefore the set does not form a group under this composition rule. With addition as a composition rule, the set does form a group, however, with e as the unit element. $\square$

In Examples 2-1 and 2-3 we have met two groups of order 2, and a closer examination of the group tables shows that they are identical except for the notation used for the elements. Two finite groups which have composition tables with this property are called *isomorphic* and are said to represent the same *abstract group*. The concept of isomorphism is extremely useful, in that it allows one to recognize that the same group properties can arise in seemingly totally different contexts.

The above definition of isomorphism between two groups is only applicable to finite groups. The concept of isomorphism is generalized to also cover infinite groups, in the following way. Consider a group G_1, where the composition of two arbitrary elements x_1 and y_1 is written $x_1 \textcircled{1} y_1$, and another group G_2, where the composition of two arbitrary elements x_2 and y_2 is written $x_2 \textcircled{2} y_2$. The two groups are then said to be isomorphic in case there exists a one-to-one correspondence between the elements of G_1 and G_2 such that whenever x_1 corresponds to x_2 and y_1 corresponds to y_2, $x_1 \textcircled{1} y_1$ also corresponds to $x_2 \textcircled{2} y_2$.

It is easily seen that this definition is equivalent to the original one when finite groups are considered. A one-to-one correspondence is here obtained when elements in the same position in the left-hand column or in the top row in the respective group tables are taken as corresponding to each other. And, conversely, if the two finite groups are isomorphic in the generalized sense, then (if necessary by changing the order in which the elements appear in the group tables) it is possible to make the two tables identical except for notation.

As an important example of isomorphism between infinite groups, we mention the group G_1 formed by the set of positive real numbers organized by multiplication, and the group G_2, formed by the set of all

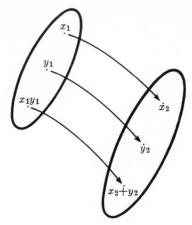

Figure 2-2

real numbers organized by addition. A one-to-one correspondence between the two sets is obtained by means of the logarithmic function; i.e., to the real positive number t_1 corresponds the real number $t_2 = \log t_1$. It is then true that whenever x_1 corresponds to x_2 (i.e., $x_2 = \log x_1$) and y_1 corresponds to y_2 (i.e., $y_2 = \log y_1$), then the product of x_1 and y_1 corresponds to the sum of x_2 and y_2 [i.e., $(x_2 + y_2) = \log(x_1 y_1)$]. Thus the two groups considered are isomorphic. One could say that the whole use of logarithms for calculations is based on this isomorphism (Fig. 2-2).

Returning again to the consideration of finite groups, one might ask how many abstract groups there are of a given order. It is clear that the number is finite and it is also clear that there is at least one group of each order. As an example of a group of order n, we can take the set consisting of all complex nth roots of 1 organized with ordinary multiplication as the composition rule. This group is Abelian and furthermore has the property of being *cyclic;* i.e., each element can be obtained as a power of a certain element of the group. The group is then said to be *generated* by this element (which is said to be a *generator* of the group).

It is quite complicated to find out precisely how many abstract groups exist of a certain order. In Table 2-5 we list the results that have been obtained for groups up to order 12. $N(n)$ is the total number of groups with order n and $N_A(n)$ is the number of Abelian groups.

Table 2-5

n	1	2	3	4	5	6	7	8	9	10	11	12
$N(n)$	1	1	1	2	1	2	1	5	2	2	1	5
$N_A(n)$	1	1	1	2	1	1	1	3	2	1	1	2

When the order of the group is a prime number, the only abstract group which can exist must be cyclic, as we shall see below (p. 104). When the order of the group is a composite number with many small factors, the number of groups can be very large. The number of groups with order larger than a few hundred is virtually unknown.

Exercises

*1. Show that the set $\{0,1,2,3\}$ organized as indicated in Table 2-6 forms an Abelian group of order 4.

Table 2-6

	0	1	2	3
0	0	1	2	3
1	1	2	3	0
2	2	3	0	1
3	3	0	1	2

Table 2-7

	1	2	3	4
1	1	2	3	4
2	2	4	1	3
3	3	1	4	2
4	4	3	2	1

*2. Show that the set $\{1,2,3,4\}$ organized as indicated in Table 2-7 forms a group which is isomorphic to the one considered in Exercise 1.

3. Corresponding to a given positive integer N consider the set $\{0,1,2,. . .,N-1\}$, organized in the following way:

$$a \oplus b = \begin{cases} a+b & \text{if } a+b < N, \\ a+b-N & \text{if } a+b \geq N. \end{cases}$$

Show that this gives an Abelian group of order N.

4. Show that the set of congruences in the plane which map a given regular N-gon onto itself (when organized by multiplication of congruences) constitutes a non-Abelian group of order $2N$.

5. Show that there are two and only two different abstract groups of order 4.

6. Show that the set of orthogonal matrices of order 2 and the set of congruences in the plane which map a given point onto itself, when organized by their respective multiplications, are isomorphic groups.

Answers

1. The set $\{0,1,2,3\}$ is closed under the given composition rule as only elements from $\{0,1,2,3\}$ appear in the table. Introducing $a \oplus b$ for the composition of a and b, it follows from the table that we have

$$a \oplus b = \begin{cases} a+b & \text{if } a+b < 4, \\ a+b-4 & \text{if } a+b \geq 4, \end{cases}$$

and therefore also

$$(a \oplus b) \oplus c = (a + b - 4\alpha) + c - 4\beta = (a + b + c) - 4(\alpha + \beta),$$
$$a \oplus (b \oplus c) = a + (b + c - 4\gamma) - 4\delta = (a + b + c) - 4(\gamma + \delta),$$

where α, β, γ, and δ are either 0 or 1. Hence $(a \oplus b) \oplus c$ and $a \oplus (b \oplus c)$ are both obtained by subtracting a multiple of 4 from $a + b + c$. As there is only one such number belonging to $\{0,1,2,3\}$, it follows that $(a \oplus b) \oplus c = a \oplus (b \oplus c)$. The element 0 is seen to be a unit element. Finally, it follows from the table that 0, 1, 2, and 3 all have inverse elements, namely 0, 3, 2, and 1, respectively.

2. Rearranging Table 2-7 as indicated, it follows that the organized set considered is isomorphic to the group of Exercise 1. From this fact it also follows that we are again considering a group.

	1	2	4	3
1	1	2	4	3
2	2	4	3	1
4	4	3	1	2
3	3	1	2	4

2-2. FINITE ABSTRACT GROUPS

The Order of an Element

Below we shall briefly discuss some concepts from the theory of finite abstract groups. In our considerations, G is an arbitrary finite group with unit element e. The order of the group is g, and all our information about the group is contained in the group multiplication table, which we assume to be given.

The nonnegative powers of an arbitrary element a in G, e, a, a^2, a^3, a^4, ..., are all elements of G, and since G is finite, these elements cannot all be distinct; i.e., for some m and n we must have $a^m = a^n$, where $m > n$. From this it follows that $a^{m-n} = e$. In a finite group some positive power of every element is thus equal to the unit element. The least positive integer α for which $a^\alpha = e$ is called the *order* of a. The following facts about the order of an element can readily be proved: (1) e is the only element of order 1; (2) a and a^{-1} have the same order; and (3) If $b = t^{-1}at$, where t is an element of G, then a and b have the same order.

Above we have defined a cyclic group as a group which can be generated by a single element. We can now also say that a group of order g is cyclic if and only if it contains an element of order g. It should be noted that this does not mean that each element in a cyclic group of order g has the order g—only that at least one element has that order.

Example 2-4. The numbers 1, -1, i, $-i$ form a cyclic group of order 4 when ordinary multiplication is used as the composition rule.

1 is the unit element and thus has the order 1. -1 has the order 2, whereas i and $-i$ both have the order 4. The group considered thus has two generators. 1 and -1 form a subgroup of order 2. $\square$

All cyclic groups of the same order are isomorphic. To show this we only need to find a generator of each group and then let equal powers of the generating elements correspond to each other. There is therefore only one abstract cyclic group of any given order and this group is Abelian.

Finite Subgroups

Consider an arbitrary subset H of the given finite group G. We define H^2 as the set of elements of G which can be written as a product of two (equal or different) elements of H. In case the elements of H occupy consecutive spaces in the left-hand column and in the top row of the composition table of G, then H^2 is the set of elements appearing (once or more) in the corresponding square part of the interior of the table.

We shall now show that a necessary and sufficient condition for the subset H to be a subgroup of G is that $H^2 = H$. In order to establish the necessity of the condition, we assume that H is a subgroup of G. It follows that H is closed with respect to the composition rule and therefore that all elements of H^2 belong to H. Thus H^2 is a subset (proper or improper) of H. We shall write this as $H^2 \subseteq H$. Furthermore, as H contains the unit element e of G, it follows that every element of H belongs to H^2. Thus $H \subseteq H^2$, which taken together with $H^2 \subseteq H$ gives $H^2 = H$.

Let us now conversely assume that $H^2 = H$. As we then have $H^2 \subseteq H$, it is obvious that H is closed under the composition rule. As G is a group, it is also obvious that the composition rule is associative in relation to the set H. Next we want to show that the unit element e of G belongs to H. To this purpose we consider the composition table of H. We already know that only elements of H will appear in this table. Furthermore, as G is a group, it is also true that the elements in any row (and in any column) of the table of H will all be distinct. Finally, as the number of elements in H is finite, it follows that every element in H will appear exactly once in every row (and in every column). We can now easily see that e belongs to H: In that row of the table which contains products of the form $h_1 x$ we also find h_1. As the equation $h_1 x = h_1$ has only one solution in G, namely, e, we conclude that e appears in the top row, which means that e belongs to H. By an analogous argument we can finally conclude that the inverse of any element in H belongs to H. Thus H is a group.

In the above proof we have supposed G (and therefore also H) to be finite. It is easily seen that G need not be finite. If, however, H is also allowed to become infinite, then the above theorem is no longer valid. Suppose, for instance, that G is the group of positive real numbers organized by ordinary multiplication and that H is the set of positive integers. We then have $H^2 = H$, even though the set of positive integers organized by multiplication is not a group.

On page 98 we proved that if a finite group G of order g has a subgroup H of order p, then $g = np$, where n is an integer, often called the *index* of the subgroup. Two simple consequences of this are that the order of any element of G is a factor of g (obviously the set of powers of any element of G forms a cyclic subgroup) and that groups of prime order have no nontrivial subgroups and are necessarily cyclic. Hence, all groups of order g are isomorphic if g is a prime number. A cyclic group of composite order, however, has nontrivial subgroups. An example of this was given in Example 2-4. Actually one can easily prove a stronger statement—that any finite group of composite order has proper subgroups.

Sets of Generators and Defining Relations

On page 100 we introduced the concept of a generator of a cyclic group. We shall now show how this concept is extended to noncyclic groups. As an example we consider the group discussed in Example 2-2. The elements E, $C_3(1)$, and $C_3(2)$ form a subgroup which is seen to be cyclic, as it can be generated, for instance, by $C_3(1)$. It is also easily verified that the elements E and C_2 form a subgroup of order 2, as does E and C_2' as well as E and C_2''. The first of these last three groups can be thought of as generated by C_2, and we shall now see that the whole group can be generated from the two elements $C_3(1)$ and C_2. This simply means that all six elements E, $C_3(1)$, $C_3(2)$, C_2, C_2', and C_2'' can be obtained as products of powers of $C_3(1)$ and C_2, and this becomes obvious when one consults the group table.

We shall, however, show it in a slightly more sophisticated manner, proving that E, $C_3(1)$, $[C_3(1)]^2$, C_2, $C_3(1)C_2$, and $[C_3(1)]^2C_2$ are distinct elements. The first three elements form a subgroup of order 3 and therefore certainly are distinct. Also the fourth element is known to be different from the first three. To see that $C_3(1)C_2$ is distinct from any of the first four, we can show that any equality would lead to a contradiction. If, for instance, $C_3(1)C_2$ were equal to $[C_3(1)]^2$, we would have $C_2 = C_3(1)$. Correspondingly, we can show that the last-mentioned element is different from the five others. If, for instance, $[C_3(1)]^2C_2$ were equal to $C_3(1)$, then $C_2 = [C_3(1)]^{-1}$, which contradicts the fact that $C_3(1)$ is an element of a subgroup which does not contain C_2. This completes the proof: $C_3(1)$ and C_2 form a *set of generators* of the group considered.

Of course, this choice of generators is not unique. As a set of generators we could also have chosen, for example, $C_3(1)$, C_2, and C_2' (or even G itself). In this case, however, the generators are not *independent*, which means that at least one of the generators can be expressed as a product of powers of the other generators. The set originally considered is seen to be independent, as is also the set consisting of $C_3(1)$ and C_2'.

Often an abstract group is defined by means of an independent set of generators together with some *defining relations* sufficient to reconstruct the composition table. In the case considered we might, for example, choose the following:

$$[C_3(1)]^3 = [C_2]^2 = [C_3(1)C_2]^2 = E.$$

In fact, by means of these relations, any product of powers of $C_3(1)$ and C_2 can be reduced to either E, $C_3(1)$, $[C_3(1)]^2$, C_2, $C_3(1)C_2$, or $[C_3(1)]^2C_2$. On the other hand, these must all be distinct, as we have seen above, using only the fact that the set of generators was independent. Hence, the group given by the above defining relations has exactly six elements. The composition table can now easily be (re)constructed. Correspondingly, the cyclic group of order 6 can be defined by means of the one generator a and the one defining relation $a^6 = e$. Of course, it is here to be understood that no smaller positive power of a would give the unit element.

The Direct Product of Two Groups

From two finite groups $H = \{h_1, h_2, \ldots, h_p\}$ and $K = \{k_1, k_2, \ldots, k_q\}$ a new group G of order $g = pq$ may be derived in the following way. The elements of G are all ordered pairs of the form (h_i, k_j), and group multiplication is defined by

$$(h_i, k_j)(h_l, k_m) = (h_i h_l, k_j k_m),$$

where the products $h_i h_l$ and $k_j k_m$ are determined by means of the composition rules in H and K, respectively. The unit element is the pair of unit elements from H and K and we have

$$(h_i, k_j)^{-1} = (h_i^{-1}, k_j^{-1}).$$

The group obtained is called the *direct product* of H and K and written $G = H \times K$. It follows immediately from the definition that the direct product of two Abelian groups is itself an Abelian group.

As an example we shall investigate the direct product of the (unique) abstract groups of order 2 and 3. To make the calculations simple we represent the two abstract groups by $H = \{1, -1\}$ and $K = \{1, \epsilon, \epsilon^2\}$, where $\epsilon = -\frac{1}{2} + i(\sqrt{3}/2)$, using ordinary multiplication as the composition rule in both cases. We then have

$$H \times K = \{(1,1), (1,\epsilon), (1,\epsilon^2), (-1,1), (-1,\epsilon), (-1,\epsilon^2)\}.$$

We want to show that this represents the sixth-order cyclic group. Since there can be no doubt about the order of the group, the only problem is to prove that a single generator suffices. We try out $(-1, \epsilon)$ as generator with the following results:

$$(-1,\epsilon)^2 = (1,\epsilon^2),$$
$$(-1,\epsilon)^3 = (-1,1),$$
$$(-1,\epsilon)^4 = (1,\epsilon),$$
$$(-1,\epsilon)^5 = (-1,\epsilon^2),$$
$$(-1,\epsilon)^6 = (1,1).$$

In this way we have proved directly that the product group represents the cyclic group of order 6.

It has already been mentioned that there exist two different abstract groups of order 6. One is the cyclic group of order 6 represented, for example, by the above direct product. The other, which is not Abelian, is represented by the group considered in Example 2-2. Both groups have subgroups of orders 2 and 3, and these must be pairwise isomorphic, as there is only one abstract group of order 2 and only one of order 3. To investigate the difference between the two order-6 groups we make the following rather natural "partial correspondence":

$$\begin{array}{cccccc} E & C_3(1) & C_3(2) & C_2 & C_2' & C_2'' \\ (1,1) & (1,\epsilon) & (1,\epsilon^2) & (-1,1) & ? & ? \end{array}$$

It looks reasonable enough to make the "correspondence" as shown for the first four elements, but after that we cannot continue: C_2' and C_2''

are "not very different" from C_2, since they are all in second-order subgroups with the unit element, but $(-1,\epsilon)$ and $(-1,\epsilon^2)$ behave quite differently, as they are not members of any proper subgroup at all. Furthermore, as the product group is Abelian, we have, for instance, $(1,\epsilon)(-1,1) = (-1,1)(1,\epsilon)$, while $C_3(1)C_2 \neq C_2 C_3(1)$.

Classes of Conjugate Elements

Finally, we shall make more precise the idea introduced above that C_2, C_2', and C_2'' have something in common. This is geometrically quite clear, as they were all obtained as reflections in a symmetry axis of the triangle originally considered. Correspondingly, $C_3(1)$ and $C_3(2)$ have something in common, both being rotations of 120°. The situation is reminiscent of the discussion leading up to the division of (symmetric) matrices into classes of similar matrices. Our main result there was the introduction of the tensor as the abstract concept which corresponded to a whole class of matrices or matrix representations.

Consider two arbitrary elements a and b of the group G. a is then said to be *conjugate* with b if for some element t of G it holds that $b = t^{-1}at$. As this equation implies $a = (t^{-1})^{-1}b(t^{-1})$, it follows that if a is conjugate with b, then b is also conjugate with a. Two such elements may therefore simply be called conjugate (with each other). Obviously any element is conjugate with itself $(a = e^{-1}ae)$. Furthermore, if a is conjugate with b and b is conjugate with c, then a is conjugate with c $[b = t^{-1}at$ and $c = s^{-1}bs$ implies $c = (ts)^{-1}a(ts)]$.

The set of elements of G which are conjugate with a is called the *class* of a. It follows from the above that no class is empty and that two classes having one element in common are identical: The set of classes constitutes a partition of the whole group G. The class of e has only e as a member $(t^{-1}et = e)$; the same is true for every element in an Abelian group $(t^{-1}at = t^{-1}ta = ea = a)$.

By using the group table given in Example 2-2 we find that the classes in this case are precisely

$$\{E\}, \quad \{C_3(1), C_3(2)\} \quad \text{and} \quad \{C_2, C_2', C_2''\},$$

so here the more intuitive idea of two elements not being very different corresponds to the formal concept of two elements belonging to the same class. It follows from a previous remark that any two elements of the same class have the same order (see p. 102). That the converse is not true may be seen by considering the cyclic group of order 3.

Exercises

*1. Show that the set $\{e,a,b,c,d\}$ organized as indicated by Table 2-8 does not constitute a group.

Table 2-8

	e	a	b	c	d
e	e	a	b	c	d
a	a	e	d	b	c
b	b	c	e	d	a
c	c	d	a	e	b
d	d	b	c	a	e

*2. Show that any finite group of composite order has proper subgroups.

3. Show that any group in which no element is of order higher than 2 is Abelian.

4. Consider the so-called quaternion group $\mathfrak{Q}$, given abstractly in the following way:

  Generators: a, b.

  Defining relations: $a^4 = e$, $a^2 = b^2 = (ab)^2$.

  Show that $ba = a^3b$. Furthermore, show that the group is of order 8. Finally, write down its composition table.

5. Determine the classes of conjugate elements for the quaternion group (cf. Exercise 4).

Answers

1. The organized set considered is closed under the composition rule, it has a unit element, and any element has an inverse element. But the associative law is not valid. For example, we have $(ab)c \neq a(bc)$.

2. In a group of order n with no proper subgroup, any element different from the unit element must also be of order n (see p. 104). Suppose G is of order $n = pq (p > 1, q > 1)$, and let a be some element of G different from the unit element e. If G has no proper subgroups we have $a^{pq} = e$. For the element $b = a^p$ we then have $b^q = e$, which shows that b is not of order n. This gives a contradiction. Hence, if G is of composite order it must have a proper subgroup.

2-3. GROUP REPRESENTATIONS

Suppose a finite group $G = \{G_1, G_2, \ldots, G_g\}$ of order g is given and furthermore a function D, which to every element G_n of G assigns a (real or complex) square matrix $D(G_n)$ such that all matrices are non-singular (i.e., with determinants different from zero) and of the same order r. The function D [or the set of matrices $D(G_n)$] is then said to be a *representation* of the group G in case it is true for arbitrary elements of G that if $G_nG_m = G_k$, then also $D(G_n)D(G_m) = D(G_k)$. Here, of course, G_nG_m is the group product of G_n and G_m, while $D(G_n)D(G_m)$ is the matrix product of the two corresponding matrices. r is called the *dimension* of the representation. It is not required that all matrices $D(G_n)$ be different. In case they are, the representation is said to be *faithful,* and the set of matrices organized by multiplication forms a group of order g isomorphic with G. In case they are not, the representation is said to be *unfaithful.* It turns out that the set of matrices still forms a group only of order h less than g. G is said to be *homomorphic* to this group. It can be shown that every matrix then corresponds to the same number of elements from G. It follows that h will always be a divisor of g.

If G_1 is the unit element of the given group, we have $G_1G_1 = G_1$. Consider an arbitrary representation D of dimension r. We then have $D(G_1)D(G_1) = D(G_1)$, where $D(G_1)$ is a nonsingular matrix of order r. As the equation $D(G_1)X = D(G_1)$ has one and only one solution, the unit matrix E of order r, it follows that $D(G_1) = E$. Hence in any representation of dimension r the matrix corresponding to the unit element of the given group is the unit matrix of order r—in the special case of $r = 1$, the real number 1. By an analogous argument, it is seen that inverse elements of the given group correspond to inverse matrices.

Every group has a (trivial) one-dimensional representation in which each element is represented by the number 1. A more interesting representation D of an arbitrary group of order g is obtained in the following way. As above, the group elements are supposed to be numbered $G_1, G_2, \ldots, G_n, \ldots, G_g$. The group element G_n is then represented by a gth-order matrix whose matrix elements $D_{ij}(G_n)$ are defined by

$$D_{ij}(G_n) = \begin{cases} 1 & \text{if } G_nG_j = G_i, \\ 0 & \text{otherwise.} \end{cases}$$

It follows from the fact that the equation $G_nG_j = G_i$ for given values of n and i has exactly one solution that every row of the matrix $D(G_n)$ has one and only one element which is not zero. Obviously the same is true for every column of $D(G_n)$. From this we conclude that $D(G_n)$ is nonsingular.

Let us now prove that D is a representation of G; i.e., let us prove that $D(G_n)D(G_m) = D(G_nG_m)$ for any n and m. We have

$$(D(G_n)D(G_m))_{ij} = \sum_{k=1}^{g} D_{ik}(G_n)D_{kj}(G_m).$$

A necessary condition for the kth term in the sum on the right side to be different from zero (that is, equal to 1) is that $D_{kj}(G_m) = 1$ or that

$G_m G_j = G_k$.   As m and j are given numbers, it follows that only one of the g terms on the right side can be different from zero.   And this will occur if and only if for the same k we have both $G_m G_j = G_k$ and $G_n G_k = G_i$, or $G_n G_m G_j = G_i$.   This means that

$$(D(G_n)D(G_m))_{ij} = \begin{cases} 1 & \text{if } G_n G_m G_j = G_i \\ 0 & \text{otherwise} \end{cases} = D_{ij}(G_n G_m),$$

which proves that D is a representation. D is said to be a *regular* representation of the group considered.   By comparing, for instance, the first rows of the matrices it is seen that the representation is faithful.

Example 2-5.   For the regular representation of the cyclic group of order 3, $\mathcal{C}_3 = \{e, a, a^2\}$, corresponding to $G_1 = e$, $G_2 = a$, and $G_3 = a^2$, we have

$$D(e) = \begin{pmatrix} 1 & 0 & 0 \\ 0 & 1 & 0 \\ 0 & 0 & 1 \end{pmatrix}, \quad D(a) = \begin{pmatrix} 0 & 0 & 1 \\ 1 & 0 & 0 \\ 0 & 1 & 0 \end{pmatrix}, \quad D(a^2) = \begin{pmatrix} 0 & 1 & 0 \\ 0 & 0 & 1 \\ 1 & 0 & 0 \end{pmatrix}. \qquad \square$$

Equivalent Representations

On page 76 we introduced the notion of similarity between real matrices: Two symmetric matrices A and B of the same order were called similar if there existed an orthogonal matrix Q such that $B = \tilde{Q}AQ$ or (since $\tilde{Q} = Q^{-1}$) $B = Q^{-1}AQ$.   For the more general case of complex matrices, the condition for similarity of the two Hermitian matrices A and B is correspondingly that there exists a unitary matrix Q such that $B = Q^\dagger AQ$ or (since $Q^\dagger = Q^{-1}$) $B = Q^{-1}AQ$ (cf. p. 91).

We shall now introduce an even more general notion, which we shall call equivalence between matrices.   Any two (real or complex) matrices A and B of the same order (not necessarily Hermitian) will be called *equivalent* if there exists a nonsingular matrix T (not necessarily unitary) such that $B = T^{-1}AT$ (and therefore also $A = S^{-1}BS$, where $S = T^{-1}$).   Obviously, similarity implies equivalence, but the converse is not true.

Let us now consider an arbitrary representation D of dimension r with matrices $D(G_1), \ldots, D(G_g)$ (some of these matrices are of course equal if the representation is unfaithful), and let T be a nonsingular matrix of order r.   We can then form a new representation D' with matrices $D'(G_1),\ldots,D'(G_g)$ by setting

$$D'(G_j) = T^{-1}D(G_j)T \qquad (j = 1,2,\ldots,g).$$

Any two representations of the same group having such a relation are said to be *equivalent*. It should be noted that not only are matrices corresponding to the same group element equivalent, but this equivalence has also to be "effected" by the same *transforming matrix T* in every case. It is easily seen that the two sets of matrices belonging to two equivalent representations form isomorphic groups also in the case of unfaithful representations.

Example 2-6. Corresponding to the above regular representation of $\mathcal{C}_3$ and

$$T = \begin{pmatrix} 1 & 0 & 0 \\ 0 & 0 & 1 \\ 0 & 1 & 0 \end{pmatrix} \; (= T^{-1}),$$

we obtain

$$D'(e) = \begin{pmatrix} 1 & 0 & 0 \\ 0 & 1 & 0 \\ 0 & 0 & 1 \end{pmatrix}, \qquad D'(a) = \begin{pmatrix} 0 & 1 & 0 \\ 0 & 0 & 1 \\ 1 & 0 & 0 \end{pmatrix}, \qquad D'(a^2) = \begin{pmatrix} 0 & 0 & 1 \\ 1 & 0 & 0 \\ 0 & 1 & 0 \end{pmatrix}.$$

D' is seen to be the regular representation corresponding to $G_1 = e$, $G_2 = a^2$, and $G_3 = a$.

Starting with the same representation of $\mathcal{C}_3$ but choosing

$$T = \begin{pmatrix} 0 & 1 & 0 \\ 1 & 1 & 2 \\ 2 & 0 & 1 \end{pmatrix} \qquad \text{and therefore } T^{-1} = \begin{pmatrix} \frac{1}{3} & -\frac{1}{3} & \frac{2}{3} \\ 1 & 0 & 0 \\ -\frac{2}{3} & \frac{2}{3} & -\frac{1}{3} \end{pmatrix},$$

we obtain

$$D'(e) = \begin{pmatrix} 1 & 0 & 0 \\ 0 & 1 & 0 \\ 0 & 0 & 1 \end{pmatrix}, \qquad D'(a) = \begin{pmatrix} \frac{4}{3} & \frac{1}{3} & \frac{5}{3} \\ 2 & 0 & 1 \\ -\frac{5}{3} & \frac{1}{3} & -\frac{4}{3} \end{pmatrix},$$

$$D'(a^2) = \begin{pmatrix} -\frac{1}{3} & 1 & \frac{1}{3} \\ 1 & 1 & 2 \\ \frac{2}{3} & -1 & -\frac{2}{3} \end{pmatrix}. \qquad \square$$

Irreducible Representations

Let us then, corresponding to the given group $G = \{G_1,G_2,\ldots,G_g\}$, consider two arbitrary representations $D^{(p)}$ and $D^{(q)}$ with dimensions d_p and d_q, respectively. From these we construct matrices all of order

$d_p + d_q$, as indicated below ($j = 1,2,\ldots,g$):

$$D^{(p)}(G_j) \oplus D^{(q)}(G_j)$$

$$= \begin{cases} D_{11}^{(p)}(G_j) \cdots D_{1d_p}^{(p)}(G_j) & 0 & \cdots & 0 \\ \vdots & & & \\ D_{d_p1}^{(p)}(G_j) \cdots D_{d_pd_p}^{(p)}(G_j) & 0 & \cdots & 0 \\ 0 \qquad\cdots\qquad 0 & D_{11}^{(q)}(G_j) & \cdots & D_{1d_q}^{(q)}(G_j) \\ \vdots & & & \\ 0 \qquad\cdots\qquad 0 & D_{d_q1}^{(q)}(G_j) & \cdots & D_{d_qd_q}^{(q)}(G_j) \end{cases}$$

$D^{(p)}(G_j) \oplus D^{(q)}(G_j)$ is called the *direct sum* of $D^{(p)}(G_j)$ and $D^{(q)}(G_j)$. It is easily verified that these matrices correspond to a new representation of the given group. A representation obtained in such a way is said to be *reducible*, since it can be "split" into two representations of lower dimension. Generally, a representation is said to be reducible if it can be obtained as above, or if there exists another representation equivalent to the one considered such that the new one can be obtained as above. A representation which is not reducible is said to be *irreducible*. It is a main problem of the theory of representations to devise ways of finding all the irreducible representations of a given group. The number of nonequivalent irreducible representations of a group can be shown to be equal to the number of classes of conjugate elements in the given group.

We shall now state without proof two theorems about irreducible representations:

Schur's lemma. Let $D^{(p)}$ and $D^{(q)}$ be two irreducible representations of G with dimensions d_p and d_q, respectively, and suppose a matrix S exists, such that

$$SD^{(p)}(G_j) = D^{(q)}(G_j)S \qquad (j = 1,2,\ldots,g).$$

Then either S is a null matrix or S is a nonsingular square matrix, in which case $d_p = d_q$ and the two representations are equivalent.

The orthogonality theorem. Consider any two irreducible representations $D^{(p)}$ and $D^{(q)}$ of dimensions d_p and d_q, respectively. For $p \neq q$ the two representations are supposed to be nonequivalent. We then have

$$\sum_{n=1}^{g} [D^{(p)}(G_n)^{-1}]_{ij} \, D_{kl}^{(q)}(G_n) = \frac{g}{d_p} \, \delta_{il} \, \delta_{jk} \, \delta_{pq}.$$

Here $[D^{(p)}(G_n)^{-1}]_{ij}$ is the i,jth matrix element in the matrix which is the inverse of $D^{(p)}(G_n)$. If in particular we consider a representation formed by a set of *unitary* matrices, then (see p. 91) $D^{(p)}(G_n)^{-1} = D^{(p)}(G_n)^\dagger$, that is, $[D^{(p)}(G_n)^{-1}]_{ij} = [D_{ji}^{(p)}(G_n)]^*$. The theorem then states that

$$\sum_{n=1}^{g} [D_{ij}^{(p)}(G_n)]^* D_{kl}^{(q)}(G_n) = \frac{g}{d_p} \, \delta_{ik} \, \delta_{jl} \, \delta_{pq}.$$

The last version of the orthogonality theorem may be interpreted in the following way. The i,jth matrix elements belonging to the representation $D^{(p)}$ of the given group can be used to construct a g-dimensional vector $(D_{ij}^{(p)}(G_1), \ldots, D_{ij}^{(p)}(G_g))$. The scalar product of this vector and the corresponding vector formed by the k,lth matrix elements belonging to the representation $D^{(q)}$ is zero unless $i = k$, $j = l$, and $p = q$, in which case it equals g/d_p.

Unitary Representations

Obviously the orthogonality theorem is especially simple when we consider representations formed by unitary matrices. It would therefore be very convenient if every representation were equivalent to such a *unitary representation*. We shall now see that this is actually the case by explicitly constructing a transforming matrix S.

Introducing for the sake of brevity $D_n = D(G_n)$, we define a matrix D by

$$D = \sum_{n=1}^{g} D_n D_n^\dagger.$$

Since the i,kth matrix element of the nth term in the right-hand sum is

$$(D_n D_n^\dagger)_{ik} = \sum_{j=1}^{r} (D_n)_{ij}(D_n^\dagger)_{jk} = \sum_{j} (D_n)_{ij}(D_n)_{kj}^*$$
$$= \sum_{j} [(D_n)_{ij}^*(D_n)_{kj}]^* = \sum_{j} [(D_n)_{kj}(D_n^\dagger)_{ji}]^* = ((D_n D_n^\dagger)^\dagger)_{ik},$$

we see that D is a sum of Hermitian matrices and therefore itself a Hermitian matrix. It was mentioned on page 91 that any Hermitian matrix can be diagonalized by a unitary matrix. Let U be such a unitary matrix diagonalizing our matrix D, and let the resulting diagonal matrix be Λ. We then have

$$\Lambda = U^{-1}DU,$$

where, as previously mentioned, the diagonal elements of Λ are real numbers. In the case under consideration, it can furthermore be shown that they are all positive. The diagonal matrix whose diagonal elements are the (positive) square roots of these is denoted $\Lambda^{1/2}$, while the inverse of this is denoted $\Lambda^{-1/2}$.

The matrix S is now defined as $S = U\Lambda^{1/2}$. We are then to show that $S^{-1}D_nS$ is a unitary matrix for $n = 1,2,\ldots,g$. To do this we prove that $(S^{-1}D_nS)(S^{-1}D_nS)^{\dagger}$ is the unit matrix E for any n. Introducing the abbreviations $D'_j = U^{-1}D_jU$, we have

$$\Lambda = \sum_{j=1}^{g} U^{-1}D_jUU^{-1}D_j^{\dagger}U = \sum_{j=1}^{g} D'_j D'^{\dagger}_j.$$

In the proof we shall have occasion to use the fact that the primed D's form a (finite) group insofar as any of the primed D's is obtained once and only once as $D'_nD'_j$ when n is fixed and j runs through the numbers $1,2,\ldots,g$.

The proof is now carried through in the following way:

$$(S^{-1}D_nS)(S^{-1}D_nS)^{\dagger} = (\Lambda^{-1/2}D'_n\Lambda^{1/2})(\Lambda^{-1/2}D'_n\Lambda^{1/2})^{\dagger}$$

$$= \Lambda^{-1/2}D'_n \left(\sum_{j=1}^{g} D'_j D'^{\dagger}_j \right) D'^{\dagger}_n\Lambda^{-1/2}$$

$$= \Lambda^{-1/2} \sum_{j=1}^{g} (D'_nD'_j)(D'_nD'_j)^{\dagger}\Lambda^{-1/2}$$

$$= \Lambda^{-1/2} \left(\sum_{k=1}^{g} D'_k D'^{\dagger}_k \right) \Lambda^{-1/2} = \Lambda^{-1/2}\Lambda\Lambda^{-1/2} = E.$$

We have thus seen that every representation is equivalent to a unitary representation for which the second formulation of the orthogonality theorem holds. We can then use this theorem to show that there is at least an upper bound on the number of nonequivalent irreducible representations of a given group.

From each class of mutually equivalent irreducible matrix representations of the given group, we choose one that is unitary. Consider one of these "special" representations and let its dimension be d. From this we get d^2 g-dimensional vectors of the type appearing in the second formulation of the orthogonality theorem. Any two of these are mutually orthogonal and orthogonal on any one coming from one of the other special representations. As there exist no more than g mutually orthogonal g-dimensional vectors, it follows that the sum of the squares of the dimensions of all the special representations is less than or equal to g. By a more elaborate argument it can be shown that it is in fact the equality which holds. The existence of an upper bound on the number of nonequivalent irreducible representations follows immediately. As already mentioned, the number of such representations is equal to the number of classes of conjugate elements of the group considered.

Example 2-7. The regular representation of the group $\mathcal{C}_3$ given in Example 2-5 is unitary, as can be verified immediately. The representation is not directly reducible, but there exists an equivalent representation which breaks up into three one-dimensional representations. To see this we transform by means of a matrix T, where

$$T = \frac{1}{\sqrt{3}} \begin{Bmatrix} 1 & 1 & 1 \\ 1 & \epsilon^2 & \epsilon \\ 1 & \epsilon & \epsilon^2 \end{Bmatrix}, \qquad T^{-1} = \frac{1}{\sqrt{3}} \begin{Bmatrix} 1 & 1 & 1 \\ 1 & \epsilon & \epsilon^2 \\ 1 & \epsilon^2 & \epsilon \end{Bmatrix}.$$

Here $\epsilon = -\frac{1}{2} + i(\sqrt{3}/2)$, giving $\epsilon^2 = -\frac{1}{2} - i(\sqrt{3}/2)$ and $\epsilon^3 = 1$. In this way we get

$$T^{-1}D(e)T = \begin{Bmatrix} 1 & 0 & 0 \\ 0 & 1 & 0 \\ 0 & 0 & 1 \end{Bmatrix}, \qquad T^{-1}D(a)T = \begin{Bmatrix} 1 & 0 & 0 \\ 0 & \epsilon & 0 \\ 0 & 0 & \epsilon^2 \end{Bmatrix},$$

$$T^{-1}D(a^2)T = \begin{Bmatrix} 1 & 0 & 0 \\ 0 & \epsilon^2 & 0 \\ 0 & 0 & \epsilon \end{Bmatrix},$$

which shows directly that C_3 has the three irreducible representations listed in Table 2-9. It is obvious that $D^{(1)}$ is not equivalent to either of the other two representations. Furthermore, $D^{(2)}$ and $D^{(3)}$ are not equivalent, for in order for them to be, there should exist a number t such that $t^{-1}\epsilon t = \epsilon^2$, and that is clearly impossible. The two groups formed by the representations $D^{(2)}$ and $D^{(3)}$ are, however, isomorphic. Whereas equivalence, as already mentioned, implies isomorphism, the converse, therefore, is not true.

Table 2-9

	$D^{(1)}$	$D^{(2)}$	$D^{(3)}$
e	1	1	1
a	1	ϵ	ϵ^2
a^2	1	ϵ^2	ϵ

As the sum of the squares of the dimensions of these three representations equals the order of the group, namely 3, it follows that our list is complete. A fourth irreducible representation (nonequivalent to the above three) does not exist. □

Example 2-8. Let us consider the abstract group introduced in Example 2-2 to find a complete set of irreducible representations. We shall first consider the one-dimensional representations. All of these will of course be irreducible and mutually nonequivalent (cf. Example 2-7). As already mentioned, we must have $D(E) = 1$. From the fact that $C_2^2 = E$ we get $D(C_2)^2 = 1$ or $D(C_2) = \pm 1$. Correspondingly we get $D(C_2') = \pm 1$ and $D(C_2'') = \pm 1$. And—as $[C_3(1)]^3 = E$ —we must have $D(C_3(1))$ equal to 1, ϵ, or ϵ^2, where $\epsilon = -\frac{1}{2} + i(\sqrt{3}/2)$ (cf. Example 2-7). As $C_2'C_2 = C_3(1)$ and therefore also $D(C_2')D(C_2) = D(C_3(1))$, we can exclude the possibility of $D(C_3(1))$ being equal to ϵ or ϵ^2. Hence $D(C_3(1)) = 1$, and—by the same line of argument— $D(C_3(2)) = 1$. Continuing in this way, we find that if $D(C_2)$ equals 1, then the same holds for $D(C_2')$ and $D(C_2'')$, while $D(C_2) = -1$ gives $D(C_2') = D(C_2'') = -1$. As a result, we get two possible one-dimensional representations. Both of these are seen to satisfy all conditions. They are given below as $D^{(1)}$ and $D^{(2)}$. $D^{(1)}$ is the trivial one-dimensional representation.

Let us then investigate the possibility of finding irreducible representations of a higher dimension. Since $1^2 + 1^2 + 2^2 = 6$, the only possibility is to find a two-dimensional representation. In such a representation E must be represented by the two-dimensional unit matrix. As the group has C_2 and $C_3(1)$ as a set of generators, we concentrate upon finding matrices representing these two elements of the group. From $C_2^2 = E$ we conclude that the square of $D(C_2)$ must be equal to the unit matrix (of order 2). This does not determine $D(C_2)$ uniquely. However, our aim is only to find some irreducible two-dimensional representation of the group. We therefore simply try some matrix with the property mentioned, for example, the unitary matrix

$$\begin{pmatrix} -1 & 0 \\ 0 & 1 \end{pmatrix}.$$

As to $D(C_3(1))$, it follows from the fact that $[C_3(1)]^3 = E$ that the cube of $D(C_3(1))$ must be equal to the unit matrix. Once more we are in a situation where the necessary condition stated admits an infinity of solutions. We therefore add convenient extra conditions. First of all, we also want this matrix to be real and unitary, i.e., orthogonal. This implies that we must choose the matrix as

$$\begin{pmatrix} a & -b \\ b & a \end{pmatrix} \quad \text{or} \quad \begin{pmatrix} a & b \\ b & -a \end{pmatrix}$$

where $a^2 + b^2 = 1$. Choosing the first possibility we get

$$\begin{pmatrix} a & -b \\ b & a \end{pmatrix}^3 = \begin{pmatrix} a^3 - 3ab^2 & b^3 - 3a^2b \\ 3a^2b - b^3 & a^3 - 3ab^2 \end{pmatrix} = \begin{pmatrix} 1 & 0 \\ 0 & 1 \end{pmatrix}.$$

The condition on the off-diagonal elements in the cubed matrix gives $3a^2 - b^2 = 0$ ($b = 0$ turns out to give a reducible representation). Together with $a^2 + b^2 = 1$, this leads to $a^2 = \frac{1}{4}$, $b^2 = \frac{3}{4}$. The condition on the diagonal elements gives $a(a^2 - 3b^2) = 1$, which determines a to be $-\frac{1}{2}$. Finally, choosing $b = -\sqrt{3}/2$, $D(C_3(1))$ is determined. From the two matrices representing a set of generators, the remaining matrices are uniquely determined. The result is given in Table 2-10 as $D^{(3)}$, which is seen to form a faithful representation of the group

Table 2-10

	$D^{(1)}$	$D^{(2)}$	$D^{(3)}$
E	1	1	$\begin{pmatrix} 1 & 0 \\ 0 & 1 \end{pmatrix}$
$C_3(1)$	1	1	$\dfrac{1}{2}\begin{pmatrix} -1 & \sqrt{3} \\ -\sqrt{3} & -1 \end{pmatrix}$
$C_3(2)$	1	1	$\dfrac{1}{2}\begin{pmatrix} -1 & -\sqrt{3} \\ \sqrt{3} & -1 \end{pmatrix}$
C_2	1	-1	$\begin{pmatrix} -1 & 0 \\ 0 & 1 \end{pmatrix}$
C_2'	1	-1	$\dfrac{1}{2}\begin{pmatrix} 1 & \sqrt{3} \\ \sqrt{3} & -1 \end{pmatrix}$
C_2''	1	-1	$\dfrac{1}{2}\begin{pmatrix} 1 & -\sqrt{3} \\ -\sqrt{3} & -1 \end{pmatrix}$

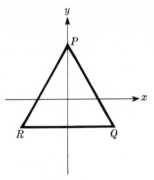

Figure 2-3

considered.   As a reducible and faithful representation of dimension 2 cannot be formed from $D^{(1)}$ and $D^{(2)}$, it follows finally that $D^{(3)}$ is irreducible.

The representation $D^{(3)}$ is, of course, not unique; there are infinitely many other equivalent representations—also if we restrict ourselves to consideration of unitary representations.   The one obtained has a very simple geometric interpretation.   Interpreting the abstract group considered as in Example 2-2, the different matrices are seen to represent the corresponding mappings of the whole plane onto itself in the coordinate system indicated in Fig. 2-3.   □

Characters

On page **77** we defined the trace, Tr A, of an arbitrary square matrix A as the sum of its diagonal elements.   Consider now any two matrices A and B of the same order.   By direct evaluation it is easily seen that $\text{Tr}(AB) = \text{Tr}(BA)$.   Suppose that B is nonsingular.   For the matrix $B^{-1}AB$ we then have $\text{Tr}(B^{-1}(AB)) = \text{Tr}((AB)B^{-1})$ or $\text{Tr}(B^{-1}AB) = \text{Tr } A$.   Hence any two matrices of the form $B^{-1}AB$ and A have the same trace; i.e., equivalent matrices have the same trace.   We shall use this theorem below.

The fact that the irreducible representations of a given group in general are not unique makes it desirable to characterize the representations by something which is *invariant* under an equivalence transformation, i.e., by something which is common to all equivalent representations.   The most convenient invariant has turned out to be the trace of the matrices.   Consider an arbitrary representation D of the given group G.   We now define a function χ which to every element

G_i of the group assigns the (complex) number $\chi_i = \text{Tr}(D(G_i))$. χ is called the *character* of the representation D, while χ_i is called the character of the element G_i in the representation D. Consider another representation D', equivalent to D, with matrices $D'(G_i) = T^{-1}D(G_i)T$, and let χ' be the character of this representation. It follows immediately from the above theorem that we have

$$\text{Tr}(T^{-1}D(G_i)T) = \text{Tr}(D(G_i)) \qquad \text{or} \qquad \chi_i' = \chi_i \quad (i = 1,2,\ldots,g),$$

which means that the two functions χ and χ' are identical, or that the character of a representation really is invariant under an equivalence transformation.

Returning again to the consideration of one particular representation D, we find that conjugate elements of the given group have the same character: Let G_i and G_j be conjugate. This means that there exists a group element G_h such that $G_j = G_h^{-1}G_iG_h$. It follows [as $D(G_h^{-1}) = D(G_h)^{-1}$] that we have $D(G_j) = D(G_h)^{-1}D(G_i)D(G_h)$, and therefore also $\chi_j = \chi_i$. The character χ_i of an element G_i thus only depends on which class of conjugate elements G_i belongs to. As a consequence, the character is often referred to as a *class function*.

Let $D^{(1)},D^{(2)},\ldots,D^{(s)}$ be a complete set of nonequivalent irreducible representations and let $\chi^{(1)},\chi^{(2)},\ldots,\chi^{(s)}$ be the corresponding characters. We shall then prove the following theorem:

$$\sum_{i=1}^{g} (\chi_i^{(p)})^* \chi_i^{(q)} = g\delta_{pq}.$$

The above representations need not be unitary. As any class of equivalent representations contains some which are unitary, and the characters of equivalent representations are identical, we may, however, in the proof suppose that all the above representations are unitary. This implies that we can use the second formulation of the orthogonality theorem:

$$\sum_{i=1}^{g} (\chi_i^{(p)})^* \chi_i^{(q)} = \sum_{i=1}^{g} \sum_{k=1}^{d_p} (D_{kk}^{(p)}(G_i))^* \sum_{l=1}^{d_q} D_{ll}^{(q)}(G_i)$$

$$= \sum_{i,k,l} (D_{kk}^{(p)}(G_i))^* D_{ll}^{(q)}(G_i)$$

$$= \sum_{k,l} \frac{g}{d_p} \delta_{kl}\,\delta_{kl}\,\delta_{pq} = g\,\delta_{pq}.$$

From this theorem we can immediately draw the conclusion that nonequivalent irreducible representations have different characters: Suppose the two representations $D^{(p)}$ and $D^{(q)}(p \neq q)$ had identical characters. We would then have $\Sigma_{i=1}^{g} \left| \chi_i^{(p)} \right|^2 = 0$, which is not possible, since the character of the unit element of the given group is never zero.

Let us then consider a reducible representation D, which is at first supposed to be a *direct sum* of some of the above s irreducible nonequivalent representations, for example, $D^{(m)}, D^{(n)}, \ldots, D^{(p)}, D^{(q)}$:

$$D(G_i) = D^{(m)}(G_i) \oplus D^{(n)}(G_i) \oplus \cdots \oplus D^{(p)}(G_i) \oplus D^{(q)}(G_i)$$
$$(i = 1,2,\ldots,g).$$

Here, of course, the same representation may occur more than once. Since the trace of a direct sum of matrices is the sum of the traces of the matrices which enter into the direct sum, we have correspondingly,

$$\chi_i = \chi_i^{(m)} + \chi_i^{(n)} + \cdots + \chi_i^{(p)} + \chi_i^{(q)} \qquad (i = 1,2,\ldots,g).$$

This last expression is more conveniently written

$$\chi_i = \sum_{k=1}^{s} c_k \chi_i^{(k)},$$

where the nonnegative integer c_k then denotes the number of times $D^{(k)}$ occurs in the direct sum expansion of D. If we multiply on both sides by $(\chi_i^{(l)})^*$ and sum over i we get, by virtue of the above theorem,

$$c_l = \frac{1}{g} \sum_{i=1}^{g} (\chi_i^{(l)})^* \chi_i \qquad (l = 1,2,\ldots,s).$$

This means that we can use the trace of the given representation D to determine the irreducible representations into which it can be split up.

Until now we have supposed D to be a direct sum of irreducible representations. Our conclusion is, however, also valid for any other reducible representation. This follows simply from the fact that any reducible representation is equivalent to one of the above forms combined with the fact that equivalent representations have identical characters.

We have already shown that equivalent representations have identical characters whether or not they are reducible. From the above it is now possible to show that the converse is also true: Representations having identical characters are also equivalent even if they are not irreducible.

Table 2-11

	E	$C_3(1)$	$C_3(2)$	C_2	C_2'	C_2''
$D^{(1)}$	1	1	1	1	1	1
$D^{(2)}$	1	1	1	-1	-1	-1
$D^{(3)}$	2	-1	-1	0	0	0
D	6	0	0	0	0	0

Example 2-9. Let us consider the regular representation D of the group discussed in Example 2-2 corresponding to $G_1 = E$, $G_2 = C_3(1)$, $G_3 = C_3(2)$, $G_4 = C_2$, $G_5 = C_2'$, and $G_6 = C_2''$.
Using the composition table given in Example 2-2, we get

$$D(C_3(1)) = D_2 = \begin{pmatrix} 0 & 0 & 1 & 0 & 0 & 0 \\ 1 & 0 & 0 & 0 & 0 & 0 \\ 0 & 1 & 0 & 0 & 0 & 0 \\ 0 & 0 & 0 & 0 & 0 & 1 \\ 0 & 0 & 0 & 1 & 0 & 0 \\ 0 & 0 & 0 & 0 & 1 & 0 \end{pmatrix},$$

$$D(C_2) = D_4 = \begin{pmatrix} 0 & 0 & 0 & 1 & 0 & 0 \\ 0 & 0 & 0 & 0 & 0 & 1 \\ 0 & 0 & 0 & 0 & 1 & 0 \\ 1 & 0 & 0 & 0 & 0 & 0 \\ 0 & 0 & 1 & 0 & 0 & 0 \\ 0 & 1 & 0 & 0 & 0 & 0 \end{pmatrix}.$$

The other matrices are found in a similar way, and from this we can construct the *character table* for D. Table 2-11 lists the characters for D and for the three irreducible representations found in Example 2-8.
For the coefficients c_k in the expansion

$$\chi_i = c_1\chi_i^{(1)} + c_2\chi_i^{(2)} + c_3\chi_i^{(3)},$$

we have

$$c_1 = \tfrac{1}{6} \sum_{i=1}^{6} (\chi_i^{(1)})^* \chi_i$$
$$= \tfrac{1}{6}[1 \cdot 6 + 1 \cdot 0 + 1 \cdot 0 + 1 \cdot 0 + 1 \cdot 0 + 1 \cdot 0] = 1,$$
$$c_2 = \tfrac{1}{6}[1 \cdot 6 + 1 \cdot 0 + 1 \cdot 0 + (-1) \cdot 0 + (-1) \cdot 0 + (-1) \cdot 0] = 1,$$
$$c_3 = \tfrac{1}{6}[2 \cdot 6 + (-1) \cdot 0 + (-1) \cdot 0 + 0 \cdot 0 + 0 \cdot 0 + 0 \cdot 0] = 2.$$

The regular representation therefore is equivalent to a (any) direct sum of $D^{(1)}$, $D^{(2)}$, $D^{(3)}$, and $D^{(3)}$. ☐

Exercises

*1. Find all irreducible representations of the group $\mathfrak{D}_2$ given by Table 2-12.

Table 2-12

	e	a	b	c
e	e	a	b	c
a	a	e	c	b
b	b	c	e	a
c	c	b	a	e

2. Show that the six matrices

$$\begin{pmatrix} 1 & 0 & 0 \\ 0 & 1 & 0 \\ 0 & 0 & 1 \end{pmatrix}, \quad \begin{pmatrix} 1 & 0 & 0 \\ 0 & 0 & 1 \\ 0 & 1 & 0 \end{pmatrix}, \quad \begin{pmatrix} 0 & 1 & 0 \\ 0 & 0 & 1 \\ 1 & 0 & 0 \end{pmatrix},$$

$$\begin{pmatrix} 0 & 1 & 0 \\ 1 & 0 & 0 \\ 0 & 0 & 1 \end{pmatrix}, \quad \begin{pmatrix} 0 & 0 & 1 \\ 1 & 0 & 0 \\ 0 & 1 & 0 \end{pmatrix}, \quad \begin{pmatrix} 0 & 0 & 1 \\ 0 & 1 & 0 \\ 1 & 0 & 0 \end{pmatrix}$$

constitute a faithful representation of the group considered in Example 2-2. Determine by means of characters a direct sum of irreducible representations equivalent to the above representation. As a control, evaluate the matrices of the representation equivalent to the given one corresponding to the transforming matrix

$$T = \begin{pmatrix} 1 & \sqrt{3} & 1 \\ 1 & 0 & -2 \\ 1 & -\sqrt{3} & 1 \end{pmatrix}.$$

*3. Find a complete set of irreducible representations of the eighth-order group $\mathfrak{D}_4$, which is the set of congruences mapping a given square onto itself.

*4. Find the regular representation of $\mathfrak{D}_2$ (see Exercise 1) and determine a unitary matrix T transforming the regular representation into one consisting entirely of diagonal matrices.

Answers

1.

	e	a	b	c
$D^{(1)}$	1	1	1	1
$D^{(2)}$	1	-1	-1	1
$D^{(3)}$	1	1	-1	-1
$D^{(4)}$	1	-1	1	-1

3. The group elements are symmetry operations on a planar square and we introduce the following names for the group elements:

$E:$ The identity congruence

$C_4(1):$ The 90° clockwise rotation of the square around the center

$C_4(2)$: The 90° counterclockwise rotation of the square around the center
C_2: The rotation of 180° around the center
$C_2'(1)$ and $C_2'(2)$: Reflections in the diagonals
$C_2''(1)$ and $C_2''(2)$: Reflections in the lines through the center parallel to the sides of the square

	E	$C_4(1)$	$C_4(2)$	C_2	$C_2'(1)$	$C_2'(2)$	$C_2''(1)$	$C_2''(2)$
$D^{(1)}$	1	1	1	1	1	1	1	1
$D^{(2)}$	1	1	1	1	-1	-1	-1	-1
$D^{(3)}$	1	-1	-1	1	1	1	-1	-1
$D^{(4)}$	1	-1	-1	1	-1	-1	1	1

$$D^{(5)} \begin{Bmatrix}1 & 0 \\ 0 & 1\end{Bmatrix} \begin{Bmatrix}0 & 1 \\ -1 & 0\end{Bmatrix} \begin{Bmatrix}0 & -1 \\ 1 & 0\end{Bmatrix} \begin{Bmatrix}-1 & 0 \\ 0 & -1\end{Bmatrix} \begin{Bmatrix}0 & 1 \\ 1 & 0\end{Bmatrix} \begin{Bmatrix}0 & -1 \\ -1 & 0\end{Bmatrix} \begin{Bmatrix}1 & 0 \\ 0 & -1\end{Bmatrix} \begin{Bmatrix}-1 & 0 \\ 0 & 1\end{Bmatrix}$$

4.

$$D(e) = \begin{Bmatrix} 1 & 0 & 0 & 0 \\ 0 & 1 & 0 & 0 \\ 0 & 0 & 1 & 0 \\ 0 & 0 & 0 & 1 \end{Bmatrix}$$

$$D(a) = \begin{Bmatrix} 0 & 1 & 0 & 0 \\ 1 & 0 & 0 & 0 \\ 0 & 0 & 0 & 1 \\ 0 & 0 & 1 & 0 \end{Bmatrix}$$

$$D(b) = \begin{Bmatrix} 0 & 0 & 1 & 0 \\ 0 & 0 & 0 & 1 \\ 1 & 0 & 0 & 0 \\ 0 & 1 & 0 & 0 \end{Bmatrix}$$

$$D(c) = \begin{Bmatrix} 0 & 0 & 0 & 1 \\ 0 & 0 & 1 & 0 \\ 0 & 1 & 0 & 0 \\ 1 & 0 & 0 & 0 \end{Bmatrix}$$

$$T = \frac{1}{2} \begin{Bmatrix} 1 & 1 & 1 & 1 \\ 1 & -1 & -1 & 1 \\ 1 & 1 & -1 & -1 \\ 1 & -1 & 1 & -1 \end{Bmatrix} \quad \text{(for example)}$$

2-4. SOME IMPORTANT FINITE GROUPS

The Cyclic and the Dihedral Groups

Above we have as examples considered different groups. We shall now more systematically treat a few important types of abstract finite groups. Corresponding to an arbitrary natural number n we have *the cyclic group* of order n, often denoted $\mathcal{C}_n$. Abstractly, it can be defined as follows:

$$\mathfrak{C}_n \left\{ \begin{array}{l} \text{Generator: } a. \\ \text{Defining relation: } a^n = e. \end{array} \right.$$

Obviously, this group is Abelian; hence there are exactly n different classes of conjugate elements—each class having only one member (cf. p. 107). As the number of nonequivalent irreducible representations is equal to the number of such classes, and as the sum of the squares of their dimensions is equal to the order of the group, it follows that any irreducible representation of a cyclic group is of dimension 1. In Example 2-7 we considered the case of $n = 3$.

The dihedral group $\mathfrak{D}_n$ $(n \geq 3)$ may be defined geometrically in the following way: Its elements are exactly those congruences in the plane which map a given regular n-gon onto itself. It is organized such that the product ab of a and b is the congruence obtained by first performing b and then a (cf. p. 97). The order of the group is $2n$: The center O of the n-gon must always be mapped onto itself. As to the image of a given vertex A of the n-gon there are n possibilities. Corresponding to each of these there are two congruences, one is a rotation, the other may be obtained by a reflection in the line OA followed by the same rotation. It follows from these considerations that any of the group elements can be obtained as a power of the rotation of $360°/n$, possibly multiplied by the above-mentioned reflection. In view of this, it might be expected that the group $\mathfrak{D}_n$ could be defined abstractly in this way:

$$\mathfrak{D}_n \left\{ \begin{array}{l} \text{Generators: } a, b. \\ \text{Defining relations: } a^n = b^2 = (ab)^2 = e. \end{array} \right.$$

To show that this is correct, we may argue as follows: Obviously the elements $e, a, a^2, \ldots, a^{n-1}$ and $b, ab, a^2b, \ldots, a^{n-1}b$ are all distinct. Furthermore, any other expression in a and b can be reduced to one of these. Let us consider a group element of the form $c = \cdots ba \cdots$. From $abab = e$ we get $a^{n-1}ababb = a^{n-1}b$, or $ba = a^{n-1}b$. Hence, $c = \cdots a^{n-1}b \cdots$. Repeating this procedure a sufficient number of times, all occurrences of the element b may be moved to the right, and c finally identified with one of the $2n$ elements mentioned above. As the dihedral group $\mathfrak{D}_n$ obviously satisfies the above defining relations when a is interpreted as the rotation of $360°/n$ and b as the reflection in the line OA, our proof is complete.

It is immediately seen that $\mathcal{C}_n$ is a subgroup of $\mathcal{D}_n$, and also that $\mathcal{D}_n$ is non-Abelian. It can be shown that any irreducible representation of $\mathcal{D}_n$ is of dimension 1 or 2. In Example 2-8 the case of $n = 3$ was considered.

Permutation Groups

A permutation of the natural number $1,2,. . .,n$ may be looked upon as a mapping which to any of these numbers assigns as its image one of these same numbers, and in such a way that different numbers always have different images. Corresponding to this point of view, a permutation may be written

$$a = \begin{pmatrix} 1 & 2 & & n \\ a(1) & a(2) & \cdots & a(n) \end{pmatrix},$$

where the numbers appearing in the second row are the images of the corresponding numbers in the first row. The number of different permutations of $1,2,. . .,n$ is $n!$ The set of all these is now organized by what is generally called *composition of functions* (cf. p. 97, where the case of congruences in the plane was considered): The product of two arbitrary permutations a and b is defined as the mapping given by

$$c(i) = a(b(i)) \qquad (i = 1,2,. . .,n).$$

It is easily seen that the above set of permutations organized as explained forms a group. This is called *the symmetric group of degree n*, and is often denoted $\mathcal{S}_n$. It is of order $n!$ For $n \geq 3$ it is non-Abelian. As subgroups of $\mathcal{S}_n$ we have $\mathcal{D}_n$ as well as $\mathcal{C}_n$. Another important subgroup is *the alternating group* of degree n, $\mathcal{A}_n$, which has as its elements all even permutations of the numbers $1,2,. . .,n$ (cf. p. 37). This subgroup is of order $n!/2$.

Example 2-10. The elements of $\mathcal{S}_3$ may be written as follows (see Table 2-13):

$$e = \begin{pmatrix} 1 & 2 & 3 \\ 1 & 2 & 3 \end{pmatrix}, \qquad a = \begin{pmatrix} 1 & 2 & 3 \\ 2 & 3 & 1 \end{pmatrix}, \qquad b = \begin{pmatrix} 1 & 2 & 3 \\ 3 & 1 & 2 \end{pmatrix},$$

$$c = \begin{pmatrix} 1 & 2 & 3 \\ 1 & 3 & 2 \end{pmatrix}, \qquad d = \begin{pmatrix} 1 & 2 & 3 \\ 3 & 2 & 1 \end{pmatrix}, \qquad f = \begin{pmatrix} 1 & 2 & 3 \\ 2 & 1 & 3 \end{pmatrix}.$$

In this case ($n = 3$) we have $\mathcal{S}_3 = \mathcal{D}_3$, and also $\mathcal{A}_3 = \mathcal{C}_3$. $\square$

Table 2-13

	e	a	b	c	d	f
e	e	a	b	c	d	f
a	a	b	e	f	c	d
b	b	e	a	d	f	c
c	c	d	f	e	a	b
d	d	f	c	b	e	a
f	f	c	d	a	b	e

Consider an arbitrary finite group G of order g with elements $G_1, G_2, \ldots, G_g$. Corresponding to the group element G_i we introduce the following permutation of the group elements:

$$\gamma_i = \begin{pmatrix} G_1 & G_2 & \cdots & G_g \\ G_iG_1 & G_iG_2 & & G_iG_g \end{pmatrix} \qquad (i = 1,2,\ldots,g).$$

Obviously, permutations corresponding to different group elements are different. For the product of two such permutations γ_j and γ_i, we have

$$\gamma_j\gamma_i = \begin{pmatrix} G_1 & G_2 & \cdots & G_g \\ G_jG_iG_1 & G_jG_iG_2 & & G_jG_iG_g \end{pmatrix},$$

which is exactly the permutation corresponding to the group element G_jG_i. It follows that the above set of permutations organized by composition of functions forms a group which is isomorphic with the given group G. We have thus shown that any finite group of order g is isomorphic with a subgroup of the symmetric group of degree g.

Survey of Groups up to Order 8

We shall now briefly specify all abstract groups up to order 8. As already shown (p. 103), there is only one abstract group of given order n, in case n is a prime number, namely, the cyclic group $\mathcal{C}_n$. Hence, $\mathcal{C}_2$, $\mathcal{C}_3$, $\mathcal{C}_5$, and $\mathcal{C}_7$ are the only groups of order 2, 3, 5, and 7, respectively.

There are two abstract groups of order 4, both of which are Abelian (cf. p. 101). One of these is $\mathcal{C}_4$. The other therefore is not cyclic; i.e., it has no element of order 4. Since the order of any element must be 1, 2, or 4, and only one element can be of order 1, it follows that there must be three elements of order 2. This is realized by the group $\mathcal{C}_2 \times \mathcal{C}_2$, often denoted $\mathcal{V}$ and called the *four-group* ("Vierergruppe") (Table 2-14). It is also denoted $\mathcal{D}_2$, as it can be obtained geomet-

Table 2-14

	e	a	b	c
e	e	a	b	c
a	a	e	c	b
b	b	c	e	a
c	c	b	a	e

rically as the set of congruences in the plane mapping a given line segment onto itself.

There are two abstract groups of order 6, namely, $\mathcal{C}_6$ and $\mathfrak{D}_3$. The latter, which is non-Abelian, has been considered several times already. Finally, there are five groups of order 8. Of these three are Abelian and two are non-Abelian. The Abelian ones may be obtained as $\mathcal{C}_8$, $\mathcal{C}_4 \times \mathcal{C}_2$, and $\mathcal{C}_2 \times \mathcal{C}_2 \times \mathcal{C}_2$. Abstractly they can be represented as follows:

$\mathcal{C}_8$ $\begin{cases} \text{Generator: } a. \\ \text{Defining relation: } a^8 = e. \end{cases}$

$\mathcal{C}_4 \times \mathcal{C}_2$ $\begin{cases} \text{Generators: } a, b. \\ \text{Defining relations: } a^4 = b^2 = e, \, ab = ba. \end{cases}$

$\mathcal{C}_2 \times \mathcal{C}_2 \times \mathcal{C}_2$ $\begin{cases} \text{Generators: } a, b, c. \\ \text{Defining relations: } a^2 = b^2 = c^2 = e, \, ab = ba, \\ \qquad\qquad\qquad\qquad bc = cb, \, ca = ac \end{cases}$

To construct the remaining two groups, we note that if all group elements are of order 1 or 2, the group is Abelian. Suppose a and b are arbitrary elements of a group with no element of order more than 2. We then have $a^2 = b^2 = (ab)^2 = e$, and therefore also $a^{-1} = a$, $b^{-1} = b$, and $(ab)^{-1} = ab$. But in any group we have $(ab)^{-1} = b^{-1}a^{-1}$. On substitution we get $ab = (ab)^{-1} = b^{-1}a^{-1} = ba$, which shows that the group is Abelian. We can conclude that both the remaining groups of order 8 must have at least one element of order 4 (the existence of an element of order 8 means that the group is cyclic and therefore also Abelian). Abstractly the two remaining groups can be represented in the following way:

$\mathfrak{D}_4$ $\begin{cases} \text{Generators: } a, b. \\ \text{Defining relations: } a^4 = b^2 = (ab)^2 = e. \end{cases}$

$\mathcal{Q}$ $\begin{cases} \text{Generators: } a, b. \\ \text{Defining relations: } a^4 = e, \, a^2 = b^2 = (ab)^2. \end{cases}$

Q is the so-called *quaternion group*, deriving its name from the quaternions, which are "hypercomplex" numbers of the form $a_0 + a_1 i + a_2 j + a_3 k$, where the coefficients a_0, a_1, a_2, and a_3 are real, and where the "units" i, j, and k satisfy the relations

$$i^2 = j^2 = k^2 = -1, \quad ij = -ji = k, \quad jk = -kj = i, \quad ki = -ik = j.$$

It is easily verified that the set $\{1, -1, i, -i, j, -j, k, -k\}$ represents the group Q when the above-defined multiplication is used as the composition rule.

An Application of Group Theory

Group theory is used widely in discussing molecular structure and in classifying crystal symmetries. Most of these applications require a rather extensive use of differential equations, and we can therefore not treat them here. We shall, however, give one very simple application of the above theory in crystallography.

Example 2-11. Consider three linearly independent three-dimensional vectors a_1, a_2, and a_3. By the corresponding *lattice* we shall understand the set of all linear combinations $n_1 a_1 + n_2 a_2 + n_3 a_3$, where n_1, n_2, and n_3 are integers (positive, negative, or zero). Drawn as position vectors from a fixed point O, these determine a set of points in space which we shall call an (infinite) space crystal. If we introduce a coordinate system S' with O as its origin and with a_1, a_2, and a_3 as its base vectors, the points belonging to the crystal are exactly those which have integral coordinates.

A linear vector function which maps the lattice as a whole onto itself is said to leave the lattice *invariant*. In the above coordinate system S' such a vector function will appear as a matrix with only integral elements, and therefore also with integral trace. Consider now the set of all the matrices which in S' represent linear vector functions leaving the lattice invariant. When organized by usual matrix multiplication, these form a group G', often called a *crystallographic point group*.

Suppose finally that an *orthogonal* coordinate system S, also with its origin at O, is introduced. The set of matrices representing the above-mentioned vector functions in this other system also form a group G when organized by matrix multiplication. Obviously, the two groups G and G' are equivalent: Let A and A' be matrices which in S and S', respectively, represent the same vector function. We then have

$A' = T^{-1}AT$, where the columns of T are the coordinates of $\mathbf{a}_1$, $\mathbf{a}_2$, and $\mathbf{a}_3$ in system S (cf. p. 67). As the trace is left unchanged by an equivalence transformation, we know also that the elements of G have integral trace. From this fact we can easily draw a conclusion regarding the possible rotations leaving the lattice invariant.

Consider an arbitrary rotation around the Z-axis of the coordinate system S. In S such a rotation will appear as a matrix of the form

$$\left\{ \begin{matrix} \cos\theta & -\sin\theta & 0 \\ \sin\theta & \cos\theta & 0 \\ 0 & 0 & 1 \end{matrix} \right\}.$$

If this is to be an element of G, it must have integral trace; i.e., $2\cos\theta + 1$ must be integral. The only possibilities for $\cos\theta$ are therefore 0, $\pm\frac{1}{2}$, ± 1, which shows that θ must be $0°$, $60°$, $90°$, or $120°$ $(+n \cdot 180°)$. The same argument may of course be applied to any other axis passing through the point O. Our conclusion is that any symmetry axis through a point of our space crystal must be either twofold, threefold, fourfold, or sixfold. An axis with fivefold symmetry, for instance, is impossible.

It can be shown that there exist 32 inequivalent crystallographic point groups. Among these there are 18 nonisomorphic groups. □

Exercises

1. Consider a regular tetrahedron $ABCD$ with center O. Show that the set of all rotations around an axis through O mapping the tetrahedron as a whole onto itself defines a group of order 12 (the tetrahedral group), when the product ab of two such rotations a and b is defined as the rotation obtained by first performing b and then a.

2. There are two Abelian groups of order 9. Determine their composition tables.

*3. Investigate the group generated by the matrices

$$a = \left\{ \begin{matrix} 0 & i \\ i & 0 \end{matrix} \right\} \quad \text{and} \quad b = \left\{ \begin{matrix} 0 & 1 \\ -1 & 0 \end{matrix} \right\}$$

when matrix multiplication is used as the composition rule.

4. Show by means of the defining relations that the number of classes of conjugate elements in the group $\mathfrak{D}_n$ is $(n+3)/2$ if n is odd and $(n+6)/2$ if n is even.

Answer

3. $a^4 = e$, $a^2 = b^2 = (ab)^2$. The group is the quaternion group $\mathfrak{Q}$.

Part II
Functions of One and Several Variables

3

Functions of One Variable

3-1. REAL-VALUED FUNCTIONS OF ONE REAL VARIABLE

The Notion of a Function

In the following we shall consider what are called real-valued functions of one real variable. Before we do that we want to say a few words about the notion of a *function* in general.

Suppose A and B are given sets of any kind. A *function f from A to B* or a *mapping of A into B* is then determined when to every element of A there is associated one and only one element of B. If x is any element in A, then the element in B associated with x is denoted $f(x)$ and is called the *value* which the function f assumes at the *argument* x or the *image* of x under the function f.

A is called the *domain* of the function. Those elements of B that are images of at least one element in A form the *range* of the function. The range may or may not be the whole of B; in case it is, f is said to be a mapping of A *onto* B. The mapping is said to be *one-to-one* if every element in the range is the image of only one element in A (Fig. 3-1).

If f is a one-to-one mapping of A onto B, a new function f^{-1}, called the *inverse of f*, is defined as the function from B to A which has the following property: The image $f^{-1}(y)$ of an arbitrary element y in B is the uniquely determined element in A whose image under f is y. For

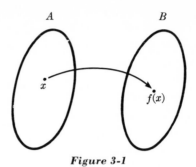

Figure 3-1

any element y in B we thus have, by definition, $f(f^{-1}(y)) = y$. It immediately follows that we correspondingly have for any element x in $A : f^{-1}(f(x)) = x$.

In the preceding we have already considered an important class of functions, the linear vector functions from the set of N-dimensional vectors to the set of N-dimensional vectors. We saw that such a function has an inverse function in the case where the determinant belonging to the defining matrix is different from zero.

Real Functions

In the following paragraphs we shall consider *real-valued functions of one real variable*, or, briefly, *real functions*, i.e., functions from some set A to some set B, where A as well as B are sets of real numbers.

The image of an arbitrary element x in the domain of such a function f is often denoted y. We then have $y = f(x)$. Insofar as $f(x)$ is an explicit expression for the image of x (and the sets A and B appear from the context), this equation completely determines the function: Substituting any element from A in the right side of the equation, we get the corresponding element in B. Here x is often called the *independent variable*, y the *dependent variable*, and y is said to be a function of x.

The statement that the function f has an inverse function is then equivalent to saying that the equation $y = f(x)$, where y is any element in B, has one and only one solution x belonging to A. As already mentioned, this solution is denoted $f^{-1}(y)$. The inverse function may thus be represented by the equation $x = f^{-1}(y)$, where now y is the independent variable and x the dependent variable.

The *graph* of the function f in a (usual right-angled) coordinate system XY is of course (cf. p. 7) the set of points with coordinates (x,y) such that x belongs to A and $y = f(x)$. The same set of points may be considered as forming the graph of the inverse function (if it exists) insofar as this is represented by the equation $x = f^{-1}(y)$.

If we want to reserve the letter x for the independent variable (and y for the dependent one), the inverse of f will be represented by the equation $y = f^{-1}(x)$. In this case the graph of f^{-1} is obtained by reflecting the graph of f in the straight line $y = x$.

Given two real functions f and g with a common domain A, the *sum*, $f + g$, of the two functions is defined as the function with domain A, for which the image of an arbitrary element x in A is $f(x) + g(x)$. Correspondingly the *difference*, $f - g$, the *product*, $f \cdot g$, and—provided zero does not belong to the range of g—the *quotient*, f/g, is defined.

Finally the *composite* of two functions g and f, where the range of g is included in the domain of f, is defined as the function, whose domain is that of g and such that the image of an arbitrary element x in this domain is $f(g(x))$. The composite of g and f is written $f \circ g$.

Above we have used the letter f to denote the function itself, while $f(x)$ has been used to denote some value of the function. In practice it will often be convenient to allow deviations from such a principle. We shall permit ourselves to speak of "the function $y = f(x)$" or even "the function $f(x)$". In these cases the domain of the function considered—unless otherwise stated—will be the most extensive set of real numbers for which the expression $f(x)$ has a meaning. From time to time we will also write "$y = y(x)$", which may be read "y is a function of x"; the meaning of this will of course be that we are considering some function f where the independent variable is x, while the dependent variable is y.

In accordance with these conventions we may, for example, restate some of the above definitions as follows: The sum of the two functions $y = f(x)$ and $y = g(x)$ is the function $y = f(x) + g(x)$; the composite of the two functions $u = g(x)$ and $y = f(u)$ is the function $y = f(g(x))$.

Example 3-1. Let us consider the function f from the set of all real numbers to the set of all real numbers such that the image of the arbitrary real number x is $f(x) = 2x - 3$. According to the above, this function may be referred to simply as the function $y = 2x - 3$,

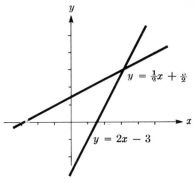

Figure 3-2

$-\infty < x < \infty$, or, more simply, $y = 2x - 3$, it being understood that the domain of the function is the set of all real numbers. As previously shown, the graph of the function is a straight line.

Solving the equation with respect to x, it is seen that the function has an inverse function which is defined for all y, as corresponding to each y exactly one solution $x = \frac{1}{2}y + \frac{3}{2}$ is obtained. This is then an expression for the inverse function (Fig. 3-2).

The graph is unchanged. On interchanging the names of the variables, we obtain the expression $y = \frac{1}{2}x + \frac{3}{2}$ for the inverse function. The graph of this is obtained from the previous one by a reflection in the line $y = x$.

The function $f \cdot f$ is here $y = (2x - 3)^2$ or $y = 4x^2 - 12x + 9$, while the function $f \circ f$ is $y = 2(2x - 3) - 3$ or $y = 4x - 9$.   □

Sequences

The notion of an infinite sequence is an important tool in the consideration of a large number of problems concerning functions.

An (*infinite*) *sequence* is simply a function whose domain is the set of all positive integers. If the sequence is called a, its value at n is usually denoted a_n and is called the nth *element* of the sequence. The sequence itself is often written $a_1, a_2, \ldots, a_n, \ldots$

In the following we are concerned with sequences of real numbers, i.e., sequences whose elements are real numbers. Such a sequence a is said to be *convergent* with the *limit* α, or to *converge* to α in case the following is true: Corresponding to any given positive number ϵ, however small, it is possible to determine a number N such that the inequality $|a_n - \alpha| < \epsilon$ is satisfied for every $n > N$. This is written

$a_n \to \alpha$ as $n \to \infty$ [a_n approaches α as n tends to (plus) infinity] or as $\lim_{n\to\infty} a_n = \alpha$ [the limit of a_n, as n tends to (plus) infinity, is α].

Example 3-2. $a_n = k \to k$ as $n \to \infty$, as $|k - k| < \epsilon$ is already satisfied for all positive n independently of ϵ. $b_n = 1/n \to 0$ as $n \to \infty$, as $|(1/n) - 0| < \epsilon$ whenever $n > 1/\epsilon$. $a_n = (-1)^n$ has no limit. □

If a sequence a has no limit, it is said to be *divergent* or to *diverge*. In particular the sequence is said to diverge to (plus) infinity (minus infinity) when corresponding to any given number K, however large, it is possible to determine a number N such that the inequality $a_n > K$ ($a_n < -K$) is satisfied for every $n > N$. This is written $a_n \to \infty$ ($-\infty$) as $n \to \infty$.

Example 3-3. $a_n = \sqrt{n} \to \infty$ as $n \to \infty$, since $\sqrt{n} > K$ whenever $n > K^2$. $b_n = (n^2 - 2n) \to \infty$ as $n \to \infty$, as $(n^2 - 2n) > K$ whenever $n > 1 + \sqrt{1 + K}$. $c_n = n(-1)^n$ is divergent without tending either to plus or minus infinity. □

Given two sequences a and b, we can combine them to give the new sequences $a + b$, $a - b$, $a \cdot b$ and a/b. In the last case it must be assumed, however, that zero does not belong to the range of b. In case a and b are convergent with limits α and β, respectively, then the new sequences will also be convergent, and with limits $\alpha + \beta$, $\alpha - \beta$, $\alpha \cdot \beta$, and, provided β is different from zero, α/β, respectively. The proof of these basic *rules of operation* for convergent sequences follows from the definition of convergence.

Jointly, these rules show that an arbitrary series of elementary mathematical operations on the nth elements of a number of given convergent sequences is "carried over" in the limit: The resulting sequence will be convergent and with a limit which is obtained by carrying out the same series of operations with the corresponding limits of the given sequences (with the usual condition that no denominator can be 0).

Example 3-4

$$a_n = \frac{5n^2 + 1}{n^2 - n} = \frac{5 + (1/n)(1/n)}{1 - (1/n)} \to \frac{5 + 0 \cdot 0}{1 - 0} = 5$$

as $n \to \infty$. □

Limits of Functions

In the following we shall use the expressions "the number x" and "the point x" at random. By the δ-*neighborhood of the point* x_0, we then understand the set of real numbers x such that $|x - x_0| < \delta$, while the *deleted* δ-*neighborhood* of x_0 means the set of real numbers x, such that $0 < |x - x_0| < \delta$.

Now let f be a function which is defined in a deleted neighborhood of some point x_0, but not necessarily at the point x_0 itself. f is then said to have the *limit* c at x_0, when for every sequence $x_1, x_2, . . ., x_n, . . .$ the elements of which are all different from x_0 and within the domain of f it is valid that if the sequence converges to x_0, the corresponding sequence of f-values converges to c: $f(x_1), f(x_2), . . ., f(x_n), . . . \to c$ as $n \to \infty$. The statement that f has the limit c at x_0 is written $f(x) \to c$ as $x \to x_0$ [$f(x)$ approaches c as x approaches x_0] or $\lim_{x \to x_0} f(x) = c$ [the limit of $f(x)$, as x approaches x_0, is c].

If we confine ourselves to the consideration of sequences which converge to x_0 from the right ($x_n > x_0$) and then obtain sequences of f-values all having c as a limit, then the function is naturally said to have c as a *right-hand limit* at x_0 [$f(x) \to c$ as $x \to x_0 + 0$ or $\lim_{x \to x_0 + 0} f(x) = c$]. In an analogous manner, the statement that the function has a left-hand limit at x_0 [$f(x) \to c$ as $x \to x_0 - 0$] is defined.

If the function has a limit at x_0, then of course it also has a right-hand limit and a left-hand limit. The converse need not be true, as the two one-sided limits may be different.

The given "dynamic" definition of a limit is equivalent to the following "static" definition, which does not make use of the notion of a sequence: $f(x) \to c$ as $x \to x_0$, when corresponding to any given positive number ϵ, however small, it is possible to determine a positive number δ such that $f(x)$ belongs to the ϵ-neighborhood of c whenever x belongs to the deleted δ-neighborhood of x_0.

The four above-mentioned basic rules for convergent sequences are easily seen to give rise to corresponding rules for limits of functions. Suppose we have $f(x) \to c$ as $x \to x_0$ and $g(x) \to d$ as $x \to x_0$. Then we also have $f(x) \pm g(x) \to c \pm d$ as $x \to x_0$, $f(x)g(x) \to c \cdot d$, and (provided $d \neq 0$) $f(x)/g(x) \to c/d$ as $x \to x_0$. It follows from this that a series of elementary mathematical operations carried out on functions which all have limits at a point x_0 will give a new function which also has a limit at x_0 and which is obtained by carrying out the same series of operations with the corresponding limits of the given functions (provided that zero does not occur as a denominator).

The statements $f(x) \to \infty (-\infty)$ as $x \to x_0, f(x) \to c$ as $x \to \infty(-\infty)$, and $f(x) \to \infty(-\infty)$ as $x \to \infty(-\infty)$ are defined exactly in analogy with the above in either the "dynamic" or "static" manner.

Continuity of Functions

Let f be a real function defined in some neighborhood of the point x_0. f is then said to be *continuous* at x_0, if it has a limit at x_0 and if this limit equals $f(x_0)$, i.e., if $f(x) \to f(x_0)$ as $x \to x_0$. Correspondingly, the function is said to be continuous from the right (left) at x_0, when $f(x) \to f(x_0)$ as $x \to x_0 + 0(x \to x_0 - 0)$.

The four basic rules for limits of functions immediately show that any series of permissible elementary mathematical operations carried out on functions which are continuous at x_0 yields a function which is also continuous at this point.

That the function f is continuous in a whole interval simply means that it is continuous at each point in the interval. Graphically this signifies that it is without "jumps" in the interval.

In the following, the *closed interval* with *end points* a and b, i.e., the set of real numbers x such that $a \leq x \leq b$, will be written $[a,b]$. The corresponding *open interval*, where the end points do not belong to the set, will be written $]a,b[$.

A series of important rules apply to a function f which is continuous in a closed interval $[a,b]$. Together these state that the range of the function in this case also is a closed interval whose end points are *the absolute maximum value* and *the absolute minimum value* of the function considered.

When the function furthermore is increasing (decreasing), then it has an inverse function f^{-1} which is also increasing (decreasing) and continuous in the corresponding interval $[f(a),f(b)]([f(b),f(a)])$.

Example 3-5

$$f(x) = \begin{cases} x^2 & \text{if } x < 0, \\ x^2 + 1 & \text{if } 0 < x < 1, \\ (3/x) - 1 & \text{if } 1 < x. \end{cases}$$

The function is continuous in the whole of its domain ($x \neq 0$ and 1) (Fig. 3-3). $f(x) \to 0$ as $x \to 0 - 0$; $f(x) \to 1$ as $x \to 0 + 0$. The function is said to make a (finite) *jump* at the point 0.

For $x = 1$, the function has a limit from the left as well as from the right. As these are equal $(= 2), f(x) \to 2$ as $x \to 1$ without restriction. If the function is extended to take on the value 2 at the point 1 (its

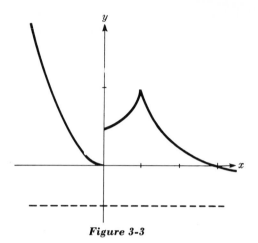

Figure 3-3

so-called *true value* here), then it will still be continuous in all of its domain. $f(x) \to \infty$ as $x \to -\infty$, $f(x) \to -1$ as $x \to \infty$. □

Vanishing Functions

When a function of x approaches 0 as x approaches x_0, then it is said to be an *infinitely small quantity* or to be *vanishing* as $x \to x_0$.

Given two functions of x, α and β, which are both infinitely small as $x \to x_0$, then when β is different from 0 in some deleted neighborhood of x_0, the function α/β will be defined in the same deleted neighborhood.

Nothing can be said beforehand regarding the values of this function as $x \to x_0$. If it also vanishes as $x \to x_0$, then α is said to be infinitely small of a *higher order* than β, and we write $\alpha(x) = o(\beta(x))$ as $x \to x_0$.

Example 3-6. $\alpha(x) = (x-1)^2$, $\beta(x) = x^2 - 1$. Both functions vanish as $x \to 1$.

$$\frac{\alpha(x)}{\beta(x)} = \frac{(x-1)^2}{x^2 - 1} = \frac{x-1}{x+1} \to 0$$

as $x \to 1$; hence $(x-1)^2 = o((x^2 - 1))$ as $x \to 1$. □

Exercises

*1. Find explicit expressions for the inverses of each of the following functions:

(a) $y = x^2 - 6x + 7$, $-3 \le x \le 3$.

(b) $y = \begin{cases} x^2 - 2x + 3 & \text{if } x < 1, \\ -x^2 + 2x + 1 & \text{if } x \ge 1. \end{cases}$

(c) $y = x^2 + x \cdot |x+1| + 3x$, $-2 \le x \le 1$.

2. Suppose that f and g are one-to-one mappings of the set of all real numbers onto itself. Show that the following formula is valid:

$$(g \circ f)^{-1} = f^{-1} \circ g^{-1}.$$

3. Show that the set of all one-to-one mappings of the set of all real numbers onto itself forms a non-Abelian group when organized by composition of functions.

*4. Investigate the following sequences:

(a) $a_n = (n^2 - 2n)/(3n^2 + 1)$.   (d) $a_n = \sqrt[n]{n}$.
(b) $a_n = n^2/(2n + 1) - 2n^2/(4n + 1)$.   (e) $a_n = n!/2^n$.
(c) $a_n = \sqrt[n]{2}$.   (f) $a_n = \sqrt[n]{n!}$.

*5. Determine those values of x_0 for which it is true that $f(x) \to 5$ as $x \to x_0$, in each of the following cases:

(a) $f(x) = x^2 - 4x$.   (b) $f(x) = \begin{cases} -x^2 - 4x + 2 & \text{if } x < -3, \\ x^2 + 2x + 2 & \text{if } -3 < x \le 1, \\ -x^2 - 4x + 2 & \text{if } x > 1. \end{cases}$

6. Consider the functions $f_1(x) = x - 1$, $f_2(x) = x^3 - 1$, $f_3(x) = (x - 1)^3$, $f_4(x) = \sqrt[3]{x - 1}$, and $f_5(x) = \sqrt[3]{x} - 1$, which all vanish as $x \to 1$. Determine all pairs of functions $(f_i(x), f_k(x))$ for which $f_i(x) = o(f_k(x))$ as $x \to 1$.

Answers

1. (a) $x = 3 - \sqrt{2 + y}$ $-2 \le y \le 34$

     (b) $x = \begin{cases} 1 - \sqrt{y - 2} & y > 2 \\ 1 + \sqrt{2 - y} & y \le 2 \end{cases}$

     (c) $x = \begin{cases} -1 + \sqrt{1 + y/2} & -2 \le y \le 6 \\ y/2 & -4 \le y \le -2 \end{cases}$

4. The limits are

(a) $\frac{1}{3}$.   (d) 1.
(b) $-\frac{1}{8}$.   (e) The sequence diverges to $+\infty$.
(c) 1.   (f) The sequence diverges to $+\infty$.

5. (a) $x_0 = 5$ or -1.   (b) $x_0 = -3$.

3-2. DEFINITE INTEGRALS

Definition of a Definite Integral

Consider a function f which in a closed interval $[a,b]$ is bounded and has at most a finite number of discontinuities.

We now divide the given interval into n subintervals with the lengths $\Delta_1 x, \Delta_2 x, \ldots, \Delta_n x$ and choose a point in each of these subintervals, respectively, $x_1, x_2, \ldots, x_n$ (Fig. 3-4). Corresponding to this we define an *average sum* as follows:

$$f(x_1)\,\Delta_1 x + f(x_2)\,\Delta_2 x + \cdots + f(x_n)\,\Delta_n x = \sum_{i=1}^{n} f(x_i)\,\Delta_i x.$$

If such a process is carried out corresponding to each positive integer

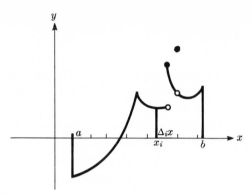

Figure 3-4

n, then a sequence of average sums is obtained. Naturally the resulting sequence will in general depend on the subintervals chosen as well as on the points chosen in these subintervals. However, all sequences formed in this manner turn out to be convergent and with the same limit if only the length of the greatest subinterval in each sequence approaches 0, as n tends to infinity.

This limit is named the *definite integral* of the function f from a to b and is written $\int_a^b f(x)\, dx$ (or $\int_a^b f$). The function f under the *integral sign* is called the *integrand*, a the *lower limit* of integration, and b the *upper limit* of integration.

A Geometric Interpretation

Let $f(x)$ be greater than or equal to zero and continuous in the interval $[a,b]$. In this case the curve together with the X-axis and (if necessary) the two straight lines $x = a$ and $x = b$ enclose a region in the plane (Fig. 3-5).

Geometrically, the average sum is seen here to give the area of a

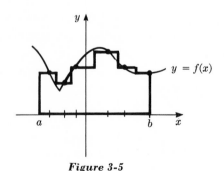

Figure 3-5

"step figure" built up around the given curve. Correspondingly the definite integral gives what is called the *area* of the region considered, as it can be shown that this and only this number is greater than or equal to the area of any polygon contained in the region and at the same time less than or equal to the area of any polygon containing the region.

When $f(x) \le 0$ and continuous in the interval, then the area between the curve and the X-axis is obtained as the negative of the definite integral. More generally, the area of a region enclosed by two continuous curves $y = f(x)$ and $y = g(x)$, where $f(x) \ge g(x)$ $(a \le x \le b)$, and by the lines $x = a$ and $x = b$ is given by $\int_a^b (f(x) - g(x))\, dx$.

Example 3-7. Determine $\int_1^3 (x + 1)\, dx$. The interval $1 \le x \le 3$ is divided into n equally large parts, and in each subinterval the value of the function is chosen at the right end point (Fig. 3-6). Corresponding to this the following average sum is obtained:

$$S_n = \left(\left(1 + \frac{2}{n}\right) + 1\right)\frac{2}{n} + \left(\left(1 + \frac{4}{n}\right) + 1\right)\frac{2}{n} + \cdots$$
$$+ \left(\left(1 + \frac{2n}{n}\right) + 1\right)\frac{2}{n}$$
$$= \sum_{i=1}^{n}\left(\left(1 + \frac{2i}{n}\right) + 1\right)\frac{2}{n} = \frac{4}{n^2}\sum_{i=1}^{n} i + \frac{4}{n}\sum_{i=1}^{n} 1$$
$$= \frac{4}{n^2}\frac{n}{2}(n + 1) + \frac{4}{n}n = 6 + \frac{2}{n}.$$

Thus $S_n \to 6$ as $n \to \infty$.

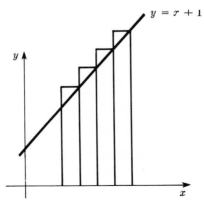

$y = x + 1$

Figure 3-6

As here the length of the greatest subinterval automatically approaches zero as n tends to infinity, we have found the value of the desired definite integral to be 6—in agreement with a well-known formula for the area of a trapezium.   □

Some Rules for Definite Integrals

From the corresponding relations between average sums, it is easily seen that the following rules are valid: a linearity rule,

$$\int_a^b (\alpha f(x) + \beta g(x))\, dx = \alpha \int_a^b f(x)\, dx + \beta \int_a^b g(x)\, dx,$$

an additivity rule,

$$\int_a^b f(x)\, dx = \int_a^c f(x)\, dx + \int_c^b f(x)\, dx \qquad (a < c < b),$$

and the inequality

$$\int_a^b f(x)\, dx \le \int_a^b g(x)\, dx,$$

whenever $f(x) \le g(x)$ in the whole interval.

If we change the values of the integrand in a finite number of points in the interval, the integrand will still satisfy the conditions for the existence of the definite integral. Furthermore its value will not be changed by this, as in choosing a usable sequence of average sums it is possible to avoid applying the values of the function at the "new" points.

So far it has been assumed throughout that the lower limit is less than the upper limit $(a < b)$. For the case $a \ge b$ we now define

$$\int_a^b f(x)\, dx = - \int_b^a f(x)\, dx.$$

Thus in particular a definite integral for which both limits are the same has the value zero. This extension of the concept of a definite integral does not invalidate the linearity and the additivity rules.

We shall see later that in certain cases it is also possible to define a definite integral in case the integrand is not bounded, or the integration interval is not finite. Such integrals will then be said to be improper integrals.

The Mean Value Theorem for Integrals

Let the integrand now be continuous in the closed interval given by the limits of integration a and b $(a < b)$. The integrand in this case takes on a maximum value M and a minimum value m in the interval (cf. p. 137).

Clearly we have the following:

$$m(b - a) \le \int_a^b f(x)\,dx \le M(b - a) \qquad \text{or} \qquad m \le \frac{\int_a^b f(x)\,dx}{b - a} \le M.$$

As the integrand takes on all values between its minimum and maximum values, then there exists in the interval (at least) one point c such that

$$\frac{\int_a^b f(x)\,dx}{b - a} = f(c).$$

From this the *mean value theorem for integrals* is obtained (Fig. 3-7):

$$\int_a^b f(x)\,dx = (b - a)f(c).$$

$f(c)$ is the so-called *mean value* of the integrand in the interval considered.

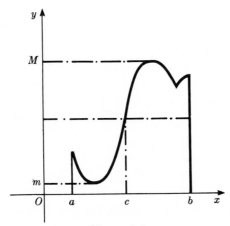

Figure 3-7

The formula holds generally only for a continuous integrand.   However, it is also valid for $a \geq b$.

Exercises

1. Prove (for example by induction) the formula

$$\sum_{i=1}^{n} i^2 = \frac{n(n + 1)(2n + 1)}{6},$$

and use this to evaluate the definite integral $\int_0^1 x^2 \, dx$.

2. Prove (for example by induction) the formula

$$\sum_{i=1}^{n} i^3 = \frac{n^2(n + 1)^2}{4},$$

and use this to evaluate the definite integral $\int_0^1 x^3 \, dx$.

*3. Show that

$$\int_0^a x^p \, dx = a^{p+1} \int_0^1 x^p \, dx,$$

where a is a real number and p a positive integer.

Answer

3. $\int_0^a x^p \, dx = \lim_{n\to\infty} \sum_{i=1}^{n} \left(\frac{a}{n} i\right)^p \frac{a}{n} = a^{p+1} \lim_{n\to\infty} \sum_{i=1}^{n} \left(\frac{i}{n}\right)^p \frac{1}{n}$

$$= a^{p+1} \int_0^1 x^p \, dx.$$

3-3. DIFFERENTIABLE FUNCTIONS

Definition of a Derivative

Let the function $y = f(x)$ be defined in some neighborhood of the point x_0, and let x be another point belonging to this neighborhood. We may look upon x as the result of giving x_0 an *increment* $\Delta x = h = x - x_0$. Corresponding to this, the function takes an increment $\Delta y = f(x_0 + h) - f(x_0)$.

The quantity

$$\frac{\Delta y}{\Delta x} = \frac{f(x_0 + h) - f(x_0)}{h}$$

is called the *difference quotient* of the function.   It depends only on h for a given function and a fixed x_0.

If the difference quotient has a limit as h approaches 0, the function $y = f(x)$ is said to be *differentiable* at the point x_0 and the limit is called the *derivative* or the *differential quotient* of the function at x_0. The limit is written $f'(x_0)$:

$$\frac{\Delta y}{\Delta x} = \frac{f(x_0 + h) - f(x_0)}{h} \rightarrow f'(x_0)$$

as $h \rightarrow 0$.

As the denominator of the difference quotient approaches zero as $h \rightarrow 0$, it is a necessary condition for the differentiability of the function that the numerator also approach zero, or, in other words, that the given function is continuous at x_0. This condition, however, is not sufficient (Examples 3-5 and 3-9).

As to a geometric interpretation of the above considerations, it is seen that the difference quotient gives the slope of the secant determined by the points $(x_0, f(x_0))$ and $(x_0 + h, f(x_0 + h))$ on the graph of the given function.

The existence of a derivative therefore means that the secant approaches a "limit line" as h approaches 0. This limit is by definition the *tangent* line of the given curve at the point $(x_0, f(x_0))$. It has the equation $y = f'(x_0)(x - x_0) + f(x_0)$ (Fig. 3-8).

Suppose a given function f is differentiable at every point of some interval. It is then said to be differentiable *in* that interval. The function f', whose value at the arbitrary point x is $f'(x)$, is called the (*first*) *derivative* of f. Conversely f is called a *primitive* or an *antiderivative* of f'. The process of obtaining f' from f is called *differentiation*.

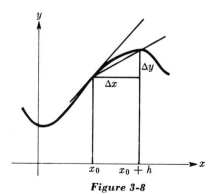

Figure 3-8

Corresponding to the equation $y = f(x)$ we shall also write $y' = f'(x)$. In this way y' becomes a new symbol for the derivative of f at the point x. Occasionally we shall write $y'(x)$ instead of y', as it is then possible to show at which point the derivative is taken.

Suppose the (first) derivative of f also is differentiable; then $(f')'$ or f'' is called the *second derivative* of f. Analogously the nth *derivative* of f is defined (if it exists); it is written $f^{(n)}$.

Rules for Differentiation

From the above definition one immediately obtains the following results: The function $f(x) = c$, where c is a constant, is differentiable for all x with $f'(x) = 0$. The function $f(x) = x$ is differentiable for all x with $f'(x) = 1$. The function $f(x) = x^n$, where $n > 1$ and an integer, is similarly differentiable for all x:

$$\frac{\Delta y}{\Delta x} = \frac{f(x + h) - f(x)}{h} = \frac{(x + h)^n - x^n}{(x + h) - x} = (x + h)^{n-1} + (x + h)^{n-2}x$$
$$+ \cdots + (x + h)x^{n-2} + x^{n-1} \to nx^{n-1}$$

as $h \to 0$. From this $f'(x) = nx^{n-1}$.

Furthermore, from the definition, four general rules can be obtained which state that the sum, difference, product, and quotient of two functions, differentiable at a point x_0, are also differentiable at x_0. In the last case the denominator, of course, must not be 0 at x_0:

$$\phi(x) = f(x) \pm g(x) \qquad \phi'(x_0) = f'(x_0) \pm g'(x_0)$$
$$\phi(x) = f(x)g(x) \qquad \phi'(x_0) = f'(x_0)g(x_0) + f(x_0)g'(x_0)$$
$$\phi(x) = \frac{f(x)}{g(x)} \qquad \phi'(x_0) = \frac{g(x_0)f'(x_0) - f(x_0)g'(x_0)}{(g(x_0))^2}.$$

Combined with the previously found derivatives, these rules show that every polynomial and every rational function (i.e., quotient of two polynomials) is differentiable in the whole of its domain.

Example 3-8. $f(x) = x^{-p} = 1/x^p$ (p positive and integer, $x \ne 0$).

$$f'(x) = \frac{x^p \cdot 0 - 1 \cdot px^{p-1}}{x^{2p}} = -\frac{p}{x^{p+1}} = (-p)x^{(-p)-1}.$$

It is thus seen that for every integer n (also 0), the function $f(x) = x^n$ is differentiable within its whole domain with $f'(x) = nx^{n-1}$. □

Example 3-9

$$f(x) = \begin{cases} x^2 & \text{if } x \le 0, \\ x^2 + 1 & \text{if } 0 < x < 1, \\ (3/x) - 1 & \text{if } 1 \le x. \end{cases}$$

Aside from the points $x = 0$ and $x = 1$, the function is seen to be differentiable with

$$f'(x) = \begin{cases} 2x & \text{if } \quad x < 0, \\ 2x & \text{if } 0 < x < 1, \\ -3/x^2 & \text{if } 1 < x. \end{cases}$$

At $x = 0$, the function makes a jump, and is thus discontinuous, and therefore not differentiable. At $x = 1$, the function is continuous, but not differentiable:

$$\frac{((1+h)^2 + 1) - 2}{h} \to 2 \qquad \text{as } h \to 0 - 0,$$

$$\frac{\left(\dfrac{3}{1+h} - 1\right) - 2}{h} \to -3 \qquad \text{as } h \to 0 + 0.$$

The difference quotient has a limit as $h \to 0$ from the left as well as from the right, but these two limits are not equal.

The function is said to be *differentiable from the left* with a derivative of 2 and correspondingly from the *right* with a derivative of -3. At the point (1,2), the curve has two *half-tangents*, which do not lie on the same line. The curve is said to show a *cusp* at the point considered (Fig. 3-9). □

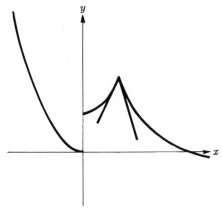

Figure 3-9

Differentials

The definition of differentiability given above is readily seen to be equivalent to the following. The function $y = f(x)$ is said to be differentiable at a point x_0 with the derivative (differential quotient) $f'(x_0)$ when the increment of the function, $f(x_0 + h) - f(x_0)$, corresponding to an increment h of the independent variable, can be written in the form

$$\Delta y = f(x_0 + h) - f(x_0) = f'(x_0)h + o(h),$$

where $o(h)$ is a function of h such that $o(h)/h \to 0$ as $h \to 0$ (cf. p. 138).

The quantity $f'(x_0)h$ is called the *differential* of the function at the point under question corresponding to the increment h of the independent variable. The differential is also written dy or $df(x)$; these latter symbols are not very informative, as they contain neither x_0 nor h, but they will prove very useful later.

For the special function $y = x$ we now obtain the differential $dx = 1 \cdot h$. If we then choose the same increment h for the two functions $y = f(x)$ and $y = x$, we obtain on substitution $dy = f'(x_0)\,dx$ or $df(x) = f'(x_0)\,dx$, which on dividing by dx becomes

$$f'(x_0) = \frac{dy}{dx} \quad \text{or} \quad f'(x_0) = \frac{df(x)}{dx}.$$

Again these new symbols are not very informative, as they do not contain x_0. Sometimes they are written more carefully as $(dy/dx)_{x=x_0}$ or $(df(x)/dx)_{x=x_0}$. However, usually it will appear from the context at what point the derivative is to be taken.

The quantity which we have already called the differential quotient (of y with respect to x) appears in this way really as a quotient of two differentials, the differentials of the dependent and the independent variables corresponding to a common increment h. Based on analogous considerations, we write for the second derivative of the given function $f''(x_0) = d(dy)/(dx)^2 = d^2y/(dx)^2$, and so forth.

When we introduce $y_0 = f(x_0)$, $x = x_0 + h$ and, corresponding to this, $y = f(x_0 + h)$, the condition for differentiability becomes $y - y_0 = f'(x_0)(x - x_0) + o(x - x_0)$.

While the increment of the function itself, $y - y_0$, can depend in a very complicated way on x, the differentiability states that we can as an approximation replace the increment by the differential dy, i.e., by the very simple (linear) function $f'(x_0)(x - x_0)$. The error introduced by this is $o(x - x_0)$, which for $f'(x_0) \neq 0$ is vanishing of an order higher than the linear expression, and thus in general small in comparison with this.

Geometrically the approximation means that we replace the given curve $y = f(x)$ by a straight line $y = f'(x_0)(x - x_0) + f(x_0)$, which is (of course) the tangent of the curve at the point $(x_0, f(x_0))$.

Composite Functions

In addition to the above rules of differentiation we need rules for differentiation of composite functions and inverse functions. These will now be considered.

Suppose f and g are two functions such that the range of g is included in the domain of f. As already mentioned (p. 133), the composite $f \circ g$ of the two functions g and f may also be written $y = f(g(x))$ or, introducing u as an *auxiliary variable*, as $y = f(u)$, $u = g(x)$. In what follows this notation will be used.

Now if $u = g(x)$ is continuous at the point x_0 and $y = f(u)$ is continuous at the corresponding point $u_0 = g(x_0)$, it follows from the definition of continuity that the composite function also is continuous at x_0.

Let the two functions f and g also be differentiable at the points u_0 and x_0, respectively, with the differential quotients $f'(u_0) = f'(g(x_0))$ and $g'(x_0)$. We then have

$$f(u) - f(u_0) = f'(u_0)(u - u_0) + o(u - u_0)$$

and

$$u - u_0 = g(x) - g(x_0)$$
$$= g'(x_0)(x - x_0) + o(x - x_0).$$

Introducing ϵ as a function such that

$$\epsilon(u - u_0) = \begin{cases} \dfrac{o(u - u_0)}{u - u_0} & \text{for } u - u_0 \neq 0, \\ 0 & \text{for } u - u_0 = 0, \end{cases}$$

it follows that ϵ is continuous at the point zero. On substitution we get

$$f(u) - f(u_0) = f'(u_0)g'(x_0)(x - x_0) + f'(u_0)o(x - x_0)$$
$$+ \epsilon(u - u_0)(u - u_0).$$

But

$$\frac{f'(u_0)o(x - x_0) + o(u - u_0)}{x - x_0} \to f'(u_0) \cdot 0 + 0 \cdot g'(x_0) = 0$$

as $x \to x_0$. Thus

$$f(g(x)) - f(g(x_0)) = f'(g(x_0))g'(x_0)(x - x_0) + o(x - x_0).$$

This means that the composite function is differentiable at x_0 and that its differential quotient can be obtained as the product of $f'(g(x_0))$ and $g'(x_0)$. This important result (the so-called *chain rule*) may also be written $dy/dx = (dy/du)(du/dx)$.

The proof of this rule can be obtained perhaps more simply from consideration of the appropriate difference quotients. The method used here can, however, immediately be extended to functions of several variables.

Example 3-10. $y = f(u) = u^2$, $u = g(x) = 3x + 5$.

$$\frac{dy}{dx} = \frac{dy}{du}\frac{du}{dx} = 2u \cdot 3 = 2(3x + 5) \cdot 3.$$

Of course, this can also easily be obtained from the explicit expression for the composite function $y = (3x + 5)^2 = 9x^2 + 30x + 25$. □

Inverse Functions

Consider now, in a given interval, a monotone continuous function $y = f(x)$ which is differentiable at a point x_0 in the interval with $dy/dx = f'(x_0)$ different from zero.

When Δx and Δy represent corresponding increments to the two variables from the point x_0, we have $\Delta y/\Delta x \to f'(x_0)$ as $\Delta x \to 0$.

It follows from the above that there exists an inverse function $x = f^{-1}(y)$ which is at least continuous at the point $y_0 = f(x_0)$. For the difference quotient at the point y_0 we obtain

$$\frac{\Delta x}{\Delta y} = \frac{1}{\Delta y/\Delta x} \to \frac{1}{f'(x_0)}$$

as $\Delta y \to 0$ (as in this case $\Delta x \to 0$ at the same time).

The inverse function is thus differentiable at the point y_0 and its differential quotient is obtained as the reciprocal of the derivative of the original function at the corresponding point x_0: $dx/dy = 1/(dy/dx)$.

The function $y = x^n (0 \leq x \leq a, n$ positive and integer) is increasing and continuous in the interval considered and thus has an inverse function,

$$x = \sqrt[n]{y} = y^{1/n} \qquad (0 \leq y \leq a^n).$$

Furthermore, as the given function is differentiable in its entire interval, with $dy/dx = nx^{n-1}$, then for the inverse function we obtain

$$\frac{dx}{dy} = \frac{1}{dy/dx} = \frac{1}{nx^{n-1}} = \frac{1}{n(\sqrt[n]{y})^{n-1}} = \frac{1}{n} y^{(1/n)-1} \qquad (0 < y \le a^n).$$

Changing the names of the variables, and using the fact that a can be chosen arbitrarily large, we have the following result. The function $y = \sqrt[n]{x} = x^{1/n}$ $(0 \le x < \infty)$ is differentiable for $x \ne 0$ and has as its differential quotient $y' = (1/n)x^{(1/n)-1}$.

The function $y = \sqrt[q]{x^p} = x^{p/q}$ (q a positive integer, p an integer) may be written $y = u^{1/q}$, $u = x^p$. This composite function is seen to be differentiable for $x > 0$ with the differential quotient

$$\frac{dy}{dx} = \frac{dy}{du}\frac{du}{dx} = \frac{1}{q} u^{(1/q)-1} px^{p-1} = \frac{1}{q} (x^p)^{(1/q)-1} px^{p-1} = \frac{p}{q} x^{(p/q)-1}.$$

A closer investigation shows finally that the result obtained is valid for any point of the domain of the function if only the expression given above for the differential quotient has a meaning (all x, $x \ne 0$, $x \ge 0$, $x > 0$).

We have now shown that every function of the form $y = x^a$ (a rational) is differentiable with a differential quotient $y' = ax^{a-1}$ (see also p. 183, where the case of irrational a is treated).

Example 3-11. As the function $x = y^3$ is increasing and continuous, and maps the set of all real numbers onto the set of all real numbers, the inverse function $y = x^{1/3}$ similarly is increasing and continuous with the set of all real numbers as its domain. $dx/dy = 3y^2 \ne 0$ for $y \ne 0$. Thus the function $y = x^{1/3}$ is differentiable for $x \ne 0$ with the differential quotient (Fig. 3-10)

$$\frac{dy}{dx} = \frac{1}{3y^2} = \frac{1}{3x^{2/3}} = \frac{1}{3} x^{-2/3}.$$

For $x = 0$ we obtain

$$\frac{\Delta y}{\Delta x} = \frac{(\Delta x)^{1/3}}{\Delta x} = (\Delta x)^{-2/3} \to \infty$$

as $\Delta x \to 0$. The function is thus not differentiable at $x = 0$. This is in agreement with the above, as the expression $\frac{1}{3}x^{-2/3}$ is not defined at $x = 0$.

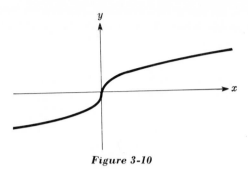

Figure 3-10

The graph of the function $y = x^{1/3}$ has a *vertical* tangent at the point $x = 0$, which agrees with the fact that the graph of the function $x = y^3$ (looked at from the Y-axis) has a horizontal tangent at this point. □

The Mean Value Theorem for Derivatives

For a function f continuous in $[a,b]$ and differentiable in $]a,b[$, the *mean value theorem for derivatives* can be shown to hold. Geometrically, this states that the graph of f in $]a,b[$ has at least one tangent which is parallel to the straight line determined by the end points $(a,f(a))$ and $(b,f(b))$ of the curve (Fig. 3-11). Thus there exists at least one number c $(a < c < b)$ such that $(f(b) - f(a))/(b - a) = f'(c)$, or $f(b) - f(a) = (b - a)f'(c)$.

In the special case when $f(a) = f(b) = 0$, *Rolle's theorem* $[f'(c) = 0]$ is obtained.

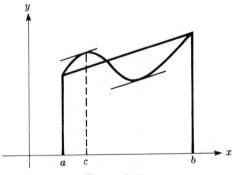

Figure 3-11

Later, under the name of Taylor's formula, we shall meet an extension of the mean value theorem where higher-order derivatives also are taken into consideration.

Already from the theorem formulated here, important rules follow regarding the increase and decrease of differentiable functions. When the function $y = f(x)$ satisfies the conditions of the mean value theorem in the interval $[a,b]$ and if $f'(x)$ in the entire open interval $]a,b[$ is either negative, 0, or positive, then the function in the entire closed interval will be, respectively, either decreasing, constant, or increasing.

Furthermore, it is already evident from the definition of differentiability that a necessary condition for a relative maximum or minimum of the function at a point c inside the interval is that the derivative here is 0.

If this is satisfied and if, moreover, $f'(x)$ is positive to the left of c and negative to the right of c, then the function has a relative *maximum* at the point. The opposite order of signs indicates a relative *minimum*, while the same sign both to the right and to the left of the point indicates that there is no relative extremum at c. In this case the curve is said to have a (horizontal) point of *inflection* (see also p. 163).

In all cases, the function is said to have a *stationary value* at every point where the derivative is 0 and the tangent of the graph is thus parallel to the X-axis (horizontal).

Example 3-12. Sketch the curve $y = x^5 - x^3 (-\frac{4}{3} < x \leq \frac{4}{3})$. Rewriting the equation $y = x^3(x + 1)(x - 1)$ immediately gives the sign of y:

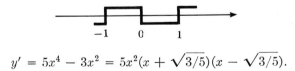

$$y' = 5x^4 - 3x^2 = 5x^2(x + \sqrt{3/5})(x - \sqrt{3/5}).$$

From this we obtain the sign of y':

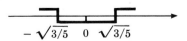

The curve is seen to have a relative maximum at the point $(-\sqrt{3/5}, \frac{6}{25} \cdot \sqrt{3/5})$ and a relative minimum at the point $(\sqrt{3/5}, -\frac{6}{25} \cdot \sqrt{3/5})$.

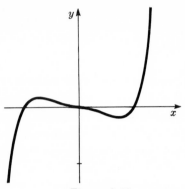

Figure 3-12

At the point (0,0) there is a horizontal point of inflection. In connection with this it is noted that $y'' = 0$ and $y''' < 0$ at the point (0,0) (cf. p. 163).

The curve is symmetric about (0,0); the function has no absolute minimum in the given interval, but an absolute maximum which is assumed at the point $x = \frac{4}{3}$ (Fig. 3-12). □

Exercises

*1. Find all values of the parameter a for which the function

$$f(x) = \begin{cases} a^2 x & \text{if } x \le 2, \\ x^2 - 3x + 2 - 2a \cdot |a| & \text{if } x > 2, \end{cases}$$

is continuous in the whole of its domain. Next, find possible values of a for which f is differentiable in the whole of its domain.

2. Show that the rules about differentiation of composite and inverse functions may be stated as follows:

$$(g \circ f)' = (g' \circ f) \cdot f' \qquad \text{and} \qquad (f^{-1})' = \frac{1}{f' \circ f^{-1}},$$

where the denominator in the last formula denotes the constant function $y = 1$.

*3. For each of the following functions determine those values of x for which it is differentiable and give its derivative:

$$f(x) = \sqrt{1 + \sqrt{1 + x}},$$
$$g(x) = \sqrt{x + \sqrt{x + 1}},$$
$$h(x) = \sqrt{2x + \sqrt{2x + 2}}.$$

4. Sketch the following two curves:

(a) $y = \dfrac{x^2 - 1}{x - 2}$.

(b) $y = \dfrac{2x^2 - 4x}{x^2 - 4x + 3}$.

*5. Given the line l through the points $(0,2)$ and $(3,3)$ together with the two points $A = (0,0)$ and $B = (4,0)$. Corresponding to an arbitrary point P on l, consider the ratio between the squares of the lengths of the line segments AP and BP. Show that this ratio has an absolute maximum value, and determine the point P_0 corresponding to this.

Answers

1. $f(x)$ continuous for $a \leq 0$; $f(x)$ differentiable for $a = -1$.

3. $f'(x) = [4\sqrt{1+x}\sqrt{1+\sqrt{1+x}}]^{-1}; x > -1$

$$g'(x) = (2\sqrt{1+x}+1)[4\sqrt{1+x}\sqrt{x+\sqrt{1+x}}]^{-1}; x > \frac{1}{2} - \frac{\sqrt{5}}{2}$$

$$h'(x) = (2\sqrt{2x+2}+1)[2\sqrt{2x+2}\sqrt{2x+\sqrt{2x+2}}]^{-1}; x > -\frac{1}{2}$$

5. $P_0 = (2 + \sqrt{10}, \frac{8}{3} + \frac{1}{3}\sqrt{10})$.

3-4. INDEFINITE INTEGRALS

Existence of Primitive Functions

In the previous section the determination of the derivative corresponding to a given function has been considered. We shall now proceed in the reverse manner and search for the primitive functions belonging to a given function f.

We then have to solve the equation $dy/dx = f(x)$, where $f(x)$ is given in a certain interval. In other words, we are looking for all the functions $y = F(x)$ which are differentiable in the given interval and which have $f(x)$ as their differential quotient.

If such a function $F(x)$ really exists, it is immediately clear that there are also infinitely many others, namely, all the functions $G(x) = F(x) + k$, where k is an arbitrary constant. However no more primitive functions exist, as the difference between two functions must be constant when their derivatives are equal (p. 152).

The question now is which functions have primitives at all. Let $f(x)$ be continuous in the interval I and let a be a point belonging to I. We now consider at some point x_0 the difference quotient of the function $F(x) = \int_a^x f(t)\, dt$, which also is defined in I:

$$\frac{\Delta F}{\Delta x} = \frac{\displaystyle\int_a^{x_0+\Delta x} f(t)\, dt - \int_a^{x_0} f(t)\, dt}{\Delta x} = \frac{\displaystyle\int_{x_0}^{x_0+\Delta x} f(t)\, dt}{\Delta x}$$

$$= \frac{\Delta x\, f(\alpha)}{\Delta x} = f(\alpha),$$

where α lies between x_0 and $x_0 + \Delta x$. As $\Delta x \to 0$, $\alpha \to x_0$, and from this follows [since $f(x)$ is continuous at x_0], that $\Delta F/\Delta x = f(\alpha) \to f(x_0)$; this means that $F(x)$ is differentiable at x_0 and has a differential quotient $f(x_0)$ at this point.

Every function continuous in some interval thus has a primitive function in the whole of this interval. Even though there also exist noncontinuous functions which have a primitive function, we shall in the following limit ourselves to consider continuous functions.

A Fundamental Theorem

It is now possible in a simple manner to express the value of a given definite integral $\int_a^b f(x)\,dx$ if only a primitive $F(x)$ of the integrand is known.

Then we must necessarily have $F(x) = \int_a^x f(t)\,dt + k$, where k is some constant. On setting $x = a$ we find $F(a) = 0 + k$; hence $\int_a^x f(t)\,dt = F(x) - F(a)$. Finally, for $x = b$ we obtain

$$\int_a^b f(t)\,dt = F(b) - F(a) \qquad \text{or} \qquad \int_a^b f(x)\,dx = F(b) - F(a);$$

this is often written $\int_a^b f(x)\,dx = [F(x)]_a^b$.

Because of this fundamental relation between a definite integral and an arbitrary primitive of the integrand, any primitive $F(x)$ of a function $f(x)$ is also called an *indefinite integral* of $f(x)$ (with respect to x) and is written $\int f(x)\,dx$. This notation will be further justified in the following. At first sight the symbol $\int f(x)\,dx$ seems a little dangerous, as it is to represent *any* primitive of $f(x)$. Thus we may have at the same time $F(x) = \int f(x)\,dx$ and $F(x) + 7 = \int f(x)\,dx$. For this reason an equals sign in parentheses is sometimes used: $F(x) (=) \int f(x)\,dx$. In practice, however, this prudence does not seem necessary.

The general solution of the equation $dy/dx = f(x)$ may now be written $y = \int f(x)\,dx$. The indefinite integral then represents an infinite number of different functions which, however, differ among themselves only by a constant. In any concrete problem, $\int f(x)\,dx$ is naturally thought of as representing one single function.

Integration Formulas

The above relation suggests that it will be very important to develop methods of *integration*, i.e., methods of determining indefinite integrals.

It is obvious that after differentiation of some randomly chosen functions we can at once in reverse write down formulas for a corresponding number of indefinite integrals. In this way a number of important results are obtained.

Example 3-13. As $d(k)/dx = 0$, we have $\int 0 \cdot dx = k$; correspondingly, $(d/dx)(x^{a+1}/a + 1) = x^a$ gives $\int x^a \, dx = x^{a+1}/(a + 1)$ $(a \neq -1)$. □

At the same time certain general rules will be needed for integration. These are now introduced, supplemented by a number of simple examples which are, however, not fitted to show the extreme scope of these results.

The constant rule: $\int kf(x) \, dx = k \int f(x) \, dx.$
The sum rule: $\int (f(x) + g(x)) \, dx = \int f(x) \, dx + \int g(x) \, dx.$
Integration by parts: $\int f(x)g(x) \, dx = f(x)\int g(x) \, dx - \int [f'(x)\int g(x) \, dx] \, dx.$
Integration by substitution: $\int f(\phi(x))\phi'(x) \, dx = \{\int f(u) \, du\}_{u=\phi(x)}.$

The validity of these rules can be proved directly, as on differentiation the right sides give the corresponding integrands found on the left sides.

The last formula gives rise to another important method of integration, also called *integration by substitution*. We must in this case assume that the function $u = \phi(x)$ is monotone in the considered interval. It then has an inverse function $x = \psi(u)$.

On substitution of this into both sides we obtain

$$\{\int f(\phi(x))\phi'(x) \, dx\}_{x=\psi(u)} = \int f(u) \, du,$$

or, with changed variables,

$$\int f(x) \, dx = \{\int f(\phi(t))\phi'(t) \, dt\}_{t=\psi(x)}.$$

The first form of integration by substitution may be interpreted as follows. It is always permissible to substitute for the quantity $\phi'(x) \, dx$ the differential $d(\phi(x))$, with which it has previously been identified, although in a different connection (see p. 148). After this we must consider $\phi(x) = u$ as the integration variable and then finally introduce u as a function of x, $u = \phi(x)$.

The second form shows that it is also allowed to introduce a substitution $x = \phi(t)$ everywhere in the indefinite integral. Then $d(\phi(t))$ must be regarded as the differential of $\phi(t)$, i.e., be replaced by $\phi'(t) \, dt$. However, the function $x = \phi(t)$ has to be monotone. This is of importance when the inverse function is finally introduced.

These comments at the same time show the great suggestive value of the notation introduced for indefinite integrals.

Example 3-14

$$\int 5x^3 \, dx = 5 \int x^3 \, dx = \frac{5}{4} x^4.$$

$$\int (x^7 + x^{-6}) \, dx = \frac{1}{8} x^8 - \frac{1}{5} x^{-5}.$$

$$\int x \cdot x^4 \, dx = x \frac{x^5}{5} - \int 1 \frac{x^5}{5} \, dx = \frac{x^6}{5} - \frac{x^6}{30} = \frac{1}{6} x^6.$$

This was also obvious beforehand.

$$\int (x^3 - 2x)^4 (3x^2 - 2) \, dx = \left\{ \int u^4 \, du \right\}_{u=x^3-2x} = \left\{ \frac{u^5}{5} \right\}_{u=x^3-2x}$$
$$= \frac{(x^3 - 2x)^5}{5},$$

or, in shorter form,

$$\int (x^3 - 2x)^4 (3x^2 - 2) \, dx = \int (x^3 - 2x)^4 \, d(x^3 - 2x) = \frac{(x^3 - 2x)^5}{5}.$$

$$\int \sqrt[3]{x^2} \, dx = \left\{ \int \sqrt[3]{t^6} 3t^2 \, dt \right\}_{t=\sqrt[3]{x}} = \left\{ \int 3t^4 \, dt \right\}_{t=\sqrt[3]{x}}$$
$$= \left\{ \frac{3}{5} t^5 \right\}_{t=\sqrt[3]{x}} = \frac{3}{5} (\sqrt[3]{x})^5.$$

The substitution here is $x = t^3$, which is seen to be monotone in the interval $-\infty < t < \infty$. Corresponding to this we have $-\infty < x < \infty$; $dx = 3t^2 \, dt$. This result of course can be obtained more easily by direct use of the formula for the indefinite integral of x^a ($a = \frac{2}{3}$).   □

Definite Integrals

On introducing an upper and a lower limit into the above formulas, a corresponding number of rules are obtained for definite integration.

The first two have already been met with in connection with the linearity rule for definite integrals (p. 142). Only the last two necessitate some further remarks, as here the question of changing the limits arises:

$$\int_a^b f(\phi(x)) \phi'(x) \, dx = \left[\left\{ \int f(u) \, du \right\}_{u=\phi(x)} \right]_a^b = \int_{\phi(a)}^{\phi(b)} f(u) \, du,$$

$$\int_a^b f(x) \, dx = \left[\left\{ \int f(\phi(t)) \phi'(t) \, dt \right\}_{t=\psi(x)} \right]_a^b = \int_{\psi(a)}^{\psi(b)} f(\phi(t)) \phi'(t) \, dt.$$

Example 3-15

$$\int_1^2 (x^3 - 2x)^4 (3x^2 - 2)\, dx = \int_{-1}^4 u^4\, du = \left[\frac{u^5}{5}\right]_{-1}^4 = \frac{4^5}{5} - \frac{(-1)^5}{5}$$
$$= 205,$$

$$\int_8^{27} \sqrt[3]{x^2}\, dx = \int_2^3 3t^4\, dt = \left[\frac{3}{5}\,t^5\right]_2^3 = \frac{3}{5}\,3^5 - \frac{3}{5}\,2^5 = \frac{633}{5}.$$

The same results are of course obtained on introducing the original limits in the primitives containing the original variables. □

Exercises

1. Using integration by substitution, show the validity of the following formulas, where a, b, and c are arbitrary positive numbers:

(a) $\displaystyle\int_a^b \frac{1}{x}\, dx = \int_{ac}^{bc} \frac{1}{x}\, dx.$
(c) $\displaystyle\int_a^b \frac{1}{x}\, dx = -\int_{1/a}^{1/b} \frac{1}{x}\, dx.$

(b) $\displaystyle 2\int_a^b \frac{1}{x}\, dx = \int_{a^2}^{b^2} \frac{1}{x}\, dx.$
(d) $\displaystyle\int_a^b \frac{1}{x^2}\, dx = c\int_{ac}^{bc} \frac{1}{x^2}\, dx.$

*2. Introducing $F(x)$ and $G(x)$ as primitives of the functions $1/x$ and $1/(1 + x^2)$, respectively $(x > 0)$, evaluate the following indefinite integrals:

(a) $\displaystyle\int \frac{x}{1 + x^2}\, dx.$
(d) $\displaystyle\int \frac{1}{4 + x^2}\, dx.$
(f) $\displaystyle\int \frac{1}{x^2 + 2x + 2}\, dx.$

(b) $\displaystyle\int \frac{x^2}{1 + x^2}\, dx.$
(e) $\displaystyle\int \frac{x}{4 + x^2}\, dx.$
(g) $\displaystyle\int \frac{x}{1 + x^4}\, dx.$

(c) $\displaystyle\int \frac{x^3}{1 + x^2}\, dx.$

*3. Find all functions f satisfying the equation $f'(x) = |x - 2|$ for all real x. Show that there is exactly one solution f satisfying the extra condition $f(0) = 0$. Sketch the graph of this solution.

Answers

2. (a) $\frac{1}{2}F(1 + x^2).$ 　(d) $\frac{1}{2}G\,(x/2).$ 　(f) $G(x + 1).$
　(b) $x - G(x).$ 　(e) $\frac{1}{2}F(4 + x^2).$ 　(g) $\frac{1}{2}G(x^2).$
　(c) $\frac{1}{2}x^2 - \frac{1}{2}F(1 + x^2).$

3. $f(x) = \begin{cases} \frac{1}{2}x^2 - 2x + c & x \geq 2 \\ -\frac{1}{2}x^2 + 2x - 4 + c & x < 2 \end{cases}$

where c is an arbitrary constant which can take on all values. Only when $c = 0$ is $f(0) = 0$.

3-5. TAYLOR'S FORMULA

Taylor's formula, which, as previously mentioned, is an extension of the mean value theorem for derivatives, will now be considered.

Let $f(x)$ represent a function which we assume is differentiable n times and has a continuous differential quotient of the nth order in the closed interval determined by the points a and b.

On repeated integration by parts of the right side of the equation $f(b) - f(a) = \int_a^b f'(x)\,dx$, the following is obtained when the integrand is considered as the product $f'(x) \cdot 1$ and $(x - b)$ is used as a primitive function for 1:

$$
\begin{aligned}
f(b) - f(a) &= \int_a^b f'(x)\,dx = [f'(x)(x - b)]_a^b - \int_a^b f''(x)(x - b)\,dx \\
&= (b - a)f'(a) - \left[f''(x)\,\frac{(x - b)^2}{2} \right]_a^b \\
&\qquad + \int_a^b f^{(3)}(x)\,\frac{(x - b)^2}{2}\,dx \\
&= (b - a)f'(a) + \frac{(b - a)^2}{2}f''(a) + \left[\frac{(x - b)^3}{3!}f^{(3)}(x) \right]_a^b \\
&\qquad - \int_a^b f^{(4)}(x)\,\frac{(x - b)^3}{3!}\,dx \\
&= (b - a)f'(a) + \frac{(b - a)^2}{2!}f''(a) + \frac{(b - a)^3}{3!}f^{(3)}(a) \\
&\qquad + \int_a^b f^{(4)}(x)\,\frac{(b - x)^3}{3!}\,dx,
\end{aligned}
$$

and so forth.

After $(n - 1)$ steps we obtain

$$
f(b) - f(a) = \frac{(b - a)}{1!}f'(a) + \frac{(b - a)^2}{2!}f''(a) + \cdots
$$
$$
+ \frac{(b - a)^{n-1}}{(n - 1)!}f^{(n-1)}(a) + \int_a^b f^{(n)}(x)\,\frac{(b - x)^{n-1}}{(n - 1)!}\,dx.
$$

The last term on the right side, the so-called *remainder*, is rewritten in the following manner. If g and G represent the absolute minimum value and the absolute maximum value of the nth derivative in the integration interval, then we have $g \leq f^{(n)}(x) \leq G$. When $b > a$ it follows that

$$g \frac{(b-x)^{n-1}}{(n-1)!} \leq f^{(n)}(x) \frac{(b-x)^{n-1}}{(n-1)!} \leq G \frac{(b-x)^{n-1}}{(n-1)!},$$

so that on integration

$$g \frac{(b-a)^n}{n!} \overset{\leq}{_{(=)}} \int_a^b f^{(n)}(x) \frac{(b-x)^{n-1}}{(n-1)!} \, dx \overset{\leq}{_{(=)}} G \frac{(b-a)^n}{n!}.$$

Finally $f^{(n)}(x)$ as a continuous function takes on every value between g and G inside the integration interval:

$$\int_a^b f^{(n)}(x) \frac{(b-x)^{n-1}}{(n-1)!} \, dx = \frac{(b-a)^n}{n!} f^{(n)}(c),$$

where $a < c < b$. The same result is obtained when $b < a$, for n both even and odd.

In this form, the remainder is called *Lagrange's remainder*. Taylor's formula then finally appears as follows:

$$f(b) - f(a) = \frac{(b-a)}{1!} f'(a) + \frac{(b-a)^2}{2!} f''(a) + \cdots$$
$$+ \frac{(b-a)^{n-1}}{(n-1)!} f^{(n-1)}(a) + \frac{(b-a)^n}{n!} f^{(n)}(c).$$

For $n = 1$, the mean value theorem for derivatives is obtained.

An Application of Taylor's Formula

In a different notation, when x_0 represents a fixed point and x some other point inside an interval, in which $f(x)$ is differentiable an arbitrary number of times, we obtain

$$f(x) = f(x_0) + \frac{(x-x_0)}{1!} f'(x_0) + \frac{(x-x_0)^2}{2!} f''(x_0) + \cdots$$
$$+ \frac{(x-x_0)^{n-1}}{(n-1)!} f^{(n-1)}(x_0) + \frac{(x-x_0)^n}{n!} f^n(\xi),$$

where ξ lies between x and x_0. Here the given function is said to be *expanded* about the point x_0.

Example 3-16

$$f(x) = x^{1/3}, \qquad f'(x) = \tfrac{1}{3}x^{-2/3},$$
$$f''(x) = -\tfrac{2}{9}x^{-5/3}, \qquad f'''(x) = \tfrac{10}{27}x^{-8/3},$$
$$f''''(x) = -\tfrac{80}{81}x^{-11/3}.$$

From this

$$x^{1/3} = x_0^{1/3} + \tfrac{1}{3}x_0^{-2/3}(x - x_0) - \tfrac{1}{9}x_0^{-5/3}(x - x_0)^2 + \tfrac{5}{81}x_0^{-8/3}(x - x_0)^3$$
$$- \tfrac{10}{243}\xi^{-11/3}(x - x_0)^4.$$

With $x = 8.1$ and $x_0 = 8$, we obtain, for example,

$$\sqrt[3]{8.1} = 2 + \tfrac{1}{3}\cdot\tfrac{1}{4}\cdot 0.1 - \tfrac{1}{9}\cdot\tfrac{1}{32}\cdot 0.1^2 + \tfrac{5}{81}\cdot\tfrac{1}{256}\cdot 0.1^3 - \tfrac{10}{243}\xi^{-11/3}\cdot 0.1^4.$$

The evaluation of the error, r_4, which is made in the value of $\sqrt[3]{8.1}$ by ignoring the last term, gives $|r_4| < (10/243)(1/2^{11}) \cdot 0.1^4 < 3 \cdot 10^{-9}$.

Thus by retaining a sufficient number of figures in the calculation of the first four terms, a value for $\sqrt[3]{8.1}$ is found with an error first appearing in the ninth decimal place. $\square$

In a later section, Taylor's formula will be used to determine infinite series for a number of important functions. The problem will then be to show that the remainder for a fixed x (and x_0) approaches 0 as $n \to \infty$.

Another Form of Taylor's Formula

It will be practical to rewrite Taylor's formula to demonstrate a further application.

If $f^{(n)}(x)$ is continuous at x_0, we have $f^{(n)}(\xi) = f^{(n)}(x_0) + \epsilon(x - x_0)$, where $\epsilon(x - x_0) \to 0$ as $x \to x_0$. On substituting this, we obtain *Taylor's o-formula:*

$$f(x) = f(x_0) + \frac{(x - x_0)}{1!}f'(x_0) + \frac{(x - x_0)^2}{2!}f''(x_0) + \cdots$$
$$+ \frac{(x - x_0)^n}{n!}f^{(n)}(x_0) + o((x - x_0)^n).$$

This is especially useful for the investigation of the behavior of the function near x_0.

Apart from the last term, the right side is a polynomial in x of degree n or less. It is called *Taylor's polynomial* or the *approximating polynomial* of the (at most) nth degree belonging to the function $f(x)$ and the point x_0. It is seen to have the same value and the same derivatives up to the nth order at the point x_0; it is also the only polynomial of the (at most) nth degree with these properties.

When $n = 1$, the formula gives the second definition of differentiability (cf. p. 148). When $n = 2$, then

$$f(x) - (f(x_0) + f'(x_0)(x - x_0)) = \frac{(x - x_0)^2}{2}(f''(x_0) + \epsilon(x - x_0)).$$

From this it is seen that the curve $y = f(x)$ lies above its tangent at the point x_0 in some deleted neighborhood of x_0, in case $f''(x_0) > 0$. The curve is then said to be *concave upward* at the point x_0. Correspondingly, the curve is *concave downward* at x_0 if $f''(x_0) < 0$. When $f''(x_0) = 0$, then the o-formula with $n = 2$ gives no information regarding the position of the curve in relation to its tangent. But if $f^{(3)}(x_0) \neq 0$, then from the o-formula with $n = 3$, we see that there is a *point of inflection*. This analysis can be continued if necessary.

L'Hôpital's Rule

The o-formula can often be used to examine the quotient between two (arbitrarily often differentiable) functions $f(x)$ and $g(x)$, which are both zero at the point x_0.

Let $f^{(p)}(x_0)$ and $g^{(q)}(x_0)$ be the derivatives of the lowest order which are different from zero at the point x_0. We then have

$$\frac{f(x)}{g(x)} = \frac{q!}{p!}(x - x_0)^{p-q}\frac{f^{(p)}(x_0) + \epsilon_1(x - x_0)}{g^{(q)}(x_0) + \epsilon_2(x - x_0)}.$$

If $p > q$ we obtain $f(x)/g(x) \to 0$ as $x \to x_0$, while $p = q$ gives $f(x)/g(x) \to f^{(p)}(x_0)/g^{(p)}(x_0)$ as $x \to x_0$ and finally $p < q$ gives $|f(x)/g(x)| \to \infty$ as $x \to x_0$.

For the special case $q = 1$ (p arbitrary), we obtain $f(x)/g(x) \to f'(x_0)/g'(x_0)$ as $x \to x_0$. This can also be obtained immediately in the following way:

$$\frac{f(x)}{g(x)} = \frac{[f(x) - f(x_0)]/(x - x_0)}{[g(x) - g(x_0)]/(x - x_0)} \to \frac{f'(x_0)}{g'(x_0)} \qquad \text{as } x \to x_0.$$

Here it still has to be assumed that the given functions $f(x)$ and $g(x)$ are differentiable at the point x_0 where the value of the functions is zero.

Even if they are not differentiable at x_0, we may, however, obtain information about the quotient between the two vanishing functions if only they have derivatives in some deleted neighborhood of x_0.

For this, it is assumed that $f(x)$ and $g(x)$, which are both 0 for $x = x_0$, are continuous in some closed interval $[x_0,x_1]$ and differentiable inside this interval, but not necessarily at the end point x_0. Using Rolle's theorem on the function

$$\phi(x) = (f(x_1) - f(x_0))(g(x) - g(x_0)) - (g(x_1) - g(x_0))(f(x) - f(x_0)),$$

we obtain the so-called *extended mean value theorem:*

$$\phi'(\xi) = (f(x_1) - f(x_0))g'(\xi) - (g(x_1) - g(x_0))f'(\xi) = 0,$$

where ξ is a point in the open interval $]x_0,x_1[$.

Now if $g'(x) \neq 0$ in the open interval considered [and thus $g(x_1) \neq 0$], then, as $f(x_0) = g(x_0) = 0$, we get $f(x_1)/g(x_1) = f'(\xi)/g'(\xi)$. *L'Hôpital's rule* arises from this. It states that if two functions vanish at a point x_0 and if the ratio of the derivatives of these functions has a limit at this point, then the ratio between the two functions themselves has the same limit:

$$\frac{f(x_1)}{g(x_1)} = \frac{f'(\xi)}{g'(\xi)} \rightarrow \lim_{\xi \to x_0} \frac{f'(\xi)}{g'(\xi)}$$

as $x_1 \to x_0$ (and hence $\xi \to x_0$). A corresponding rule is seen to be valid if the ratio of the derivatives tends to $\pm \infty$.

L'Hôpital's rule can be shown to have a larger region of validity than appears from above, as it also is valid when the given functions both tend to $\pm \infty$ as $x \to x_0$. Furthermore, corresponding rules apply in the cases $x \to \pm \infty$ ("$x = \pm \infty$").

The proof for the *extended l'Hôpital's rule* will only be sketched here. Let $f(x) \to \infty$ and $g(x) \to \infty$ as $x \to x_0 - 0$. Using the extended mean value theorem on the interval $x_1 < x < x_2$ ($<x_0$), we obtain $(f(x_2) - f(x_1))g'(\xi) = (g(x_2) - g(x_1))f'(\xi)(x_1 < \xi < x_2)$, and thus

$$\frac{f(x_2)(1 - [f(x_1)/f(x_2)])}{g(x_2)(1 - [g(x_1)/g(x_2)])} = \frac{f'(\xi)}{g'(\xi)},$$

or

$$\frac{f(x_2)}{g(x_2)} = \frac{1 - [g(x_1)/g(x_2)]}{1 - [f(x_1)/f(x_2)]} \frac{f'(\xi)}{g'(\xi)}.$$

We now let x_1 and x_2 approach x_0 simultaneously, but in such a way that both $g(x_1)/g(x_2)$ and $f(x_1)/f(x_2)$ approach 0. From the hypothesis it follows that this is always possible as long as x_2 approaches x_0 suitably "faster" than x_1. At the same time ξ is forced to approach x_0. If the ratio of the derivatives has a limit at x_0 (from the left) then this is seen also to be the limit of the ratio of the given functions themselves, and the proof is carried out. A corresponding proof can be made for the case when $x_0 = \pm \infty$.

Exercises

1. Show that the following formula is valid for any positive number x and any integer $n \geq 2$:

$$1 + \frac{x}{n} - \frac{n-1}{2n^2} x^2 < \sqrt[n]{1+x} < 1 + \frac{x}{n}.$$

*2. Determine an interval $0 < x < a$, where $1 + (x/4)$ can be used as an approximation to $\sqrt[4]{1+x}$ with an error less than 1 per cent of x.

3. Show that the curve $y = (1-x)/(1+x^2)$ has three points of inflection lying on the same straight line.

Answer

2. $\sqrt[4]{1+x} = 1 + \frac{x}{4} - \frac{3}{32}(1+\xi)^{-7/4}x^2 \qquad 0 < \xi < x$

Replacing ξ by 0, we require that $(3/32)x^2 < 10^{-2}x$, giving $a = 32/300$.

3-6. INVERSES OF THE TRIGONOMETRIC FUNCTIONS

The Trigonometric Functions

Let x be an arbitrary real number. When a unit vector is drawn from the origin of an orthogonal coordinate system XY, such that the directed angle from the X-axis to the vector, measured in radians, is x, then the coordinates of the terminal point of the vector will be by definition $(\cos x, \sin x)$.

There are a large number of formulas relating the trigonometric functions *cosine* and *sine*, as defined above. Of these, we shall mention only the following:

$$\cos^2 x + \sin^2 x = 1,$$
$$\cos(u \pm v) = \cos u \cdot \cos v \mp \sin u \cdot \sin v,$$
$$\sin(u \pm v) = \sin u \cdot \cos v \pm \cos u \cdot \sin v,$$
$$(\sin x)/x \to 1 \text{ as } x \to 0.$$

On this basis it is easily shown that the two functions are differentiable in their entire domains with the following differential quotients:

$$\frac{d}{dx}(\cos x) = -\sin x \quad \text{and} \quad \frac{d}{dx}(\sin x) = \cos x.$$

Two other trigonometric functions, the *tangent* and the *cotangent*, are now defined as $\tan x = \sin x/\cos x$ ($x \neq \pi/2 + p\pi$) and $\cot x = \cos x/\sin x$ ($x \neq p\pi$). These are also seen to be differentiable in their entire domains with the differential quotients

$$\frac{d}{dx}(\tan x) = \frac{1}{\cos^2 x} \quad \text{and} \quad \frac{d}{dx}(\cot x) = -\frac{1}{\sin^2 x}.$$

Corresponding to the given differential quotients, we have at once

$$\int \sin x \, dx = -\cos x, \qquad \int \cos x \, dx = \sin x,$$

$$\int \frac{1}{\cos^2 x} \, dx = \tan x, \qquad \int \frac{1}{\sin^2 x} \, dx = -\cot x.$$

With the help of these expressions, a large number of integrals can be expressed explicitly.

Example 3-17

$$\int \sin^2 x \, dx = \int \frac{1 - \cos 2x}{2} \, dx = \frac{x}{2} - \frac{\sin 2x}{4},$$

$$\int \cos^2 x \, dx = \int \frac{1 + \cos 2x}{2} \, dx = \frac{x}{2} + \frac{\sin 2x}{4},$$

$$\int \sin^3 x \, dx = \int (1 - \cos^2 x) \sin x \, dx = - \int (1 - \cos^2 x) d \cos x$$

$$= -\cos x + \frac{\cos^3 x}{3},$$

$$\int x \sin x \, dx = -x \cos x + \int \cos x \, dx = -x \cos x + \sin x. \quad \square$$

The construction of the values of the trigonometric functions corresponding to a given angle x is shown in Fig. 3-13.

We shall now consider more closely each of these trigonometric functions. Our purpose is to introduce new important functions as inverses of the trigonometric functions.

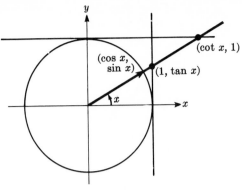

Figure 3-13

The Function Arc Cosine

The cosine function has as its domain the set of all real numbers, it is periodic with a period of 2π, and its range is the closed interval $[-1,1]$. The graph corresponding to the equation $y = \cos x$ is shown in Fig. 3-14.

To facilitate the subsequent discussion of an inverse function, we now interchange the names of the two variables. The cosine function is then written $x = \cos y$. The graph of this is obtained from the above by a reflection in the line $y = x$.

Here x is a continuous, nonmonotone function of y ($-\infty < y < \infty$) and as a result there is no inverse function (Fig. 3-15).

If, however, we restrict the domain to be the closed interval $0 \leq y \leq \pi$, then the function $x = \cos y$ is monotone-decreasing with an unchanged range, the closed interval $1 \geq x \geq -1$.

The function determined in this way therefore has an inverse function, which is written $y = \arccos x$. This new function, the *arc cosine*,

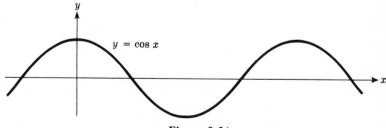

Figure 3-14

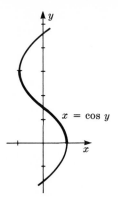

Figure 3-15

has as its domain the interval $[-1,1]$, in which it is decreasing and continuous; its range is the interval $[0,\pi]$.

The symbol arccos x may thus be considered simply as a short way of writing the following: the angle (arc), measured in radians, belonging to the interval $[0,\pi]$, which has a cosine equal to x.

Sometimes the inverse function is written $y = \cos^{-1} x$. This is in agreement with the general notation but can, however, easily be mixed up with $y = 1/\cos x$ ($= \sec x$).

Example 3-18. arccos $\frac{1}{2} = \pi/3$, as $0 \leq \pi/3 \leq \pi$ and $\cos \pi/3 = \frac{1}{2}$.

arccos $(- \sqrt{3}/2) = 5\pi/6$,

$\qquad$ as $0 \leq 5\pi/6 \leq \pi$ and $\cos 5\pi/6 = - \sqrt{3}/2$. $\square$

As the original function $x = \cos y$ is differentiable with a differential quotient $dx/dy = -\sin y$, different from 0 in the open interval $0 < y < \pi$, it follows that the inverse function also is differentiable in the corresponding open interval $1 > x > -1$ with the differential quotient

$$\frac{dy}{dx} = \frac{1}{-\sin y} = -\frac{1}{|\sin y|} = -\frac{1}{\sqrt{1 - \cos^2 y}} = -\frac{1}{\sqrt{1 - x^2}}.$$

From this we obtain

$$\int \frac{1}{\sqrt{1 - x^2}} \, dx = -\arccos x.$$

Example 3-19

$$\int \frac{1}{\sqrt{a^2 - x^2}}\, dx = \int \frac{1}{\sqrt{1 - (x/|a|)^2}}\, d\left(\frac{x}{|a|}\right) = -\arccos \frac{x}{|a|}. \qquad \square$$

The complete solution to the trigonometric equation $\cos x = a$ ($|a| \le 1$) can now be given as $x = \pm \arccos a + 2p\pi$.

The Function Arc Sine

In close analogy with the above, the function $x = \sin y$ will now be examined. Its graph is obtained from that of the previous ($x = \cos y$) by a translation of $\pi/2$ in the direction of the Y-axis [$\sin (y + (\pi/2)) = \cos y$].

The function $x = \sin y$ with the restricted domain $-\pi/2 \le y \le \pi/2$ is monotone-increasing and continuous with the range $-1 \le x \le 1$ (Fig. 3-16).

It therefore has an inverse function, the *arc sine*, which is written $y = \arcsin x$ (or $y = \sin^{-1} x$), and which is defined for $-1 \le x \le 1$, and is increasing and continuous with the range $-\pi/2 \le y \le \pi/2$.

The symbol $\arcsin x$ thus represents the angle (arc), measured in radians, in the interval $[-\pi/2, \pi/2]$, which has a sine equal to x.

Example 3-20. $\arcsin \frac{1}{2} = \pi/6$ as $-\pi/2 \le \pi/6 \le \pi/2$ and $\sin \pi/6 = \frac{1}{2}$. $\arcsin (-\sqrt{3}/2) = -\pi/3$ as $-\pi/2 \le -\pi/3 \le \pi/2$ and $\sin(-\pi/3) = -\sqrt{3}/2$. $\square$

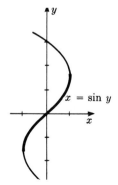

Figure 3-16

The function $y = \arcsin x$ is differentiable in the open interval $-1 < x < 1$ with the differential quotient

$$\frac{dy}{dx} = \frac{1}{\cos y} = \frac{1}{|\cos y|} = \frac{1}{\sqrt{1 - \sin^2 y}} = \frac{1}{\sqrt{1 - x^2}}.$$

From this it follows that

$$\int \frac{1}{\sqrt{1 - x^2}} \, dx = \arcsin x.$$

Example 3-21. We have now found two different expressions for $\int [1/\sqrt{1 - x^2}] \, dx$, $\arcsin x$ and $-\arccos x$. These two functions can therefore only differ from each other by a constant. The quantity $\arcsin x + \arccos x$ must thus be independent of x. On substituting $x = 0$, for example, this quantity is seen to be $\pi/2$. This can also be shown in the following way: Corresponding to an arbitrary x ($|x| \leq 1$), we determine $u = \arcsin x$; thus $-\pi/2 \leq u \leq \pi/2$ and $\sin u = x$. From this it follows that $0 \leq \pi/2 - u \leq \pi$ and $\cos(\pi/2 - u)(= \sin u) = x$, or $\pi/2 - u = \arccos x$. When the original expression for u is substituted the desired relation is obtained. The formula can also be obtained simply by comparing the graphs of the two functions. $\square$

The complete solutions to the trigonometric equation $\sin x = a$ ($|a| \leq 1$) can now be written

$$x = \begin{cases} \arcsin a + p \cdot 2\pi, \\ \pi - \arcsin a + p \cdot 2\pi. \end{cases}$$

The Function Arc Tangent

The function $y = \tan x$ is periodic with a period of π and is monotone-increasing and continuous in each of the intervals $-\pi/2 + p\pi < x < \pi/2 + p\pi$ with $-\infty < y < \infty$.

An inverse function—with the ordinary choice of variables—is obtained by considering the function $x = \tan y$ in the interval $-\pi/2 < y < \pi/2$. The inverse function corresponding to this is written $y = \arctan x$ (or $y = \tan^{-1} x$) (Fig. 3-17).

It is defined for $-\infty < x < \infty$, with $-\pi/2 < y < \pi/2$. It is increasing, continuous, and has two horizontal asymptotes $y = \pm\pi/2$. It is also differentiable for all x with differential quotient

$$\frac{dy}{dx} = \frac{1}{1/\cos^2 y} = \frac{1}{1 + \tan^2 y} = \frac{1}{1 + x^2}.$$

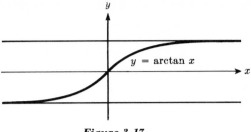

Figure 3-17

From this we obtain another important integral,

$$\int \frac{1}{1 + x^2}\, dx = \arctan x;$$

$\arctan x$ represents the angle (arc), measured in radians, in the interval $]-\pi/2, \pi/2[$, which has a tangent equal to x.

Example 3-22. $\arctan \sqrt{3} = \pi/3$ as $-\pi/2 < \pi/3 < \pi/2$ and $\tan \pi/3 = \sqrt{3}$. $\arctan (-1) = -\pi/4$ as $-\pi/2 < -\pi/4 < \pi/2$ and $\tan (-\pi/4) = -1$. □

All solutions to the trigonometric equation $\tan x = a$ can be obtained as $x = \arctan a + p\pi$.

The Function Arc Cotangent

For the sake of completeness, we shall finally mention that the inverse function to $x = \cot y$ $(0 < y < \pi, \infty > x > -\infty)$ is written $y = \text{arccot } x$ (Fig. 3-18). This function is thus defined for all x, is monotone-decreasing and continuous, has the range $\pi > y > 0$, has the asymptotes $y = \pi$ and $y = 0$, and is differentiable with the differential

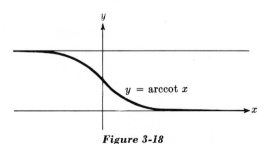

Figure 3-18

quotient

$$\frac{dy}{dx} = \frac{1}{-1/\sin^2 y} = -\frac{1}{1 + \cot^2 y} = -\frac{1}{1 + x^2}.$$

Thus

$$\int \frac{1}{1 + x^2}\, dx = -\operatorname{arccot} x.$$

From this we obtain the relation $\arctan x + \operatorname{arccot} x = $ constant $(= \pi/2)$. Together with the corresponding relation between arcsin and arccos, this shows that in practice, it is sufficient to have only two of these inverse trigonometric functions, for example, arcsin and arctan.

Some Indefinite Integrals

Having introduced inverse trigonometric functions, it is now possible explicitly to express a large number of indefinite integrals.

We shall limit ourselves to stating three important examples (where a is a positive constant):

$$(1) \quad \int \frac{1}{\sqrt{a^2 - x^2}}\, dx = \int \frac{1}{\sqrt{1 - (x/a)^2}}\, d\left(\frac{x}{a}\right) = \arcsin \frac{x}{a}.$$

$$(2) \quad \int \sqrt{a^2 - x^2}\, dx = \left\{ \int \sqrt{a^2 - a^2 \sin^2 t}\, a \cos t\, dt \right\}_{t = \arcsin x/a}$$

$$= \left\{ \int a^2 \cos^2 t\, dt \right\}$$

$$= \left\{ a^2 \left(\frac{t}{2} + \frac{\sin 2t}{4} \right) \right\}$$

$$= \left\{ a^2 \frac{t}{2} + \frac{1}{2} a \sin t \sqrt{a^2 - a^2 \sin^2 t} \right\}$$

$$= \frac{a^2}{2} \arcsin \frac{x}{a} + \frac{1}{2} x \sqrt{a^2 - x^2}.$$

In this latter case, the substitution $x = a \sin t$ is thus made. This is also adequate: x takes on all values in the domain of the integrand $-a \le x \le a$ when x traverses the interval $-\pi/2 \le t \le \pi/2$, where the substitution is really monotone. We obtain $t = \arcsin x/a$, and, as $\cos t \ge 0$, we have $\cos t = \sqrt{1 - \sin^2 t}$.

$$(3) \quad \int \frac{1}{a^2 + x^2}\, dx = \frac{1}{a} \int \frac{1}{1 + (x/a)^2}\, d\left(\frac{x}{a}\right) = \frac{1}{a} \arctan \frac{x}{a}.$$

Exercises

1. Sketch the curve $y = \cos 2x + \sin x$, and determine—as a function of a—the number of solutions in the interval $0 \le x \le 2\pi$ to the equation $\cos 2x + \sin x = a$.

*2. Find that point on the circle $x^2 + y^2 = 1$ for which the sum of the squares of the distances to the points $(3,0)$ and $(0,2)$ is the greatest possible.

3. Investigate whether the function

$$f(x) = \begin{cases} \dfrac{\sin x}{x} & \text{for } x \ne 0, \\ 1 & \text{for } x = 0 \end{cases}$$

is twice differentiable at the point $x = 0$.

*4. Determine the domains of validity of the following formulas:

(a) $\sin(\arccos x) = \sqrt{1 - x^2}$.

(b) $2 \arctan x = \arccos \dfrac{1 - x^2}{1 + x^2}$.

(c) $2 \arctan x = \arcsin \dfrac{2x}{1 + x^2}$.

*5. Evaluate the following integrals:

(a) $\displaystyle\int \arccos x \, dx$.

(b) $\displaystyle\int_0^{1/2} \arccos x \, dx$.

Finally, give a method for the evaluation of (b), where (a) is not used.

*6. Find the approximating polynomial $g(x)$ of the at-most third degree belonging to the function $f(x) = \arcsin x$ and the point $x_0 = 0$. Sketch the graphs of the two functions $f(x)$ and $g(x)$ in the same coordinate system.

Answers

2. $\left(-\dfrac{3}{\sqrt{13}}, -\dfrac{2}{\sqrt{13}} \right)$

4. (a) $-1 \le x \le 1$. (b) $x \ge 0$. (c) $-1 \le x \le 1$.

5. (a) $x \arccos x - \sqrt{1 - x^2}$

(b) $\dfrac{\pi}{6} + 1 - \dfrac{\sqrt{3}}{2} \left(= \dfrac{\pi}{6} + \displaystyle\int_{\pi/3}^{\pi/2} \cos x \, dx \right)$

6. $x + \dfrac{x^3}{6}$

3-7. LOGARITHMIC FUNCTIONS

The Natural Logarithm

Above, we have obtained explicit expressions for a number of important integrals by the introduction of the arc functions. Now another integration problem will be considered.

It can be shown that the simple indefinite integral $\int (1/x)\, dx$ cannot be expressed by any of the functions so far introduced. Nevertheless, we can easily write down a primitive of the function $1/x$, for example (for $x > 0$), the definite integral $\int_1^x (1/t)\, dt$ (cf. p. 155).

From the definition of a definite integral (or in other ways), it is possible to tabulate this function of x with arbitrary accuracy. The integration problem can then be considered as solved.

The function defined in this way for $x > 0$, $\ln x = \int_1^x (1/t)\, dt$, is called the *natural logarithm* or the *Naperian logarithm*. It is of course differentiable in its whole domain with the differential quotient $1/x$. It follows from this that the function is monotone-increasing. As $\ln 1 = \int_1^1 (1/t)\, dt = 0$, it also follows that $\ln x < 0$ for $0 < x < 1$ and $\ln x > 0$ for $x > 1$.

With the help of this function, we are then able to express any definite integral of the form $\int_a^b (1/t)\, dt$ $(ab > 0)$: The introduction of the monotone substitution $t = au$ gives

$$\int\limits_a^b \frac{1}{t}\, dt = \int\limits_1^{b/a} \frac{1}{au}\, a\, du = \ln \frac{b}{a}\cdot$$

Now, let x_1 and x_2 represent two arbitrary positive numbers. Using the additivity rule (p. 142), we then have

$$\ln (x_1 x_2) = \int\limits_1^{x_1 x_2} \frac{1}{t}\, dt = \int\limits_1^{x_1} \frac{1}{t}\, dt + \int\limits_{x_1}^{x_1 x_2} \frac{1}{t}\, dt = \ln x_1 + \ln \frac{x_1 x_2}{x_1}\cdot$$
$$= \ln x_1 + \ln x_2.$$

The natural logarithm thus satisfies in its whole domain the *functional equation* $f(x_1 x_2) = f(x_1) + f(x_2)$. From this it further follows that

$$\ln \frac{x_1}{x_2} = \ln x_1 - \ln x_2,$$
$$\ln x^n = n \ln x \quad (n \text{ whole}),$$
$$\ln \sqrt[n]{x} = \frac{1}{n} \ln x \quad (n \text{ positive and whole}).$$

From the last two rules we finally obtain $\ln x^a = a \ln x$, where a is any rational number (see also p. 181).

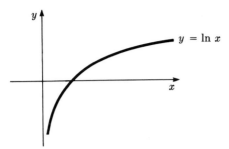

Figure 3-19

The graph of the natural logarithm, $y = \ln x$, is shown in Fig. 3-19. Although the slope of the tangent $y' = 1/x \to 0$ as $x \to \infty$, still $y \to \infty$ as $x \to \infty$. In connection with the monotony of the function, this follows from the fact that $\ln 2^n = n \ln 2 \to \infty$ as $n \to \infty$. This also implies that $\ln x \to -\infty$ as $x \to 0 + 0$ ($\ln 1/x = -\ln x \to -\infty$ as $x \to \infty$).

Together with the important result $\int(1/x)\,dx = \ln x$ $(x > 0)$, we automatically get $\int(1/x)\,dx = \ln(-x)$ $(x < 0)$. This is simply seen on differentiating the right side. Thus generally we have $\int(1/x)\,dx = \ln|x|$ $(x \neq 0)$. Having introduced the function ln, we are now able to evaluate many other indefinite integrals.

Example 3-23

$$\int \frac{1}{a+x}\,dx = \ln|a+x|$$

$$\int \frac{1}{\sin x}\,dx = \int \frac{1}{2\sin\dfrac{x}{2}\cos\dfrac{x}{2}}\,dx = \int \frac{1}{\tan x/2}\,d\left(\tan\frac{x}{2}\right) = \ln\left|\tan\frac{x}{2}\right|$$

$$\int \ln x\,dx = x\ln x - \int x\frac{1}{x}\,dx = x\ln x - x. \qquad \square$$

The equation $\ln x = 1$ is seen to have exactly one solution. This solution is always written e ($= 2.718\cdots$) and the number e is called the *base* of the natural logarithms.

Other Logarithmic Functions

The *logarithmic function to the base a* $(a > 0$ and $\neq 1)$ is defined as the function proportional to the natural logarithmic function which takes on the value 1 at the point a:

$$\log_a x = \frac{1}{\ln a} \ln x.$$

It also satisfies the above functional equation and hence the rules which follow from this. It is monotone-decreasing if $0 < a < 1$ and monotone-increasing if $a > 1$.

For $a = 10$, the *common logarithm*, or *Briggsian logarithm*, is obtained. This is the one generally used in calculations:

$$\log_{10} x = \frac{1}{\ln 10} \ln x \simeq 0.4343 \cdot \ln x.$$

The common logarithm is often written simply log, although it should be mentioned that this symbol is used for the natural logarithm in many presentations.

Using a table of a logarithmic function for arguments between 1 and 10, it is, as is well known, possible to carry out, in a simple manner, multiplications, divisions, exponentiations, and calculations of roots with an accuracy which depends only on the number of operations (and the size of the table). While in principle an arbitrary logarithmic function can be used for this, the Briggs's function is generally chosen, as in this case it is especially easy to obtain the logarithm of a number outside the range of the table.

Example 3-24
$\ln 843.0 = \ln 8.430 + \ln 100 = 2.1318 + 4.6052 = 6.7370,$
$\log 843.0 = \log 8.430 + \log 100 = 0.9259 + 2.0000 = 2.9259.$ □

The Logarithmic Scale
Consider a straight line on which an *origin* O and a *base vector* **v** are chosen. A *linear scale* (ordinary coordinate axis) is then obtained by letting the end point of position vector **OA** $= a\mathbf{v}$ be the image of the arbitrary real number a.

In a corresponding manner a so-called *logarithmic scale* is obtained when the end point of the position vector **OA** $= (\log a)\mathbf{v}$ is considered as the image of the arbitrary positive number a.

To orientate oneself easily on such a scale, it is practical just as is the case for the linear scale to mark out points corresponding to a suitable choice of numbers, writing at each point the number in question. Thus at the distance $\log a$ from the origin we now write a.

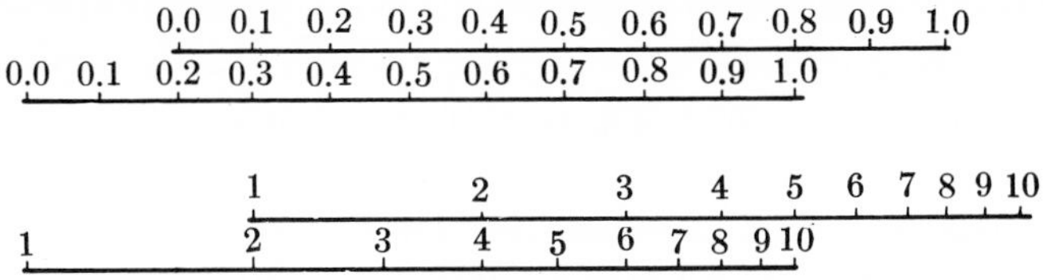

Figure 3-20

The interval between points corresponding to consecutive integral powers of 10 is then seen to have the same length as the base vector $(\log 10^{n+1} - \log 10^n = 1)$. Such an interval is called a *decade*.

By means of two mutually sliding linear scales it is possible to carry out addition and subtraction; correspondingly, with two mutually sliding logarithmic scales, it is possible to carry out multiplication and division. This is then the principle that underlies the ordinary slide rule (Fig. 3-20).

Semilogarithmic Paper

In the practical representation of a given function, a usual right-angled coordinate system drawn on *millimeter graph paper* is most often used.

However, in some cases it is advantageous to use *semilogarithmic paper*. This is divided rectangularly, corresponding to two mutually perpendicular axes. One of these has a linear scale and the other a logarithmic scale containing one or more decades further divided in a suitable manner.

Let us now use the logarithmic scale as an X-axis and the linear as a Y-axis on such paper. The ordered pair of numbers (x,y), $(x > 0)$, will then be represented by the point P on the paper which has orthogonal projections onto the two axes corresponding, respectively, to the numbers x and y. Conversely, P is then said to have the coordinates (x,y). The origin of the coordinate system has the coordinates $(1,0)$.

However, at the same time, the point P can be represented by its "true" coordinates (x',y') in a usual right-angled coordinate system $X'Y'$ with the same origin and the same orientation of the axes as that introduced above.

Let the length of a decade on the X-axis be v_1 and let the length of the chosen unit on the Y-axis be v_2, where both are measured in terms of the unit length of the primed coordinate system. We then have $(x',y') = (v_1 \log x, v_2 y)$.

The "true" equation for a straight line which is not parallel with the Y-axis is now of the form $y' = \alpha x' + q$. Thus, what is characteristic of the points on this line is that their coordinates (x,y) satisfy the equation $v_2 y = \alpha v_1 \log x + q$.

From this we obtain the following: Let $y = f(x)$ be some function with a domain of positive number. If its graphical representation is to be a straight line on semilogarithmic paper with the logarithmic scale as X-axis, the function must be of the form $y = a \log x + b$. Conversely, a function of this form will always give rise to a straight line, the line which has the "true" equation $(1/v_2)y' = (a/v_1)x' + b$.

Use of Semilogarithmic Paper

The graphical representation of the function $y = a \log x + b$ is immediately obtained as the straight line determined by two points $(x_1, a \log x_1 + b)$ and $(x_2, a \log x_2 + b)$.

Conversely, the values of a and b corresponding to a given straight line can be obtained in the following manner: b is read off at the intersection of the line with the Y-axis, and a is obtained as the difference between the y-values corresponding to $x = 10$ and $x = 1$ (Fig. 3-21). a and b can of course also be determined from two other suitably chosen points on the line.

In connection with the exponential functions we shall later consider the use of semilogarithmic paper with the logarithmic scale as the Y-axis. Here the origin has the coordinates $(0,1)$.

Logarithmic paper is divided with the help of two mutually perpendicular axes, both of which have a logarithmic scale. This will be considered more closely during the discussion of the power functions. The origin is seen here to have coordinates $(1,1)$.

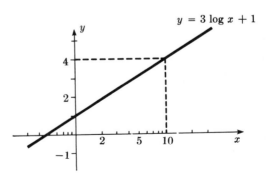

Figure 3-21

Exercises

*1. Using Taylor's formula on the function $\ln(1 + x)$, evaluate $\ln 1.02$ to 10 decimal places.

2. Sketch the curve $y = x \ln x$, and determine the area enclosed by this curve and the axes of the coordinate system.

*3. Find those values of a for which the equation $x = \log_a x$ has at least one solution.

*4. Evaluate $\lim_{x \to 1}(x/(x - 1) - (1/\ln x))$.

5. Solve the equation

$$3.85 \cdot \log x + 1.26 = -1.08 \cdot \log x + 3.17$$

graphically, using semilogarithmic paper. Check the result by calculation.

Answers

1. 0.0198026273.
3. $0 < a < 1, 1 < a \leq e^{1/e}$.
4. $\frac{1}{2}$.

3-8. EXPONENTIAL FUNCTIONS

Inverses of the Logarithmic Functions

An arbitrary logarithmic function to a positive base a ($a \neq 1$) is a one-to-one mapping of the set of all positive numbers onto the set of all real numbers. It therefore has an inverse function defined for all real numbers and with the set of all positive numbers as its range.

Let us consider the function $x = \log_a y$ more closely. As usual in analogous situations, we have used y as the independent variable. The explicit expression for the inverse function can now be obtained from this on solving with respect to y. If x is rational, this can be done without introducing new symbols: As $\log_a a^{p/q} = p/q \log_a a = p/q$ (see p. 174), we have $y = a^x$.

An expression such as a^x, with an irrational exponent, has had until now no meaning attached to it. We now state that this symbol for all real x shall represent the desired inverse function, which is called the *exponential function to the base a*.

When $a > 1$, the function $y = a^x$ is monotone-increasing with $y \to 0$ as $x \to -\infty$ and $y \to \infty$ as $x \to \infty$; when $0 < a < 1$, it is monotone-decreasing with $y \to \infty$ as $x \to -\infty$ and $y \to 0$ as $x \to \infty$. In all cases it takes on the value 1 at the point 0 (Fig. 3-22). As the function $x = \log_a y = (1/\ln a) \ln y$ is differentiable with a differential quotient $dx/dy = (1/\ln a)(1/y)$, different from zero in the whole of its domain, then the exponential function $y = a^x$ is differentiable for all x with a differential quotient $dy/dx = \ln a \cdot y = a^x \ln a$.

From this $\int a^x \, dx = a^x/\ln a$.

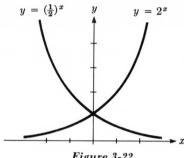

$y = (\frac{1}{2})^x$ y $y = 2^x$

Figure 3-22

As $x = \log_a y$ now generally implies $y = a^x$, then for all x the identity $\log_a a^x = x$ is valid. From the functional equation of the logarithmic function, the following is obtained:

$$\log_a(a^{x_1} a^{x_2}) = \log_a a^{x_1} + \log_a a^{x_2} = x_1 + x_2,$$

or

$$a^{x_1} a^{x_2} = a^{x_1 + x_2},$$

where x_1 and x_2 are arbitrary real numbers.

The exponential function thus satisfies in the whole of its domain the functional equation

$$f(x_1 + x_2) = f(x_1)f(x_2).$$

From this we obtain, furthermore, $a^{x_1}/a^{x_2} = a^{x_1-x_2}$ and, as a special case, $1/a^x = a^0/a^x = a^{0-x} = a^{-x}$.

The Function e^x

Corresponding to the natural logarithmic function $x = \ln y = \log_e y$, there is the especially important exponential function $y = e^x$, often written $y = \exp x$. In this case the derivative and the primitive are both equal to the function itself (Fig. 3-23).

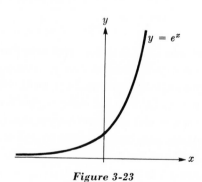

y

$y = e^x$

Figure 3-23

We can now express all other exponential functions with the help of this: As $y = a^x$ implies $x = \log_a y = (1/\ln a) \ln y$ or $\ln y = x \ln a$, then $y = e^{x \ln a}$ or $a^x = e^{x \ln a}$.

The general validity of the well-known rules used in calculations with rational exponents may be shown from this formula.

If $a = 1$ is substituted into the above formula, then the right side becomes $e^{x \cdot 0} = 1$. On this basis the (degenerate) exponential function $y = 1^x = 1$ is defined. Its graph is a straight line parallel to the X-axis. This function of course also satisfies the functional equation found above.

Example 3-25

$$I = \int e^x \cos x \, dx = e^x \sin x - \int e^x \sin x \, dx$$
$$= e^x \sin x + e^x \cos x - \int e^x \cos x \, dx$$
$$= e^x \sin x + e^x \cos x - (I + k),$$

from which $I = \tfrac{1}{2} e^x \cos x + \tfrac{1}{2} e^x \sin x \ (+k_1)$. □

Since $d^n e^x / dx^n = e^x$, the following Taylor expansion about the point 0 is obtained:

$$e^x = 1 + \frac{1}{1!} x + \frac{1}{2!} x^2 + \frac{1}{3!} x^3 + \cdots + \frac{1}{(n-1)!} x^{n-1} + \frac{e^\xi}{n!} x^n.$$

For an arbitrary fixed x the remainder r_n approaches 0 as n tends to infinity:

$$|r_n| < e^{|x|} \frac{|x|^n}{n!} \to 0 \qquad \text{for } n \to \infty.$$

We shall later return to this and see how it gives rise to a so-called "power-series expansion" of e^x valid for all x:

$$e^x = 1 + x + \frac{x^2}{2!} + \frac{x^3}{3!} + \cdots + \frac{x^n}{n!} + \cdots .$$

Exponential Functions and Semilogarithmic Paper

Let us now consider semilogarithmic paper with the linear scale as the X-axis and the logarithmic scale as the Y-axis. At the same time we introduce, as previously, a usual right-angled coordinate system $X'Y'$ with the same origin and the same orientation of the axes.

If the unit of the linear scale as measured by the unit of the primed coordinate system is v_1, and the length of a decade on the logarithmic scale is v_2, the following relationship is obtained between the coordinates (x,y) and (x',y') of an arbitrary point in the plane: $(x',y') = (v_1 x, v_2 \log y)$.

The equation for a straight line, which is not perpendicular to the X-axis, is now $y' = \alpha x' + q$, or, expressed in the coordinate system XY,

$$v_2 \log y = \alpha v_1 x + q \qquad \text{or} \qquad y = (10^{q/v_2})(10^{\alpha v_1/v_2})^x.$$

From this it is seen that such a straight line always will represent a function of the form $y = ba^x$, i.e., an exponential function multiplied by a (positive) constant.

Conversely it is seen that every function of this form $(a > 0, b > 0)$ gives rise to a straight line, and, in particular, that parallel lines correspond to exponential functions to the same base.

The graphical representation of a given function $y = ba^x$ is immediately obtained as the straight line through two points (x_1, ba^{x_1}) and (x_2, ba^{x_2}).

Conversely, the values of a and b that correspond to a given straight line l can be obtained in the following manner: b can be read directly on the logarithmic scale at the intersection of l with the scale. Corresponding to $x = 1$, the number ab is found on the Y-axis. The division with b necessary after this for the determination of a is easily carried out by considering a line parallel to l through the origin of the coordinate system. This corresponds to the function $y = 1 \cdot a^x$; thus a is obtained directly as the y-coordinate corresponding to $x = 1$. Here, the logarithmic scale has been used as a slide rule (Fig. 3-24).

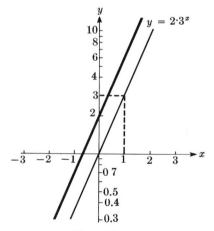

Figure 3-24

Of course, a and b can also be determined from any two other points on the line l. In many cases another choice of points will give more accurate results.

Exercises

*1. Evaluate $e^{-0.1}$ to six decimal places.

2. Sketch the following curves in the same coordinate system: $y = x^n e^{-x}$ ($n = 1,2,3$).

*3. A capital C with a rate of interest r compounded annually will after 1 year have grown to $C_1 = C(1 + r)$. Compounded semiannually at a rate $r/2$, the capital after 1 year will have grown to $C_2 = C(1 + r/2)^2$. Compounded three times a year at a rate $r/3$, the capital after 1 year will have grown to $C_3 = C(1 + r/3)^3$, etc. Find the limit of C_n as n tends to infinity ("continuous compounding").

4. Solve the equation $3.76 \cdot 1.57^x = 1.29 \cdot 2.14^{-x}$ graphically, using semilogarithmic paper. Check the result by calculation.

5. By the disintegration of a radioactive substance the following measurements were made:

Time	0	1	2	3	4	5	6	7	8	9	10	11	12
Intensity	820	770	620	530	480	400	320	300	270	220	185	150	140

Plot the results on semilogarithmic paper, and find the time it takes for the intensity to decrease to half its original value (the half-life).

Answers

1. 0.904837.

3. Ce^r.

3-9. POWER FUNCTIONS

Power Functions

By a *power function* we mean a function of the form $f(x) = x^a$, where the exponent a is an arbitrary real constant.

We have previously considered power functions with rational exponents, for which the domain in some cases also could contain negative numbers. Here the functions will be considered only in their common domain, the set of all positive numbers.

On rewriting $x^a = e^{a \ln x}$ which is valid for all positive x (and any a), it is seen that the function $y = x^a$ is differentiable in the whole of its domain with the differential quotient $dy/dx = e^{a \ln x} a(1/x) = ax^{a-1}$. From this we immediately obtain

$$\int x^a \, dx = \frac{x^{a+1}}{a + 1} \ (a \neq -1).$$

Depending on whether a is negative, 0, or positive, the function is

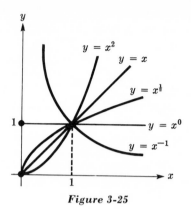

Figure 3-25

seen to be decreasing, constant ($= 1$), or increasing. Aside from the degenerate case $a = 0$, the function thus is a one-to-one mapping of the set of all positive numbers onto the set of all positive numbers.

Every function takes on the value 1 at the point 1 ($1^a = e^{a \ln 1} = 1$). If a is positive, then $x^a \to 0$ as $x \to 0 + 0$. Therefore in these cases we define $0^a = 0$. In this way the functions also become continuous if their domain is extended to include 0.

With respect to the differentiability at the point 0, it is seen that such a function has the differential quotient 0 if $a > 1$, while the graph has a vertical tangent if $0 < a < 1$ (Fig. 3-25) (see also p. 151).

Previously, we have often been able to introduce new and important functions as inverses of functions already considered. This is not the case here, as the inverse function of $y = x^a$ is seen to be $x = y^{1/a}$, which is also a power function.

Logarithmic Paper

In connection with power functions we shall finally consider the use of logarithmic paper.

If we approach the subject in a manner analogous to that used in the case of semilogarithmic paper, we obtain the following relation between the usual right-angled and "the logarithmic" coordinates: $(x',y') = (v_1 \log x, v_2 \log y)$.

In the logarithmic coordinates the equation for the straight line $y' = \alpha x' + q$ thus becomes

$$v_2 \log y = \alpha v_1 \log x + q \quad \text{or} \quad y = 10^{q/v_2} \cdot x^{\alpha v_1/v_2},$$

i.e., a power function (multiplied by a positive constant). Conversely, any function of the form $y = bx^a$ ($b > 0$) gives rise to a

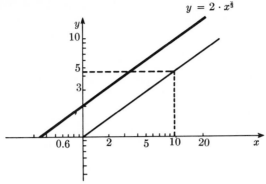

$$y = 2 \cdot x^{\frac{3}{4}}$$

Figure 3-26

straight line. Parallel lines correspond here to power functions with the same exponent.

The graphical representation of a given function $y = bx^a$ is readily obtained from two points $(x_1, bx_1{}^a)$ and $(x_2, bx_2{}^a)$. Conversely, the values of a and b which correspond to a given straight line l can be obtained in the following manner: Corresponding to $x = 1$, we obtain $y = b$; b can thus be read directly at the intersection of the line with the Y-axis. The line parallel to l through the origin has the equation $y = x^a$; the value of y corresponding to $x = 10$ is then $y = 10^a$. The (common) logarithm of this number is then equal to a (Fig. 3-26). Naturally, a and b can also be determined from two other suitably chosen points on the line.

Behavior of Some Important Functions as $x \to \infty$

We have now considered three important types of functions which all tend to infinity, as x tends to infinity: $\log_a x$ $(a > 1)$, x^a $(a > 0)$, and a^x $(a > 1)$.

In practice, the ratio between two such functions often comes into consideration. It is thus of interest to observe how this behaves as $x \to \infty$. From a comparison of each of the three types the following results are immediately obtained:

$$\frac{\log_b x}{\log_a x} = \frac{\ln a}{\ln b},$$

$$\frac{x^b}{x^a} = x^{b-a} \to \infty \qquad \text{as } x \to \infty \ (\text{in case } b > a),$$

$$\frac{b^x}{a^x} = \left(\frac{b}{a}\right)^x \to \infty \qquad \text{as } x \to \infty \ (\text{in case } b > a).$$

There remains the mutual comparison of the three types. As $1/t < 1$ for $t > 1$, then $\int_1^x (1/t)\, dt < \int_1^x 1\, dt$ or $\ln x < x - 1$ $(x > 1)$. From this,

$$\frac{\log_a x}{x^b} = \frac{2}{b \ln a}\, \frac{\ln x^{b/2}}{x^{b/2}}\, \frac{1}{x^{b/2}} < \frac{2}{b \ln a}\, \frac{1}{x^{b/2}} \to 0 \qquad \text{as } x \to \infty,$$

and also

$$\frac{x^b}{c^x} = \frac{e^{b \ln x}}{e^{x \ln c}} = e^{b \ln x - x \ln c} = \exp\left[-x\left(\ln c - b\,\frac{\ln x}{x} \right) \right] \to 0$$

$$\text{as } x \to \infty.$$

Finally, on multiplication, we find

$$\frac{\log_a x}{c^x} = \frac{\log_a x}{x^b}\, \frac{x^b}{c^x} \to 0 \cdot 0 = 0 \qquad \text{as } x \to \infty.$$

Summarizing, the following series is obtained for the functions considered:

$$\ln x,\ x^a,\ x^b,\ c^x,\ d^x \qquad (0 < a < b,\, 1 < c < d).$$

Here all the functions are "infinitely large" at "$x = \infty$," and they are also infinitely large as compared to all the preceding ones.

The same results would of course have been obtained by the use of l'Hôpital's rule (p. 164). Using the above method, however, we have had the opportunity to give a typical example of the practice of estimation in mathematics.

Example 3-26. $x \ln x \to 0$ as $x \to 0 + 0$, because $x \ln x = -\ln (1/x)/(1/x) \to 0(-0)$ as $1/x \to \infty$ or as $x \to 0 + 0$. $\quad\square$

Exercises

*1. Sketch the curve $y = x^x$. Especially, consider the curve and its tangents for small (positive) values of x.

*2. Sketch the curve $y = x^{1/x}$. Especially, consider the curve and its tangents for small (positive) values of x.

3. Solve the equation $0.432 \cdot x^{0.729} = 8.15 \cdot x^{-0.516}$ graphically, using logarithmic paper. Check the result by calculation.

Answers

1. $y \to 1$ as $x \to 0 + 0$.

   $y' \to -\infty$ as $x \to 0 + 0$.

   The curve has one minimum point $(1/e,\ e^{-1/e})$.

2. $y \to 0$ as $x \to 0 + 0$ $y \to 1$ as $x \to \infty$.
   $y' \to 0$ as $x \to 0 + 0$.
   The curve has one maximum point $(e, e^{1/e})$.

3-10. HYPERBOLIC FUNCTIONS

The following functions will now be considered: *hyperbolic cosine* (cosh), *hyperbolic sine* (sinh), *hyperbolic tangent* (tanh), and *hyperbolic cotangent* (coth). As seen from the definitions given below, they are differentiable in their entire domains with the indicated differential quotients.

$$\cosh x = \frac{e^x + e^{-x}}{2} \quad \frac{d}{dx} \cosh x = \sinh x \quad \text{(all } x)$$

$$\int \sinh x \, dx = \cosh x,$$

$$\sinh x = \frac{e^x - e^{-x}}{2} \quad \frac{d}{dx} \sinh x = \cosh x \quad \text{(all } x)$$

$$\int \cosh x \, dx = \sinh x,$$

$$\tanh x = \frac{e^x - e^{-x}}{e^x + e^{-x}} \quad \frac{d}{dx} \tanh x = \frac{1}{\cosh^2 x} \quad \text{(all } x)$$

$$\int \frac{1}{\cosh^2 x} \, dx = \tanh x,$$

$$\coth x = \frac{e^x + e^{-x}}{e^x - e^{-x}} \quad \frac{d}{dx} \coth x = - \frac{1}{\sinh^2 x} \quad (x \neq 0)$$

$$\int \frac{1}{\sinh^2 x} \, dx = - \coth x.$$

As the names already suggest, they have many properties which correspond to those of the trigonometric functions. We shall here only mention a few formulas, which are readily proved from the definitions:

$$\cosh^2 x - \sinh^2 x = 1,$$
$$\cosh(x_1 \pm x_2) = \cosh x_1 \cosh x_2 \pm \sinh x_1 \sinh x_2,$$
$$\sinh(x_1 \pm x_2) = \sinh x_1 \cosh x_2 \pm \cosh x_1 \sinh x_2.$$

From the first one, the so-called "basic relation," it is seen that $(x,y) = (\cosh t, \sinh t)$ is a parametric equation of one branch $(x > 0)$ of the hyperbola $x^2 - y^2 = 1$. This is one reason for the name hyperbolic functions.

Even if the hyperbolic functions only represent various combinations of exponential functions, they are of great use in, for example, the evaluation of many integrals by the substitution method. With this in mind we shall now briefly consider the corresponding inverse functions.

An Inverse of Cosh

As $y = \cosh x$ is monotone-increasing for $x \geq 0$, it has an inverse function in this interval which may be written $x = \cosh^{-1} y$ (cf p. 168). An explicit expression for this inverse function may be obtained by solving for e^x.

From $y = (e^x + e^{-x})/2$ we obtain $(e^x)^2 - 2ye^x + 1 = 0$, which gives $e^x = y \pm \sqrt{y^2 - 1}$ or $x = \ln(y \pm \sqrt{y^2 - 1})$ $(y \geq 1)$. Here the lower sign corresponds to negative values of x. We thus have

$$x = \cosh^{-1} y = \ln(y + \sqrt{y^2 - 1}) \qquad (1 \leq y < \infty, 0 \leq x < \infty).$$

From the basic relation we obtain $\sinh x = \pm \sqrt{\cosh^2 x - 1}$ where for $x > 0$ the upper sign has to be used. The differential quotient of the inverse function (for $y > 1$) is then

$$\frac{dx}{dy} = \frac{1}{dy/dx} = \frac{1}{\sinh x} = \frac{1}{\sqrt{\cosh^2 x - 1}} = \frac{1}{\sqrt{y^2 - 1}}.$$

The same result is naturally obtained on direct differentiation of the explicit expression for the inverse function.

At the same time we obtain an important integral:

$$\int \frac{1}{\sqrt{x^2 - 1}} \, dx = \cosh^{-1} x = \ln(x + \sqrt{x^2 - 1}),$$

valid for $x > 1$. For $x < -1$ we get $\ln|x + \sqrt{x^2 - 1}|$, which is easily verified by differentiation (Fig. 3-27).

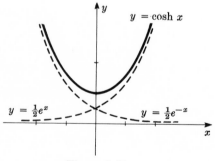

Figure 3-27

Example 3-27

$$\int \frac{1}{\sqrt{x^2 - a^2}}\, dx = \int \frac{1}{\sqrt{(x/|a|)^2 - 1}}\, d\,\frac{x}{|a|}$$

$$= \ln\left(\frac{x}{|a|} + \sqrt{\left(\frac{x}{|a|}\right)^2 - 1}\right) + k$$

$$= \ln|x + \sqrt{x^2 - a^2}| + k_1. \qquad \square$$

The Inverse of Sinh

The function $y = \sinh x$ is monotone-increasing in the whole of its domain and has as its range the set of all real numbers. It therefore has an inverse function $x = \sinh^{-1} y$ defined for all y: $y = \sinh x = (e^x - e^{-x})/2$ gives $(e^x)^2 - 2ye^x - 1 = 0$, from which $e^x = y \pm \sqrt{y^2 + 1}$. The lower sign must, in this case be cancelled, thus giving $x = \ln(y + \sqrt{y^2 + 1})$. We therefore have (Fig. 3-28)

$$x = \sinh^{-1} y = \ln(y + \sqrt{y^2 + 1}) \qquad (-\infty < y < \infty, -\infty < x < \infty).$$

From the basic relation, we obtain $\cosh x = \sqrt{\sinh^2 x + 1}$ (as $\cosh x > 0$ for all x). The differential quotient of the inverse function is then found to be

$$\frac{dx}{dy} = \frac{1}{dy/dx} = \frac{1}{\cosh x} = \frac{1}{\sqrt{1 + \sinh^2 x}} = \frac{1}{\sqrt{y^2 + 1}}$$

$$(-\infty < y < \infty).$$

Here also, the differential quotient could have been obtained from the explicit expression for the inverse function.

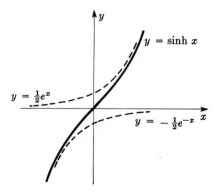

Figure 3-28

We again obtain an important integral,

$$\int \frac{1}{\sqrt{x^2 + 1}}\, dx = \ln(x + \sqrt{x^2 + 1}).$$

Example 3-28

$$\int \frac{1}{\sqrt{x^2 + a^2}}\, dx = \int \frac{1}{\sqrt{(x/|a|)^2 + 1}}\, d\left(\frac{x}{|a|}\right)$$

$$= \ln\left(\frac{x}{|a|} + \sqrt{\left(\frac{x}{|a|}\right)^2 + 1}\right) + k$$

$$= \ln(x + \sqrt{x^2 + a^2}) + k_1.$$

In connection with the previous example we now have in general

$$\int \frac{1}{\sqrt{x^2 + c}}\, dx = \ln|x + \sqrt{x^2 + c}|,$$

where c is an arbitrary real number ($\neq 0$). $\qquad \square$

Example 3-29. To evaluate the indefinite integral $\int \sqrt{x^2 - a^2}\, dx$ for $x \geq a\ (>0)$ the monotone substitution $x = a \cosh t\ (a \leq x < \infty,\ 0 \leq t < \infty)$ may be introduced. Then

$$t = \ln\left(\frac{x}{a} + \sqrt{\frac{x^2}{a^2} - 1}\right),$$

and the following is found:

$$\int \sqrt{x^2 - a^2}\, dx = \int a \sinh t\, a \sinh t\, dt = a^2 \int \frac{\cosh 2t - 1}{2}\, dt$$

$$= \frac{a^2}{4} \sinh 2t - \frac{a^2}{2} t = \frac{a^2}{2} \sinh t \cosh t - \frac{a^2}{2} t$$

$$= \frac{1}{2} a \cosh t \sqrt{a^2 \cosh^2 t - a^2} - \frac{a^2}{2} t$$

$$= \frac{1}{2} x \sqrt{x^2 - a^2} - \frac{a^2}{2} \ln\left(\frac{x}{a} + \sqrt{\frac{x^2}{a^2} - 1}\right) + k$$

$$= \frac{1}{2} x \sqrt{x^2 - a^2} - \frac{a^2}{2} \ln(x + \sqrt{x^2 - a^2}) + k_1.$$

When x is negative we may use the substitution $x = -a \cosh t$, which gives the integration interval $-\infty < x \le a$ in a monotone manner for either $-\infty < t \le 0$ or $\infty > t \ge 0$. In both cases the result can be written in the same way as above, but the argument of the logarithmic function used above now has to be substituted by its negative. In the first case it is noted that $\sinh t = -\sqrt{\cosh^2 t - 1}$.

We can handle the indefinite integral $\int \sqrt{x^2 + a^2}\, dx$, which is defined for all x, in a corresponding way. Here we choose the substitution $x = a \sinh t$, which is monotone for all t. The final result obtained is

$$\int \sqrt{x^2 + c}\, dx = \frac{x}{2} \sqrt{x^2 + c} + \frac{c}{2} \ln\left|x + \sqrt{x^2 + c}\right|,$$

where c is an arbitrary real number ($\ne 0$). The same result could also have been obtained by integration by parts. $\square$

The Inverses of Tanh and Coth

The function $y = \tanh x$ is monotone-increasing with the range $-1 < y < 1$, while the function $y = \coth x$, $(= 1/\tanh x)$, which is not defined for $x = 0$, is monotone-decreasing in each of the intervals $-\infty < x < 0$ and $0 < x < \infty$ with ranges $-1 > y > -\infty$ and $\infty > y > 1$, respectively.

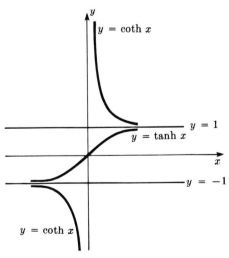

Figure 3-29

Both functions have inverses:

$$x = \tanh^{-1} y = \frac{1}{2} \ln \frac{1+y}{1-y} \qquad |y| < 1$$

and

$$x = \coth^{-1} y = \frac{1}{2} \ln \frac{y+1}{y-1} \qquad |y| > 1.$$

In both cases the differential quotient is $dx/dy = 1/(1 - y^2)$ (Fig. 3-29).

From this,

$$\int \frac{1}{1-x^2} dx = \frac{1}{2} \ln \left| \frac{1+x}{1-x} \right|.$$

The same result could also have been obtained very easily in a quite different way:

$$\int \frac{1}{1-x^2} dx = \int \left(\frac{1}{2} \frac{1}{1+x} + \frac{1}{2} \frac{1}{1-x} \right) dx$$

$$= \frac{1}{2} \ln|1+x| - \frac{1}{2} \ln|1-x|$$

$$= \frac{1}{2} \ln \left| \frac{1+x}{1-x} \right|.$$

Because of this, these two inverses do not require a further consideration.

Exercises

1. Prove the formula

$$\sinh x + \sinh y = 2 \sinh \frac{x+y}{2} \cosh \frac{x-y}{2}.$$

Also, find (and prove) analogous formulas for $\cosh x \pm \cosh y$.

2. Let P_1 and P_2 be different points with the same positive x-coordinate a, both lying on the hyperbola $x^2 - y^2 = 1$. Show that the area of the region bounded by the line segments OP_1 and OP_2 and by the hyperbola satisfies the equation $\cosh x = a$.

*3. Evaluate the following integrals:

(a) $\displaystyle\int \frac{1}{x\sqrt{1+x^2}} dx.$ (b) $\displaystyle\int \frac{1}{x\sqrt{1-x^2}} dx.$ (c) $\displaystyle\int \frac{1}{x\sqrt{x^2-1}} dx.$

Answers

3. (a) $-\ln \left| \dfrac{1 + \sqrt{1 + x^2}}{x} \right|$

(b) $-\ln \left| \dfrac{1 + \sqrt{1 - x^2}}{x} \right|$

(c) $\arccos \left(\dfrac{1}{x} \right) \quad$ for $x > 1$

$\quad -\arccos \left(\dfrac{1}{x} \right) \quad$ for $x < -1$

3-11. INDEFINITE INTEGRATION

Integration of Rational Functions

In Section 3-10 we evaluated many integrals by a combination of general integration rules and a knowledge of various functions. Some further results will now be discussed.

It may be of great importance to know whether a given integral can, on the whole, be explicitly expressed by known functions. In connection with this, we mention that the indefinite integral of any *rational function* can always be expressed as a combination of previously introduced functions: polynomials, rational functions, logarithmic functions, and arc tangent functions.

The proof of this gives at the same time a general method for carrying out the integration. It is based on an algebraic theorem which states that any rational function where the degree of the numerator is less than that of the denominator (a *proper* rational function) can be decomposed into so-called *partial fractions*. This means that it can be written as a sum of terms of the form

$$\frac{A}{(x + a)^n} \quad \text{and} \quad \frac{Bx + C}{((x + b)^2 + c^2)^n}.$$

An arbitrary rational function can always by division be rewritten as a sum of a polynomial and a proper rational function. The proof is therefore completed when methods of integrating the above forms are given. In the case of the latter expression, the following *recursion formula* will be of great help:

$$\int \frac{1}{(x^2 + 1)^n}\, dx = \frac{x}{(2n - 2)(x^2 + 1)^{n-1}} + \frac{2n - 3}{2n - 2} \int \frac{1}{(x^2 + 1)^{n-1}}\, dx.$$

Example 3-30. Evaluate

$$\int \frac{2x^5 + 3x^4 + 7x^3 - 14x^2 - 15x + 1}{x^4 + 2x^2 - 8x + 5} \, dx.$$

The integrand $f(x)$ is first rewritten as the sum of a polynomial and a proper rational function:

$$f(x) = 2x + 3 + \frac{3x^3 - 4x^2 - x - 14}{x^4 + 2x^2 - 8x + 5}.$$

Next the denominator of the last term is factored as much as possible (cf. p. 89): $x^4 + 2x^2 - 8x + 5 = (x - 1)^2(x^2 + 2x + 5)$. The last term can now be decomposed into partial fractions as follows:

$$\frac{3x^3 - 4x^2 - x - 14}{(x - 1)^2(x^2 + 2x + 5)} = \frac{A}{x - 1} + \frac{B}{(x - 1)^2} + \frac{Cx + D}{x^2 + 2x + 5}.$$

Multiplication throughout by the common denominator gives two identical polynomials, from which we obtain uniquely $A = 1, B = -2,$ $C = 2$, and $D = 1$. We then have

$$\int f(x) \, dx = \int \left(2x + 3 + \frac{1}{x - 1} - \frac{2}{(x - 1)^2} + \frac{2x + 1}{x^2 + 2x + 5} \right) dx.$$

As

$$\int \frac{2x + 1}{x^2 + 2x + 5} \, dx = \int \frac{2x + 2}{x^2 + 2x + 5} \, dx - \int \frac{1}{(x + 1)^2 + 4} \, dx$$

$$= \int \frac{1}{x^2 + 2x + 5} \, d(x^2 + 2x + 5)$$

$$- \frac{1}{2} \int \frac{1}{((x + 1)/2)^2 + 1} \, d\left(\frac{x + 1}{2} \right)$$

$$= \ln(x^2 + 2x + 5) - \frac{1}{2} \arctan \frac{x + 1}{2},$$

we finally obtain

$$\int f(x) \, dx = x^2 + 3x + \ln|x - 1| + \frac{2}{x - 1} + \ln(x^2 + 2x + 5)$$

$$- \frac{1}{2} \arctan \frac{x + 1}{2}. \qquad \square$$

Integration of Root Expressions

By use of the above, another general type of function can be integrated, all rational functions in the two variables x and y where y is the square root of a second-degree polynomial in x. The proof of this will not be considered here, but we shall mention some functions of this type that were previously integrated. The monotone substitutions used are also given:

$$\sqrt{a^2 - x^2} \quad \text{and} \quad \frac{1}{\sqrt{a^2 - x^2}}, \quad x = a \sin t,$$

$$\sqrt{x^2 - a^2} \quad \text{and} \quad \frac{1}{\sqrt{x^2 - a^2}}, \quad x = a \cosh t,$$

$$\sqrt{x^2 + a^2} \quad \text{and} \quad \frac{1}{\sqrt{x^2 + a^2}}, \quad x = a \sinh t.$$

Example 3-31

$$\int \frac{1}{\sqrt{x^2 + 2x + 5}}\, dx = \int \frac{1}{\sqrt{(x + 1)^2 + 4}}\, d(x + 1)$$
$$= \ln(x + 1 + \sqrt{x^2 + 2x + 5}),$$

$$\int \frac{x + 1}{\sqrt{x^2 + 2x + 5}}\, dx = \tfrac{1}{2} \int (x^2 + 2x + 5)^{-1/2} d(x^2 + 2x + 5)$$
$$= \sqrt{x^2 + 2x + 5}. \quad \square$$

Other types of functions which we can now generally integrate are rational functions in x and $\sqrt[n]{(ax + b)/(cx + a)}$ (substitution of, for example, $\sqrt[n]{(ax + b)/(cx + d)} = t$), and rational functions in $\sin x$ and $\cos x$. We shall limit ourselves to mentioning two important recursion formulas:

$$\int \sin^n x \cos^m x\, dx = -\frac{\sin^{n-1} x \cos^{m+1} x}{m + n}$$
$$+ \frac{n - 1}{m + n} \int \sin^{n-2} x \cos^m x\, dx$$

and

$$\int \cos^n x \sin^m x\, dx = \frac{\cos^{n-1} x \sin^{m+1} x}{m + n} + \frac{n - 1}{m + n} \int \cos^{n-2} x \sin^m x\, dx$$
$$(m + n \neq 0, m \neq -1).$$

Integration Leading to Introduction of New Functions

In practice one sometimes encounters an indefinite integral, about which it is known that it cannot be expressed in terms of the functions introduced so far.

In such a case it may be practical simply to introduce a new function. As mentioned, this was precisely the background for the introduction of the natural logarithm.

Example 3-32.   The function $f(x) = \sin x/x$ is continuous for all x ($f(0) = 1$). As a result it has a primitive function which also is defined for all x. This cannot, however, be expressed by previously introduced functions. The function *sine integral*, Si, has therefore been defined (and tabulated):

$$\mathrm{Si}\, x = \int_0^x \frac{\sin t}{t}\, dt.$$

We then have $\displaystyle\int \frac{\sin x}{x}\, dx = \mathrm{Si}\, x.$ With the help of this, a new series of integrals can be evaluated, for example,

$$\int \frac{\cos x}{(\pi/2) - x}\, dx = -\int \frac{\sin[(\pi/2) - x]}{(\pi/2) - x}\, d\left(\frac{\pi}{2} - x\right) = -\mathrm{Si}\left(\frac{\pi}{2} - x\right),$$

$$\int \frac{\sin(x^2)}{x}\, dx = \frac{1}{2} \int \frac{\sin(x^2)}{x^2}\, d(x^2) = \frac{1}{2}\,\mathrm{Si}(x^2). \qquad \square$$

There exist, of course, accurate tables of a large number of functions which have been introduced to give compact expressions for integrals and which sometimes are related in more or less simple ways. The decision as to how far a given integral should be reduced in a specific case will then often depend on the tabulated material available.

Furthermore, in many cases it may prove sufficient to use some approximation formula to evaluate a given definite integral (see Chapter 8).

Exercises

*1. Evaluate the following integrals:

(a) $\displaystyle\int \frac{3x^3 - 5x^2 + 4}{(x - 1)^2}\, dx.$

(b) $\displaystyle\int \frac{x + 4}{x^2 + 3x + 2}\, dx.$

(c) $\displaystyle\int \frac{4x + 9}{x^2 + 4x + 5}\, dx.$

(d) $\displaystyle\int \frac{2x + 3}{(x^2 + 1)^2}\, dx.$

2. Prove the following recursion formula:

$$\int_0^{\pi/2} \cos^n x\, dx = \frac{n - 1}{n} \int_0^{\pi/2} \cos^{n-2} x\, dx \qquad (n = 2,3,4,\ldots).$$

Also find (and prove) an analogous formula for sine.

*3. Evaluate the following integrals:

(a) $\int \dfrac{1}{\sin x}\, dx.$

(b) $\int \sin(2x + 3)\cos(4x + 5)\, dx.$

Answers

1. (a) $\dfrac{3}{2}x^2 + x - \ln|x - 1| - \dfrac{2}{x - 1}$

   (c) $2\ln(x^2 + 4x + 5) + \arctan(x + 2)$

   (b) $\ln\left|\dfrac{(x + 1)^3}{(x + 2)^2}\right|$

   (d) $\dfrac{3x - 2}{2(x^2 + 1)} + \dfrac{3}{2}\arctan x$

3. (a) $\ln\left|\tan\dfrac{x}{2}\right|$

   (b) $\tfrac{1}{4}\cos(2x + 2) - \tfrac{1}{12}\cos(6x + 8)$

3-12. DEFINITE INTEGRATION

Improper Integrals

As mentioned previously, it is possible in some cases to define a definite integral, even if the integrand is not bounded in the whole interval of integration, or the integration interval is not finite in length. We shall now show through a series of examples how the concept of a definite integral can be extended in this way.

Example 3-33

$$I = \int_a^1 \frac{1}{\sqrt[3]{x^2}}\, dx = 3 - 3 \cdot \sqrt[3]{a} \qquad (a > 0).$$

The integrand tends to infinity as x approaches 0. Nevertheless the definite integral has a limit, 3, as a approaches 0 (from the right).

We say that the *improper integral* $\int_0^1 (1/\sqrt[3]{x^2})\, dx$ is *convergent* and that it has the *value* 3.

Geometrically, the area enclosed by the curve $y = 1/\sqrt[3]{x^2}$, the coordinate axes, and the line $x = 1$ is considered equal to 3. □

Example 3-34

$$\int_{-2}^b \frac{1}{\sqrt[3]{x^2}}\, dx = 3 \cdot \sqrt[3]{b} + 3 \cdot \sqrt[3]{2} \to 3\sqrt[3]{2} \qquad \text{as } b \to 0(-0).$$

From this

$$\int_{-2}^0 \frac{1}{\sqrt[3]{x^2}}\, dx = 3\sqrt[3]{2}. \qquad □$$

Example 3-35. $\int_{-2}^{1} (1/\sqrt[3]{x^2})\, dx$ is also said to be convergent, and with the value

$$\int_{-2}^{1} \frac{1}{\sqrt[3]{x^2}}\, dx = \int_{-2}^{0} \frac{1}{\sqrt[3]{x^2}}\, dx + \int_{0}^{1} \frac{1}{\sqrt[3]{x^2}}\, dx = 3 \cdot \sqrt[3]{2} + 3. \qquad \square$$

Example 3-36

$$\int_{1}^{b} \frac{1}{\sqrt[3]{x^2}}\, dx = 3 \cdot \sqrt[3]{b} - 3 \to \infty \qquad \text{as } b \to \infty.$$

The improper integral $\int_{1}^{\infty} (1/\sqrt[3]{x^2})\, dx$ is said to be *divergent*. $\qquad \square$

Example 3-37

$$\int_{1}^{b} \frac{1}{x^2}\, dx = \frac{-1}{b} + 1 \to 1 \qquad \text{as } b \to \infty.$$

The improper integral is convergent: $\int_{1}^{\infty} (1/x^2)\, dx = 1.$ $\qquad \square$

Example 3-38. Using the monotone substitution $x = \tan t$ $(0 \le t \le \arctan b,\ 0 \le x \le b)$, we obtain

$$\int_{0}^{b} \frac{1}{(1 + x^2)^2}\, dx = \int_{0}^{\arctan b} \frac{1}{(1 + \tan^2 t)^2} \frac{1}{\cos^2 t}\, dt$$

$$= \int_{0}^{\arctan b} \cos^2 t\, dt = \frac{1}{2} \arctan b + \frac{1}{4} \sin(2 \arctan b)$$

$$\to \frac{1}{2} \frac{\pi}{2} + \frac{1}{4} \sin \pi = \frac{\pi}{4} \qquad \text{as } b \to \infty.$$

From this follows that

$$\int_{0}^{\infty} \frac{1}{(1 + x^2)^2}\, dx = \int_{0}^{\pi/2} \cos^2 t\, dt.$$

We observe how a substitution can transform an improper integral into a proper one; the limits are changed in the expected manner. $\qquad \square$

The improper integrals thus arise as possible limits of ordinary definite integrals (proper integrals). This may occur as the upper limit or the lower limit (or both) tend to $+\infty\,(-\infty)$ or to a point c where the integrand is not bounded in a deleted neighborhood of c. In the latter case, the integrand need not be defined at c.

If a limit is really obtained, then the improper integral is said to be convergent with the limit as its value; in case there is no limit, the improper integral is said to be divergent, and considered as having no value. The additivity rule is made to retain its validity in this extension.

The Gamma Function

Closer examination shows that the improper integral

$$\Gamma(x) = \int_0^\infty t^{x-1}e^{-t}\, dt$$

is convergent for $x > 0$ and divergent in all other cases. The function Γ determined in this way, the *gamma function*, is thus defined for all positive numbers. Corresponding to $x = 1$ we find

$$\Gamma(1) = \int_0^\infty e^{-t}\, dt = \lim_{b\to\infty}(1 - e^{-b}) = 1.$$

On integration by parts, x being any positive constant, the following is obtained:

$$\int_a^b t^x e^{-t}\, dt = [-t^x e^{-t}]_a^b + \int_a^b x t^{x-1}e^{-t}\, dt.$$

Now $-b^x e^{-b} \to 0$ as $b \to \infty$ and $a^x e^{-a} \to 0$ as $a \to 0 + 0$. Therefore,

$$\int_0^\infty t^x e^{-t}\, dt = x \int_0^\infty t^{x-1}e^{-t}\, dt \qquad \text{or} \qquad \Gamma(x+1) = x\Gamma(x).$$

The gamma function thus satisfies the functional equation $f(x+1) = xf(x)$. From this

$$\Gamma(2) = 1\Gamma(1) = 1, \qquad \Gamma(3) = 2\Gamma(2) = 2,$$
$$\Gamma(4) = 3\Gamma(3) = 3!, \ . \ .,\Gamma(n) = (n-1)!$$

(n a positive integer). The gamma function is thus an extension of the factorial function $(n-1)!$ from the set of all positive integers to the set of all positive real numbers. Furthermore,

$$\Gamma\left(\frac{1}{2}\right) = \int_0^\infty t^{-1/2}e^{-t}\, dt = \int_0^\infty \frac{1}{u}e^{-u^2}2u\, du = 2\cdot\int_0^\infty e^{-u^2}\, du.$$

Here we have used the substitution $t = u^2$ ($0 < u < \infty, 0 < t < \infty$).

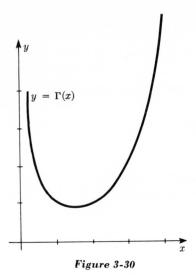

Figure 3-30

This last integral shall later be calculated to be $\sqrt{\pi}/2$ (see p. 277); thus $\Gamma(\frac{1}{2}) = \sqrt{\pi}$, and consequently, $\Gamma(\frac{3}{2}) = \frac{1}{2}\sqrt{\pi}$, $\Gamma(\frac{5}{2}) = \frac{3}{4}\sqrt{\pi}$, $\Gamma(\frac{7}{2}) = \frac{15}{8}\sqrt{\pi}$, etc.

The gamma function will be investigated in greater detail later, but we note here that it is differentiable an arbitrary number of times and tends to infinity as x approaches 0 as well as ∞ (Fig. 3-30).

Exercises

*1. Sketch each of the following curves, and investigate whether the area between the curve and the X-axis is finite. In case it is, evaluate it:

$$\text{(a)} \ y = \frac{8}{(x-2)^2 + 8}. \quad \text{(b)} \ y = \frac{1}{|x-2| + 1}. \quad \text{(c)} \ y = \frac{8}{|x-2|^3 + 8}.$$

2. Consider the function

$$f(x) = \frac{1}{x^5} \frac{1}{e^{1/ax} - 1} \quad (x > 0),$$

where a is a positive constant. Show that there is exactly one point x_0, where the function has a maximum. Furthermore, show that x_0 is inversely proportional to a, and that the area between the X-axis and the graph of the function is finite and directly proportional to a^4.

*3. Evaluate:

$$\text{(a)} \ \int_0^\infty x^3 e^{-x}\, dx. \qquad \text{(b)} \ \int_0^\infty \sqrt{x}\, e^{-x}\, dx. \qquad \text{(c)} \ \int_0^\infty x^{10} e^{-x}\, dx.$$

Answers

1. (a) $2\sqrt{2}\,\pi$. (b) Not finite. (c) $8\pi/3\,\sqrt{3}$.
3. (a) 6. (b) $\sqrt{\pi}/2$. (c) $10! \approx 3.63 \cdot 10^6$.

3-13. MATHEMATICS IN SCIENCE

Rigorism and Mathematics

In our consideration of the differential and integral calculus we have up to now tried to give a rather detailed treatment. The assumptions regarding the continuity, the differentiability, etc., which must be made in every case have been discussed. At the same time we have tried to point out where a further investigation is necessary to prove the validity of the statements made.

However, the uses of mathematics in science have been successfully developed in a less rigorous form, leaving it to the mathematicians to clear up the basis.

A condition for doing this, however, is that it has been carefully clarified at which points serious problems may arise. This then is one reason for the rather lengthy explanations given so far.

As an example of a less rigorous form, we shall once more derive an expression for the area enclosed by the positive function $y = f(x)$, the X-axis, and the lines $x = a$ and $x = b$ (Fig. 3-31).

For this we consider the "infinitely" small rectangle drawn in the figure (an *infinitesimal rectangle*) which has for its sides dx and $f(x)$. The area of this is $f(x)\,dx$. The area of the whole figure is then obtained as the *sum* of all such rectangles, i.e., as $\int_a^b f(x)\,dx$. The proof is thus complete.

With respect to the conditions necessary for the validity of the result, we assume simply that the given function is suitably *"well*

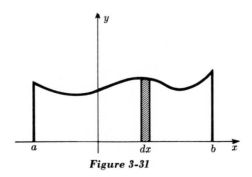

Figure 3-31

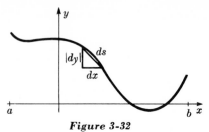

Figure 3-32

behaved." This means here, for example, that it is continuous in the closed interval $[a,b]$. Above we have understood the differentials dx to be positive. In what follows differentials *chosen by us* will always be taken as positive. In case all differentials had been chosen negative in the above proof, the infinitesimal rectangle considered would be of area $-f(x)\,dx$, while the corresponding sum would have been $\int_b^a -f(x)\,dx$. The final result would thus have been the same.

Further Examples

In order to determine the *arc length* on the curve $y = f(x)$ between the points $(a,f(a))$ and $(b,f(b))$, an *infinitesimal arc* is considered. This is the hypotenus in a right-angled triangle in which the other sides have the lengths dx and $|dy| = |f'(x)\,dx|$. Its length is therefore $ds = \sqrt{(dx)^2 + (dy)^2} = \sqrt{1 + (f'(x))^2}\,dx$ (Fig. 3-32). The entire arc length s is obtained by adding all these elements, i.e.,

$$s = \int_a^b \sqrt{1 + (f'(x))^2}\,dx.$$

Next, let the positive function $y = f(x)$, together with the lines $x = a$ and $x = b$, be rotated 360° about the X-axis (Fig. 3-33). The

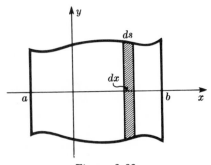

Figure 3-33

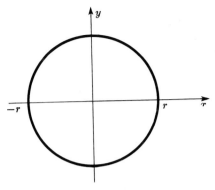

Figure 3-34

area S of the surface and the *volume* V of the solid generated by the rotation are found by considering an *infinitesimal conical frustum* with the circular bases perpendicular to the X-axis and of height dx. For the area dS and the volume dV we have $dS = 2\pi y \, ds = 2\pi f(x) \sqrt{1 + (f'(x))^2} \, dx$ and $dV = \pi y^2 \, dx = \pi (f(x))^2 \, dx$. Thus

$$S = 2\pi \int_a^b f(x) \sqrt{1 + (f'(x))^2} \, dx$$

and

$$V = \pi \int_a^b (f(x))^2 \, dx.$$

Example 3-39. For the semicircle $y = \sqrt{r^2 - x^2}$, the following well-known results are obtained (Fig. 3-34):

$$A = \int_{-r}^r \sqrt{r^2 - x^2} \, dx$$

$$= \int_{-\pi/2}^{\pi/2} r \cos v \, r \cos v \, dv$$

$$= \tfrac{1}{2}\pi r^2,$$

$$s = \int_{-r}^r \sqrt{1 + \left(\frac{-x}{\sqrt{r^2 - x^2}}\right)^2} \, dx$$

$$= \int_{-r}^r \frac{r}{\sqrt{r^2 - x^2}} \, dx = \int_{-\pi/2}^{\pi/2} r \frac{1}{r \cos v} r \cos v \, dv = \pi r,$$

$$S = 2\pi \int_{-r}^{r} \sqrt{r^2 - x^2} \, \frac{r}{\sqrt{r^2 - x^2}} \, dx = 4\pi r^2,$$

$$V = \pi \int_{-r}^{r} (r^2 - x^2) \, dx = \tfrac{4}{3}\pi r^3. \quad \square$$

Exercises

*1. Find the length of the curve $y = \ln x$ $(2\sqrt{2} \le x \le 2\sqrt{6})$.

2. The curve $y = 1/x \, (x \ge 1)$ and the line segment $x = 1$ $(0 \le y \le 1)$ are rotated 360° about the X-axis, thus bounding a funnel-shaped region in space. Investigate whether this region has (a) a finite surface area, (b) a finite volume.

*3. Sketch the curve $y = -\tfrac{4}{3}x + \tfrac{5}{3}\sqrt{x}$. Rotating this curve 360° about the line $3x - 4y = 0$, a finite solid is generated. Find its volume.

Answers

1. $2 + \ln\left(\dfrac{2}{\sqrt{3}}\right)$

3. $\dfrac{2^9 \pi}{3^3 \cdot 5^4}$

3-14. VECTOR-VALUED FUNCTIONS OF ONE REAL VARIABLE

Vector Functions

The previous sections have been concerned with functions where both the domain and the range were sets of real numbers. We shall now consider *vector-valued functions of one real variable,* or briefly, *vector functions,* i.e., functions from some set A to some set B, where A is a set of real numbers and B is a set of N-dimensional vectors. In the following we shall consider two- and three-dimensional vectors only.

To describe these, we introduce a usual right-angled coordinate system XY in the plane and a usual right-angled right-handed coordinate system XYZ in space. In this way, a vector function will be uniquely determined by two—in space three—real functions, the so-called *coordinate functions,* with a common domain. The independent variable of a vector function is also called the *parameter.* It is often represented by the letter t. The value of the vector function at the point t may be written $\mathbf{r}$ or $\mathbf{r}(t)$.

Suppose the corresponding coordinate functions in a space system with base vectors $\mathbf{i}, \mathbf{j}$, and $\mathbf{k}$ are f, g, and h, respectively. We then have

$$\mathbf{r} = \mathbf{r}(t) = f(t)\mathbf{i} + g(t)\mathbf{j} + h(t)\mathbf{k} = (f(t),g(t),h(t)).$$

This may also be written

$$\mathbf{r} = \mathbf{r}(t) = x(t)\mathbf{i} + y(t)\mathbf{j} + z(t)\mathbf{k} = (x(t),y(t),z(t)) \quad \text{or } \mathbf{r} = (x,y,z),$$

where we have introduced $x = x(t) = f(t)$, $y = y(t) = g(t)$, and $z = z(t) = h(t)$. If $h(t)$ is constant and equal to 0, then we have the two-dimensional case with all the vectors lying in the XY-plane. Of course, the vector can then be written $\mathbf{r}(t) = (f(t),g(t))$. The above notation, however, has the advantage that it may be used to represent both two- and three-dimensional vector functions.

Graphs of Vector Functions

The *graph* of the vector function $\mathbf{r}(t)$ is defined as the set of all the terminal points of the vectors $\mathbf{r}(t)$ drawn as position vectors, i.e., drawn from the origin of the coordinate system. The graph of the vector function $\mathbf{r}(t) = (f(t),g(t),h(t))$ is thus identical to the curve with parametric equations $x = f(t)$, $y = g(t)$, $z = h(t)$.

Taken as a graphical representation of the vector function $\mathbf{r}(t)$ this curve must be considered as a rather incomplete picture insofar as it does not show which of the points on the curve is the one corresponding to some given value of the independent variable t. If necessary some values of t may be written at the corresponding points of the curve.

Example 3-40. $\mathbf{r}(t) = (a \cos t, a \sin t, bt)$, $-\infty < t < \infty$.

The graph of this function is the so-called *circular helix*. It is seen to wind itself around the right circular cylinder $x^2 + y^2 = a^2$ in a "steadily increasing" manner (Fig. 3-35). $\square$

If the abscissa function f is monotone in the whole of its domain, then here the equation $x = f(t)$ can be solved with respect to t as $t = \phi(x)$. Substituting this into the other two coordinate functions, one obtains $y = g(\phi(x))$ and $z = h(\phi(x))$.

In the two-dimensional case we have $z = 0$. Thus by eliminating the parameter, a new function $y = y(x)$ is found, which has the same graph as the given vector function (if the range of f is chosen as the domain of this new function).

In the three-dimensional case, two functions are obtained, $y = y(x)$ and $z = z(x)$. The first one has as its graph a cylinder with the curve $y = y(x)$ in the XY-plane as a directrix and some line parallel to the Z-axis as its generator. The second function corresponds to a cylinder with the curve $z = z(x)$ in the XZ-plane as a directrix and some line

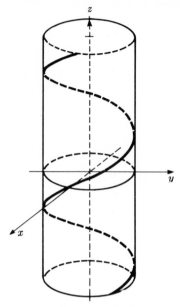

Figure 3-35

parallel to the Y-axis as its generator. The given curve is obtained as the intersection between these two cylinders (see also p. 20).

Vector Sequences

In the following, by a vector we mean a three-dimensional vector, unless otherwise stated. The set of all two-dimensional vectors is hereby considered as a subset of the set of all three-dimensional vectors—the set of all vectors with their z-coordinate equal to zero.

As an important aid in the more detailed consideration of vector functions, sequences of vectors are used. A *vector sequence* is a function from the set of all positive integers to some set of vectors (cf. p. 134). It is often written $\mathbf{r}_1, \mathbf{r}_2, \ldots, \mathbf{r}_n, \ldots$ In connection with such a vector sequence we shall often consider the three corresponding *coordinate sequences*. In the two-dimensional case, the z-sequence has all its elements equal to zero.

The vector sequence $\mathbf{r}_1, \mathbf{r}_2, \ldots, \mathbf{r}_n, \ldots$ is now said to be *convergent* with the vector $\mathbf{r}$ as its *limit* ($\mathbf{r}_n \to \mathbf{r}$ as $n \to \infty$), if corresponding to any given positive number ϵ, however small, it is possible to determine a number N such that $|\mathbf{r}_n - \mathbf{r}| < \epsilon$ for $n > N$. Geometrically, this requirement means that the end points of the position vectors $\mathbf{r}_n$

$(n > N)$ shall lie inside a sphere (in the plane a circle) with radius ϵ and the center at the end point of the position vector $\mathbf{r}$.

It is easily seen that a necessary and sufficient condition for convergence of a vector sequence is that the three corresponding coordinate sequences are all convergent with the respective coordinates of the limit vector as their limits.

Continuity of Vector Functions

A vector function $\mathbf{r}(t)$ which is defined in some deleted neighborhood of t_0 (not necessarily at the point t_0 itself) is now said to have the *limit vector* $\mathbf{c}$ at the point t_0 ($\mathbf{r}(t) \to \mathbf{c}$ as $t \to t_0$) when for every sequence $t_1, t_2, \ldots, t_n, \ldots$ which remains inside the domain of the vector function, does not contain t_0, but converges to t_0, it is true that the corresponding vector sequence $\mathbf{r}(t_1), \mathbf{r}(t_2), \ldots, \mathbf{r}(t_n), \ldots$ converges to $\mathbf{c}$.

If the vector function also is defined at t_0, and $\mathbf{r}(t_0) = \mathbf{c}$, then the vector function is said to be *continuous* at the point t_0. A necessary and sufficient condition for this is that the three coordinate functions all are continuous at the point considered.

Finally, by a *continuous curve* we mean the graph of some vector function defined in an interval and continuous in the whole of its domain. According to this definition, the graph of a continuous function $y = f(x)$ defined in an interval is also a continuous (two-dimensional) curve, as its graph can be determined by the continuous vector function $\mathbf{r}(t) = (t, f(t))$ or $\mathbf{r}(t) = (t, f(t), 0)$.

Example 3-41. $\mathbf{r}(t) = (at \cos t,\ at \sin t),\ t \geq 0$ (Fig. 3-36). The graph of this continuous vector function is the so-called *Archimedean spiral*. It is seen that corresponding to a given abscissa there is an

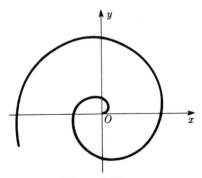

Figure 3-36

infinite number of points of the curve. Thus it will never occur as the graph of any real function. □

The *definite integral* of a vector function, continuous in the interval $\alpha \leq t \leq \beta$, $\mathbf{r}(t) = (f(t), g(t), h(t))$, can be obtained as the limit of a sequence of average vector sums corresponding to an increasingly finer partition of the parameter interval. It is seen to be

$$\int_{\alpha}^{\beta} \mathbf{r}(t)\, dt = \left(\int_{\alpha}^{\beta} f(t)\, dt, \int_{\alpha}^{\beta} g(t)\, dt, \int_{\alpha}^{\beta} h(t)\, dt \right).$$

Differentiability of Vector Functions

Let a vector function $\mathbf{r}(t)$ be defined in a neighborhood of the point t_0. We now consider the *difference quotient*

$$\frac{\Delta \mathbf{r}}{\Delta t} = \frac{\mathbf{r}(t_0 + \Delta t) - \mathbf{r}(t_0)}{\Delta t} = \left(\frac{f(t_0 + \Delta t) - f(t_0)}{\Delta t}, \frac{g(t_0 + \Delta t) - g(t_0)}{\Delta t}, \right.$$
$$\left. \frac{h(t_0 + \Delta t) - h(t_0)}{\Delta t} \right) = \left(\frac{\Delta f}{\Delta t}, \frac{\Delta g}{\Delta t}, \frac{\Delta h}{\Delta t} \right)$$

as $\Delta t \to 0$. If a limit is thus obtained, then the vector function is said to be *differentiable* at the point t_0 with the limit vector as its *differential quotient* or *derivative* at the point considered:

$$\frac{\Delta \mathbf{r}}{\Delta t} \to \frac{d\mathbf{r}}{dt} = \mathbf{r}'(t_0) \qquad \text{as } \Delta t \to 0.$$

A necessary and sufficient condition for this to occur is that the three coordinate functions are differentiable at t_0. Then $\mathbf{r}'(t_0) = (f'(t_0), g'(t_0), h'(t_0))$ (Fig. 3-37).

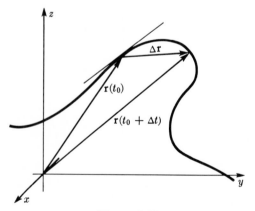

Figure 3-37

Geometrically, $\Delta\mathbf{r}$ and thus also $\Delta\mathbf{r}/\Delta t$ are vectors on a secant to the graph of the vector function. If $\mathbf{r}'(t_0) \neq \mathbf{0}$, it follows that the secant has a limit position as $\Delta t \to 0$, and the curve thus a *tangent line* which contains the vector $\mathbf{r}'(t_0)$. As parametric equations of the tangent line the following may serve:

$$(x,y,z) = (f(t_0) + f'(t_0)u, g(t_0) + g'(t_0)u, h(t_0) + h'(t_0)u),$$

where $-\infty < u < \infty$.

As a result of this, a *differentiable curve* is now defined as the graph of a vector function, defined and differentiable in an interval with a derivative different from $\mathbf{0}$. Further, this derivative is required to be continuous in the interval considered. An arbitrary differentiable curve thus has a tangent at every point on it.

The graph of a function $y = f(x)$, which is defined and differentiable in some interval with a continuous derivative, in this way becomes a (plane) differentiable curve, because the same curve is the graph of the vector function $\mathbf{r}(t) = (t, f(t), 0)$. As $\mathbf{r}'(t) = (1, f'(t), 0)$ here, the necessary conditions are seen to be fulfilled.

Example 3-42. The circular helix previously considered is a differentiable curve as $\mathbf{r}'(t) = (-a\sin t, a\cos t, b)$ is continuous and different from $\mathbf{0}$ for all t. $\quad\square$

On consideration of the coordinate functions, it is seen that the sum, difference, scalar product, and vector product of two vector functions differentiable at a point t_0 also are differentiable at that point:

$$\mathbf{r}(t) = \mathbf{r}_1(t) \pm \mathbf{r}_2(t), \qquad \mathbf{r}'(t_0) = \mathbf{r}_1'(t_0) \pm \mathbf{r}_2'(t_0),$$
$$\phi(t) = \mathbf{r}_1(t) \cdot \mathbf{r}_2(t), \qquad \phi'(t_0) = \mathbf{r}_1'(t_0) \cdot \mathbf{r}_2(t_0) + \mathbf{r}_1(t_0) \cdot \mathbf{r}_2'(t_0),$$
$$\mathbf{r}(t) = \mathbf{r}_1(t) \times \mathbf{r}_2(t), \qquad \mathbf{r}'(t_0) = \mathbf{r}_1'(t_0) \times \mathbf{r}_2(t_0) + \mathbf{r}_1(t_0) \times \mathbf{r}_2'(t_0).$$

A corresponding rule is valid for the product of a real function and a vector function:

$$\mathbf{r}(t) = \phi(t)\mathbf{r}_1(t), \qquad \mathbf{r}'(t_0) = \phi'(t_0)\mathbf{r}_1(t_0) + \phi(t_0)\mathbf{r}_1'(t_0).$$

Taylor's Formula

From the second definition of differentiability of a real function, we obtain for the vector function $\mathbf{r}(t)$, differentiable at t_0,

$$\Delta\mathbf{r} = \mathbf{r}(t_0 + \Delta t) - \mathbf{r}(t_0) = (f(t_0 + \Delta t) - f(t_0), g(t_0 + \Delta t) - g(t_0),$$
$$h(t_0 + \Delta t) - h(t_0))$$
$$= (f'(t_0), g'(t_0), h'(t_0))\,\Delta t + (o_1(\Delta t), o_2(\Delta t), o_3(\Delta t))$$
$$= \mathbf{r}'(t_0)\,\Delta t + \mathbf{o}(\Delta t) = d\mathbf{r} + \mathbf{o}(\Delta t),$$

where $o(\Delta t)$ is a vector function of Δt such that $o(\Delta t)/\Delta t \rightarrow 0$ as $\Delta t \rightarrow 0$.

The quantity $d\mathbf{r} = \mathbf{r}'(t_0)\,\Delta t$ is the *differential* of the vector function at the considered point corresponding to the increment Δt of the parameter.

For the real function $\phi(t) = t$ we have, corresponding to the same increment Δt, a differential $dt = 1 \cdot \Delta t$. Introducing this, we find $d\mathbf{r} = \mathbf{r}'(t_0)\,dt = (f'(t_0), g'(t_0), h'(t_0))\,dt = (df, dg, dh)$ or, on dividing, $d\mathbf{r}/dt = \mathbf{r}'(t_0)$. In this way the symbol $d\mathbf{r}/dt$ and the name differential quotient already used for the derivative may be justified.

With a different notation we then have $\mathbf{r}(t) - \mathbf{r}(t_0) = \mathbf{r}'(t_0)(t - t_0) + o(t - t_0)$. If $\mathbf{r}'(t_0) \neq 0$, the last term on the right side will be vanishing of an order higher than the first term as t approaches t_0. To ignore the last term means geometrically to replace the curve by its tangent at the point. If, however, the exact position of the curve with respect to its tangent is of interest, then this approximation is not sufficient.

Let us now assume that the coordinate functions are differentiable an arbitrary number of times in an open interval containing t_0. Then by the use of Taylor's o-formula for each of these we get the following, which is *Taylor's formula* for vector functions:

$$\mathbf{r}(t) = \mathbf{r}(t_0) + \frac{\mathbf{r}'(t_0)}{1!}(t - t_0) + \frac{\mathbf{r}''(t_0)}{2!}(t - t_0)^2 + \cdots$$
$$+ \frac{\mathbf{r}^{(n)}(t_0)}{n!}(t - t_0)^n + o((t - t_0)^n).$$

Using this formula, information regarding the curve in a neighborhood of t_0 may now be derived (cf. p. 162). We limit ourselves to noting that a curve, which at the point t_0 has $\mathbf{r}'(t) = 0$—and therefore is not a differentiable curve—but which has $\mathbf{r}''(t_0) \neq 0$, has a cusp at the point in question with a *half-tangent* in the direction $\mathbf{r}''(t_0)$. This arises from Taylor's formula with $n = 2$.

Example 3-43. A *cycloid* is a plane curve which is traced out by a fixed point on a circle which rolls without slipping on a straight line (Fig. 3-38). For the case shown in the figure, a corresponding vector function is $\mathbf{r}(t) = (a(t - \sin t), a(1 - \cos t))$, $-\infty < t < \infty$, where t gives the angle between the radius to the point P on the curve and the radius to the instantaneous point of contact Q of the circle. We

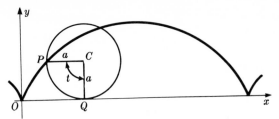

Figure 3-38

obtain $\mathbf{r}'(t) = (a(1 - \cos t), \ a \sin t)$, $\mathbf{r}''(t) = (a \sin t, \ a \cos t)$ and $\mathbf{r}^{(3)}(t) = (a \cos t, \ -a \sin t)$. As $\mathbf{r}'(p2\pi) = \mathbf{0}$, the entire curve is not differentiable. However, $\mathbf{r}''(p2\pi) = (0,a) \neq \mathbf{0}$; hence the curve has at all the points $(p2\pi a, 0)$ a (vertical) half-tangent. Furthermore, $\mathbf{r}^{(3)}(p2\pi) = (a,0)$ is linearly independent of the second derivative; thus the two parts of the curve corresponding to Δt positive and Δt negative will lie each on either side of the half-tangent (Taylor's formula with $n = 3$). $\quad\square$

Arc Length

Finally, we shall, in a less rigorous way, derive an expression for the *arc length* of a differentiable curve corresponding to a vector function $\mathbf{r}(t) = (f(t), g(t), h(t))$ and a parametric interval $[\alpha, \beta]$.

Consider the length of the infinitesimal part of the curve PP_1 which corresponds to a parameter interval $[t, \ t + dt]$ (Fig. 3-39). This portion of the curve is a diagonal in a parallelepiped with sides $|dx| = |f'(t) \ dt|$, $|dy| = |g'(t) \ dt|$, and $|dz| = |h'(t) \ dt|$ parallel to the axes. Its length is therefore

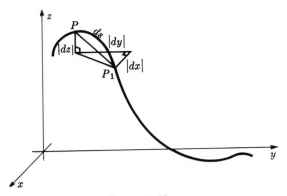

Figure 3-39

$$ds = \sqrt{(dx)^2 + (dy)^2 + (dz)^2}$$
$$= \sqrt{(f'(t))^2 + (g'(t))^2 + (h'(t))^2} \, dt = \left| \mathbf{r}'(t) \right| dt.$$

The whole arc length is then obtained as the sum of all these elements, or as

$$s = \int_\alpha^\beta \sqrt{(f'(t))^2 + (g'(t))^2 + (h'(t))^2} \, dt = \int_\alpha^\beta \left| \mathbf{r}'(t) \right| dt.$$

For the plane differentiable curve $y = f(x)$ ($a \le x \le b$), the result is $s = \int_a^b \sqrt{1 + (f'(t))^2} \, dt$, in agreement with the previous result (p. 202).

Example 3-44. For the curve corresponding to the parameter interval $[0,2\pi]$ on the circular helix (a single turn), we obtain

$$s = \int_0^{2\pi} \left| \mathbf{r}'(t) \right| dt = \int_0^{2\pi} \sqrt{a^2 + b^2} \, dt$$
$$= 2\pi \sqrt{a^2 + b^2}.$$

For the length of a single cycloid arc ($0 \le t \le 2\pi$) we obtain

$$s = \int_0^{2\pi} \sqrt{a^2(1 - \cos t)^2 + a^2 \sin^2 t} \, dt$$
$$= 2a \int_0^{2\pi} \sqrt{\frac{1 - \cos t}{2}} \, dt = 2a \int_0^{2\pi} \sin \frac{t}{2} \, dt = 8a. \qquad \square$$

Motion of a Particle

An important use of vector functions occurs in physics where the *motion* of a particle is represented by a vector function $\mathbf{r}(t)$. The parameter t is interpreted as the *time* and the value $\mathbf{r}(t)$ of the vector function as the *position* vector determined by the particle at the time t. The *velocity* of the particle is then obtained as $\mathbf{r}'(t)$, and the *acceleration* as $\mathbf{r}''(t)$.

Example 3-45. With this interpretation, the above vector function, having as its graph a cycloid (p. 210), represents the motion of a fixed point on a circle rolling with *angular velocity* 1.

As $\mathbf{OP} = \mathbf{r}(t) = (a(t - \sin t), a(1 - \cos t))$, and $\mathbf{OQ} = (at,0)$, then $\mathbf{PQ} = (a \sin t, a(\cos t - 1))$. The vector $\mathbf{PQ}$ is perpendicular to

$\mathbf{r}'(t) = (a(1 - \cos t),\ a \sin t)$, because $\mathbf{PQ} \cdot \mathbf{r}(t) = 0$. This is also intuitively clear as the instantaneous motion must be a rotation about the point of contact Q. Suppose the circle is not rolling with the constant angular velocity 1 but in some other way, such that the angle PCQ is a monotone-increasing function $\phi(t)$ of the time t. The angular velocity then becomes $\phi'(t)$ and the following vector function must be used:

$$\mathbf{r}_\phi(t) = (a(\phi(t) - \sin \phi(t)),\ a(1 - \cos \phi(t))).$$

The velocity is then

$$\mathbf{r}'_\phi(t) = (a(1 - \cos \phi(t))\phi'(t),\ a(\sin \phi(t))\phi'(t)) = \mathbf{r}'(t)\phi'(t).$$

The direction of the velocity, which also is the direction of the tangent, naturally is not changed by this. The absolute value of the velocity (the *speed*) changes in the expected manner.   □

Exercises

*1. On the outside of a circle with radius $2a$ there rolls a circle with radius a. In a suitably chosen coordinate system, find parametric equations for the curve traced by a fixed point on the rolling circle. Find the length of this curve (an epicycloid).

2. Show that the curve given by the vector function

$$\mathbf{r}(t) = (t^3 - 9t^2 + 24t + 2,\ t^3 - 3t^2 + 1)$$

has exactly one cusp, and investigate whether the curve is symmetrical about its (half-) tangent at this point.

3. Sketch the graph of the vector function

$$\mathbf{r}(t) = \left(\cos t,\ \sin t,\ \cos \frac{t}{2}\right) \qquad (0 \le t \le 4\pi).$$

*4. The motion of a point P in an orthogonal coordinate system with origin O and base vectors $\mathbf{i}$, $\mathbf{j}$, and $\mathbf{k}$ is given by the vector function

$$OP = \mathbf{r}(t) = e^{-t} \cos t\, \mathbf{i} + e^{-t} \sin t\, \mathbf{j} + e^{-t}\mathbf{k}.$$

Show that the angle between the acceleration and the velocity is constant, and that the angle between the acceleration and the plane containing the velocity and the position vector is constant. Find the length $s(t)$ of the curve traced by P in the time interval from 0 to t, and determine $\lim_{t \to \infty} s(t)$.

Answers

1. $\mathbf{r}(t) = (3a \cos t - a \cos 3t,\ 3a \sin t - a \sin 3t);\ 0 \le t \le 2\pi$

    $s = 24a$

4. $s(t) = \sqrt{3}\,(1 - e^{-t});\ \lim\limits_{t \to \infty} s(t) = \sqrt{3}$

3-15. POLAR COORDINATES

Coordinate Systems

Except for some comments regarding logarithmic papers, we have in this chapter only used orthogonal coordinate systems (usual right-angled coordinate systems). In Chapter 1 we also considered the more general parallel coordinate systems, in which the base vectors could be of different lengths and not necessarily mutually perpendicular. However, in addition to these, there is an infinite number of other possibilities. As a *coordinate system* we may consider any method of specifying the position of an arbitrary point by means of numbers.

We shall now introduce other important types of coordinate systems, the so-called *polar coordinate systems*. These are usually introduced in a specific position in relation to a previously fixed orthogonal system. One type will be considered for the planar case, two for the spacial case.

Plane Polar Coordinates

Consider in a plane an orthogonal coordinate system XY with origin O. As usual the plane will be orientated so that the angle from the X-axis to the Y-axis is $+\pi/2$.

Suppose P is an arbitrary point in the plane. The length of the position vector **OP**, $|\text{OP}| = r$, is then called the *radial distance* of the point P, and any directed angle θ from the X-axis to the position vector **OP** is called a *polar angle* of P. The ordered pair of numbers (r,θ) are then called *polar coordinates* of P, corresponding to O as the *pole* and the positive half of the X-axis as the *polar axis*.

While the radial distance for any point is uniquely determined, the polar angle is determined only to a multiple of 2π, with one exception: For the pole, the polar angle is completely indefinite (while the radial distance is 0). On the other hand, there corresponds to an arbitrary ordered pair of numbers (r,θ), where $r \geq 0$, only one point in the plane with this pair as its polar coordinates (Fig. 3-40).

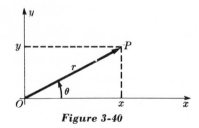

Figure 3-40

The relation between the usual right-angled coordinates (x,y) and the polar coordinates (r,θ) to an arbitrary point in the plane is given by $x = r \cos \theta$, $y = r \sin \theta$, or

$$r = \sqrt{x^2 + y^2},$$

$$\cos \theta = \frac{x}{\sqrt{x^2 + y^2}}, \qquad \sin \theta = \frac{y}{\sqrt{x^2 + y^2}}.$$

Example 3-46. $(x,y) = (\sqrt{3},1)$ corresponds to $(r,\theta) = (2, \pi/6 + p2\pi)$.

$(r,\theta) = (4, (5\pi/6) + p2\pi)$ corresponds to $(x,y) = (-2\sqrt{3}, 2)$. $\square$

It may occur that negative values of the radial distance are also used. The point (r,θ) is then identical with the point $(-r, \theta + \pi)$. In some situations, however, it may be advantageous to require $r \geq 0$ and $0 \leq \theta < 2\pi$. Then the polar coordinates of any point except the pole will be uniquely determined.

Equations in Polar Coordinates

The graph in a given polar coordinate system of an equation $\phi(r,\theta) = 0$ is of course the set of all points in the plane which have polar coordinates (r,θ) that satisfy the given equation. The case where the given equation can be solved uniquely with respect to r, as $r = \phi(\theta)$, is of special interest here.

Example 3-47. $r = a\theta \ (0 \leq \theta < \infty)$. On transformation to usual right-angled coordinates (x,y), we obtain

$$\left. \begin{array}{l} x = r \cos \theta = a\theta \cos \theta \\ y = r \sin \theta = a\theta \sin \theta \end{array} \right\} \quad (0 \leq \theta < \infty).$$

These are parametric equations of the previously considered Archimedean spiral (p. 207). Its equation in polar coordinates is thus that introduced above. As already mentioned, this curve could not be represented by a single function in a coordinate system XY, but we have now seen that this is possible in polar coordinates. $\square$

For the straight line $\alpha x + \beta y + \gamma = 0$, where $\alpha^2 + \beta^2 = 1$, we find on introducing polar coordinates $r\alpha \cos \theta + r\beta \sin \theta + \gamma = 0$, or if $(\alpha,\beta) = (\cos \theta_0, \sin \theta_0)$, $r \cos(\theta - \theta_0) + \gamma = 0$. This is also readily obtained from pure geometric considerations (Fig. 3-41).

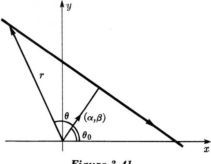

Figure 3-41

For a circle with center $(a,0)$ and radius a, we find—either from its equation in usual right-angled coordinates (x,y), or immediately from geometry—the equation $r = 2a \cos \theta$ (Fig. 3-42).

Infinitesimal Considerations

In order to investigate more closely a curve which in polar coordinates has the equation $r = \phi(\theta)$, one can, of course, choose to consider the corresponding parametric equations $x = \phi(\theta) \cos \theta$, $y = \phi(\theta) \sin \theta$. From these an equation for the curve in usual right-angled coordinates may be obtained by elimination of the parameter θ.

It is, however, also possible to retain the polar form, transferring the general theory to the polar system. We limit ourselves to the deduction of some important results. These will not be rigorously developed.

Let $P = (r,\theta)$ and $P_1 = (r + dr, \theta + d\theta)$ be two neighboring points on the curve $r = \phi(\theta)$. The section of curve PP_1 is then the hypotenuse of a right-angled triangle which has the two other sides on the circle through P with center at the pole O and on the straight line OP_1. The lengths of these are respectively $r\,d\theta$ and $|dr|$ (Fig. 3-43).

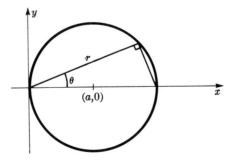

Figure 3-42

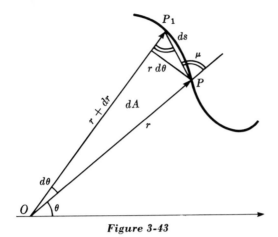

Figure 3-43

The angle μ between the position vector **OP** and the tangent to the curve at P, orientated by increasing θ, is given by

$$\cot \mu = \frac{dr}{r\,d\theta} = \frac{1}{r}\frac{dr}{d\theta} = \frac{1}{\phi(\theta)}\,\phi'(\theta).$$

The area A enclosed by the curve $r = \phi(\theta)$, $\alpha \le \theta \le \beta$ ($\beta - \alpha \le 2\pi$), and, if necessary, the lines $\theta = \alpha$ and $\theta = \beta$, is obtained as a sum of infinitesimal circular sectors having areas $dA = \tfrac{1}{2}r\,r\,d\theta$. Thus

$$A = \tfrac{1}{2}\int_{\alpha}^{\beta} (\phi(\theta))^2 \, d\theta.$$

The arc length s of the curve considered is obtained as a sum of infinitesimal arc elements having lengths

$$ds = \sqrt{(r\,d\theta)^2 + (dr)^2} = \sqrt{r^2 + \left(\frac{dr}{d\theta}\right)^2}\,d\theta.$$

Hence

$$s = \int_{\alpha}^{\beta} \sqrt{(\phi(\theta))^2 + (\phi'(\theta))^2}\, d\theta.$$

This result can also be obtained by substitution of the above-mentioned parametric equations into the previously derived general formula for arc length (p. 212).

Example 3-48. The following results are now obtained for the Archimedean spiral:

$$\cot \mu = \frac{1}{r}\frac{dr}{d\theta} = \frac{1}{a\theta}a = \frac{1}{\theta}.$$

The angle μ is monotone-increasing from 0 to $\pi/2$. At the first intersection with the polar axis $(\theta = 2\pi)$, $\cot \mu = 1/(2\pi)$, $\mu = 80.96°$. The area enclosed by the first turn and the polar axis is

$$A = \tfrac{1}{2}\int_0^{2\pi} (a\theta)^2 \, d\theta = \tfrac{4}{3}\pi^3 a^2,$$

while the corresponding arc length is

$$s = \int_0^{2\pi} \sqrt{(a\theta)^2 + a^2}\, d\theta$$
$$= a(\pi\sqrt{4\pi^2 + 1} + \tfrac{1}{2}\ln(2\pi + \sqrt{4\pi^2 + 1})). \qquad \square$$

Spherical Coordinates

Consider, in space, a usual right-angled right-handed coordinate system XYZ with origin O. A point P is said to have the *spherical coordinates* (r,θ,ϕ) corresponding to the *origin O*, the *axis Z*, and the *plane ZX*, when the distance of the point from O is r, the angle from the Z-axis to the position vector **OP** is θ, and the angle from the X-axis to the projection of **OP** into the XY-plane, $\mathbf{OP}_1$, is ϕ (Fig. 3-44).

Requiring $r \geq 0$, $0 \leq \theta \leq \pi$, and $0 \leq \phi < 2\pi$, then each point with the exception of the points on the Z-axis has exactly one set of polar

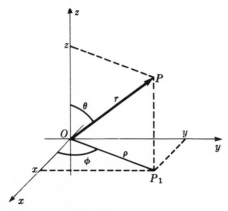

Figure 3-44

coordinates. Points on the Z-axis have an infinite number of sets of coordinates, as ϕ is indefinite in this case. At O, θ is also indefinite.

The relation between the usual coordinates (x,y,z) and the polar coordinates (r,θ,ϕ) of an arbitrary point in space is

$$x = r \sin \theta \cos \phi,$$
$$y = r \sin \theta \sin \phi,$$
$$z = r \cos \theta.$$

Cylindrical Coordinates

The *cylindrical coordinates* (ρ,ϕ,z) of a point P in space corresponding to the *origin O*, the *axis Z*, and the *plane XY* are obtained by giving the plane polar coordinates (ρ,ϕ) for the projection P_1 of the point into the XY-plane, together with the Z-coordinate, z, of the point P.

Also in this case points on the Z-axis will have an infinite number of sets of coordinates, even within the limits $\rho \geq 0$ and $0 < \phi < 2\pi$, as ϕ is indefinite.

The transformation formulas relating the usual coordinates (x,y,z) and the cylindrical coordinates (ρ,ϕ,z) of an arbitrary point in space are thus $x = \rho \cos \phi$, $y = \rho \sin \phi$, $z = z$.

Later, in connection with calculations of the so-called "space integrals," we shall make use of the important spacial coordinate systems we have introduced here.

Exercises

1. Sketch the curve $r = e^\theta$ $(0 \leq \theta \leq 2\pi)$. Find the length of the curve and the area of the region bounded by the curve and the polar axis.

*2. Sketch the curve $r = 2a(1 - \cos \theta)$, and find the area of the region bounded by the curve (a cardioid). A rectangle is circumscribed about the curve such that two of its sides are parallel to the polar axis. Find the area of this rectangle.

*3. Corresponding to given angles α, b, and c between 0 and π, consider the three points A, B, and C with spherical coordinates $(1,0,0)$, $(1,c,0)$, and $(1,b,\alpha)$. Prove the law of cosines for the spherical triangle ABC by evaluating the scalar product $\mathbf{OB} \cdot \mathbf{OC}$.

Answers

2. $6\pi a^2;\ \dfrac{27\sqrt{3}}{2}\,a^2$

3. $\mathbf{OB} \cdot \mathbf{OC} = (\sin c,\ 0,\ \cos c) \cdot (\sin b \cos \alpha,\ \sin b \sin \alpha,\ \cos b)$
   or
   $$\cos a = \sin b \sin c \cos \alpha + \cos b \cos c$$

3-16. COMPLEX-VALUED FUNCTIONS

Complex Numbers and Polar Coordinates

By introducing polar coordinates in the complex plane, the arbitrary complex number $a + ib$ can be represented by polar coordinates (r,v) of the point (a,b). These are called, respectively, the *modulus* (or the *absolute value*) and the *argument* of the complex number under consideration (see also p. 88). Then we have

$$A = a + ib = r \cos v + ir \sin v = r(\cos v + i \sin v),$$

where the last factor sometimes is called the *phase* of the complex number. It is, in contrast to the argument, uniquely determined (in the case $r \neq 0$).

Previously it was possible to give a simple geometric interpretation of the addition of complex numbers A_1 and A_2. This is now also possible for the case of multiplication, as the modulus and argument of the product is obtained as the product and sum of the moduli and arguments of the two factors, respectively:

$$A_1 A_2 = (r_1 \cos v_1 + ir_1 \sin v_1)(r_2 \cos v_2 + ir_2 \sin v_2)$$
$$= r_1 r_2 \cos (v_1 + v_2) + ir_1 r_2 \sin (v_1 + v_2).$$

The following inequalities are seen to hold for the absolute values of two complex numbers A_1 and A_2 (Fig. 3-45):

$$\left| |A_1| - |A_2| \right| \le \left| A_1 \pm A_2 \right| \le |A_1| + |A_2|,$$

$$|A_1 A_2| = |A_1| \, |A_2| \quad \text{and} \quad \left| \frac{A_1}{A_2} \right| = \frac{|A_1|}{|A_2|}.$$

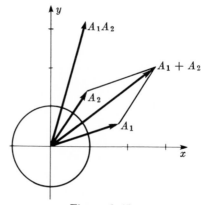

Figure 3-45

Complex-Valued Functions of One Complex Variable

A complex-valued function of one complex variable is a function for which the domain as well as the range is some set of complex numbers. Graphically such a function may be represented by a mapping of points in one complex plane onto points in another complex plane.

Example 3-49. The function

$$u + iv = \frac{1}{x + iy}\left(= \frac{x - iy}{x^2 + y^2}\right)$$

thus gives a mapping of the points in the complex XY-plane $((x,y) \neq (0,0))$ onto the points in the complex UV-plane $((u,v) \neq (0,0))$.

Here every so-called *generalized circle* (i.e., a circle or a straight line) is mapped onto a generalized circle.

For example, for the straight line $x = 2$, $y = t(-\infty < t < \infty)$, the following is obtained:

$$u = \frac{x}{x^2 + y^2} = \frac{2}{4 + t^2},$$

$$v = \frac{-y}{x^2 + y^2} = \frac{-t}{4 + t^2},$$

which on elimination of t becomes (Figs. 3-46 and 3-47)

$$(u - \tfrac{1}{4})^2 + v^2 = \tfrac{1}{16} \ ((u,v) \neq (0,0)). \qquad \square$$

In the theory of complex functions, notions such as the limit of a complex sequence, the limit of a complex function, continuity, and

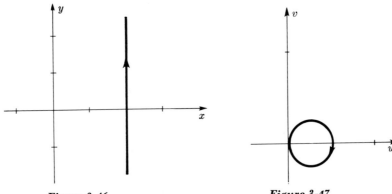

Figure 3-46   **Figure 3-47**

differentiability of a complex function are introduced as generalizations of the corresponding notions in the theory of real functions.

We shall, however, postpone a consideration of this wide subject to a later chapter, limiting ourselves here to a short discussion of certain problems in connection with the narrower notion of a *complex function of one real variable*. Such a function can always be written $F(x) = f_1(x) + if_2(x)$, where the independent real variable is x and the functions $f_1(x)$ and $f_2(x)$ are real functions with a common domain. The values of the function, when mapped into the complex plane, will then make up some curve which is identical with the graph of the two-dimensional vector function $\mathbf{r}(t) = (f_1(t), f_2(t))$.

Complex-Valued Functions of One Real Variable

For complex-valued functions of one real variable the notions of limit, continuity, definite integral, and differentiability are defined in a similar way to those for vector functions.

The condition that a complex function defined in a certain interval is *continuous* is then that both the real and the imaginary parts of the function are continuous.

The *definite integral* of the complex function $F(x) = f_1(x) + if_2(x)$ continuous in the interval $a \leq x \leq b$ is obtained as

$$\int_a^b F(x)\, dx = \int_a^b f_1(x)\, dx + i \int_a^b f_2(x)\, dx.$$

The condition that the function under consideration is *differentiable* is that both the real and the imaginary parts of the function are differentiable. The differential quotient is then

$$\frac{dF}{dx} = F'(x) = f_1'(x) + if_2'(x).$$

The sum, difference, product, and quotient of two continuous complex functions with a common domain are themselves new continuous complex functions with the usual exception of zeros in the denominator. When both of the given functions are differentiable, the resulting functions are also differentiable. This can be shown by the use of the corresponding rules for real functions.

The Complex Exponential Function

We have already defined e^a for any real number a. We now extend the definition to include *complex exponents* as follows:

$$e^{a+ib} = e^a(\cos b + i \sin b),$$

where a and b are arbitrary real numbers. For $b = 0$ this is seen to give simply $e^a = e^a$.

As an especially important example of a complex-valued function of one real variable we shall consider the *complex exponential function*

$$F(x) = e^{(a+ib)x} = e^{ax}(\cos bx + i \sin bx),$$

where a and b are arbitrary real numbers. This function is differentiable for all x with the differential quotient

$$F'(x) = (ae^{ax} \cos bx - be^{ax} \sin bx) + i(ae^{ax} \sin bx + be^{ax} \cos bx)$$
$$= (a + ib)e^{(a+ib)x}.$$

This is obtained formally in the same manner as when the coefficient of x is real. The function also satisfies the functional equation for the real exponential functions:

$$F(x_1)F(x_2) = e^{ax_1}(\cos bx_1 + i \sin bx_1)e^{ax_2}(\cos bx_2 + i \sin bx_2)$$
$$= e^{a(x_1+x_2)}(\cos b(x_1 + x_2) + i \sin b(x_1 + x_2))$$
$$= e^{(a+ib)(x_1+x_2)} = F(x_1 + x_2).$$

Important use will be made of this function in connection with the solution of certain simple differential equations.

From $e^{ix} = \cos x + i \sin x$ and $e^{-ix} = \cos x - i \sin x$, the so-called *Euler formulas* are obtained:

$$\cos x = \frac{e^{ix} + e^{-ix}}{2} \quad \text{and} \quad \sin x = \frac{e^{ix} - e^{-ix}}{2i}.$$

These show a further analogy between trigonometric and hyperbolic functions.

The Euler formulas can be used with advantage to rewrite expressions of the form $\cos^m x \sin^n x$, which may be of interest, for example, in connection with integrations of trigonometric function.

Example 3-50

$$\cos^4 x = \left(\frac{e^{ix} + e^{-ix}}{2}\right)^4 = \frac{e^{4ix} + 4e^{2ix} + 6 + 4e^{-2ix} + e^{-4ix}}{16}$$
$$= \tfrac{1}{8} \cos 4x + \tfrac{1}{2} \cos 2x + \tfrac{3}{8}. \qquad \square$$

Exercises

1. The equation $u + iv = (x + iy)^2$ defines a mapping of the complex XY-plane into the complex UV-plane. Determine the image of the straight line $(x,y) = (1,t)$.

*2. Defining cosine of z, where z is in arbitary complex number, as

$$\cos z = \frac{e^{iz} + e^{-iz}}{2},$$

solve the equations:

(a) $\cos z = 2.6$.

(b) $\cos z = 2.4i$.

3. Prove the following formula:

$$\tfrac{1}{2} + \cos x + \cos 2x + \cdots + \cos nx = \frac{\sin (n + \tfrac{1}{2})x}{2 \sin (x/2)} \qquad (x \neq 2p\pi).$$

Answer

2. (a) $z = \pm i \ln 5 + 2p\pi$. (b) $z = \pm \left(\dfrac{3\pi}{2} + i \ln 5 \right) + 2p\pi$.

4

Functions of Several Variables

4-1. REAL-VALUED FUNCTIONS OF SEVERAL REAL VARIABLES

Let f be a function from a set of ordered pairs of real numbers to a set of real numbers; then f is said to be a *real-valued function of two real variables*, or, briefly, a *real function of two variables*. The value that f assumes at the argument (x,y) is naturally written $f(x,y)$. Often this value is also called z. We then have $z = f(x,y)$, where x and y are the *independent variables* and z the *dependent variable*.

Corresponding to what was the case for functions of one variable, we shall often represent a function of two variables by an equation such as $z = f(x,y)$. We may then speak of "the function $z = f(x,y)$" or even "the function $f(x,y)$." In these cases—unless otherwise stated—the domain of f is thought of as the most extensive set of ordered pairs (x,y) for which the expression $f(x,y)$ has a meaning. Occasionally we shall write "$z = z(x,y)$," which means that we are considering some function of two variables where the independent variables are x and y and the dependent variable is z.

To obtain a graphical representation of such a function f, we introduce a (usual right-angled right-handed) coordinate system XYZ. By the *graph* of f we then mean the set of all points P in space with coordinates (x,y,z) such that $z = f(x,y)$. This is quite natural considering our previous definition of the graph of an equation $F(x,y,z) = 0$ in three real unknowns (p. 18).

While the graph of a real function of one variable usually is a curve, it turns out that the graph of a real function of two variables usually will be a *surface*. In many situations such a surface may be of great help, illustrating important properties of the function considered.

In some cases, however, a better general view will be obtained on sketching some *level curves* of the function. These are graphs in a coordinate system XY of equations of the form $f(x,y) = c$, where c is a constant belonging to the range of f. A level curve may thus be considered as the projection into the XY-plane of the curve of intersection of the surface $z = f(x,y)$ and a plane parallel to the XY-plane (a "horizontal" plane).

Let A be the domain of the function $z = f(x,y)$. The *graph* of A is then also a set of points, the projection of the graph of f into the XY-plane. In view of this, the following geometric terminology will appear quite natural—whether a graphical representation is thought of or not.

An arbitrary ordered pair of real numbers will also be called a *point*. The δ-*neighborhood* of the point (x_0,y_0), where δ is a positive real number, is the set of all points inside the circle having center (x_0,y_0) and radius δ, i.e., the set of all points (x,y) such that $(x - x_0)^2 + (y - y_0)^2 < \delta^2$. The *deleted* δ-*neighborhood* of (x_0,y_0) is correspondingly the set of all points (x,y) such that $0 < (x - x_0)^2 + (y - y_0)^2 < \delta^2$.

Now let M be an arbitrary set of ordered pairs of real numbers. The point $P_0 = (x_0,y_0)$ is then said to be an *interior point* of M, if there exists a neighborhood of P_0 the whole of which belongs to M. If, on the other hand, there exists a neighborhood of P_0 the whole of which does not belong to M, then P_0 is said to be an *exterior point* of M. The point P_0 is a *boundary point* of M in case it is neither an interior point nor an exterior point.

M is said to be an *open set* if all the points of M are interior points, while M is said to be a *closed set* in case all the boundary points of M belong to M. The set M will be called *connected* if any two points belonging to M can be connected by a broken line the whole of which belongs to M. M is *bounded* in case the whole set can be enclosed in a circle of sufficiently large radius.

Corresponding to an open interval in the one-dimensional case, we now define an *open region* as an open connected set of points. Adding to su $^{-\mathsf{L}}$ an open region some or all of its boundary points we obtain what v ` be called a *region*. This need not be connected. Finally, a *closed r. ion* is obtained if all the boundary points of the open region are added and if the set is bounded. This concept may then be considered as corresponding to the concept of a closed interval in the one-dimensional case.

Limits

A *point sequence* $(x_1,y_1),(x_2,y_2),. . .,(x_n,y_n),. . .$ or $P_1,P_2,. . .,P_n,. . .$ is said to be *convergent* with the *limit* $(x_0,y_0) = P_0$ [$(x_n,y_n) \rightarrow (x_0,y_0)$ as $n \rightarrow \infty$ or $P_n \rightarrow P_0$ as $n \rightarrow \infty$] if the corresponding sequence of position vectors $OP_1, OP_2,. . .,OP_n,. . .$ has the vector OP_0 as its limit (cf. p. 206). Using this notion we are now also able to define the fundamental concepts of limit and continuity for functions of two variables.

The function $f(x,y) = f(P)$ is said to have the *limit* c at the point $(x_0,y_0) = P_0$ [$f(x,y) \rightarrow c$ as $(x,y) \rightarrow (x_0,y_0)$, or $f(P) \rightarrow c$ as $P \rightarrow P_0$] when for any point sequence which is within the domain of f and does not contain P_0, but converges to P_0, it is true that the corresponding sequence of f-values converges to c.

Here the function f does not need to be defined at P_0. If the domain of f contains a neighborhood of P_0, then there will be many possibilities for the choice of a converging point sequence. These possibilities are somewhat limited if this is not the case. The only condition that will be placed on the domain of the function is that any deleted neighborhood of P_0 shall contain at least one element of the domain.

Correspondingly, the statement $f(P) \rightarrow \infty (-\infty)$ as $P \rightarrow P_0$ means that the sequences of f-values considered above all tend to $\infty (-\infty)$.

Equivalent to the above definition of a limit of a function of two variables is the following, which does not make use of the notion of point sequences: $f(P) \rightarrow c$ as $P \rightarrow P_0$, when for any $\epsilon > 0$ it is possible to determine a $\delta > 0$ such that $|f(P) - c| < \epsilon$ for every point P which at the same time belongs to the domain of f and the deleted δ-neighborhood of P_0. Geometrically this means that the graph of f corresponding to points in the XY-plane inside the circle with center P_0 and

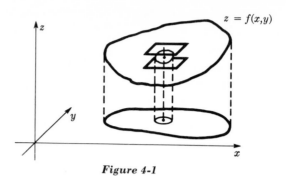

$z = f(x,y)$

Figure 4-1

radius δ altogether lies between the two planes $z = c - \epsilon$ and $z = c + \epsilon$ (Fig. 4-1).

The usual four basic rules are easily seen to be valid also for limits of real functions of two variables (cf. p. 136).

Continuity

The function f is said to be *continuous* at the point P_0 if it has a limit at P_0 which is equal to the value $f(P_0)$ of the function at this point. It is not required that the domain of f contains a neighborhood of P_0, but naturally the point itself must belong to the domain.

For functions of two variables, continuous at some point P_0, as seen previously in the one-dimensional case, it is true that addition, subtraction, multiplication, and division produce new functions which are also continuous at this point (if only the domains of the resulting functions satisfy the above-mentioned conditions). Particularly it should be noted that every polynomial and every rational function of two variables will be continuous in all of its domain.

For a function of two variables defined and continuous in a closed region it can be shown that the range of the function is a closed interval. Such a function thus has an absolute maximum value and an absolute minimum value (cf. p. 137).

Example 4-1. An especially simple example of a real function of two variables is the *linear function* $z = ax + by + c$, where a, b, and c are given constants. This function is continuous in the open region consisting of the whole XY-plane. As previously mentioned (p. 18), its graph is the plane which contains the point $(0,0,c)$ and has $(a,b,-1)$ as a normal vector. If we assume $(a,b) \neq (0,0)$, then the plane is not parallel to the XY-plane. The level curves of this surface will then be mutually parallel straight lines. The absolute maximum and minimum values of the function in the closed region $x^2 + y^2 \leq R^2$ are then both assumed only at the boundary: $(x,y) = (R \cos t,\ R \sin t)$ $(0 \leq t < 2\pi)$ (Fig. 4-2). Expressed with the parameter t, the values of the function at the boundary are determined by a function of one variable, $\phi(t) = aR \cos t + bR \sin t + c$. The values of t corresponding to the extreme values can be obtained as solutions to the equation $\phi'(t) = -aR \sin t + bR \cos t = 0$.

In the open region $x^2 + y^2 < R^2$, the function has no extreme values. □

The ideas presented above are immediately extended to *real-valued functions of several real variables*.

The domain of such a function of N variables, $u = f(x_1,x_2,. . .,x_N)$, or $u = f(P)$, is a set of points in N-dimensional space, while its range is a set of real numbers. For $N = 3$, the domain of f can be mapped into a spacial coordinate system, but there will no longer be room for the values of the function. For $N > 3$, not even the domain can be mapped into the spacial coordinate system.

Exercises

1. Consider the function $f(x,y) = x^2 - y^2$.
   (a) Sketch its graph in a coordinate system XYZ.
   (b) Sketch some level curves belonging to the function.
   (c) Explain how the surface considered may be obtained by the translation of one parabola in such a way that its vertex moves along another parabola.

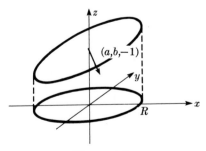

Figure 4-2

*2. Find an equation for the surface which is obtained by the translation of the parabola $x = y^2$, $z = 0$, when its vertex moves along the curve $z = x + \sin x$, $y = 0$.

*3. Find the absolute maximum value of the function $z = 3x + 2y - 1$ having the closed region bounded by the curve $(x,y) = (\cos t, 2 \sin t)$ $(0 \leq t < 2\pi)$ as its domain.

Answers

2. $z = x - y^2 + \sin (x - y^2)$.
3. 4.

4-2. DIFFERENTIABLE FUNCTIONS OF SEVERAL REAL VARIABLES

Partial Derivatives

In the following it will be assumed, unless otherwise stated, that the functions considered are real functions of two variables defined in some open region.

Our first task will be to define the notion of differentiability of a function $z = f(x,y)$ at a point (x_0,y_0) belonging to the domain of the function. In analogy with the one-dimensional case, it will be a question of imposing conditions on the increment of the function in addition to the conditions for continuity.

As a neighboring point to (x_0,y_0) in the domain of f we choose $(x_0 + h, y_0 + k)$. We shall then consider the corresponding increment of the function:

$$\Delta z = f(x_0 + h, y_0 + k) - f(x_0,y_0).$$

The existence of two independent variables allows greater freedom in the choice of a neighboring point. We shall now first consider a special case and set k equal to 0.

We then obtain a function of the one variable x, $z = f(x,y_0)$. The corresponding difference quotient can be written $\Delta z/h$ and its behavior as $h \to 0$ can be investigated in the usual manner. If a limit arises, this is called the *partial derivative (partial differential quotient)* of f *with respect to* x at the point (x_0,y_0). It is written $\partial z/\partial x$ (or $\partial f/\partial x$), or $f_x'(x_0,y_0)$:

$$\frac{\Delta z}{h} = \frac{f(x_0 + h, y_0) - f(x_0,y_0)}{h} \to \frac{\partial z}{\partial x} = f_x'(x_0,y_0) \qquad \text{as } h \to 0.$$

The quantity obtained is seen to give the slope of the tangent at the

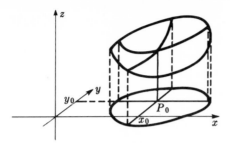

Figure 4-3

point x_0 for the curve of intersection of the surface $z = f(x,y)$ and the plane $y = y_0$ (Fig. 4-3).

Analogously, the increment of the function can be investigated for $h = 0$. In this way the existence of a *partial derivative with respect to y* may be established:

$$\frac{\Delta z}{k} = \frac{f(x_0, y_0 + k) - f(x_0,y_0)}{k} \rightarrow \frac{\partial z}{\partial y} = f_y'(x_0,y_0) \qquad \text{as } k \rightarrow 0.$$

This quantity is then the slope of the tangent at the point y_0 for the curve of intersection of the given surface and the plane $x = x_0$.

Differentiability

The two partial derivatives will in general not be equal, even for very simple functions. A condition that the limit of the difference quotient of the function at the point considered be independent of the direction of approach to this point would thus be unnecessarily strong, even if, as above, only neighboring points in the directions of the axes were taken into consideration.

In closer analogy to the previously mentioned second formulation of the definition of differentiability for a function of one variable, we consider instead the increment Δz and define that the function $z = f(x,y)$ is to be called *differentiable* at the point (x_0,y_0), if this increment can be written

$$\Delta z = f(x_0 + h, y_0 + k) - f(x_0,y_0) = ah + bk + o(\rho).$$

Here a and b are constants, $\rho = \sqrt{h^2 + k^2}$ is the distance between the point (x_0,y_0), and the neighboring point $(x_0 + h, y_0 + k)$ and $o(\rho)$ is a function of h and k such that $o(\rho)/\rho \rightarrow 0$ as $(h,k) \rightarrow (0,0)$.

By specially choosing $k = 0$, we obtain $\Delta z = ah + o(h)$, or $\Delta z/h = a + [o(h)/h] \to a$ as $h \to 0$. From this it follows that the differentiable function has a partial derivative with respect to x at the point considered, and that this is equal to a. Analogously it is seen (by choosing $h = 0$) that the partial derivative with respect to y also exists at the point and is equal to b. We then have

$$\Delta z = \frac{\partial z}{\partial x} h + \frac{\partial z}{\partial y} k + o(\rho) = dz + o(\rho),$$

where the quantity

$$dz = \frac{\partial z}{\partial x} h + \frac{\partial z}{\partial y} k$$

is called *the (total) differential* of the function at the point considered corresponding to the increments h and k of the independent variables x and y.

A Sufficient Condition for Differentiability

The existence of partial derivatives of a function with respect to the two independent variables at a given point is thus a necessary condition for the differentiability of the function at this point. To show that this condition is not sufficient, the following function may be considered:

$$z = \begin{cases} 1 & \text{for } xy \neq 0, \\ 0 & \text{for } xy = 0. \end{cases}$$

This has partial derivatives (both equal to 0) at the point (0,0), but it is not continuous here. It is therefore not differentiable, since continuity is a necessary condition for differentiability:

$$\Delta z = ah + bk + o(\rho) \to 0 \qquad \text{as } (h,k) \to (0,0).$$

It can be shown, however, that a function of two variables is differentiable at a point when it has partial derivatives not only at the point itself but also in a neighborhood of the point, and when these are continuous at the point itself.

This means that the majority of the functions arising in applications are differentiable at every point of their domains with the exception, perhaps, of a limited number of points.

Example 4-2

$$z = f(x,y) = 3x^2y + \frac{x}{y} \quad (y \neq 0),$$

$$\Delta z = f(x_0 + h, y_0 + k) - f(x_0,y_0) = \left[3(x_0 + h)^2(y_0 + k) + \frac{x_0 + h}{y_0 + k} \right.$$
$$\left. - \left(3x_0^2 y_0 + \frac{x_0}{y_0} \right) \right]$$

$$= 6x_0 y_0 h + 3y_0 h^2 + 3x_0^2 k + 6x_0 h k + 3h^2 k + \frac{y_0 h - x_0 k}{y_0^2}$$
$$+ \frac{x_0 y_0 k^2 - y_0^2 h k}{y_0^3(y_0 + k)}$$

$$= \left(6x_0 y_0 + \frac{1}{y_0} \right) h + \left(3x_0^2 - \frac{x_0}{y_0^2} \right) k + \left(3y_0 h^2 + 6x_0 h k + 3h^2 k \right.$$
$$\left. + \frac{x_0 k^2 - y_0 h k}{y_0^2(y_0 + k)} \right)$$

$$= ah + bk + o(\rho).$$

As the last term really has the required property of being $o(\rho)$, the given function is seen to be differentiable in the whole of its domain. In this case we have been able to show the differentiability of the function directly from the definition. In agreement with theory we have that

$$a = f'_x(x_0,y_0) \quad \text{and} \quad b = f'_y(x_0,y_0). \quad \square$$

The Total Differential

Let the function $z = f(x,y)$ be differentiable at the point (x_0,y_0). The following is then valid:

$$\Delta z = f(x_0 + h, y_0 + k) - f(x_0,y_0) = ah + bk + o(\rho),$$

or, when we introduce $x_0 + h = x$ and $y_0 + k = y$,

$$z - z_0 = f(x,y) - f(x_0,y_0,) = a(x - x_0) + b(y - y_0) + o(\rho),$$
$$\rho = \sqrt{(x - x_0)^2 + (y - y_0)^2}.$$

While the increment $f(x,y) - f(x_0,y_0)$ itself may depend in a very complicated way on x and y, the differentiability expresses that as an approximation we can replace the increment by the very simple (linear) function $a(x - x_0) + b(y - y_0)$, i.e., the differential dz. The error thus introduced is $o(\rho)$, which is vanishing of a higher order than the linear expression, or in general small in comparison with this.

Whether such an approximation is sufficient will depend on the application. Later, in connection with the determination of extreme values of functions of two variables, we shall meet a case where the approximation is not good enough. When in the following we speak—less rigorously—about *"sufficient approximation,"* it will always indicate an approximation which in the limit can be shown to have no consequences, i.e., an approximation such that the results obtained by the subsequent limiting process are exactly valid.

Geometrically the above approximation means that the given surface $z = f(x,y)$ is replaced by the plane $z - z_0 = a(x - x_0) + b(y - y_0)$, which is called the *tangent plane* to the surface at the point $P_0(x_0,y_0,z_0)$ (see also p. 237). A normal vector to the surface (i.e., to its tangent plane) at the point P_0 is therefore

$$(a,b,-1) = (f'_x(x_0,y_0),f'_y(x_0,y_0),-1).$$

Let us now consider the special case of the simple function of two variables, $z = f_1(x,y) = x$. For this we have

$$\Delta z = f_1(x_0 + h, \, y_0 + k) - f_1(x_0,y_0) = (x_0 + h) - x_0$$
$$= 1 \cdot h + 0 \cdot k + 0.$$

Thus $dz = dx = h$. Correspondingly, for the function $z = f_2(x,y) = y$ we obtain $dz = dy = k$. For the arbitrary function $z = f(x,y)$, differentiable at the point (x_0,y_0), we finally have

$$dz = \frac{\partial z}{\partial x} h + \frac{\partial z}{\partial y} k.$$

Let us then consider the two functions $z = x$ and $z = y$ together with the function $z = f(x,y)$. When in all three cases we allow x_0 and y_0 equally great increments, h and k, respectively, then on introducing $h = dx$ and $k = dy$, the following expression for the differential of f at the point (x_0,y_0) is found:

$$dz = \frac{\partial z}{\partial x} dx + \frac{\partial z}{\partial y} dy \quad \text{or} \quad df = \frac{\partial f}{\partial x} dx + \frac{\partial f}{\partial y} dy.$$

This is the form in which the differential usually appears. The expression is of course exactly valid, as it is a consequence only of suitable definitions. The question of approximation will first arise when the differential is taken as the increment Δz of the function itself, since then we neglect the quantity $o(\rho)$.

Generalization to Several Variables

The ideas introduced above are easily extended to functions of several variables. Consider a function of N variables $u = f(x_1, x_2, \ldots, x_N)$. This is said to be *differentiable* at the point $P_0 = (x_1^{(0)}, x_2^{(0)}, \ldots, x_N^{(0)})$ in the N-dimensional space if the increment Δu of the function corresponding to increments $h_1, h_2, \ldots, h_N$ of the independent variables $x_1, x_2, \ldots, x_N$, respectively, can be written in the form

$$\Delta u = f(x_1^{(0)} + h_1, x_2^{(0)} + h_2, \ldots, x_N^{(0)} + h_N) - f(x_1^{(0)}, x_2^{(0)}, \ldots, x_N^{(0)})$$
$$= a_1 h_1 + a_2 h_2 + \cdots + a_N h_N + o(\rho) = du + o(\rho).$$

Here the a's are constants, $\rho = \sqrt{h_1{}^2 + h_2{}^2 + \cdots + h_N{}^2}$, and $o(\rho)$ is a function of the h's such that $o(\rho)/\rho \to 0$ as $(h_1, h_2, \ldots, h_N) \to (0, 0, \ldots, 0)$, while du as defined by the equation is the *(total) differential* of f at P_0 corresponding to the increments considered.

A necessary condition for the differentiability is that the N partial derivatives $\partial u / \partial x_i$ exist at the point. These are defined as follows:

$$\frac{\partial u}{\partial x_i} = \lim_{h_i \to 0} \frac{f(x_1^{(0)}, \ldots, x_i^{(0)} + h_i, \ldots, x_N^{(0)}) - f(x_1^{(0)}, \ldots, x_i^{(0)}, \ldots, x_N^{(0)})}{h_i}.$$

A sufficient condition for the differentiability is that the partial derivatives exist in a neighborhood of the point and are continuous at the point itself.

The following expression is then obtained for the differential du:

$$du = \frac{\partial u}{\partial x_1} dx_1 + \frac{\partial u}{\partial x_2} dx_2 + \cdots + \frac{\partial u}{\partial x_N} dx_N.$$

Composite Functions

Suppose we have q real-valued functions, $u_1 = g_1(P)$, $u_2 = g_2(P)$, $\ldots, u_q = g_q(P)$, defined in a common open region A of the N-dimensional space. We can then define a new function g, also with domain A, as follows: $g(P) = (g_1(P), g_2(P), \ldots, g_q(P))$. The values of g are thus points in the q-dimensional space. Suppose furthermore that we have a real-valued function f defined in an open region of the q-dimensional space and such that this domain includes the range of g: $v = f(u_1, u_2, \ldots, u_q)$, or $v = f(Q)$.

On these conditions the *composite function* $f \circ g$ exists. It has A as its domain and its values are real numbers. It may be written $v = f(g(P))$, or, introducing $P = (x_1, x_2, \ldots, x_N)$, as

$$v = f(g_1(x_1, x_2, \ldots, x_N), g_2(x_1, x_2, \ldots, x_N), \ldots, g_q(x_1, x_2, \ldots, x_N)).$$

Let us now consider a point $P_0 = (x_1^{(0)}, x_2^{(0)}, \ldots, x_N^{(0)})$ in A and let Q_0 be the value of g at this point:

$$Q_0 = g(P_0) = (g_1(P_0), g_2(P_0), \ldots, g_q(P_0)).$$

If all the functions g_i are continuous at P_0 and the function f is continuous at Q_0, it follows easily from the definition of continuity that the composite function $f \circ g$ is also continuous at P_0. Correspondingly, it can be shown that the differentiability of the given functions g_i and f at P_0 and Q_0, respectively, implies that the composite function $f \circ g$ will be differentiable at P_0.

In this connection the so-called *chain rule* is often of great interest. This rule gives the partial derivatives of the composite function in terms of the partial derivatives of the originally given functions. It can be looked upon as a generalization of the previously mentioned chain rule for functions of one variable (see p. 150).

For the differentials of the given functions we have

$$du_1 = \frac{\partial u_1}{\partial x_1} dx_1 + \cdots + \frac{\partial u_1}{\partial x_N} dx_N;$$

$$\vdots$$

$$du_q = \frac{\partial u_q}{\partial x_1} dx_1 + \cdots + \frac{\partial u_q}{\partial x_N} dx_N,$$

$$dv = \frac{\partial v}{\partial u_1} du_1 + \cdots + \frac{\partial v}{\partial u_q} du_q.$$

On substituting in the last expression, we obtain

$$dv = \frac{\partial v}{\partial u_1} \left(\frac{\partial u_1}{\partial x_1} dx_1 + \cdots + \frac{\partial u_1}{\partial x_N} dx_N \right)$$

$$+ \cdots + \frac{\partial v}{\partial u_q} \left(\frac{\partial u_q}{\partial x_1} dx_1 + \cdots + \frac{\partial u_q}{\partial x_N} dx_N \right)$$

$$= \left(\frac{\partial v}{\partial u_1} \frac{\partial u_1}{\partial x_1} + \cdots + \frac{\partial v}{\partial u_q} \frac{\partial u_q}{\partial x_1} \right) dx_1 + \cdots$$

$$+ \left(\frac{\partial v}{\partial u_1} \frac{\partial u_1}{\partial x_N} + \cdots + \frac{\partial v}{\partial u_q} \frac{\partial u_q}{\partial x_N} \right) dx_N.$$

The following is, however, also valid for the differential of the composite function:

$$dv = \frac{\partial v}{\partial x_1} dx_1 + \cdots + \frac{\partial v}{\partial x_N} dx_N.$$

From this we finally obtain the chain rule:

$$\frac{\partial v}{\partial x_1} = \frac{\partial v}{\partial u_1}\frac{\partial u_1}{\partial x_1} + \cdots + \frac{\partial v}{\partial u_q}\frac{\partial u_q}{\partial x_1},$$

.

.

.

$$\frac{\partial v}{\partial x_N} = \frac{\partial v}{\partial u_1}\frac{\partial u_1}{\partial x_N} + \cdots + \frac{\partial v}{\partial u_q}\frac{\partial u_q}{\partial x_N}.$$

The partial derivatives of the composite function are here said to be determined by *differentiation through* the q *auxiliary variables*.

However, it should be noted that the formal substitutions used above strictly speaking do not give any proof, either for the differentiability of the composite function or for the chain rule. To carry out such a proof it would be necessary to consider the (finite) increments $\Delta u_1, \Delta u_2, \ldots, \Delta u_q$ and Δv corresponding to the (finite) increments $h_1, h_2, \ldots, h_N$ of the independent variables $x_1, x_2, \ldots, x_N$ and then to perform the calculations with the o-terms. We shall not go into these details here, however.

Directional Derivatives

For the case $N = 1$ we obtain

$$\frac{dv}{dx} = \frac{\partial v}{\partial u_1}\frac{du_1}{dx} + \frac{\partial v}{\partial u_2}\frac{du_2}{dx} + \cdots + \frac{\partial v}{\partial u_q}\frac{du_q}{dx},$$

where the derivatives with respect to x naturally should be written with the usual d's.

It is now possible to give a further basis for the previously introduced names: tangent plane and normal vector to the surface $z = f(x,y)$ at the point $(x_0, y_0, f(x_0, y_0))$ (see p. 234).

Let $(x,y) = (\phi(t), \psi(t))$ be a parametric equation for an arbitrary differentiable curve in the XY-plane which for $t = t_0$ passes through the point (x_0, y_0). Corresponding to this curve in the XY-plane there is on the surface a curve $\mathbf{r}(t) = (\phi(t), \psi(t), f(\phi(t), \psi(t)))$, which at the point P_0 has a tangent vector $\mathbf{r}'(t_0) = (\phi'(t_0), \psi'(t_0), f'_x(x_0, y_0)\phi'(t_0) + f'_y(x_0, y_0)\psi'(t_0))$, which is different from the zero vector.

By considering a scalar product, this vector is seen to be perpendicular to what we have called a normal vector to the surface at P_0. Thus the considered spacial curve, which is contained in the surface and which passes through the point P_0, has its tangent at this point lying in the tangent plane of the surface.

Example 4-3

$$z = f(x,y), \quad \left. \begin{array}{l} x = x_0 + \alpha t \\ y = y_0 + \beta t \end{array} \right\} \alpha^2 + \beta^2 = 1,$$

$$\frac{df}{dt} = \frac{\partial f}{\partial x}\frac{dx}{dt} + \frac{\partial f}{\partial y}\frac{dy}{dt} = \frac{\partial f}{\partial x}\alpha + \frac{\partial f}{\partial y}\beta.$$

As (α,β) is a unit vector on the given line in the XY-plane, then t is the distance from the point (x_0,y_0) to the point (x,y) on the line. As a result of this, df/dt is called the *directional derivative* of the function f in the direction (α,β) at the point considered. The directional derivative appears as the scalar product of the two vectors $(\partial f/\partial x, \partial f/\partial y)$ and (α,β) (Fig. 4-4). The function $z = f(x,y)$ thus increases at its fastest in a direction given by the partial derivatives. This is also intuitively clear, as a normal vector to the surface at the point $(x_0,y_0,f(x_0,y_0))$ is $(\partial f/\partial x, \partial f/\partial y, -1)$. □

Homogeneous Function

A function of several variables $f(x_1,x_2,\ldots,x_N)$ is said to be *homogeneous of the pth degree* when it satisfies the functional equation $f(\lambda x_1,\lambda x_2,\ldots,\lambda x_N) = \lambda^p f(x_1,x_2,\ldots,x_N)$.

Suppose f is differentiable. On differentiation of the above equation with respect to λ the following is obtained:

$$\sum_{i=1}^{N} \frac{\partial f(\lambda x_1,\lambda x_2,\ldots,\lambda x_N)}{\partial(\lambda x_i)} \frac{d(\lambda x_i)}{d\lambda} = p\lambda^{p-1}f(x_1,x_2,\ldots,x_N),$$

or

$$\sum_{i=1}^{N} \frac{\partial f(\lambda x_1,\lambda x_2,\ldots,\lambda x_N)}{\partial(\lambda x_i)} x_i = p\lambda^{p-1}f(x_1,x_2,\ldots,x_N).$$

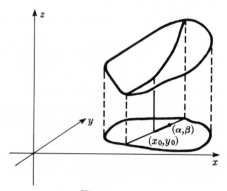

Figure 4-4

On making the special substitution $\lambda = 1$, the so-called *Euler's theorem* on homogeneous functions is obtained:

$$\sum_{i=1}^{N} x_i \frac{\partial f(x_1, x_2, \ldots, x_N)}{\partial x_i} = pf(x_1, x_2, \ldots, x_N).$$

When the differential of a function of several variables is known and, furthermore, the function is known to be homogeneous of the pth degree, then from Euler's theorem an explicit expression for the function can be obtained immediately. In the case when $N = 2$ and the differential

$$df(x,y) = \frac{\partial f}{\partial x}\, dx + \frac{\partial f}{\partial y}\, dy$$

is known, we have simply

$$f(x,y) = \frac{1}{p}\left(\frac{\partial f}{\partial x}\, x + \frac{\partial f}{\partial y}\, y\right).$$

Leibniz' Rule

For the evaluation of definite integrals the so-called *Leibniz' rule* often proves of great value. According to this we have

$$\frac{d}{dy}\int_a^b f(x,y)\, dx = \int_a^b \frac{\partial}{\partial y} f(x,y)\, dx \qquad (y_1 < y < y_2)$$

if the two real functions $f(x,y)$ and $f'_y(x,y)$ are continuous in the closed region $a \le x \le b$, $y_1 \le y \le y_2$. The above formula is also valid for improper integrals (for example, for "$b = \infty$") in case $f(x,y)$ and $f'_y(x,y)$ are continuous in the corresponding region (for example, $a \le x < \infty$, $y_1 \le y \le y_2$) and certain extra conditions as to the convergence of the integral on the right side (uniform convergence) are fulfilled.

As an example we consider the definite integral $\int_0^\infty e^{-x^2}\, dx$, which later (p. 277) will be proved to be $\frac{1}{2}\sqrt{\pi}$. Introducing $x = \sqrt{a}\cdot y$ we have

$$\sqrt{a}\int_0^\infty e^{-ay^2}\, dy = \frac{1}{2}\sqrt{\pi} \qquad \text{or} \qquad \int_0^\infty e^{-ay^2}\, dy = \frac{1}{2}\sqrt{\frac{\pi}{a}}.$$

Differentiation on both sides with respect to a and use of Leibniz' rule then gives

$$\int_0^\infty -y^2 e^{-ay^2}\, dy = -\frac{1}{4}\frac{\sqrt{\pi}}{a\sqrt{a}} \qquad \text{or} \qquad \int_0^\infty x^2 e^{-ax^2}\, dx = \frac{\sqrt{\pi}}{4a\sqrt{a}}.$$

By continued differentiation with respect to a, obviously any integral of the form $\int_0^\infty x^{2n} e^{-ax^2}\, dx$ can be evaluated.

Exercises

1. Consider the function $z = x^2 + 2y^2$. Find dz and Δz at the point $(x,y) = (3,4)$ corresponding to increments h and k of the independent variables x and y. Using the results obtained, show that $\Delta z = dz + o(\sqrt{h^2 + k^2})$ at the point considered.

*2. Find all functions $z = z(x,y)$ $(y > 0)$ satisfying the equations

$$\frac{\partial z}{\partial x} = 3y^2 + \frac{3x^2}{y} + 2, \qquad \frac{\partial z}{\partial y} = 6xy - \frac{x^3}{y^2} - 2y.$$

3. Find $\partial v/\partial x_1$ and $\partial v/\partial x_2$ when

$$v = u_1^2 + 3u_1 u_2 + 4u_2^2$$

and

$$u_1 = 2 - 2x_1 x_2^2, \qquad u_2 = 1 + x_1 x_2^2$$

by means of (a) the chain rule, and (b) substitution of u_1 and u_2 in v.

*4. In a solution, the concentration c of component A is determined by the function $c = F(x,y,z)$. For an arbitrary point P, find the direction in which there is the greatest increase in concentration.

Answers

2. $z = 3xy^2 + \dfrac{x^3}{y} - y^2 + 2x + C.$

4. $(F'_x(P), F'_y(P), F'_z(P)).$

4-3. TAYLOR'S FORMULA

Partial Derivatives of Higher Order

We have seen above how the differentiability of a function of two variables at a given point means that the values of the function at neighboring points can be expressed with a certain approximation by the value of the function and its two partial derivatives at the given point itself. Below, in close analogy to the one-dimensional case, a better approximation will be derived by means of what will be called *Taylor's formula for real functions of two variables.*

Suppose the function $z = f(x,y)$ has partial derivatives with respect to both x and y in an open region of the XY-plane. Then two new functions of two variables can be obtained by differentiation:

$$\frac{\partial z}{\partial x} = f'_x(x,y) \qquad \text{and} \qquad \frac{\partial z}{\partial y} = f'_y(x,y).$$

If these also have partial derivatives in the region considered, another four new functions can be obtained. These are the *partial derivatives of the second order:*

$$\frac{\partial}{\partial x}\left(\frac{\partial z}{\partial x}\right) = \frac{\partial^2 z}{\partial x^2} = f''_{x^2}(x,y), \qquad \frac{\partial}{\partial y}\left(\frac{\partial z}{\partial x}\right) = \frac{\partial^2 z}{\partial x\,\partial y} = f''_{xy}(x,y),$$

$$\frac{\partial}{\partial x}\left(\frac{\partial z}{\partial y}\right) = \frac{\partial^2 z}{\partial y\,\partial x} = f''_{yx}(x,y), \qquad \frac{\partial}{\partial y}\left(\frac{\partial z}{\partial y}\right) = \frac{\partial^2 z}{\partial y^2} = f''_{y^2}(x,y).$$

The partial derivatives of higher order are defined in an analogous manner. Thus there will be in all 2^n partial derivatives of the nth order. However, if all the partial derivatives of the different orders are continuous in the open region considered, then it can be shown that the *order of differentiation* is immaterial, so that among the partial derivatives of the nth order there will be, at most, $(n + 1)$ different functions:

$$\frac{\partial^n z}{\partial x^n} = f^{(n)}_{x^n}(x,y), \qquad \frac{\partial^n z}{\partial x^{n-1}\,\partial y} = f^{(n)}_{x^{n-1}y}(x,y),$$

$$\frac{\partial^n z}{\partial x^{n-2} y^2} = f^{(n)}_{x^{n-2}y^2}(x,y), \dots , \frac{\partial^n z}{\partial y^n} = f^{(n)}_{y^n}(x,y).$$

Example 4-4

$f(x,y) = x^y \qquad (x > 0),$

$\quad f'_x = yx^{y-1}, \qquad f'_y = x^y \ln x,$

$\quad f''_{x^2} = y(y - 1)x^{y-2}, \qquad f''_{xy} = x^{y-1} + yx^{y-1} \ln x,$

$$f''_{yx} = yx^{y-1} \ln x + x^y \frac{1}{x}, \qquad f''_{y^2} = x^y(\ln x)^2,$$

$f'''_{x^3} = y(y - 1)(y - 2)x^{y-3},$

$$f'''_{x^2y} = (y - 1)x^{y-2} + yx^{y-2} + y(y - 1)x^{y-2} \ln x,$$

$f'''_{xyx} = (y - 1)x^{y-2} + y(y - 1)x^{y-2} \ln x + yx^{y-1} \frac{1}{x}, \qquad \text{etc.} \qquad \square$

Taylor's Formula for Functions of Two Variables

Suppose the function $z = f(x,y)$ has continuous partial derivatives of the nth order in an open region ω of the XY-plane.   Let (x_0,y_0) be a point within this, and let $(x_0 + h,\ y_0 + k)$ be a neighboring point, which, together with the line segment $x = x_0 + ht,\ y = y_0 + kt$ $(0 \leq t \leq 1)$, also belongs to ω.

For the (composite) function of the one variable t, $F(t) = f(x_0 + ht,\ y_0 + kt)$ $(0 \leq t \leq 1)$, the following is obtained:

$$F'(t) = \frac{\partial f}{\partial x}\frac{dx}{dt} + \frac{\partial f}{\partial y}\frac{dy}{dt} = f'_x(P_t)h + f'_y(P_t)k,$$

where $P_t = (x_0 + ht,\ y_0 + kt)$.   Furthermore,

$$F''(t) = \left(\frac{\partial}{\partial x}(f'_x(P_t))\frac{dx}{dt} + \frac{\partial}{\partial y}(f'_x(P_t))\frac{dy}{dt}\right)h$$
$$+ \left(\frac{\partial}{\partial x}(f'_y(P_t))\frac{dx}{dt} + \frac{\partial}{\partial y}(f'_y(P_t))\frac{dy}{dt}\right)k$$
$$= \{f'_x(P_t)h + f'_y(P_t)k\}^{(2)},$$

where the last symbolic expression means that first the term in parentheses is raised to the second power; then $(f'_x(P_t))^2$ is replaced by $f''_{x^2}(P_t)$, $f'_x(P_t)f'_y(P_t)$ by $f''_{xy}(P_t)$ and $(f'_y(P_t))^2$ by $f''_{y^2}(P_t)$.   On continuing the differentiation, the derivatives of higher order are obtained.   In a corresponding way these can be written symbolically as follows:

$$F'''(t) = \{f'_x(P_t)h + f'_y(P_t)k\}^{(3)},$$

$$\cdot$$
$$\cdot$$
$$\cdot$$

$$F^{(n)}(t) = \{f'_x(P_t)h + f'_y(P_t)k\}^{(n)}.$$

Using Taylor's formula for functions of one variable (p. 161), expanding the function F about the point 0 we find

$$F(1) = F(0) + \frac{1}{1!}F'(0) + \frac{1}{2!}F''(0) + \cdots + \frac{1}{(n-1)!}F^{(n-1)}(0)$$
$$+ \frac{1}{n!}F^{(n)}(\theta) \qquad (0 < \theta < 1).$$

Finally, introducing the original function f, *Taylor's formula for functions of two variables* is obtained:

$$f(x_0 + h, y_0 + k) = f(x_0,y_0) + \frac{1}{1!}\{hf'_x(x_0,y_0) + kf'_y(x_0,y_0)\}$$

$$+ \frac{1}{2!}\{hf'_x(x_0,y_0) + kf'_y(x_0,y_0)\}^{(2)}$$

$$\cdots$$

$$+ \frac{1}{(n-1)!}\{hf'_x(x_0,y_0) + kf'_y(x_0,y_0)\}^{(n-1)}$$

$$+ \frac{1}{n!}\{hf'_x(x_0 + \theta h, y_0 + \theta k)$$

$$+ kf'_y(x_0 + \theta h, y_0 + \theta k)\}^{(n)}.$$

For $n = 1$, the so-called *mean value theorem* for functions of two variables is obtained.

Because of the continuity of the nth derivatives, the last term on the right side, the *remainder* R_n, can be written

$$R_n = \frac{1}{n!}\{hf'_x(x_0,y_0) + kf'_y(x_0,y_0)\}^{(n)} + o(\rho^n),$$

where $\rho = \sqrt{h^2 + k^2}$. Introducing this, *Taylor's o-formula* for functions of two variables is obtained:

$$f(x_0 + h, y_0 + k) = f(x_0,y_0) + \frac{1}{1!}\{hf'_x(x_0,y_0) + kf'_y(x_0,y_0)\} + \cdots$$

$$+ \frac{1}{n!}\{hf'_x(x_0,y_0) + kf'_y(x_0,y_0)\}^{(n)} + o(\rho^n).$$

For $n = 1$ this restates the definition of differentiability of the given function at the point (x_0,y_0).

Corresponding results may be obtained for functions of several variables.

Extreme Values of Functions of Two Variables

As an important application of Taylor's o-formula, methods shall now be derived for the determination of extreme values of functions of two variables.

The continuous function $z = f(x,y)$ is said to have a *relative maximum* at an interior point of its domain if the value of the function at this point is greater than all the values of the function in some deleted neighborhood of the point considered.   *A relative minimum* is defined in a corresponding way.

If the function is differentiable, it follows immediately that a necessary condition for a relative extremum (i.e., a relative maximum or a relative minimum) is that the partial derivatives of the first order at the point under consideration are 0.   Geometrically this means that the tangent plane at the corresponding point of the graph must be parallel to the XY-plane.   Any such point is called a *stationary point* (Fig. 4-5).

In order to obtain a sufficient condition for a relative extremum, we assume further that the function has continuous partial derivatives of the second order in its domain.   Taylor's o-formula for $n = 2$, about a point (x_0, y_0) where the two first-order derivatives are zero, then gives

$$f(x_0 + h,\ y_0 + k) = f(x_0,y_0) + \tfrac{1}{2}(f''_{x^2}(x_0,y_0)h^2 + 2f''_{xy}(x_0,y_0)hk$$
$$+ f''_{y^2}(x_0,y_0)k^2) + o(\rho^2),$$

or, introducing $r_0 = f''_{x^2}(x_0,y_0)$, $s_0 = f''_{xy}(x_0,y_0)$, and $t_0 = f''_{y^2}(x_0,y_0)$:

$$\Delta z = \tfrac{1}{2}(r_0 h^2 + 2s_0 hk + t_0 k^2) + o(\rho^2).$$

Neglecting for the moment the o-term, the problem will be to discuss the sign of the quadratic form $r_0 h^2 + 2s_0 hk + t_0 k^2$.   Interpreting h and k as coordinates in a "local" coordinate system, it follows that this problem may be solved using the theory of the reduction of quadratic forms (p. 79): By a suitable substitution procedure, the given expression can be brought into the form $\lambda_1 h'^2 + \lambda_2 k'^2$.

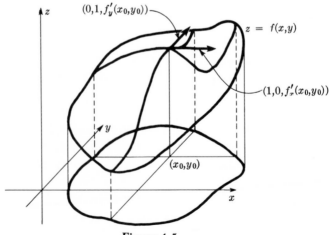

Figure 4-5

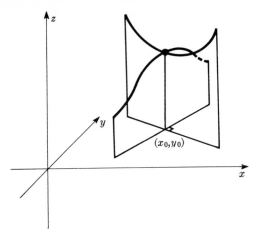

Figure 4-6

Here we do not need to concern ourselves with the relation between the unprimed and the primed coordinates, but only with the sign of the quadratic form. In case λ_1 and λ_2 are both positive, the quadratic form itself is always positive (unless both coordinates are 0). But then there must exist a deleted δ-neighborhood of the point (x_0, y_0), such that Δz is also positive, as the o-term cannot have any influence on the sign of Δz if only δ is chosen sufficiently small. As a result of this, the given function will have a *relative minimum* at the point considered. Correspondingly, there will be a *relative maximum* if both λ_1 and λ_2 are negative. However, if λ_1 and λ_2 have opposite signs, the function will have a relative maximum in a certain "direction" and a relative minimum in the direction at right angles to this. It follows that the function has no relative extremum at the point considered. The graph of the function in this case is said to have a *saddle point* (Fig. 4-6). Finally if one or both of the λ's is 0, no conclusions can be drawn, as the sign of Δz in at least one direction is determined by the o-term, the sign of which is not known.

We now only have to express the distinctions introduced here with regard to the λ's with the help of the given qualities r_0, s_0, and t_0. As shown previously, λ_1 and λ_2 are obtained as the roots of the characteristic equation

$$\begin{vmatrix} r_0 - \lambda & s_0 \\ s_0 & t_0 - \lambda \end{vmatrix} = 0 \qquad \text{or} \qquad \lambda^2 - (r_0 + t_0)\lambda + (r_0 t_0 - s_0^2) = 0.$$

Thus $\lambda_1 + \lambda_2 = r_0 + t_0$ and $\lambda_1\lambda_2 = r_0t_0 - s_0^2$. From this the following important results are obtained.

At a point (x_0,y_0) where the partial derivatives of the first order of a given function are both 0, a relative extremum is obtained if $r_0t_0 - s_0^2 > 0$; this is a relative maximum if r_0 and t_0 are both negative, and a relative minimum if they are both positive. For $r_0t_0 - s_0^2 < 0$, a saddle point is obtained. Finally, if $r_0t_0 - s_0^2 = 0$, the values of the function near the point have to be investigated in another manner.

Example 4-5

$$z = x^3 - 3x - y^2,$$
$$z'_x = 3x^2 - 3 = 3(x + 1)(x - 1),$$
$$z'_y = -2y.$$

The only stationary points of the surface are $(-1,0,2)$ and $(1,0,-2)$. Furthermore, $z''_{x^2} = 6x$, $z''_{xy} = 0$, $z''_{y^2} = -2$. Thus at the point $(-1,0,2)$ we get

$$rt - s^2 = \begin{vmatrix} -6 & 0 \\ 0 & -2 \end{vmatrix} > 0.$$

This is a relative maximum point, as the diagonal elements are negative. At the point $(1,0,-2)$ we find

$$rt - s^2 = \begin{vmatrix} 6 & 0 \\ 0 & -2 \end{vmatrix} < 0.$$

This is therefore a saddle point (Fig. 4-7).

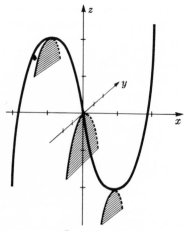

Figure 4-7

These results are not surprising, as the surface obviously may be obtained by a translation of the parabola $z = -y^2$ in the YZ-plane in such a way that its vertex moves along the third-degree curve $z = x^3 - 3x$ in the XZ-plane.

The absolute maximum value of the function considered in a given closed region is assumed either at the point $(-1,0)$ or at a point of the boundary. The absolute minimum value must necessarily be assumed at a point of the boundary. $\square$

Exercises

*1. Evaluate the first- and second-order partial derivatives of the function $f(x,y) = x^2 \ln(x^y)$.

2. Show that the function $u = (x^2 + y^2 + z^2)^{-1/2}$ satisfies the Laplace equation

$$\frac{\partial^2 u}{\partial x^2} + \frac{\partial^2 u}{\partial y^2} + \frac{\partial^2 u}{\partial z^2} = 0.$$

3. Sketch the following two surfaces:

(a) $z = 3x^2 - 3y^2 + 8xy$.   (b) $z = (x^3 - x)(y^2 + 1)$.

4. Find the absolute maximum value and the absolute minimum value of the function

$$f(x,y) = x(x - 1)^2 + y^2 \qquad (-1 \le x \le 2, \; -1 \le y \le 1).$$

*5. Examine the stationary points of the surface

$$z = 4x^3 - 6x^2 y - 2y^3 + 3x^2 - 6xy + 6y.$$

6. Find the box, which:

(a) For a given volume has the least possible surface area.

(b) For a given surface area has the greatest possible volume.

*7. Consider a box with sides a, b, and c, where $4a + 3b + 2c = 24$. Find values of a, b, and c such that (a) the volume and (b) the surface area of the box has an extremum, and decide whether this is a maximum or a minimum.

Answers

1. $\dfrac{\partial f}{\partial x} = 2xy \ln x + xy; \quad \dfrac{\partial f}{\partial y} = x^2 \ln x$

$\dfrac{\partial^2 f}{\partial x^2} = 2y \ln x + 3y; \quad \dfrac{\partial^2 f}{\partial x \, \partial y} = \dfrac{\partial^2 f}{\partial y \, \partial x} = 2x \ln x + x; \quad \dfrac{\partial^2 f}{\partial y^2} = 0$

5. max at $(-1/2, \sqrt{5}/2)$, min at $(-1/2, -\sqrt{5}/2)$; saddle points at $(1/2, 1/2)$ and $(-1, -1)$.

7. (a) $a = 2$, $b = \frac{8}{3}$, $c = 4$ max.

     (b) $a = \frac{24}{23}$, $b = \frac{72}{23}$, $c = \frac{120}{23}$ max.

4-4. TOTAL DIFFERENTIALS

Primitive Functions of Two Variables

When the notion of a differentiable function of two variables was introduced, an expression such as

$$\frac{\partial z}{\partial x}\,dx + \frac{\partial z}{\partial y}\,dy$$

was called the total differential of the function $z = z(x,y)$.

Now suppose $L(x,y)$ and $M(x,y)$ are arbitrary functions of two variables continuous in an open region of the XY-plane, and let us consider the corresponding *differential expression* $L(x,y)\,dx + M(x,y)\,dy$. A natural question, which also proves of great importance in applications, is whether this expression will always be a total differential, or, in other words, whether there must necessarily exist a differentiable function of two variables, $u(x,y)$, which has the given expression as its total differential.

The corresponding problem for functions of one variable has been previously considered, and it was concluded that when $f(x)$ was an arbitrary function continuous in an open interval, the expression $f(x)\,dx$ was the differential of any primitive function $F(x) = \int f(x)\,dx$. However, in the two-dimensional case now under consideration, the situation turns out to be different. It is not always possible to find what we shall call a *primitive function* of the differential expression considered.

A Necessary Condition

Suppose the differential expression $L(x,y)\,dx + M(x,y)\,dy$ has a primitive function $u(x,y)$:

$$du = \frac{\partial u}{\partial x}\,dx + \frac{\partial u}{\partial y}\,dy = L(x,y)\,dx + M(x,y)\,dy.$$

The problem of finding $u(x,y)$ is then equivalent to solving the two related partial differential equations

$$\frac{\partial u}{\partial x} = L(x,y) \qquad \text{and} \qquad \frac{\partial u}{\partial y} = M(x,y).$$

It is immediately clear that from a single solution $u_0(x,y)$, an infinite number of other solutions can be obtained by the addition of an arbitrary constant: $u(x,y) = u_0(x,y) + c$. However, it can be proved that these are all the solutions when, as assumed, the domain of L and M is connected.

At present we shall limit ourselves to consideration of cases where the two functions $L(x,y)$ and $M(x,y)$ have continuous partial derivatives in their common domain. Then a necessary condition for the given expression to be a total differential is readily found: From $\partial u/\partial x = L(x,y)$ and $\partial u/\partial y = M(x,y)$ we obtain $\partial^2 u/\partial x\,\partial y = L'_y(x,y)$ and $\partial^2 u/\partial y\,\partial x = M'_x(x,y)$; thus $L'_y(x,y) = M'_x(x,y)$. On "*cross-differentiation*," identical functions must be obtained. This is a necessary condition, but it is in general not sufficient. It is, however, also sufficient in case the given open region in addition is *simply connected* (see p. 279). This means that all the interior points of any polygon will belong to the region if all the sides of the polygon do, i.e., if the region is without "holes."

Later, in connection with the introduction of the notion of a line integral, we shall obtain a generally applicable criterion for the existence of a primitive function (p. 259). Then it will be assumed only that the functions $L(x,y)$ and $M(x,y)$ are continuous in an open region (which does not need to be simply connected).

Example 4-6

$$(2xy + 1)\,dx + (x^2 + 2y)\,dy.$$

As the functions $2xy + 1$ and $x^2 + 2y$ both have continuous partial derivatives in the whole XY-plane (which is simply connected) and furthermore

$$\frac{\partial}{\partial y}\,(2xy + 1) = 2x = \frac{\partial}{\partial x}\,(x^2 + 2y),$$

the given expression is a total differential.

Determining a primitive function $u(x,y)$, we have $\partial u/\partial x = 2xy + 1$, giving $u = x^2 y + x + f(y)$, where $f(y)$ is an arbitrary differentiable function of y, and $\partial u/\partial y = x^2 + 2y$, giving $u = x^2 y + y^2 + g(x)$, where $g(x)$ is correspondingly an arbitrary differentiable function of x. On equating the two expressions for $u(x,y)$ we find

$$f(y) = y^2 + C \qquad \text{and} \qquad g(x) = x + C,$$

or

$$u(x,y) = x^2 y + y^2 + x + C. \qquad \square$$

Example 4-7

$$(2x^2 y + x)\,dx + (x^3 + 2xy)\,dy.$$

This is not a total differential, as the cross-differentiation condition is not satisfied:

$$\frac{\partial}{\partial y} (2x^2 y + x) = 2x^2 \neq 3x^2 + 2y = \frac{\partial}{\partial x} (x^3 + 2xy). \qquad \Box$$

Example 4-8

$$\frac{-y}{x^2 + y^2} \, dx + \frac{x}{x^2 + y^2} \, dy \qquad (x,y) \neq (0,0).$$

The open region is not simply connected.

$$\frac{\partial}{\partial y} \left(\frac{-y}{x^2 + y^2} \right) = \frac{y^2 - x^2}{(x^2 + y^2)^2} = \frac{\partial}{\partial x} \left(\frac{x}{x^2 + y^2} \right).$$

Even though the cross-differentiation condition is satisfied in the whole region, the given expression is not a total differential.

To show this we only need to consider one of the two related partial differential equations: $\partial u / \partial x = -y/(x^2 + y^2)$. In the half-plane $y > 0$ all the solutions of this are

$$u = \int \frac{-y}{x^2 + y^2} \, dx + f_1(y) = -\arctan\frac{x}{y} + f_1(y).$$

On the half-line $y = 0$, $x > 0$, u is constant $(= k_1)$. This is also the case on the half-line $y = 0$, $x < 0$: $u = k_2$. In the half-plane $y < 0$ we finally obtain $u = -\arctan(x/y) + f_2(y)$.

As a possible primitive function must be continuous in the whole of the open region, the following is obtained:

$$u(1,y) \to k_1 \quad \text{as } y \to 0 + 0 \qquad \text{or}$$
$$\left. \begin{array}{l} -\dfrac{\pi}{2} + f_1(0) = k_1 \\[2mm] u(1,y) \to k_1 \quad \text{as } y \to 0 - 0 \qquad \text{or} \\[2mm] \dfrac{\pi}{2} + f_2(0) = k_1 \end{array} \right\} f_1(0) - f_2(0) = \pi,$$

and

$$u(-1,y) \to k_2 \quad \text{as } y \to 0 + 0 \qquad \text{or}$$
$$\left. \begin{array}{l} \dfrac{\pi}{2} + f_1(0) = k_2 \\[2mm] u(-1,y) \to k_2 \quad \text{as } y \to 0 - 0 \qquad \text{or} \\[2mm] -\dfrac{\pi}{2} + f_2(0) = k_2 \end{array} \right\} f_1(0) - f_2(0) = -\pi.$$

It is impossible to satisfy these requirements at one time. Thus no primitive function exists in the open region considered.

However, if the region is suitably restricted, for example by the removal of a half-line with its end point at (0,0), then a simply connected open region is obtained inside which the given differential expression must be a total differential.

Thus if the half-line $y = 0$, $x < 0$, is removed, we can use as a primitive function

$$u(x,y) = \begin{cases} -\arctan\dfrac{x}{y} + \dfrac{\pi}{2} & \text{if } y > 0, \\[2ex] 0 & \text{if } y = 0 \text{ (and } x > 0), \\[2ex] -\arctan\dfrac{x}{y} - \dfrac{\pi}{2} & \text{if } y < 0. \end{cases}$$

The inconsistency found above has now disappeared; the function is differentiable and calculation shows it to have the given expression as its differential. We shall return to this example later (p. 265), where a physical interpretation of the results obtained is given. □

Integrating Factors

If a given differential expression, $L(x,y)\,dx + M(x,y)\,dy$, is not a total differential, then for any simply connected open region, where L and M are not both zero and have continuous partial derivatives at every point, it is possible to prove that there exists an infinite number of so-called *integrating factors*. The function $\mu(x,y)$ is said to be an integrating factor of the expression considered when $\mu(x,y)L(x,y)\,dx + \mu(x,y)M(x,y)\,dy$ is a total differential.

Example 4-9. An integrating factor of the previously considered differential expression $(2x^2y + x)\,dx + (x^3 + 2xy)\,dy$ is the function $\mu_0(x,y) = (1/x)(x \neq 0)$, as on multiplication by this the total differential considered in Example 4-6 is obtained. Moreover, any function of the form $\mu(x,y) = (1/x)\Phi(x^2y + y^2 + x)$, where Φ is an arbitrary continuous function of one variable, is also seen to be an integrating factor. □

For a differential expression of the form $f_1(x)g_1(y)\,dx + f_2(x)g_2(y)\,dy$, an integrating factor is immediately found as $\mu_0(x,y) = 1/g_1(y)f_2(x)$: On multiplication by $\mu_0(x,y)$, the expression

$$\frac{f_1(x)}{f_2(x)}\,dx + \frac{g_2(y)}{g_1(y)}\,dy$$

is obtained; the variables here are said to be *separated*. A primitive function of this latter expression is

$$u(x,y) = \int \frac{f_1(x)}{f_2(x)}\, dx + \int \frac{g_2(y)}{g_1(y)}\, dy.$$

Generalizations to Several Variables

The above considerations may be generalized to functions of more than two variables.

For functions of three variables and with assumptions analogous to those previously made, a necessary condition for the expression

$$L(x,y,z)\, dx + M(x,y,z)\, dy + N(x,y,z)\, dz$$

to be a total differential is that on cross-differentiation identical results are obtained:

$$\frac{\partial M}{\partial z} = \frac{\partial N}{\partial y}, \qquad \frac{\partial N}{\partial x} = \frac{\partial L}{\partial z}, \qquad \frac{\partial L}{\partial y} = \frac{\partial M}{\partial x}.$$

For certain simple regions in space this condition is also sufficient.

However, it is not always possible to determine integrating factors. For functions of three variables, a condition for this is that the following is satisfied (cf. p. 309):

$$L\left(\frac{\partial N}{\partial y} - \frac{\partial M}{\partial z}\right) + M\left(\frac{\partial L}{\partial z} - \frac{\partial N}{\partial x}\right) + N\left(\frac{\partial M}{\partial x} - \frac{\partial L}{\partial y}\right) = 0.$$

Exercises

*1. Find a primitive function of the total differential

$$(3x^2y + y^2 - 2x)\, dx + (x^3 + 2xy - 1)\, dy.$$

*2. Show that the following differential expression is not a total differential:

$$(8xy^2 - 5x^2y)\, dx + (6x^2y - 2x^3)\, dy.$$

Next, try to guess an integrating factor.

*3. Find a primitive function of the total differential

$$(4x^3 + 2xyz + z^3 - y)\, dx + (x^2z + 3y^2 + 2yz - x)\, dy$$
$$+ (x^2y + 3xz^2 + y^2 - 2z)\, dz.$$

Answers

1. $x^3y + xy^2 - x^2 - y + C.$
2. x^2y (for example).
3. $x^4 + x^2yz + xz^3 + y^3 + y^2z - xy - z^2 + C.$

4-5. LINE INTEGRALS

Suppose there is given a (time-independent) force field in the XY-plane. This means that corresponding to every point (x,y) of the plane there is given a vector $\mathbf{K}(x,y) = (L(x,y),M(x,y))$, indicating length as well as the direction of the force acting at that point. Suppose further that a particle under the influence of this force field moves along a curve k, given by the vector function $\mathbf{r}(t) = (f(t),g(t))$, $\alpha \leq t \leq \beta$, where t indicates the time.

It then seems intuitively clear that it is meaningful to talk about the amount of work done by the force field on the particle during the time interval $[\alpha,\beta]$. As is well known, in case the particle moves along a line segment AB and the force field is constant ($= \mathbf{F}$), then the amount of work done is given by the scalar product $\mathbf{F} \cdot \mathbf{AB}$. The problem now is how to extend this definition in a reasonable way to the general case where the path of the particle need not be rectilinear and the force field not constant.

In the special case where the particle moves along the X-axis from a point $(a,0)$ to a point $(b,0)$ we have already a way to express the amount of work: Considering the definition of a definite integral as the limit of a sequence of average sums (p. 139), the only reasonable definition of the amount of work W seems to be (Fig. 4-8)

$$W = \int_a^b L(x,0)\, dx.$$

Here the motion of the particle is given by the vector function $\mathbf{r}(t) = (f(t),0)$, $\alpha \leq t \leq \beta$, where $f(\alpha) = a$ and $f(\beta) = b$. On introducing the monotone substitution $x = f(t)$ in the above integral, we obtain

$$W = \int_\alpha^\beta L(f(t),0)f'(t)\, dt.$$

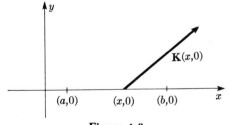

Figure 4-8

In the general case, the amount of work done is defined as

$$W = \int_{\alpha}^{\beta} [L(f(t),g(t))f'(t) + M(f(t),g(t))g'(t)] \, dt,$$

which is also written

$$W = \int_{k} \mathbf{K}(x,y) \, d\mathbf{r} \quad \text{or} \quad W = \int_{k} L(x,y) \, dx + M(x,y) \, dy.$$

Here the expression appearing on the right of the equals sign is called the line integral of the force field $\mathbf{K}$ along the curve k.

That this definition of work is reasonable will be evident from the following section, where the concept of a line integral is introduced as a purely mathematical construction without any reference to the applications.

Definition of the Line Integral

Suppose $L(x,y)$ and $M(x,y)$ are continuous functions of two variables with an open region in the XY-plane as their common domain. Let the vector-valued function $\mathbf{K}$ of two real variables (the *vector field* $\mathbf{K}$) be defined by the equation $\mathbf{K}(x,y) = (L(x,y),M(x,y))$. Further let k be a differentiable curve within the domain of L and M, given by the vector function $\mathbf{r}(t) = (f(t),g(t))$, $\alpha \leq t \leq \beta$. Here k is thought of as having a positive direction corresponding to increasing values of t. Thus $A = (f(\alpha),g(\alpha))$ is the *initial point* of k, while $B = (f(\beta),g(\beta))$ is the *terminal point* of k.

We now divide the parametric interval $[\alpha,\beta]$ into n subintervals with the lengths $\Delta_i t$ ($i = 1,2,. . .,n$) choosing in each of these subintervals a point t_i. Corresponding to this we obtain a subdivision of the given curve k into smaller curve segments and on each of these a point

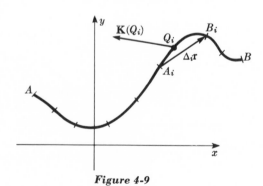

Figure 4-9

$Q_i = (f(t_i), g(t_i))$. Let the initial and terminal points of the ith curve segment be A_i and B_i. Introducing $\Delta_i \mathbf{r} = (\Delta_i x, \Delta_i y) = \mathbf{A}_i \mathbf{B}_i$, we then consider the following *average sum* (Fig. 4-9):

$$\sum_{i=1}^{n} \mathbf{K}(Q_i) \, \Delta_i \mathbf{r} = \sum_{i=1}^{n} L(f(t_i), g(t_i)) \, \Delta_i x + M(f(t_i), g(t_i)) \, \Delta_i y.$$

Using the mean-value theorem for derivatives on the functions f and g, this average sum may be rewritten as follows, where t_i^* and t_i^{**} both belong to the ith subinterval of length $\Delta_i t$:

$$\sum_{i=1}^{n} [L(f(t_i), g(t_i)) f'(t_i^*) + M(f(t_i), g(t_i)) g'(t_i^{**})] \, \Delta_i t.$$

It is evident that this quantity in general will depend on the different choices made. However, it can be shown that the sum approaches a certain limit, which is the same in all cases, if only the length of the greatest subinterval approaches zero as n tends to infinity. This limit is written

$$\int_k \mathbf{K}(x,y) \, d\mathbf{r} \qquad \text{or} \qquad \int_k L(x,y) \, dx + M(x,y) \, dy$$

and called the *line integral of the vector field* $\mathbf{K}$ *along the curve* k.

As to the value of the line integral, the following formula can be shown to be valid:

$$\int_k L(x,y) \, dx + M(x,y) \, dy = \int_\alpha^\beta [L(f(t), g(t)) f'(t) + M(f(t), g(t)) g'(t)] \, dt.$$

Formally this result may be obtained by identifying t_i, t_i^*, and t_i^{**} in the above expression, as this then becomes a usual average sum for the definite integral considered.

From the definition of the line integral it follows that its value is

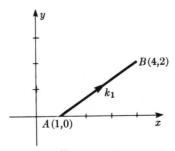

Figure 4-10

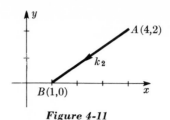

Figure 4-11

independent of the particular parametric equation for the "path of integration" k. This may also be seen on introducing a monotone substitution in the definite integral. In case $M(x,y) = 0$, the line integral is of course written $\int_k L(x,y)\, dx$; corresponding, $\int_k M(x,y)\, dy$ in case $L(x,y) = 0$.

Example 4-10. Evaluate $\int_k y^2\, dx + xy\, dy$ along the following four paths (Figs. 4-10 and 4-11):

(1) $k_1\colon (x,y) = (1 + 3t, 2t),\ 0 \le t \le 1$.

$$I_1 = \int_0^1 ((2t)^2 \cdot 3 + (1 + 3t)2t \cdot 2)\, dt$$
$$= [8t^3 + 2t^2]_0^1 = 10.$$

(2) $k_2\colon (x,y) = (4 - 3t, 2 - 2t),\ 0 \le t \le 1$.

$$I_2 = \int_0^1 ((2 - 2t)^2(-3) + (4 - 3t)(2 - 2t)(-2))\, dt$$
$$= [-8t^3 + 26t^2 - 28t]_0^1 = -10.$$

We see how a change in the positive direction of the curve gives the opposite sign to the integral; this is also an immediate consequence of the definition of the line integral

(3) k_3: the broken line ACB (Fig. 4-12).

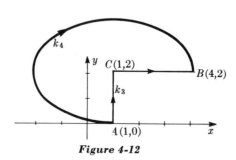

Figure 4-12

Here the path of integration shows a kink. The integration is then to be carried out in two terms:

$$I_3 = \int_{AC} + \int_{CB}.$$

$$AC: (x,y) = (1,t),\ 0 \le t \le 2.$$
$$CB: (x,y) = (t,2),\ 1 \le t \le 4.$$

$$I_3 = \int_0^2 (t^2 \cdot 0 + 1 \cdot t \cdot 1)\, dt + \int_1^4 (2^2 \cdot 1 + t \cdot 2 \cdot 0)\, dt$$

$$= [\tfrac{1}{2}t^2]_0^2 + [4t]_1^4 = 14.$$

(4) $k_4: (x,y) = (1 + 3\cos t,\ 2 - 2\sin t),\ \dfrac{\pi}{2} \le t \le 2\pi.$

$$I_4 = \int_{\pi/2}^{2\pi} [(2 - 2\sin t)^2(-3\sin t)$$

$$+ (1 + 3\cos t)(2 - 2\sin t)(-2\cos t)]\, dt$$

$$= 9\pi + 18.$$

It is seen how the results in cases (1), (3), and (4) are different even if in all cases it is a question of integrating the same expression from $A = (1,0)$ to $B = (4,2)$. Generally the *path of integration* thus has an effect on the value of the integral. □

Example 4-11. $\int_k y\, dx + x\, dy.$ Corresponding to the cases (1), (3), and (4) we obtain

(1) $I_1 = \displaystyle\int_0^1 ((2t) \cdot 3 + (1 + 3t) \cdot 2)\, dt = [6t^2 + 2t]_0^1 = 8.$

(3) $I_3 = \displaystyle\int_0^2 (t \cdot 0 + 1 \cdot 1)\, dt + \int_1^4 (2 \cdot 1 + t \cdot 0)\, dt = [t]_0^2 + [2t]_1^4 = 8.$

(4) $I_4 = \displaystyle\int_{\pi/2}^{2\pi} ((2 - 2\sin t)(-3\sin t) + (1 + 3\cos t)(-2\cos t))\, dt$

$$= [6\cos t - 2\sin t - 3\sin 2t]_{\pi/2}^{2\pi} = 8.$$

Here the results are the same for the three different paths of integration. □

The quantity under the integral sign in Example 4-11 is a total differential; this is not the case in Example 4-10. This is by no means accidental, as we shall see below.

Line Integrals and Total Differentials

The following theorem will now be considered. The value of a line integral is independent of the path of integration insofar as it only depends on its initial and terminal points in case the quantity under the integral sign is a total differential. Conversely, if the value of a line integral is independent of the path which connects any two points in a given open region, the quantity under the integral sign is a total differential in this open region.

Thus let the expression $L(x,y)\, dx + M(x,y)\, dy$ be the total differential of a function $u(x,y)$. The line integral along a curve k from A to B is then obtained, using the above notation and introducing the function $U(t) = u(f(t),g(t))$, as follows:

$$
\begin{aligned}
\int_k L(x,y)\, dx + M(x,y)\, dy &= \int_k \frac{\partial u}{\partial x}\, dx + \frac{\partial u}{\partial y}\, dy \\
&= \int_\alpha^\beta \left[\frac{\partial u}{\partial x}\frac{dx}{dt} + \frac{\partial u}{\partial y}\frac{dy}{dt} \right] dt = \int_\alpha^\beta \frac{dU}{dt}\, dt \\
&= [U(t)]_\alpha^\beta = U(\beta) - U(\alpha) \\
&= u(f(\beta),g(\beta)) - u(f(\alpha),g(\alpha)) \\
&\qquad\qquad\qquad\qquad = u(B) - u(A).
\end{aligned}
$$

From this it is evident that the value of the line integral considered is independent of the path. Thus the first part of the theorem is proved.

In such a case the value of the line integral is uniquely determined by the symbol $\int_A^B L(x,y)\, dx + M(x,y)\, dy$, and we then have in close analogy with the one-dimensional case the formula

$$
\int_A^B L(x,y)\, dx + M(x,y)\, dy = u(B) - u(A),
$$

where u is a primitive function of the differential expression under the integral sign.

Example 4-12. A primitive function in Example 4-11 is $u(x,y) = xy$. Hence we may obtain the value of the line integral considered as $u(4,2) - u(1,0) = 4 \cdot 2 - 1 \cdot 0 = 8$. $\qquad\square$

The proof of the second part of the theorem will only be outlined here. Let (x_0,y_0) be a fixed point inside the given open region. From what is given it then follows that the line integral

$$u = \int_{(x_0,y_0)}^{(x,y)} L(x,y)\, dx + M(x,y)\, dy$$

depends on x and y only: $u = u(x,y)$. Now u is shown to be a differentiable function with precisely the quantity under the integral sign as its differential. Thus this quantity really has a primitive function, and the proof is complete.

By means of the above theorem we now obtain an important method of determining whether a given differential expression in a given open region is a total differential (cf. p. 249): A necessary and sufficient condition for this is that the corresponding line integral in the given open region is independent of the path, or—as it is often formulated— that the line integral along an arbitrary *closed curve* in the region is 0. Furthermore, in case this condition is fulfilled, it follows from the above how an explicit expression for a primitive function may be obtained.

Example 4-13. We have shown earlier (Example 4-8) that the differential expression

$$\frac{-y}{x^2 + y^2}\, dx + \frac{x}{x^2 + y^2}\, dy$$

was not a total differential in the whole of its domain.

This is now readily seen upon calculation of the corresponding line integral along a closed curve which surrounds the point $(0,0)$. $k: (x,y) = (\cos t, \sin t)$, $0 \le t \le 2\pi$.

$$I = \int_0^{2\pi} \left[\frac{-\sin t}{\cos^2 t + \sin^2 t} (-\sin t) + \frac{\cos t}{\cos^2 t + \sin^2 t} (\cos t) \right] dt$$

$$= \int_0^{2\pi} dt = 2\pi \neq 0. \qquad \square$$

Applications of Line Integrals in Thermodynamics

We have already seen how line integrals may be used in connection with calculations of work in two-dimensional motion. In this section we shall consider a few examples of applications of line integrals in thermodynamics.

Consider 1 mole of an ideal gas. The pressure P and the absolute temperature T will be used as the independent variables. Then the volume V is given by the equation $V = RT/P$, where R is the gas

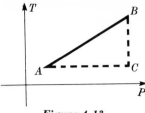

Figure 4-13

constant. By infinitesimal increments of pressure (dP) and temperature (dT), the volume is increased by

$$dV = \frac{\partial V}{\partial P} dP + \frac{\partial V}{\partial T} dT = -\frac{RT}{P^2} dP + \frac{R}{P} dT.$$

We wish now to calculate the increase in volume when P and T are changed reversibly from the values P_1 and T_1 to P_2 and T_2. Of course, this process can be carried out in many ways, but in each single case the reversible process can be represented by a curve k in a PT-coordinate system. The total increase in volume may be obtained from this as the sum of all the infinitesimal increments, in other words, as the line integral

$$\int_k dV = \int_k -\frac{RT}{P^2} dP + \frac{R}{P} dT.$$

We first consider the process corresponding to the line segment with initial point $A = (P_1, T_1)$ and terminal point $B = (P_2, T_2)$ (Fig. 4-13).

$$AB: (P,T) = \left(t, T_1 + \frac{T_2 - T_1}{P_2 - P_1} (t - P_1) \right) \qquad (P_1 \le t \le P_2).$$

$$\int_{AB} dV = \int_{P_1}^{P_2} \left[-\frac{R\{T_1 + [(T_2 - T_1)/(P_2 - P_1)](t - P_1)\}}{t^2} \cdot 1 \right.$$
$$\left. + \frac{R}{t}\frac{T_2 - T_1}{P_2 - P_1} \right] dt$$

$$= \int_{P_1}^{P_2} \left[-\frac{RT_1}{t^2} + \frac{RP_1}{t^2}\left(\frac{T_2 - T_1}{P_2 - P_1}\right) \right] dt$$

$$= \frac{-RT_1 P_2 + RP_1 T_2}{P_2 - P_1} \int_{P_1}^{P_2} \frac{1}{t^2} dt$$

$$= \frac{-RT_1 P_2 + RP_1 T_2}{P_2 - P_1} \left(-\frac{1}{P_2} + \frac{1}{P_1} \right) = \frac{RT_2}{P_2} - \frac{RT_1}{P_1}.$$

Next consider the process which is obtained by first holding the temperature constant and changing the pressure to P_2, and then holding the pressure constant and changing the temperature to T_2. This corresponds to the dashed line ACB in Fig. 4-13.

$$AC: (P,T) = (t,T_1), \; P_1 \leq t \leq P_2.$$
$$CB: (P,T) = (P_2,t), \; T_1 \leq t \leq T_2.$$

$$\int_k dV = \int_{P_1}^{P_2} \left[-\frac{RT_1}{t^2} \cdot 1 + \frac{R}{t} \cdot 0 \right] dt + \int_{T_1}^{T_2} \left[-\frac{Rt}{P_2^2} \cdot 0 + \frac{R}{P_2} \cdot 1 \right] dt$$
$$= \left[\frac{RT_1}{t} \right]_{P_1}^{P_2} + \left[\frac{RT}{P_2} \right]_{T_1}^{T_2} = \frac{RT_2}{P_2} - \frac{RT_1}{P_1}.$$

Here it is a question of integration of a total differential:

$$\frac{\partial}{\partial T}\left(-\frac{RT}{P^2} \right) = -\frac{R}{P^2} = \frac{\partial}{\partial P}\left(\frac{R}{P} \right),$$

so the result will naturally be the same in both cases. This result could also have been found directly as

$$V(P_2,T_2) - V(P_1,T_1) = \frac{RT_2}{P_2} - \frac{RT_1}{P_1}$$

because a primitive function to the integrand, the volume, was known beforehand from the equation of state.

For the infinitesimal work done in the process we have

$$\delta W = P\, dV = -\frac{RT}{P}\, dP + R\, dT.$$

This quantity is not a total differential:

$$\frac{\partial}{\partial T}\left(\frac{-RT}{P} \right) = \frac{-R}{P} \neq 0 = \frac{\partial}{\partial P}\, R.$$

Therefore the differential expression is represented by the special symbol δW.

As expected, the same work is not obtained for the two processes considered:

$$AB: \int_{P_1}^{P_2} \left[-\frac{R\{T_1 + [(T_2 - T_1)/(P_2 - P_1)](t - P_1)\}}{t} \cdot 1 \right.$$

$$\left. + R\frac{T_2 - T_1}{P_2 - P_1} \right] dt$$

$$= \int_{P_1}^{P_2} \left[-\frac{RT_1}{t} + \frac{RP_1}{t}\frac{T_2 - T_1}{P_2 - P_1} \right] dt = R\frac{T_2P_1 - P_2T_1}{P_2 - P_1} \ln \frac{P_2}{P_1}.$$

$$ACB: \int_{P_1}^{P_2} \left[-\frac{RT_1}{t} \cdot 1 + R \cdot 0 \right] dt + \int_{T_1}^{T_2} \left[-\frac{RT}{P_2} \cdot 0 + R \cdot 1 \right] dt$$

$$= -RT_1 \ln \frac{P_2}{P_1} + R(T_2 - T_1).$$

As is well known, a thermodynamic quantity is called a *function of state,* if on a change of the state of the thermodynamic system the change of this quantity depends only on the original and final states of the system. The volume V of the ideal gas is thus a function of state $(= RT/P)$, but the work done by the system is not.

Generalization to Several Variables

The ideas introduced can be immediately extended to functions of three (or more) variables. The *line integral* of the *vector field* $\mathbf{K}(x,y,z) = (L(x,y,z), M(x,y,z), N(x,y,z))$ along the curve k given by the vector function $\mathbf{r}(t) = (f(t),g(t),h(t))$, $\alpha \leq t \leq \beta$, is thus written

$$\int_k \mathbf{K}(x,y,z) \, d\mathbf{r}$$

and may be calculated from the formula

$$\int_k \mathbf{K}(x,y,z) \, d\mathbf{r} = \int_\alpha^\beta [L(f(t),g(t),h(t))f'(t) + M(f(t),g(t),h(t))g'(t)$$

$$+ N(f(t),g(t),h(t))h'(t)] \, dt.$$

It is independent of the path—or 0 along an arbitrary closed curve— if and only if the expression under the integral sign is a total differential. In this case the value of the line integral may be expressed as above by means of a primitive function of the total differential and, conversely, such a primitive function may be obtained with the help of the line integral. All this is in close analogy with the above-considered two-dimensional case.

Applications of Line Integrals in Mechanics

We have already considered the concept of work in a two-dimensional motion. Correspondingly, the above three-dimensional line integral may be interpreted as the work done by the three-dimensional force field $\mathbf{K}(x,y,z)$ on a particle moving along the space curve $\mathbf{r}(t)$.

Corresponding to the infinitesimal displacement $d\mathbf{r} = (dx,dy,dz) = \mathbf{r}'(t)\,dt$ of the particle in the time interval dt, the work done is given by $\mathbf{K}(x,y,z)\,d\mathbf{r}$ and therefore the total work done is (Fig. 4-14)

$$\int_k \mathbf{K}(x,y,z)\,d\mathbf{r} = \int_\alpha^\beta \mathbf{K}(f(t),g(t),h(t))\,\mathbf{r}'(t)\,dt.$$

The fact that the value of a line integral is independent of the parametric equation of the path of integration here simply means that the work done by the force field is the same, no matter how the particle traverses its path.

If the quantity under the integral sign is a total differential, then the force field is said to be conservative. In this case the negative of a primitive function of the total differential defines a so-called *potential energy*. Then the work done by the conservative force field will be equal to the loss in potential energy, and the components of the force field may be obtained as the negative of the partial derivatives of a potential energy.

Example 4-14. Consider a gravitational field arising from a point mass at the origin of the coordinate system. The force on a second point mass is one of attraction, decreasing as the square of the distance

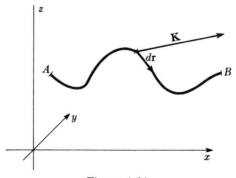

Figure 4-14

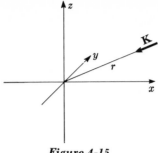

Figure 4-15

(Fig. 4-15).   We therefore obtain, with a suitable choice of units,

$$\mathbf{K} = -\frac{\mathbf{r}}{r}\frac{1}{r^2} = \left(\frac{-x}{(x^2+y^2+z^2)^{3/2}}, \frac{-y}{(x^2+y^2+z^2)^{3/2}}, \frac{-z}{(x^2+y^2+z^2)^{3/2}}\right).$$

If the second mass moves along the curve k, then the work done is

$$\int_k \mathbf{K}\,d\mathbf{r} = \int_k -\frac{x}{r^3}\,dx - \frac{y}{r^3}\,dy - \frac{z}{r^3}\,dz.$$

The quantity under the integral sign is the total differential of the function

$$U(x,y,z) = \frac{1}{r} = \frac{1}{(x^2+y^2+z^2)^{1/2}}, \quad \text{as} \quad \frac{\partial U}{\partial x} = -\frac{x}{(x^2+y^2+z^2)^{3/2}}$$

and similarly for y and z.   Thus the force field is conservative and the work done only depends on the initial point P_1 and the terminal point P_2 of the path.   It is obtained immediately as $U(P_2) - U(P_1)$.

For the potential energy the function $V = -U$ can be used.   The work gained is then $U(P_2) - U(P_1) = V(P_1) - V(P_2)$, or exactly the loss in potential energy.   At the same time we have

$$\mathbf{K} = \left(-\frac{\partial V}{\partial x}, -\frac{\partial V}{\partial y}, -\frac{\partial V}{\partial z}\right). \qquad \square$$

Example 4-15.   For the case of a "magnetic north pole" placed beside a straight conductor which has a constant current passing through it, the force on the pole has the following expression when a

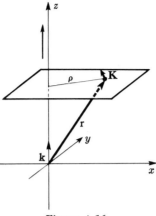

Figure 4-16

suitable system of units is chosen and the notation is as shown in Fig. 4-16:

$$\mathbf{K} = \frac{\mathbf{k} \times \mathbf{r}}{\rho^2} = \left(-\frac{y}{x^2 + y^2}, \frac{x}{x^2 + y^2}, 0 \right).$$

The force is thus inversely proportional to the distance from the conductor and perpendicular to the plane determined by the conductor and the magnetic pole.

The following expression, previously considered in the XY-plane (p. 250) is obtained for the infinitesimal work

$$-\frac{y}{x^2 + y^2} \, dx + \frac{x}{x^2 + y^2} \, dy.$$

This expression is not a total differential. This is easily seen now, as, for example in moving along a unit circle in the XY-plane in the positive sense of rotation, the movement is always in the direction of the force; thus work is gained. The amount of work corresponding to one revolution was previously (p. 259) found to be 2π. This is also quite obvious now. □

Exercises

1. Given the points $A = (1,0)$, $B = (2,3)$, and $C = (-1,1)$ and the vector field $\mathbf{K}(x,y) = (3x^2 + 2y, 2x - 1)$, evaluate the line integral of $\mathbf{K}(x,y)$ along the following line segments:

   (a) AB.　　　(b) BA.　　　(c) AC.　　　(d) BC.

*2. Evaluate the following two line integrals.

(a) $\int_k \left(\frac{1}{y} - 1\right) dx + \left(y^2 - \frac{x}{y^2}\right) dy,$ (b) $\int_k (y - y^2) \, dx + (y^4 - x) \, dy,$

where k is the arc AB on the parabola $y = 1 + x^2$, $A = (-1,2)$, $B = (1,2)$.

3. An electric charge e is placed at the point $(a,0,0)$ $(a \neq 0)$. Determine the work done by its field on a unit electric charge, when this moves from the point $(0,0,0)$ to infinity along the half-line containing the unit vector (α,β,γ) $(\alpha \neq 1)$.

*4. Consider a force field where the force $\mathbf{K}(P)$ at an arbitrary point P is directed toward a fixed point A, and where $|\mathbf{K}(P)|$ is proportional to the distance between A and P. Introducing a coordinate system, give a coordinate expression for the force field, show that the field is conservative, and find a potential energy.

Answers

2. (a) -1. (b) $-12/5$.

4. $\mathbf{K}(x,y,z) = -k(x - x_0, y - y_0, z - z_0)$

$V(x,y,z) = \dfrac{k}{2}[(x - x_0)^2 + (y - y_0)^2 + (z - z_0)^2]$ $\left.\right\}$ $k > 0$, $A = (x_0,y_0,z_0)$

4-6. DOUBLE INTEGRALS

Definition of a Double Integral

Previously we have seen that the definite integral of a positive function of one variable gives the area between the corresponding curve and the axis of the independent variable. We shall now consider a two-dimensional analogue: The *double integral* of a positive function of two variables gives the volume between the surface determined by the function and the plane of the independent variables.

Consider a function of two variables $z = F(x,y)$ which is continuous in a closed region ω of area A (Fig. 4-17).

The region ω is divided into a number of smaller *subregions*. In each of these an arbitrary point Q is chosen and the product of the value $F(Q)$ of the function at Q and the area ΔA of the corresponding subregion is then determined. The sum of these products from all the subregions represents a type of *average sum* $\Sigma_i F(Q_i) \, \Delta_i A$, which on increasingly finer division exhibits a limit which is independent of the manner in which the limiting process is carried out if only the maximum diagonal of the subregions approaches zero.

This limit is called the *double integral* (or *plane integral*) *of the function F over the region ω* and is written

$$\iint_\omega F(x,y) \, dA \qquad \text{or} \qquad \int_\omega F(x,y) \, dA.$$

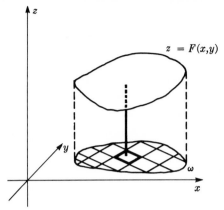

Figure 4-17

In case $F(x,y) \geq 0$ it follows from the above that the double integral really gives what must be considered the *volume* of the solid Ω bounded by the surface $z = F(x,y)$, the XY-plane, and a cylinder with a cross section ω. If $F(x,y) = 1$, the double integral simply gives the area of ω.

Reduction in Right-Angled Coordinates

The evaluation of a double integral is generally carried out by two successive (definite) integrations as a so-called *repeated integration* or *iterated integration*.

Suppose the region of integration ω is bounded by the curves $y = g(x)$ and $y = f(x)$ $(g(x) \geq f(x))$ and (if necessary) the lines $x = a$ and $x = b$.

To obtain a suitable division of the region ω we proceed as follows: The projection of ω on the X-axis, i.e., the interval $[a,b]$ on the X-axis, is divided into subintervals and in each of these a point is chosen. Let the length of the ith subinterval be $\Delta_i x$ and the point belonging to this be x_i. The projection of ω on the Y-axis is treated analogously; here the length of the jth subinterval is called $\Delta_j y$ and the corresponding point y_j. Using the two divisions on the axes, the region ω is now divided by means of straight lines perpendicular to the axes (Fig. 4-18).

Ignoring irregularities near the boundary, ω is thus divided into small rectangles. The area of a typical rectangle is $\Delta_i x \, \Delta_j y$. As a point belonging to this rectangle we may choose (x_i, y_j). Consider now the following sum:

$$S_2 = \sum_{i,j} F(x_i, y_j)\, \Delta_i x\, \Delta_j y,$$

where the two summations on i and j are not independent, as only contributions from rectangles for which the point (x_i, y_j) belongs to ω are to be taken into account.

This sum is only an approximation of an average sum as defined in the preceding section. It is, however, a sufficient approximation insofar as the error introduced can be shown to have no consequences in the limit (cf. p. 234). S_2 is now rewritten as follows:

$$S_2 = \sum_i \left[\sum_j F(x_i, y_j)\, \Delta_j y \right] \Delta_i x.$$

This may be considered as a specification of the order of summation: First, the contributions from all rectangles in the ith strip perpendicular to the X-axis are added. Second, the total contributions from all these strips are added.

As the division on the Y-axis becomes increasingly finer, the quantity $\Sigma_j F(x_i, y_j)\, \Delta_j y$ will in the limit become the definite integral

$$\int_{f(x_i)}^{g(x_i)} F(x_i, y)\, dy,$$

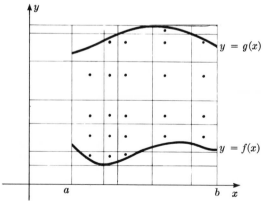

Figure 4-18

i.e., the value of the point x_i of the function (Fig. 4-19)

$$\phi(x) = \int_{f(x)}^{g(x)} F(x,y)\, dy.$$

In case $F(x_i,y) \geq 0$ this limit gives the area of a cross section perpendicular to the X-axis of the solid Ω.

Introducing the limit in S_2 we obtain the quantity $S_1 = \Sigma_i \phi(x_i)\, \Delta_i x$, which in the limit again becomes

$$\int_a^b \phi(x)\, dx \qquad \text{or} \qquad \int_a^b \left[\int_{f(x)}^{g(x)} F(x,y)\, dy \right] dx,$$

often written

$$\int_a^b dx \int_{f(x)}^{g(x)} F(x,y)\, dy.$$

The above loose consideration can be developed into an exact proof. We then have as a final result the following important formula:

$$\int_\omega F(x,y)\, dA = \int_a^b dx \int_{f(x)}^{g(x)} F(x,y)\, dy$$

or, briefly,

$$\int_\omega F(x,y)\, dA = \iint_\omega F(x,y)\, dx\, dy.$$

The evaluation of the double integral is said to be carried out by a reduction in *right-angled coordinates*. This corresponds to using as an *infinitesimal plane element* a rectangle with sides dx and dy parallel to the axes. The area of this plane element is then $dA = dx\, dy$.

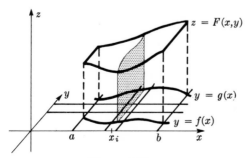

Figure 4-19

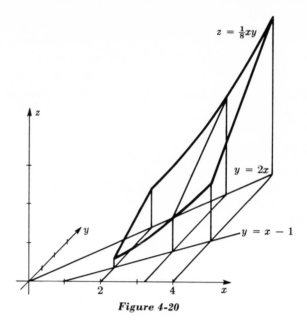

Figure 4-20

Example 4-16. $F(x,y) = \frac{1}{8}xy$; ω: $g(x) = 2x$, $f(x) = x - 1$, $a = 2$, $b = 4$ (Fig. 4-20).

$$\int_\omega \tfrac{1}{8}xy \, dA = \int_2^4 dx \int_{x-1}^{2x} \tfrac{1}{8}xy \, dy.$$

We first calculate $\phi(x)$, holding x constant:

$$\phi(x) = \int_{y=x-1}^{y=2x} \tfrac{1}{8}xy \, dy = [\tfrac{1}{16}xy^2]_{y=x-1}^{y=2x}$$
$$= \tfrac{1}{16}x(4x^2 - x^2 + 2x - 1)$$
$$= \tfrac{3}{16}x^3 + \tfrac{1}{8}x^2 - \tfrac{1}{16}x.$$

In the case under consideration, the cross section perpendicular to

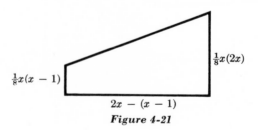

Figure 4-21

the X-axis is a trapezium. The area of this can of course also be found without integration (Fig. 4-21):

$$\phi(x) = (2x - (x - 1)) \frac{\frac{1}{8}x(x - 1) + \frac{1}{8}x \cdot 2x}{2}$$

$$= \tfrac{3}{16}x^3 + \tfrac{1}{8}x^2 - \tfrac{1}{16}x.$$

On the introduction of $\phi(x)$, in any case we obtain

$$\int_\omega \tfrac{1}{8}xy \, dA = \int_2^4 (\tfrac{3}{16}x^3 + \tfrac{1}{8}x^2 - \tfrac{1}{16}x) \, dx$$

$$= [\tfrac{3}{64}x^4 + \tfrac{1}{24}x^3 - \tfrac{1}{32}x^2]_2^4 = 13\tfrac{5}{24}. \qquad \square$$

Example 4-17. $F(x,y) = x^2/2y$; ω: $\triangle ABC$, $A = (1,1)$, $B = (2,1)$, and $C = (2,2)$ (Fig. 4-22).

$$\int_\omega \frac{x^2}{2y} \, dA = \int_1^2 dx \int_1^x \frac{x^2}{2y} \, dy$$

$$= \int_1^2 dx \, [\tfrac{1}{2}x^2 \ln y]_{y=1}^{y=x}$$

$$= \int_1^2 \tfrac{1}{2}x^2 \ln x \, dx$$

$$= \left[\frac{1}{6} x^3 \ln x - \int \frac{1}{6} x^3 \frac{1}{x} \, dx \right]_{x=1}^{x=2}$$

$$= [\tfrac{1}{6}x^3 \ln x - \tfrac{1}{18}x^3]_1^2 = \tfrac{4}{3} \ln 2 - \tfrac{7}{18}.$$

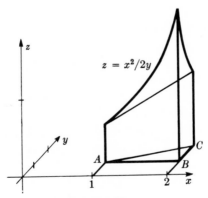

Figure 4-22

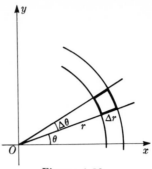

Figure 4-23

The region ω is in this case of a type such that the *reversed order of integration* can be used advantageously. In the average sum this corresponds simply to carrying out, first, the summation of all contributions from subregions in individual strips perpendicular to the Y-axis, and second, the summation of the contributions from all these strips:

$$\int_\omega \frac{x^2}{2y} \, dA = \int_1^2 dy \int_y^2 \frac{x^2}{2y} \, dx = \int_1^2 dy \left[\frac{x^3}{6y}\right]_{x=y}^{x=2} = \int_1^2 \left(\frac{4}{3y} - \frac{y^2}{6}\right) dy$$

$$= \left[\frac{4}{3}\ln y - \frac{y^3}{18}\right]_1^2 = \frac{4}{3}\ln 2 - \frac{7}{18}.$$

The result is of course the same.   □

Reduction in Polar Coordinates

The double integral has been evaluated above through a reduction in right-angled coordinates corresponding to a division of the XY-plane by lines parallel to the axes. Sometimes calculations become simpler by the use of another method of division, which leads to the so-called *reduction in polar coordinates*.

In this case the division is carried out by means of circles with their centers at the origin and half-lines with their initial points at the origin. In polar coordinates this corresponds to holding constant either the radial distance r or the polar angle θ. To a sufficiently good approximation the area of a subregion is then of the form $r \, \Delta\theta \, \Delta r$ (Fig. 4-23).

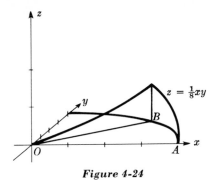

Figure 4-24

When at the same time the given function is expressed in polar coordinates, an average sum is obtained as $\Sigma F(r \cos \theta, r \sin \theta) r \, \Delta\theta \, \Delta r$. In the limit this gives

$$\int_\omega F(x,y) \, dA = \iint F(r \cos \theta, r \sin \theta) r \, dr \, d\theta,$$

corresponding to the infinitesimal formula $dA = r \, dr \, d\theta$.

Example 4-18. $F(x,y) = \frac{1}{8}xy$; ω: the section AOB of a circle, where $A = (4,0)$ and $B = (2\sqrt{2}, 2\sqrt{2})$. The region of integration (and the integrand) is here of such a type that a reduction in polar coordinates is natural (Fig. 4-24).

If it is decided first to integrate the contributions corresponding to a fixed value of θ (in this case r varies from 0 to 4), and then to integrate with respect to θ (from 0 to $\pi/4$), then the calculations are as follows:

$$\int_\omega \tfrac{1}{8}xy \, dA = \int_0^{\pi/4} d\theta \int_0^4 \tfrac{1}{8} r \cos \theta \, r \sin \theta \, r \, dr$$

$$= \int_0^{\pi/4} d\theta \, [\tfrac{1}{32} r^4 \cos \theta \sin \theta]_{r=0}^{r=4}$$

$$= \int_0^{\pi/4} 8 \cos \theta \sin \theta \, d\theta = [4 \sin^2 \theta]_0^{\pi/4} = 2.$$

If the order of integration is the reverse, that is, if we first integrate the contributions corresponding to a fixed value of r, then we obtain

$$\int_\omega \tfrac{1}{8}xy \, dA = \int_0^4 dr \int_0^{\pi/4} \tfrac{1}{8}r \cos\theta \, r \sin\theta \, r \, d\theta$$

$$= \int_0^4 dr \, [\tfrac{1}{16}r^3 \sin^2\theta]_{\theta=0}^{\theta=\pi/4}$$

$$= \int_0^4 \frac{1}{32}r^3 \, dr = \left[\frac{r^4}{128}\right]_0^4 = 2.$$

On a reduction in right-angled coordinates, if the y-integration is carried out first, the following is obtained:

$$\int_\omega \tfrac{1}{8}xy \, dA = \int_0^4 dx \int_0^{g(x)} \tfrac{1}{8}xy \, dy,$$

where

$$g(x) = \begin{cases} x & \text{if } 0 \le x \le 2\sqrt{2}, \\ \sqrt{16 - x^2} & \text{if } 2\sqrt{2} \le x \le 4. \end{cases}$$

Thus

$$\int_\omega \frac{1}{8}xy \, dA = \int_0^4 \frac{1}{8}x\frac{1}{2}(g(x))^2 \, dx = \int_0^{2\sqrt{2}} \frac{1}{16}x^3 \, dx + \int_{2\sqrt{2}}^4 \frac{x}{16}(16 - x^2) \, dx$$

$$= \left[\frac{x^4}{64}\right]_0^{2\sqrt{2}} + \left[\frac{x^2}{2} - \frac{x^4}{64}\right]_{2\sqrt{2}}^4 = 1 + 8 - 4 - 4 + 1 = 2.$$

Finally with the reversed order of integration,

$$\int_\omega \tfrac{1}{8}xy \, dA = \int_0^{2\sqrt{2}} dy \int_y^{\sqrt{16-y^2}} \tfrac{1}{8}xy \, dx = \int_0^{2\sqrt{2}} dy \, [\tfrac{1}{16}x^2y]_{x=y}^{x=\sqrt{16-y^2}}$$

$$= \int_0^{2\sqrt{2}} (\tfrac{1}{16}(16 - y^2)y - \tfrac{1}{16}y^3) \, dy$$

$$= [\tfrac{1}{2}y^2 - \tfrac{1}{32}y^4]_0^{2\sqrt{2}} = 4 - 2 = 2. \qquad \square$$

Example 4-19. $F(x,y) = \tfrac{1}{8}xy$; ω: the region in the first quadrant bounded by the semicircle with OA as its diameter, $A = (4,0)$ (Fig. 4-25).

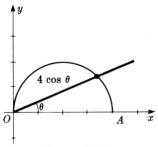

Figure 4-25

As the equation of the semicircle in polar coordination is $r = 4 \cos \theta$, $0 \le \theta \le \pi/2$, then for θ fixed, r will vary from 0 to $4 \cos \theta$. The limits for θ are 0 and $\pi/2$.

$$\int_\omega \frac{1}{8} xy \, dA = \int_0^{\pi/2} d\theta \int_0^{4\cos\theta} \frac{1}{8} r \cos\theta \, r \sin\theta \, r \, dr$$

$$= \int_0^{\pi/2} d\theta \left[\frac{r^4}{32} \cos\theta \sin\theta \right]_{r=0}^{r=4\cos\theta}$$

$$= \int_0^{\pi/2} 8 \cos^5\theta \sin\theta \, d\theta = \left[-\frac{4}{3} \cos^6\theta \right]_0^{\pi/2} = \frac{4}{3}.$$

If the other order of integration is chosen, the first problem is to find the limits for θ when r is fixed. The equation of the semicircle, when solved with respect to θ, gives $\theta = \arccos r/4$, $0 \le r \le 4$. The limits of θ are then 0 and $\arccos r/4$; r varies from 0 to 4 (Fig. 4-26).

$$\int_\omega \frac{1}{8} xy \, dA = \int_0^4 dr \int_0^{\arccos r/4} \frac{1}{8} r \cos\theta \, r \sin\theta \, r \, d\theta$$

$$= \int_0^4 dr \left[-\frac{r^3}{16} \cos^2\theta \right]_{\theta=0}^{\theta=\arccos r/4}$$

$$= \int_0^4 \left(-\frac{r^3}{16} \cdot \frac{r^2}{16} + \frac{r^3}{16} \right) dr = \left[-\frac{r^6}{3 \cdot 2^9} + \frac{r^4}{64} \right]_0^4$$

$$= -\frac{8}{3} + 4 = \frac{4}{3}. \quad \square$$

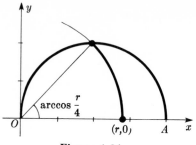

Figure 4-26

Example 4-20. $F(x,y) = e^{-x^2-y^2}$; $\omega: x^2 + y^2 \leq R^2$ (Fig. 4-27).

$$V(R) = \int_\omega e^{-x^2-y^2}\, dA$$

$$= \int_0^R dr \int_0^{2\pi} e^{-r^2} r\, d\theta$$

$$= \int_0^R dr\, [e^{-r^2}\theta r]_{\theta=0}^{\theta=2\pi}$$

$$= \int_0^R 2\pi r e^{-r^2}\, dr$$

$$= [-\pi e^{-r^2}]_0^R = \pi(1 - e^{-R^2}).$$

The integration with respect to θ is in this case of an especially simple type, and its result can be written down immediately: The contribution to the double integral from the region between circles with centers at O and radii r and $r + dr$ will be $e^{-r^2}2\pi r\, dr$, as the area is $2\pi r\, dr$ and

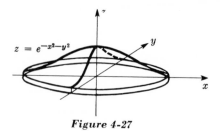

$$z = e^{-x^2-y^2}$$

Figure 4-27

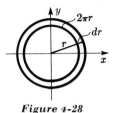

Figure 4-28

the integrand is constant in this region. Integration from 0 to R then, as above, gives the desired double integral (Fig. 4-28).

On reduction in right-angled coordinates, we obtain

$$V^{(R)} = \int_{-R}^{R} dx \int_{-\sqrt{R^2-x^2}}^{\sqrt{R^2-x^2}} e^{-x^2-y^2}\, dy.$$

This leads to a consideration of the indefinite integral $\int e^{-y^2}\, dy$, which cannot be expressed by functions introduced up to now. Nevertheless, as we have seen, the double integral can be evaluated by a reduction in polar coordinates.

If R increases without limit, then the plane integral converges to π. The quantity thus found is called the *improper double integral* of the given function over the whole plane.

On a reduction in right-angled coordinates, we obtain in this case

$$\pi = \int_{-\infty}^{\infty} dx \int_{-\infty}^{\infty} e^{-x^2-y^2}\, dy = \int_{-\infty}^{\infty} dx \left\{ e^{-x^2} \int_{-\infty}^{\infty} e^{-y^2}\, dy \right\},$$

or, introducing $\int_{-\infty}^{\infty} e^{-y^2}\, dy = I$, which is a finite quantity (the integral is convergent),

$$\pi = \int_{-\infty}^{\infty} I e^{-x^2}\, dx = I \int_{-\infty}^{\infty} e^{-x^2}\, dx = I^2,$$

and

$$I = \int_{-\infty}^{\infty} e^{-t^2}\, dt = \sqrt{\pi}.$$

In this way, surprisingly, it is possible to evaluate an ordinary improper integral, even if direct calculation is not possible (cf. p. 200). The success of this method is seen partly to be due to the possibility of separating the two variables x and y, i.e., of rewriting the given integrand as a product of two functions each of which is dependent upon only one of the two variables. The same method cannot be used for finite values of R, as the integration limits on y then depend on x. ☐

Green's Theorem

In this section we shall consider an important relation between line integrals and double integrals, the so-called *Green's theorem*.

Suppose a closed region ω in the XY-plane can at the same time be represented by inequalities $a \leq x \leq b, f(x) \leq y \leq g(x)$ and by inequalities $c \leq y \leq d, h(y) \leq x \leq i(y)$, where f, g, h, and i are functions with continuous derivatives in their respective domains (Fig. 4-29).

Consider now the double integral

$$I = \int_{\omega} [M'_x(x,y) - L'_y(x,y)] \, dA,$$

where L and M have continuous partial derivatives in an open region containing ω. On reduction in right-angled coordinates the following may be obtained:

$$I = \int_{\omega} M'_x(x,y) \, dA - \int_{\omega} L'_y(x,y) \, dA$$

$$= \int_c^d dy \int_{h(y)}^{i(y)} M'_x(x,y) \, dx - \int_a^b dx \int_{f(x)}^{g(x)} L'_y(x,y) \, dy$$

$$= \int_c^d [M(i(y),y) - M(h(y),y)] \, dy - \int_a^b [L(x,g(x)) - L(x,f(x))] \, dx.$$

Introducing k as the boundary curve of ω, assigned with a counter-clockwise direction, we further consider the line integral

$$J = \int_k L(x,y) \, dx + M(x,y) \, dy = \int_k L(x,y) \, dx + \int_k M(x,y) \, dy,$$

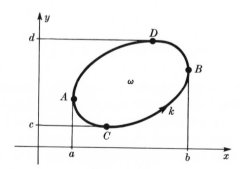

Figure 4-29

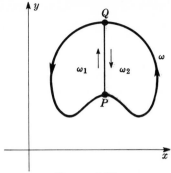

Figure 4-30

which may be rewritten as follows:

$$J = \int_{A\hat{C}B} L(x,y) \, dx - \int_{A\hat{D}B} L(x,y) \, dx + \int_{C\hat{B}D} M(x,y) \, dy$$
$$- \int_{C\hat{A}D} M(x,y) \, dy$$
$$= \int_a^b L(t,f(t)) \cdot 1 \, dt - \int_a^b L(t,g(t)) \cdot 1 \, dt + \int_c^d M(i(t),t) \cdot 1 \, dt$$
$$- \int_c^d M(h(t),t) \cdot 1 \, dt.$$

This completes the proof of Green's theorem for the region ω considered:

$$\oint_k L(x,y) \, dx + M(x,y) \, dy = \int_\omega [M'_x(x,y) - L'_y(x,y)] \, dA.$$

Here the circle with an arrow on it introduced in the formula simply emphasizes that the path of integration k, as mentioned, is to be traversed in the counterclockwise direction.

Green's theorem is valid also for more complicated regions. Suppose for example that ω is as suggested in Fig. 4-30. The theorem is easily seen to apply to both of the regions ω_1 and ω_2. Addition of the two resulting equations immediately gives the double integral wanted. But also the sum of the line integrals gives the line integral wanted as the two contributions from the line segment PQ cancel each other.

By means of Green's theorem a proof may be given for the previously mentioned sufficient condition for a given differential expression to be a total differential in a simply connected region (see p. 249). Also, Green's theorem has important applications in physics.

Applications of Double Integrals

In the above examples we have considered only positive functions, and the results obtained could all be interpreted as volumes of certain solids.

In general, the volume of a solid bounded by two surfaces $z = F(x,y)$ and $z = G(x,y)$, ($F(x,y) \leq G(x,y)$) with a common domain ω is obtained as $\int_\omega (G(x,y) - F(x,y)) \, dA$.

However, double integrals are not only used to calculate volumes. The determination of the center of mass of a given plane mass distribution is a typical example of other possible applications. This problem will now be considered.

The center of a system composed of two masses m_1 and m_2 located at the points P_1 and P_2, respectively, is the point C on the line segment P_1P_2 which divides this internally in the inverse ratio of the masses (Fig. 4-31). If the coordinates of P_1 and P_2 are (x_1,y_1) and (x_2,y_2), respectively, then the coordinates of the center of mass are thus obtained as

$$(x_c,y_c) = (x_1,y_1) + \frac{m_2}{m_1 + m_2}(x_2 - x_1, y_2 - y_1)$$
$$= \left(\frac{x_1m_1 + x_2m_2}{m_1 + m_2}, \frac{y_1m_1 + y_2m_2}{m_1 + m_2}\right).$$

Analogously, the coordinates of the center of mass for a total of n masses $m_1,m_2,\ldots,m_n$ located at points $(x_1,y_1),(x_2,y_2),\ldots,(x_n,y_n)$ are

$$(x_c,y_c) = \left(\frac{\sum_{i=1}^n x_im_i}{\sum_{i=1}^n m_i}, \frac{\sum_{i=1}^n y_im_i}{\sum_{i=1}^n m_i}\right).$$

The abscissa (ordinate) of the center of mass is thus obtained as the ratio of what is called the *static moment* of the mass distribution with respect to the Y-axis (X-axis) and the total mass of the system.

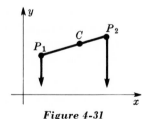

Figure 4-31

Consider now a region ω in the XY-plane with a distribution of mass given by the density function $\mu(x,y)$. Here the mass of an area element dA around the point (x,y) is $\mu(x,y)\, dA$. The total mass of the region is then obtained by a summation of all these, i.e., as $\int_\omega \mu(x,y)\, dA$.

The contributions of the individual area elements to the static moments with respect to the axes Y and X are $x\mu(x,y)\, dA$ and $y\mu(x,y)\, dA$. The total static moments will then be, respectively, $\int_\omega x\mu(x,y)\, dA$ and $\int_\omega y\mu(x,y)\, dA$. From this the coordinates of the center of mass are finally obtained as

$$(x_c, y_c) = \left(\frac{\displaystyle\int_\omega x\mu(x,y)\, dA}{\displaystyle\int_\omega \mu(x,y)\, dA}, \frac{\displaystyle\int_\omega y\mu(x,y)\, dA}{\displaystyle\int_\omega \mu(x,y)\, dA} \right).$$

For a plane curve, $\mathbf{r}(t) = (f(t), g(t))$, $\alpha \le t \le \beta$, with a distribution of mass given by the density function $\mu(t)$, the coordinates of the center of mass are obtained in a corresponding manner as

$$(x_c, y_c) = \left(\frac{\displaystyle\int_\alpha^\beta f(t)\mu(t)\left|\mathbf{r}'(t)\right| dt}{\displaystyle\int_\alpha^\beta \mu(t)\left|\mathbf{r}'(t)\right| dt}, \frac{\displaystyle\int_\alpha^\beta g(t)\mu(t)\left|\mathbf{r}'(t)\right| dt}{\displaystyle\int_\alpha^\beta \mu(t)\left|\mathbf{r}'(t)\right| dt} \right),$$

i.e., by means of ordinary definite integrals (see p. 212).

As might be expected, the coordinates of the center of mass for a three-dimensional mass distribution are found by the aid of so-called "triple integrals." These will be considered next.

Exercises

*1. Sketch the surface $z = x^2 + 4y^2$, $(|x| \le 1, |y| \le 1)$, and calculate the volume between this surface and the XY-plane.

*2. Sketch the surface $z = x^2 + 4y^2$, $(x^2 + y^2 \le 1)$, and calculate the volume between this surface and the XY-plane.

3. Evaluate the plane integral of the function $z = (x + y)/(x^2 + y^2)$ over the region between the circles with centers at $(1,0)$ and $(2,0)$ and radii 1 and 2, respectively.

*4. Find the center of gravity of a homogeneously weighted region in the XY-plane bounded by the parabola $y = x^2$ and the straight line $y = x + 6$.

5. Find the center of gravity of a 90° sector of a circle when (a) it is homogeneously weighted, (b) the mass density increases proportional to the square of the distance from the center.

*6. Find the center of gravity of a homogeneously weighted single cycloid arc.

7. Find the center of gravity of a homogeneously weighted region bounded by a single cycloid arc and the line between its end points.

Answers
1. $20/3$.
2. $5\pi/4$.
4. $(\frac{1}{2},4)$.
6. $(\pi a, \frac{4}{3}a)$.

4-7. TRIPLE INTEGRALS

Definition of a Triple Integral

The notion of a triple integral of a function of three variables is defined in complete analogy with the double integral.

Consider a function of three variables $F(x,y,z)$ continuous in a closed region Ω which has a volume V. The region Ω is divided into a number of smaller subregions. In each of these, an arbitrary point Q is chosen, and the product of the value $F(Q)$ and the volume ΔV of the corresponding subregion is determined (Fig. 4-32).

The sum of these products from all the subregions represents an *average sum*

$$\sum_i F(Q_i)\, \Delta_i V,$$

which with increasingly finer division exhibits a limit which is independent of the manner in which the limiting process is carried out if only the maximum diagonal of the subregions approaches zero. This limit is the *triple integral* (or volume integral) *of the function F over the region* Ω and is written

$$\iiint_\Omega F(x,y,z)\, dV \qquad \text{or} \qquad \int_\Omega F(x,y,z)\, dV.$$

There is no possibility of an obvious geometric interpretation here.

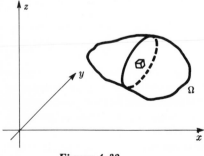

Figure 4-32

The domain of F involves all three dimensions of space; thus, as previously discussed (p. 229), not even a simple graphical representation of the function is possible. However, in the case of $F(x,y,z) = 1$, the triple integral simply gives the volume of Ω.

As an example of other applications of triple integrals we just mention the problem of determining the center of mass of a given spacial mass distribution. In case the density function is $\mu(x,y,z)$ (with domain Ω), then the coordinates of the center of mass may be expressed by triple integrals as

$$(x_c, y_c, z_c) = \left(\frac{\int_\Omega x\mu\, dV}{\int_\Omega \mu\, dV}, \frac{\int_\Omega y\mu\, dV}{\int_\Omega \mu\, dV}, \frac{\int_\Omega z\mu\, dV}{\int_\Omega \mu\, dV} \right).$$

Reduction in Right-Angled Coordinates

The evaluation of a triple integral is in general carried out by three consecutive (definite) integrations. We shall first consider a reduction in right-angled coordinates.

Let the region of integration Ω be bounded by the surfaces $z = g(x,y)$ and $z = f(x,y,)$ $(g(x,y) \geq f(x,y))$, where the functions g and f are defined and continuous in a common closed region ω, and (if necessary) a cylinder with cross section ω in the XY-plane (Fig. 4-33).

The projection of Ω on the XY-plane, i.e., ω, is now divided into (plane) subregions and in each of these a point is chosen. The area of the ith subregion is $\Delta_i A$ and the corresponding point (x_i, y_i). At the same time the projection of Ω on the Z-axis is divided into subintervals

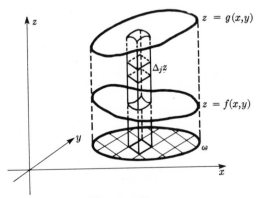

Figure 4-33

and a point is chosen in each of these. The length of the jth subinterval is $\Delta_j z$, while the corresponding point is z_j.

Corresponding to all this we obtain a division of Ω into (spacial) subregions such that the volume of a typical subregion containing the point (x_i, y_i, z_j) becomes $\Delta_i A \, \Delta_j z$. Ignoring again irregularities at the boundary (cf. p. 267), we may as an average sum use

$$S_2 = \sum_{i,j} F(x_i, y_i, z_j) \, \Delta_i A \, \Delta_j z = \sum_i \left[\sum_j F(x_i, y_i, z_j) \, \Delta_j z \right] \Delta_i A.$$

Here the latter expression may be considered as a specification of the order of summation: First, the contributions from all subregions in the ith "column" perpendicular to the XY-plane are added. Second, the contributions from the different columns are added.

As the division on the Z-axis becomes increasingly finer, the quantity $\Sigma_j F(x_i, y_i, z_j) \, \Delta_j z$ will in the limit become the definite integral

$$\int_{f(x_i, y_i)}^{g(x_i, y_i)} F(x_i, y_i, z) \, dz,$$

i.e., the value at the point $(x_i, y_i,)$ of the function

$$\phi(x,y) = \int_{f(x,y)}^{g(x,y)} F(x,y,z) \, dz.$$

Introducing this in S_2 we obtain $S_1 = \Sigma_i \phi(x_i, y_i) \, \Delta_i A$, which again in the limit becomes the double integral

$$\int_\omega \phi(x,y) \, dA = \int_\omega \left\{ \int_{f(x,y)}^{g(x,y)} F(x,y,z) \, dz \right\} dA \qquad \text{or}$$

$$\int_\omega dA \int_{f(x,y)}^{g(x,y)} F(x,y,z) \, dz.$$

Also here, the above "step-wise" limiting process can be developed into an exact proof (cf. p. 269):

$$\int_\Omega F(x,y,z) \, dV = \int_\omega dA \int_{f(x,y)}^{g(x,y)} F(x,y,z) \, dz.$$

Thus for the evaluation of the triple integral, an ordinary integration followed by a double integration is required.

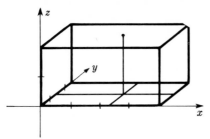

Figure 4-34

If the latter is carried out by a reduction in right-angled coordinates, the triple integral is also said to be evaluated by a *reduction in right-angled coordinates*:

$$\int_{\Omega} F(x,y,z)\, dV = \iiint_{\Omega} F(x,y,z)\, dx\, dy\, dz.$$

Here a box with sides dx, dy, and dz parallel to the axes is considered as the *infinitesimal space element*. The volume of this is $dV = dx\, dy\, dz$.

Example 4-21. $F(x,y,z) = x + y + z$. $\Omega: 0 \le x \le 4, 0 \le y \le 3$, $0 \le z \le 2$ (Fig. 4-34).

$$\begin{aligned}
\int_{\Omega} (x + y + z)\, dV &= \int_0^4 dx \int_0^3 dy \int_0^2 (x + y + z)\, dz \\
&= \int_0^4 dx \int_0^3 dy[xz + yz + \tfrac{1}{2}z^2]_{z=0}^{z=2} \\
&= \int_0^4 dx \int_0^3 (2x + 2y + 2)\, dy \\
&= \int_0^4 (6x + 9 + 6)\, dx = 108.
\end{aligned}$$

The three integrations are carried out just as readily in any other order. □

Example 4-22. $F(x,y,z) = 1/x^2$; Ω: the region considered in Example 4-16 (p. 270).

We wish to evaluate the triple integral by a reduction in right-angled coordinates with order of integration z,y,x. As the intervals of integration we then have $0 \le z \le \tfrac{1}{8}xy$, $x - 1 \le y \le 2x$, and $2 \le x \le 4$.

$$\int_\Omega \frac{1}{x^2} \, dV = \int_2^4 dx \int_{x-1}^{2x} dy \int_0^{\frac{1}{4}xy} \frac{1}{x^2} \, dz$$

$$= \int_2^4 dx \int_{x-1}^{2x} dy \left[\frac{z}{x^2}\right]_{z=0}^{z=\frac{1}{4}xy} = \int_2^4 dx \int_{x-1}^{2x} \frac{y}{8x} \, dy$$

$$= \int_2^4 dx \left[\frac{y^2}{16x}\right]_{y=x-1}^{y=2x} = \int_2^4 \left(\frac{(2x)^2}{16x} - \frac{(x-1)^2}{16x}\right) dx$$

$$= \int_2^4 \left(\frac{3}{16} x + \frac{1}{8} - \frac{1}{16x}\right) dx$$

$$= \left[\tfrac{3}{32}x^2 + \tfrac{1}{8}x - \tfrac{1}{16}\ln x\right]_2^4$$

$$= \tfrac{3}{2} + \tfrac{1}{2} - \tfrac{1}{16}\ln 4 - \tfrac{3}{8} + \tfrac{1}{16}\ln 2 - \tfrac{1}{4}$$

$$= 1\tfrac{5}{8} - \tfrac{1}{16}\ln 2.$$

Here the integrand $F(x,y,z) = 1/x^2$ is dependent only on x and therefore appears as a constant in the first two integrations. Furthermore, as any cross section perpendicular to the X-axis of the solid considered is a trapezium which has an area that can be found without integration, the problem of evaluating the given triple integral can at once be reduced to a single integration:

Consider an infinitesimal disk of the solid bounded by two planes perpendicular to the X-axis through the points x and $x + dx$. The volume of this disk is $(\tfrac{3}{16}x^3 + \tfrac{1}{8}x^2 - \tfrac{1}{16}x) \, dx$ (see p. 271). Furthermore, the value of the integrand in the disk may be considered as a constant equal to $1/x^2$. Therefore the contribution to the triple integral from this disk is $(1/x^2)(\tfrac{3}{16}x^3 + \tfrac{1}{8}x^2 - \tfrac{1}{16}x) \, dx$. The value of the triple integral is then obtained by integrating the individual infinitesimal contributions:

$$\int_\Omega \frac{1}{x^2} \, dV = \int_2^4 \frac{1}{x^2} (\tfrac{3}{16}x^3 + \tfrac{1}{8}x^2 - \tfrac{1}{16}x) \, dx = 1\tfrac{5}{8} - \tfrac{1}{16}\ln 2. \qquad \square$$

Reduction in Cylindrical Coordinates

If the double integration mentioned on page 284 is carried out by a reduction in polar coordinates (ρ,ϕ), then the triple integral considered is said to be evaluated by a *reduction in cylindrical coordinates* (cf. p. 219):

$$\int_\Omega F(x,y,z) \, dV = \iiint_\Omega F(\rho \cos \phi, \rho \sin \phi, z)\rho \, d\rho \, d\phi \, dz.$$

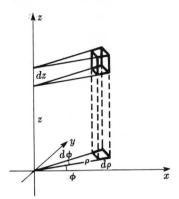

Figure 4-35

The infinitesimal space element used here is a solid bounded by surfaces corresponding to constant values of each of the three cylindrical coordinates: Two right circular cylinders having the Z-axis as their axis and radii ρ and $\rho + d\rho$, two half-planes bounded by the Z-axis at angles of ϕ and $\phi + d\phi$ to the XZ-plane, and two planes perpendicular to the Z-axis through the points z and $z + dz$ respectively (Fig. 4-35).

The "sides" of the infinitesimal space element, which is to be considered as a box, are then $d\rho$, $\rho \, d\phi$, and dz; hence the volume of the space element is $dV = \rho \, d\rho \, d\phi \, dz$, in agreement with the formula.

Example 4-23. $F(x,y,z) = xyz$; Ω: $0 \leq z \leq 3$, $0 \leq \rho \leq 2$, $0 \leq \phi \leq \pi/2$. The form of the region of integration makes a reduction

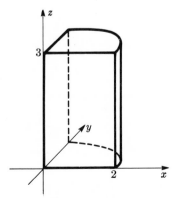

Figure 4-36

in cylindrical coordinates natural. The three integrations may here be carried out in any order (Fig. 4-36).

$$\int_\Omega xyz\, dV = \int_0^3 dz \int_0^2 d\rho \int_0^{\pi/2} \rho \cos\phi\, \rho \sin\phi\, z\, \rho\, d\phi$$

$$= \int_0^3 dz \int_0^2 d\rho \left[-\frac{z\rho^3}{4} \cos 2\phi \right]_{\phi=0}^{\phi=\pi/2}$$

$$= \int_0^3 dz \int_0^2 \frac{z\rho^3}{2}\, d\rho = \int_0^3 dz \left[\frac{z\rho^4}{8} \right]_{\rho=0}^{\rho=2}$$

$$= \int_0^3 2z\, dz = 9. \qquad \square$$

Reduction in Spherical Coordinates

As a third possibility for the evaluation of triple integrals we shall now consider a *reduction in spherical coordinates*.

In the division, spheres with centers at O are used together with right circular cones with the Z-axis as their axis and half-planes bounded by the Z-axis, i.e., surfaces corresponding to constant values of each of the three spherical coordinates r, θ, and ϕ (Fig. 4-37 and p. 218).

The infinitesimal space element is then bounded by two spheres with radii r and $r + dr$, two cones with half-vertex angles θ and $\theta + d\theta$, and

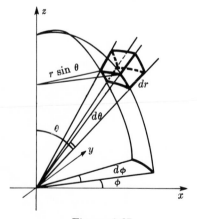

Figure 4-37

two half-planes which are at angles of ϕ and $\phi + d\phi$, respectively, to the XZ-plane. Also this infinitesimal space element is to be considered as a box. Its sides are dr, $r\, d\theta$, and $r \sin \theta\, d\phi$, giving a volume of $dV = r^2 \sin \theta\, dr\, d\theta\, d\phi$:

$$\int_\Omega F(x,y,z)\, dV$$
$$= \iiint_\Omega F(r \sin \theta \cos \phi, r \sin \theta \sin \phi, r \cos \theta) r^2 \sin \theta\, dr\, d\theta\, d\phi.$$

Example 4-24. $F(x,y,z) = xyz$; $\Omega: 0 \leq r \leq 2, 0 \leq \theta \leq \pi/2\ 0 \leq \phi \leq \pi/2$ (Fig. 4-38). The form of the region of integration makes a reduction in spherical coordinates natural:

$$\int_\Omega xyz\, dV = \int_0^2 dr \int_0^{\pi/2} d\theta \int_0^{\pi/2} r \sin \theta \cos \phi\, r \sin \theta \sin \phi\, r \cos \theta\, r^2 \sin \theta\, d\phi$$
$$= \int_0^2 dr \int_0^{\pi/2} d\theta \left[r^5 \sin^3 \theta \cos \theta \frac{\sin^2 \phi}{2} \right]_{\phi=0}^{\phi=\pi/2}$$
$$= \int_0^2 dr \int_0^{\pi/2} \frac{r^5}{2} \sin^3 \theta \cos \theta\, d\theta$$
$$= \int_0^2 dr \left[\frac{r^5}{8} \sin^4 \theta \right]_{\theta=0}^{\theta=\pi/2}$$
$$= \int_0^2 \frac{r^5}{8}\, dr = \frac{4}{3}. \qquad \square$$

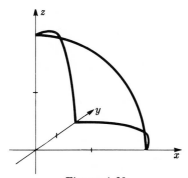

Figure 4-38

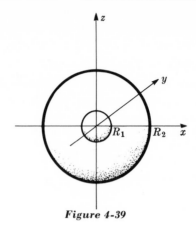

Figure 4-39

Example 4-25. $F(x,y,z) = 1/(x^2 + y^2 + z^2)^2$; Ω: $R_1 \leq r \leq R_2$, $0 \leq \theta \leq \pi$, $0 \leq \phi \leq 2\pi$ (Fig. 4-39).

$$\int_\Omega \frac{1}{(x^2 + y^2 + z^2)^2} \, dV = \int_{R_1}^{R_2} dr \int_0^\pi d\theta \int_0^{2\pi} \frac{1}{r^4} r^2 \sin\theta \, d\phi$$

$$= \int_{R_1}^{R_2} dr \int_0^\pi \frac{2\pi}{r^2} \sin\theta \, d\theta$$

$$= \int_{R_1}^{R_2} \frac{4\pi}{r^2} \, dr = 4\pi \left(\frac{1}{R_1} - \frac{1}{R_2} \right).$$

In this case the result of the first two integrations can immediately be written. The volume of an infinitesimal spherical shell bounded by spheres with centers at O and radii r and $r + dr$ is $4\pi r^2 \, dr$. As the integrand inside this is constant and equal to $1/r^4$, the spherical shell contributes $(1/r^4) \, 4\pi r^2 \, dr = (1/r^2) \, 4\pi \, dr$ to the triple integral. The value of the triple integral is then obtained as above by integration with respect to r:

$$\int_\Omega \frac{1}{(x^2 + y^2 + z^2)^2} \, dV = \int_{R_1}^{R_2} \frac{4\pi}{r^2} \, dr = 4\pi \left(\frac{1}{R_1} - \frac{1}{R_2} \right).$$

In case R_2 tends to infinity, then a limit of $4\pi/R_1$ is obtained. The triple integral extended over the entire space, except for a sphere with center at O, is thus convergent. The triple integral is seen to diverge, however, as R_1 approaches 0. □

Change of Variables in Triple Integrals

It has been shown above how the evaluation of a triple integral can be carried out in different ways. If we consider the reductions in right-angled and spherical coordinates, we have

$$\iiint_{\Omega} F(x,y,z)\ dx\ dy\ dz$$
$$= \iiint_{\Omega} F(r \sin \theta \cos \phi, r \sin \theta \sin \phi, r \cos \theta) r^2 \sin \theta\ dr\ d\theta\ d\phi.$$

This formula can be said to give a procedure for a *change of variables* in a triple integral.

The corresponding situation is well known in the study of ordinary definite integrals under the name of integration by substitution. Here a new variable is introduced by means of a monotone function $x = \phi(t)$, which has a continuous derivative. The conditions on ϕ assure the existence of an inverse continuous function ϕ^{-1}. Suppose $a < b$ and let the interval $[a,b]$ be mapped onto the interval $[\alpha,\beta]$ by the function ϕ^{-1}. The previously mentioned formula (p. 158) may then be rewritten

$$\int_a^b f(x)\ dx = \int_\alpha^\beta f(\phi(t)) |\phi'(t)|\ dt.$$

Above we found a few rules for change of variables in triple integrals by direct geometrical considerations of infinitesimal space elements; we shall now see how the whole problem can be considered from a more general point of view.

Let the new coordinates in space be introduced by means of the following equations:

$$x = f(u,v,w), \qquad y = g(u,v,w), \qquad z = h(u,v,w).$$

Here f, g, and h are functions of three variables having continuous partial derivatives and giving a one-to-one correspondence between what shall be considered as the *new coordinates* (u,v,w) and the old usual right-angled coordinates (x,y,z) of an arbitrary point in an open region of space.

Even if this may lead to a very complicated relationship between the new and the old coordinates, we still have, as an approximation, a very simple (linear) relationship between the corresponding *increments* of the coordinates:

$$\Delta x = \frac{\partial x}{\partial u} \Delta u + \frac{\partial x}{\partial v} \Delta v + \frac{\partial x}{\partial w} \Delta w,$$

$$\Delta y = \frac{\partial y}{\partial u} \Delta u + \frac{\partial y}{\partial v} \Delta v + \frac{\partial y}{\partial w} \Delta w,$$

$$\Delta z = \frac{\partial z}{\partial u} \Delta u + \frac{\partial z}{\partial v} \Delta v + \frac{\partial z}{\partial w} \Delta w.$$

Here the coefficients which occur are constants, the values of the derivatives considered at the point from which the increments are calculated. Let this point have the old coordinates (x_0, y_0, z_0) and the new coordinates (u_0, v_0, w_0).

Ignoring temporarily the origin of the above equations, we consider $(\Delta u, \Delta v, \Delta w)$ and $(\Delta x, \Delta y, \Delta z)$ as vectors in a usual right-angled coordinate system. The connection between these two vectors is then given by a linear vector function:

$$
\begin{Bmatrix} \Delta x \\ \Delta y \\ \Delta z \end{Bmatrix}
=
\begin{pmatrix}
\dfrac{\partial x}{\partial u} & \dfrac{\partial x}{\partial v} & \dfrac{\partial x}{\partial w} \\
\dfrac{\partial y}{\partial u} & \dfrac{\partial y}{\partial v} & \dfrac{\partial y}{\partial w} \\
\dfrac{\partial z}{\partial u} & \dfrac{\partial z}{\partial v} & \dfrac{\partial z}{\partial w}
\end{pmatrix}
\begin{Bmatrix} \Delta u \\ \Delta v \\ \Delta w \end{Bmatrix}.
$$

We have already considered linear vector functions and found that the points inside a box spanned by vectors lying on the axes of the coordinate system, in case the determinant of the transformation matrix is different from zero, are mapped onto the points inside a parallelepiped. Furthermore, it was found that the absolute value of this determinant gave the scale of volume (see p. 49).

We may now return to the original problem, that of expressing a given triple integral $\int_\Omega F(x,y,z)\, dV$ in the new coordinates (u,v,w). As a subregion of Ω we naturally choose a set of points (u,v,w) determined by inequalities such as

$$u_0 \leq u \leq u_0 + \Delta_0 u, \qquad v_0 \leq v \leq v_0 + \Delta_0 v, \qquad w_0 \leq w \leq w_0 + \Delta_0 w.$$

The form of the subregion obtained is clearly dependent on the type of the new coordinates. However, it will always—to the approximation used—be a parallelepiped. When described in the old coordinates, which have the usual geometrical interpretation, the subregion is seen to be the parallelepiped spanned by the vectors

$$\Delta_0 u \begin{Bmatrix} \dfrac{\partial x}{\partial u} \\[4pt] \dfrac{\partial y}{\partial u} \\[4pt] \dfrac{\partial z}{\partial u} \end{Bmatrix}, \qquad \Delta_0 v \begin{Bmatrix} \dfrac{\partial x}{\partial v} \\[4pt] \dfrac{\partial y}{\partial v} \\[4pt] \dfrac{\partial z}{\partial v} \end{Bmatrix}, \qquad \Delta_0 w \begin{Bmatrix} \dfrac{\partial x}{\partial w} \\[4pt] \dfrac{\partial y}{\partial w} \\[4pt] \dfrac{\partial z}{\partial w} \end{Bmatrix}.$$

The volume of the subregion is therefore (cf. p. 39):

$$\Delta V = \Delta_0 u \, \Delta_0 v \, \Delta_0 w \cdot \left\| \begin{matrix} \dfrac{\partial x}{\partial u} & \dfrac{\partial x}{\partial v} & \dfrac{\partial x}{\partial w} \\[6pt] \dfrac{\partial y}{\partial u} & \dfrac{\partial y}{\partial v} & \dfrac{\partial y}{\partial w} \\[6pt] \dfrac{\partial z}{\partial u} & \dfrac{\partial z}{\partial v} & \dfrac{\partial z}{\partial w} \end{matrix} \right\|,$$

where the last factor is the absolute value of the so-called *Jacobian*, i.e., the determinant corresponding to the linear vector function discussed above. The Jacobian is also written $\partial(x,y,z)/\partial(u,v,w)$. The contribution to the average sum of the subregion considered is thus

$$F(x_0,y_0,z_0)\,\Delta V$$
$$= F(f(u_0,v_0,w_0),g(u_0,v_0,w_0),h(u_0,v_0,w_0)) \left| \frac{\partial(x,y,z)}{\partial(u,v,w)} \right| \Delta_0 u \, \Delta_0 v \, \Delta_0 w.$$

When the whole region of integration is divided in a similar manner, then an average sum is obtained which in the limit gives the formula wanted:

$$\int_\Omega F(x,y,z)\,dV = \iiint_\Omega F(f(u,v,w),g(u,v,w),h(u,v,w)) \left| \frac{\partial(x,y,z)}{\partial(u,v,w)} \right| du\,dv\,dw.$$

For spherical coordinates we obtain

$$\frac{\partial(x,y,z)}{\partial(u,v,w)} = \frac{\partial(x,y,z)}{\partial(r,\theta,\phi)} = \begin{vmatrix} \sin\theta\cos\phi & r\cos\theta\cos\phi & -r\sin\theta\sin\phi \\ \sin\theta\sin\phi & r\cos\theta\sin\phi & r\sin\theta\cos\phi \\ \cos\theta & -r\sin\theta & 0 \end{vmatrix}$$
$$= \cos\theta(r^2\cos\theta\sin\theta) + r\sin\theta(r\sin^2\theta) = r^2\sin\theta,$$

in agreement with the previous result.

A Misuse of Infinitesimals

A corresponding formula is easily seen to be valid for a change of variables in double integrals. Thus for a change from right-angled to polar coordinates in the plane we obtain

$$\frac{\partial(x,y)}{\partial(u,v)} = \frac{\partial(x,y)}{\partial(r,\theta)} = \begin{vmatrix} \cos\theta & -r\sin\theta \\ \sin\theta & r\cos\theta \end{vmatrix} = r.$$

This of course agrees completely with our previous results:

$$\iint_\omega F(x,y)\, dx\, dy = \iint_\omega F(r\cos\theta,\, r\sin\theta) r\, dr\, d\theta.$$

We shall now try another procedure to carry out a change of variables in a multiple integral, a method which superficially would appear to be satisfactory. We shall consider the above-mentioned two-dimensional case, where for the sake of simplicity we choose $F(x,y) = 1$. From $x = r\cos\theta$ and $y = r\sin\theta$, we obtain

$$dx = \cos\theta\, dr - r\sin\theta\, d\theta,$$
$$dy = \sin\theta\, dr + r\cos\theta\, d\theta.$$

On substitution this gives

$$\int_\omega 1\, dx\, dy = \int_\omega 1(\cos\theta\, dr - r\sin\theta\, d\theta)(\sin\theta\, dr + r\cos\theta\, d\theta)$$

$$= \int_\omega \cos\theta\sin\theta\, dr\, dr + \int_\omega r(\cos^2\theta - \sin^2\theta)\, dr\, d\theta$$

$$- \int_\omega r^2\cos\theta\sin\theta\, d\theta\, d\theta.$$

The first and the last terms on the right side are meaningless. Therefore the method obviously must be abandoned.

However, as in the previous we have been able—successfully—to use similar less rigorous considerations, it is of some interest to see why the above procedure does not lead to the desired result.

Consider a typical subregion. After the introduction of polar coordinates, this is composed of the points in the plane which have polar coordinates (r,θ) that satisfy inequalities of the form $r_0 \leq r \leq r_0 + \Delta r$, $\theta_0 \leq \theta \leq \theta_0 + \Delta\theta$. To successfully carry out further calculations, an expression must be found which to "a sufficient approximation" gives the area ΔA of the subregion considered. As discussed previously, this is the case with $\Delta r \cdot r\, \Delta\theta$.

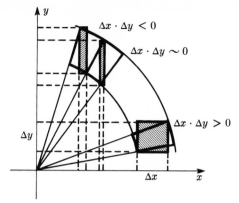

Figure 4-40

In the above formal calculations, we have used as an expression for ΔA the product $\Delta x \cdot \Delta y$, or—again to a sufficient approximation—the expression

$$(\cos \theta_0 \Delta r - r_0 \sin \theta_0 \Delta \theta)(\sin \theta_0 \Delta r + r_0 \cos \theta_0 \Delta \theta).$$

Geometrically, this gives the area of a rectangle with sides parallel to the axes determined by the points (r_0, θ_0) and $(r_0 + \Delta r, \theta_0 + \Delta \theta)$.

However, this quantity has no unique relation to ΔA. For a given value of ΔA we can by suitable choice of (positive values) for Δr and $\Delta \theta$ about an arbitrary point even obtain a negative value of the product (Fig. 4-40). Thus it is clear that further formal calculation will not give any definite numerical result, much less the correct result.

The notion of *multiple integrals* can be extended further to integrals of functions of more than three variables over regions of the corresponding space. Jacobians are also defined and can be used as above.

Exercises

*1. Evaluate the triple integral of the function xyz over the region Ω, where the interior of Ω consists of those points between the surface $z = xy$ and the XY-plane whose projection in the XY-plane lies inside the triangle OAB ($A = (2,2)$, $B = (2,4)$).

*2. Find the volume of the solid bounded by the surface with the equation $r = 2 + \cos \theta$ in spherical coordinates.

3. Evaluate the triple integral $\int_{\Omega} (x^2 + y^2 + z^2) \, dV$, where Ω is the sphere with radius R and center $(0,0,0)$.

4. Find the total electric charge of a cylinder of rotation with radius R and height H when the charge density increases exponentially with the square of the distance from the axis of the cylinder.

5. Find the center of gravity of a homogeneously dense semisphere.
*6. The axes of two cylinders of rotation with the same radius R intersect at a right angle. Find the volume of the body thus bounded.

Answers
1. 60.
2. $40\pi/3$.
6. $16R^3/3$.

4-8. SURFACE INTEGRALS

Definition of a Surface Integral

Another important type of integral, the so-called *surface integral*, will now be discussed.

Consider in space a surface F which has an area S together with a function of three variables, $G(x,y,z)$, which is continuous in a region of space containing the surface. The surface is imagined to be divided into a number of smaller parts. On each of these an arbitrary point Q is chosen, and the product of $G(Q)$ and the area ΔS of the corresponding part of the surface is determined (Fig. 4-41).

The sum of all such products defines an *average sum* $\Sigma_i G(Q_i)\,\Delta_i S$, which on increasingly finer division of the surface exhibits a limit which is independent of the way in which the limiting process is carried out if only the maximum diagonal of the parts of the surface approaches zero.

This limit is called the *surface integral of the function G over the surface F*. It is written

$$\iint\limits_{F} G(x,y,z)\,dS \qquad \text{or} \qquad \int\limits_{F} G(x,y,z)\,dS.$$

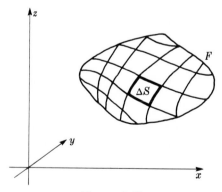

Figure 4-41

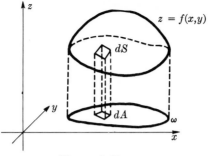

Figure 4-42

If $G(x,y,z) = 1$, then the surface integral simply gives the area S of the given surface. The problem of determining the center of mass corresponding to a given distribution on a surface F may also be solved by means of surface integrals. If the density function is $\mu(x,y,z)$ (with domain F), then

$$(x_c,y_c,z_c) = \left(\frac{\int_F x\mu \, dS}{\int_F \mu \, dS}, \frac{\int_F y\mu \, dS}{\int_F \mu \, dS}, \frac{\int_F z\mu \, dS}{\int_F \mu \, dS} \right).$$

Evaluation of Surface Integrals

The problem of evaluating a surface integral can generally be reduced to that of evaluating a double integral.

We limit ourselves to consideration of a surface F appearing as the graph of a function $z = f(x,y)$. This function is assumed to have continuous partial derivatives in its domain ω which is a closed region of the XY-plane.

Corresponding to an infinitesimal plane element of area dA about the point (x,y) in the region ω, an infinitesimal surface element of area dS is obtained on F about the point $(x,y, f(x,y))$ (Fig. 4-42).

As a vector on the normal to the surface at this point we may choose $(f'_x(x,y), f'_y(x,y), -1)$. A unit vector on the normal is then

$$\frac{1}{\sqrt{f'^2_x + f'^2_y + 1}} \, (f'_x, f'_y, -1).$$

For the determination of the angle ϕ between dA and dS we therefore have

$$\cos \phi = (0,0,-1) \cdot \frac{1}{\sqrt{f_x'^2 + f_y'^2 + 1}} (f_x',f_y',-1) = \frac{1}{\sqrt{f_x'^2 + f_y'^2 + 1}}.$$

But dA arises from dS by a (normal) projection through the angle ϕ:

$$dA = dS \left|\cos \phi\right| \quad \text{or} \quad dS = \sqrt{(f_x'(x,y))^2 + (f_y'(x,y))^2 + 1}\, dA.$$

The contribution to the surface integral from the surface element considered thus becomes

$$G(x,y,f(x,y)) \sqrt{(f_x'(x,y))^2 + (f_y'(x,y))^2 + 1}\, dA.$$

Hence the whole surface integral is obtained as

$$\int_F G(x,y,z)\, dS = \int_\omega G(x,y,f(x,y)) \sqrt{(f_x'(x,y))^2 + (f_y'(x,y))^2 + 1}\, dA.$$

Example 4-26. Determine the center of mass of a semispherical surface with a homogeneous mass distribution (Fig. 4-43). With the positioning used in the figure, the abscissa and the ordinate of the center of mass from considerations of symmetry are seen to be 0. This can, of course, also be proved by calculation.

The given surface has the equation $z = \sqrt{R^2 - x^2 - y^2}$. Thus

$$\frac{\partial z}{\partial x} = -\frac{x}{z}, \qquad \frac{\partial z}{\partial y} = -\frac{y}{z},$$

and

$$dS = \sqrt{\frac{x^2}{R^2 - x^2 - y^2} + \frac{y^2}{R^2 - x^2 - y^2} + 1}\, dA = \frac{R}{\sqrt{R^2 - x^2 - y^2}}\, dA.$$

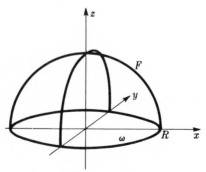

Figure 4-43

As the mass density is constant, the z-coordinate of the center of mass is found as

$$z_c = \frac{\int_F \mu z \, dS}{\int_F \mu \, dS} = \frac{\int_F z \, dS}{\int_F dS}.$$

Here

$$\int_F dS = \int_\omega \frac{R}{\sqrt{R^2 - x^2 - y^2}} \, dA = \int_0^{2\pi} d\theta \int_0^R \frac{R}{\sqrt{R^2 - r^2}} \, r \, dr$$

$$= \int_0^{2\pi} d\theta [-R \sqrt{R^2 - r^2}]_0^R = 2\pi R^2.$$

This is in agreement with the well-known formula for the area of a spherical surface. Further,

$$\int_F z \, dS = \int_\omega \sqrt{R^2 - x^2 - y^2} \, \frac{R}{\sqrt{R^2 - x^2 - y^2}} \, dA = \int_\omega R \, dA = \pi R^3.$$

From this is finally obtained $z_c = \pi R^3 / 2\pi R^2 = R/2$. Incidentally, this final result could also have been found without integration, as the areas of spherical segments which have the same heights are known to be equal. □

Exercises

*1. Evaluate the area of the surface $z = \sqrt{2xy}$ $(0 \leq x \leq 2, 0 \leq y \leq x)$.
*2. Evaluate the area of the surface $z = 1 - x^2 - y^2$ $(x^2 + y^2 \leq 1)$.

Answers
1. $8\sqrt{2}/3$.
2. $(\pi/6)(5\sqrt{5} - 1)$.

4-9. VECTOR ANALYSIS

Scalar and Vector Fields

A function from some set of points in three-dimensional space to the set of real numbers is often called a *scalar field*. Similarly, a function from a set of points in space to the set of (three-dimensional) vectors is called a *vector field*.

Introducing a (usual right-angled right-handed) coordinate system S, a scalar field will be represented by a real-valued function ϕ of three real variables, where $\phi(x,y,z)$ is the value of the scalar field at the point which in S has coordinates (x,y,z). Similarly, a vector field will be represented by one vector-valued function $\mathbf{V}$ of three real variables or by three real-valued functions V_x, V_y, and V_z of three real variables, where $\mathbf{V}(x,y,z) = (V_x(x,y,z), V_y(x,y,z), V_z(x,y,z))$ represents the value, as it appears in S, of the vector field at the point which in S has coordinates (x,y,z).

In this appearance we have previously had examples of both scalar fields (mass densities, p. 283) and vector fields (force fields, p. 263). In the following we shall always assume that such functions of three variables are sufficiently "well-behaved" (cf. p. 201).

However, it must be emphasized that the notion of a scalar field or a vector field is introduced without reference to any particular coordinate system. Thus a given scalar (vector) field will in general be represented by different real functions in different coordinate systems. The problems arising in this connection may be considered as extensions of the transformation problems regarding scalars and vectors treated previously (Section 1-3). Only now there is an infinity of scalars (vectors), each of these being attached to a definite point in space with coordinates depending upon the coordinate system considered.

Different Representations of a Given Field

Let S and S^1 be two usual right-angled right-handed coordinate systems in space, and let (x,y,z) and (x^1,y^1,z^1) be the coordinates in S and S^1, respectively, of an arbitrary point in space. The relation between these coordinates is then of the form

$$\begin{Bmatrix} x \\ y \\ z \end{Bmatrix} = \begin{Bmatrix} x_0 \\ y_0 \\ z_0 \end{Bmatrix} + \begin{Bmatrix} \alpha_1 & \beta_1 & \gamma_1 \\ \alpha_2 & \beta_2 & \gamma_2 \\ \alpha_3 & \beta_3 & \gamma_3 \end{Bmatrix} \begin{Bmatrix} x^1 \\ y^1 \\ z^1 \end{Bmatrix}$$

(cf. p. 21). Here the square matrix

$$Q = \begin{Bmatrix} \alpha_1 & \beta_1 & \gamma_1 \\ \alpha_2 & \beta_2 & \gamma_2 \\ \alpha_3 & \beta_3 & \gamma_3 \end{Bmatrix}$$

is orthogonal, with a positive determinant (cf. p. 66).

If a scalar field is given in the system S by the function $\phi(x,y,z)$, then the function of the field in system S^1 is obtained as

$$\phi^1(x^1,y^1,z^1) = \phi(x_0 + \alpha_1 x^1 + \beta_1 y^1 + \gamma_1 z^1, \; y_0 + \alpha_2 x^1 + \beta_2 y^1 + \gamma_2 z^1, \\ z_0 + \alpha_3 x^1 + \beta_3 y^1 + \gamma_3 z^1).$$

This can be written briefly as $\phi(x,y,z) = \phi^1(x^1,y^1,z^1)$. It is understood here that on the left side x, y, and z are to be expressed in terms of x^1, y^1, and z^1—or conversely, on the right side, x^1, y^1, and z^1 in terms of x, y, and z. The only important thing is that the point coordinates appearing from systems S and S^1 in the above equation belong to the same point in space.

Similarly, the relation between the two vector functions

$$\mathbf{V}(x,y,z) = (V_x(x,y,z), \; V_y(x,y,z), \; V_z(x,y,z)),$$
$$\mathbf{V}^1(x^1,y^1,z^1) = (V_x^{1}(x^1,y^1,z^1), \; V_y^{1}(x^1,y^1,z^1), \; V_z^{1}(x^1,y^1,z^1)),$$

which describe the same vector field in the two systems S and S^1, respectively, is

$$\begin{Bmatrix} V_x(x,y,z) \\ V_y(x,y,z) \\ V_z(x,y,z) \end{Bmatrix} = \begin{Bmatrix} \alpha_1 & \beta_1 & \gamma_1 \\ \alpha_2 & \beta_2 & \gamma_2 \\ \alpha_3 & \beta_3 & \gamma_3 \end{Bmatrix} \begin{Bmatrix} V_x^{1}(x^1,y^1,z^1) \\ V_y^{1}(x^1,y^1,z^1) \\ V_z^{1}(x^1,y^1,z^1) \end{Bmatrix}$$

(p. 22). Again the independent variables (x,y,z) and (x^1,y^1,z^1) which appear belong to the same point in space.

The Gradient Field

From a given scalar field it is possible in a simple manner to derive a vector field. This is the so-called *gradient field* of the scalar field.

In an arbitrary system of coordinates its components are obtained as the partial derivatives of the function representing the given scalar field. Using the same notation as above, we thus have the following: In S we get the gradient of ϕ as

$$\mathbf{grad} \; \phi(x,y,z) = \left(\frac{\partial \phi(x,y,z)}{\partial x}, \; \frac{\partial \phi(x,y,z)}{\partial y}, \; \frac{\partial \phi(x,y,z)}{\partial z} \right),$$

while in S^1 we get

$$\mathbf{grad}^1 \; \phi^1(x^1,y^1,z^1) = \left(\frac{\partial \phi^1(x^1,y^1,z^1)}{\partial x^1}, \; \frac{\partial \phi^1(x^1,y^1,z^1)}{\partial y^1}, \; \frac{\partial \phi^1(x^1,y^1,z^1)}{\partial z^1} \right).$$

It is obvious that $(\partial\phi/\partial x, \; \partial\phi/\partial y, \; \partial\phi/\partial z)$ defines a vector field, by giving its representation in S. Also it is obvious that $(\partial\phi^1/\partial x^1, \; \partial\phi^1/\partial y^1, \; \partial\phi^1/\partial z^1)$ defines a vector field—by giving its representation in

S^1. The problem is to show that the same vector field results in either case. Only then will it be permissible to talk about the gradient field as something existing independent of a particular coordinate system, i.e., as a field derived only from the given scalar field.

By means of the chain rule (p. 237) a proof is easily obtained:

$$\frac{\partial \phi^1}{\partial x^1} = \frac{\partial \phi}{\partial x}\frac{\partial x}{\partial x^1} + \frac{\partial \phi}{\partial y}\frac{\partial y}{\partial x^1} + \frac{\partial \phi}{\partial z}\frac{\partial z}{\partial x^1} = \alpha_1 \frac{\partial \phi}{\partial x} + \alpha_2 \frac{\partial \phi}{\partial y} + \alpha_3 \frac{\partial \phi}{\partial z},$$

$$\frac{\partial \phi^1}{\partial y^1} = \frac{\partial \phi}{\partial x}\frac{\partial x}{\partial y^1} + \frac{\partial \phi}{\partial y}\frac{\partial y}{\partial y^1} + \frac{\partial \phi}{\partial z}\frac{\partial z}{\partial y^1} = \beta_1 \frac{\partial \phi}{\partial x} + \beta_2 \frac{\partial \phi}{\partial y} + \beta_3 \frac{\partial \phi}{\partial z},$$

$$\frac{\partial \phi^1}{\partial z^1} = \frac{\partial \phi}{\partial x}\frac{\partial x}{\partial z^1} + \frac{\partial \phi}{\partial y}\frac{\partial y}{\partial z^1} + \frac{\partial \phi}{\partial z}\frac{\partial z}{\partial z^1} = \gamma_1 \frac{\partial \phi}{\partial x} + \gamma_2 \frac{\partial \phi}{\partial y} + \gamma_3 \frac{\partial \phi}{\partial z},$$

or

$$\begin{Bmatrix} \dfrac{\partial \phi^1}{\partial x^1} \\[2mm] \dfrac{\partial \phi^1}{\partial y^1} \\[2mm] \dfrac{\partial \phi^1}{\partial z^1} \end{Bmatrix} = \tilde{Q} \begin{Bmatrix} \dfrac{\partial \phi}{\partial x} \\[2mm] \dfrac{\partial \phi}{\partial y} \\[2mm] \dfrac{\partial \phi}{\partial z} \end{Bmatrix}.$$

On multiplication from the left by Q, we finally obtain

$$\begin{Bmatrix} \dfrac{\partial \phi}{\partial x} \\[2mm] \dfrac{\partial \phi}{\partial y} \\[2mm] \dfrac{\partial \phi}{\partial z} \end{Bmatrix} = \begin{Bmatrix} \alpha_1 & \beta_1 & \gamma_1 \\[2mm] \alpha_2 & \beta_2 & \gamma_2 \\[2mm] \alpha_3 & \beta_3 & \gamma_3 \end{Bmatrix} \begin{Bmatrix} \dfrac{\partial \phi^1}{\partial x^1} \\[2mm] \dfrac{\partial \phi^1}{\partial y^1} \\[2mm] \dfrac{\partial \phi^1}{\partial z^1} \end{Bmatrix}.$$

In this manner, a purely analytical procedure has shown the vector character of the gradient.

Geometric Interpretation of the Gradient Vector

Another proof, which at the same time gives a geometric interpretation of the gradient vector, is obtained in the following way:

The equation $\phi(x,y,z) = $ constant determines a surface in space. If we allow the constant to assume different values, then we get a collection of surfaces, which of course have no points in common. Now let $\mathbf{r}(t) = (f(t),g(t),h(t))$ be a differentiable curve in space which lies on the surface $\phi(x,y,z) = c$. We then have $\phi(f(t),g(t),h(t)) = c$. On differentiation with respect to t, we obtain

$$\frac{\partial \phi}{\partial x} f'(t) + \frac{\partial \phi}{\partial y} g'(t) + \frac{\partial \phi}{\partial z} h'(t) = 0,$$

or $(\mathbf{grad}\ \phi) \cdot \mathbf{r}'(t) = 0$. This means that a tangent vector at an arbitrary point of the curve is perpendicular to the local gradient vector (which we assume to be different from the zero vector).

As this is valid for every differentiable curve which is contained in the surface and which passes through the point, we conclude that the gradient vector is a normal to the surface at the point considered (cf. p. 237). From this it is seen that the line on which the gradient vector lies is independent of the coordinate system chosen.

The change of the scalar field in the direction given by the unit vector $\mathbf{v} = (\alpha,\beta,\gamma)$ from the point $P_0 = (x_0,y_0,z_0)$ is determined next (cf. Example 4-3). Introducing $(x,y,z) = (x_0 + \alpha t, y_0 + \beta t, z_0 + \gamma t)$, t represents the distance from P_0 to the point (x,y,z) on the line. The *directional derivative* of ϕ in the direction of $\mathbf{v}$ at the point P_0 is then obtained as

$$\frac{d\phi}{dt} = \frac{\partial \phi}{\partial x} \frac{dx}{dt} + \frac{\partial \phi}{\partial y} \frac{dy}{dt} + \frac{\partial \phi}{\partial z} \frac{dz}{dt} = \mathbf{v} \cdot \mathbf{grad}\ \phi.$$

The local ϕ-value thus increases most rapidly in the direction given by $\mathbf{grad}\ \phi$ (Fig. 4-44). The increment per unit length is here exactly $d\phi/dt = |\mathbf{grad}\ \phi|$. From this it is seen that both the orientation and the length of the gradient vector are geometrically determined quantities and therefore independent of the coordinate system used. Thus it follows once more that the gradient actually determines a vector field.

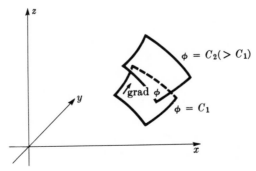

Figure 4-44

The Divergence and the Rotation of a Vector Field

From a given vector field it is also possible in a simple manner to derive a scalar field, the so-called *divergence field*, belonging to the vector field considered.

In S the divergence of $\mathbf{V}$ is obtained as

$$\text{div } \mathbf{V}(x,y,z) = \frac{\partial V_x(x,y,z)}{\partial x} + \frac{\partial V_y(x,y,z)}{\partial y} + \frac{\partial V_z(x,y,z)}{\partial z},$$

while in S^1 it is

$$\text{div}^1 \mathbf{V}^1(x^1,y^1,z^1) = \frac{\partial V_{x^1}^1(x^1,y^1,z^1)}{\partial x^1} + \frac{\partial V_{y^1}^1(x^1,y^1,z^1)}{\partial y^1} + \frac{\partial V_{z^1}^1(x^1,y^1,z^1)}{\partial z^1}.$$

By means of calculations similar to those carried out above, it is possible to show that a scalar field has actually been defined in this way:

$$\text{div } \mathbf{V}(x,y,z) = \text{div}^1 \mathbf{V}^1(x^1,y^1,z^1).$$

In the following we shall also make use of the so-called *rotation field* or *curl field* belonging to a given vector field. In the system S, the rotation of $\mathbf{V}$ is defined as

$$\text{rot } \mathbf{V}(= \text{curl } \mathbf{V}) = \left(\frac{\partial V_z}{\partial y} - \frac{\partial V_y}{\partial z}, \frac{\partial V_x}{\partial z} - \frac{\partial V_z}{\partial x}, \frac{\partial V_y}{\partial x} - \frac{\partial V_x}{\partial y} \right),$$

and analogously in S^1 as

$$\text{rot}^1 \mathbf{V}^1(= \text{curl}^1 \mathbf{V}^1) = \left(\frac{\partial V_{z^1}^1}{\partial y^1} - \frac{\partial V_{y^1}^1}{\partial z^1}, \frac{\partial V_{x^1}^1}{\partial z^1} - \frac{\partial V_{z^1}^1}{\partial x^1}, \frac{\partial V_{y^1}^1}{\partial x^1} - \frac{\partial V_{x^1}^1}{\partial y^1} \right).$$

In this way a *pseudovector field* is obtained (cf. p. 27). However, as long as we limit ourselves to consideration of right-handed systems, such a pseudovector field does not differ from an ordinary vector field.

Relationships between the Fields Introduced

With the aid of the symbolic vector *del* or *nabla*, $\nabla = (\partial/\partial x, \partial/\partial y, \partial/\partial z)$, the quantities introduced above can formally be written

$$\nabla \phi = \left(\frac{\partial}{\partial x}, \frac{\partial}{\partial y}, \frac{\partial}{\partial z} \right) \phi = \left(\frac{\partial \phi}{\partial x}, \frac{\partial \phi}{\partial y}, \frac{\partial \phi}{\partial z} \right) = \text{grad } \phi,$$

$$\nabla \cdot \mathbf{V} = \left(\frac{\partial}{\partial x}, \frac{\partial}{\partial y}, \frac{\partial}{\partial z} \right) \cdot (V_x, V_y, V_z) = \frac{\partial V_x}{\partial x} + \frac{\partial V_y}{\partial y} + \frac{\partial V_z}{\partial z} = \text{div } \mathbf{V},$$

$$\nabla \times \mathbf{V} = \left(\frac{\partial}{\partial x}, \frac{\partial}{\partial y}, \frac{\partial}{\partial z} \right) \times (V_x, V_y, V_z) = \begin{vmatrix} \mathbf{i} & \mathbf{j} & \mathbf{k} \\ \frac{\partial}{\partial x} & \frac{\partial}{\partial y} & \frac{\partial}{\partial z} \\ V_x & V_y & V_z \end{vmatrix} = \text{rot } \mathbf{V}.$$

This notation is very useful, as on further formal calculations, a series of important formulas may be obtained. For example, we have $\nabla \times \nabla \phi = 0$ (a vector product of two parallel vectors), or **rot (grad ϕ)** $= 0$, and $\nabla \cdot (\nabla \times \mathbf{V}) = 0$ (a scalar triple product with two equal vectors), or div (**rot V**) $= 0$. By straightforward calculation, both of these formulas are seen to be valid.

In this connection we just mention two very important theorems which may be considered as converse statements of the above:

Every rotation-free vector field **V** (**rot V** $= 0$) may be written as the gradient of a scalar field which (except for the sign) is a *scalar potential field* belonging to **V** (cf. p. 263—certain conditions must, however, be imposed on the domain of **V**; see Example 4-15).

Every divergence-free vector field **V** (div **V** $= 0$) may be written as the rotation of a vector field, which is a so-called *vector potential field* belonging to **V** (also here certain conditions must be imposed on the domain of **V**).

From the above one should expect that the formula **V · rot V** $= 0$ is generally valid, as the left side expressed by del is $\mathbf{V} \cdot (\nabla \times \mathbf{V})$, i.e., a scalar triple product with two equal vectors. However, this formula is not generally valid. Therefore formal calculations with del must always subsequently be controlled by other methods.

Gauss's Theorem

Consider a closed surface F in space bounding a region Ω, and let $\mathbf{n} = \mathbf{n}(x,y,z)$ be the unit outer normal to the surface at the point (x,y,z) of F. For an arbitrary vector field $\mathbf{V} = \mathbf{V}(x,y,z)$ which is defined both on F and inside F, it is then possible to prove *Gauss's theorem* (*the divergence theorem*) (Fig. 4-45):

$$\int_F \mathbf{V} \cdot \mathbf{n} \, dF = \int_\Omega \text{div } \mathbf{V} \, d\Omega.$$

The surface integral appearing on the left side is called the *flux* of the given vector field across the surface: If **V** is interpreted as the velocity field of a fluid with the constant mass density 1, then the infinitesimal contribution $\mathbf{V} \cdot \mathbf{n} \, dF$ to the surface integral is seen to give the amount of mass of fluid which per unit time flows cut through the surface element dF (see also p. 306).

According to Gauss's theorem, the flux across the surface can now be

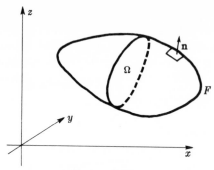

Figure 4-45

obtained by evaluating the triple integral of the divergence of the given vector field over the region bounded by the surface.

Application of Gauss's Theorem

To show an application of Gauss's theorem, we shall consider the motion of a fluid in space. Here the velocities of the fluid particles define a vector field which in general will depend on time, while the local mass densities define a scalar field which may also be time-dependent.

In a given coordinate system XYZ, the velocities define a time-dependent vector function $\mathbf{V} = \mathbf{V}(x,y,z;t)$ and the mass densities a time-dependent scalar function $\rho = \rho(x,y,z;t)$. As we want to be able to choose $\mathbf{V}$ and ρ independently of each other, the possibility of both creation and annihilation of fluid at any point and at any time must be considered. Thus let $\phi(x,y,z;t)\,d\Omega\,dt$ give the amount of mass created in the volume element $d\Omega$ and in the time interval dt about the point (x,y,z) and the time t. Here, of course, a negative value of ϕ corresponds to an annihilation.

We now first seek an expression for the mass of fluid which in a time interval dt about the time t moves through the surface element dF placed through the point (x,y,z) with the unit vector $\mathbf{n}$ as a normal.

The mass of fluid considered is seen to fill a cylinder with cross section dF and side line $\mathbf{V}(x,y,z;t)\,dt$ (Fig. 4-46). The volume of this is $dF\mathbf{V}\cdot\mathbf{n}\,dt$. Here a positive value of the volume indicates that the fluid is passing through the surface element into the half-space determined by $\mathbf{n}$. The corresponding mass is then

$$\rho(x,y,z;t)\mathbf{V}(x,y,z;t)\cdot\mathbf{n}(x,y,z)\,dF\,dt.$$

The total mass which in a period of time dt leaves the region Ω bounded by the surface F is obtained from this as

$$\left(\int_F \rho \mathbf{V} \cdot \mathbf{n} \, dF \right) dt,$$

where $\mathbf{n}$ is the unit outer normal to the surface.

On using Gauss's theorem on the vector field $\rho \mathbf{V}$ at the time t, this integral may be rewritten

$$\left(\int_\Omega \text{div} \, (\rho \mathbf{V}) \, d\Omega \right) dt.$$

During the same time interval the following amount of mass will be created in Ω:

$$\left(\int_\Omega \phi \, d\Omega \right) dt.$$

The total increase of mass in Ω is thus

$$\left(\int_\Omega \phi \, d\Omega \right) dt - \left(\int_\Omega \text{div}(\rho \mathbf{V}) \, d\Omega \right) dt = \left(\int_\Omega [\phi - \text{div}(\rho \mathbf{V})] \, d\Omega \right) dt.$$

This last quantity can, however, also be expressed by means of the density alone:

$$\int_\Omega \rho(x,y,z; t + dt) \, d\Omega - \int_\Omega \rho(x,y,z; t) \, d\Omega$$

$$= \int_\Omega (\rho(x,y,z; t + dt) - \rho(x,y,z; t)) \, d\Omega$$

$$= \left(\int_\Omega \frac{\partial \rho}{\partial t} \, d\Omega \right) dt.$$

Equating these two expressions (and dividing by dt) the following equation is finally obtained:

$$\int_\Omega [\phi(x,y,z; t) - \text{div}(\rho(x,y,z; t) \mathbf{V}(x,y,z; t))] \, d\Omega = \int_\Omega \frac{\partial}{\partial t} \, \rho(x,y,z; t) \, d\Omega.$$

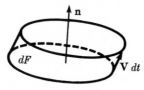

Figure 4-46

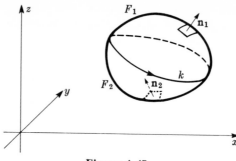

Figure 4-47

As this result is valid for any region Ω at any time t, we may conclude that the two integrands are equal:

$$\phi(x,y,z; t) - \mathrm{div}(\rho(x,y,z; t)\mathbf{V}(x,y,z; t)) = \frac{\partial\rho(x,y,z; t)}{\partial t}.$$

If we introduce $\rho = 1$, thus considering the movement of an incompressible fluid with density 1, then div $\mathbf{V} = \phi$. In this way a simple hydrodynamic interpretation of the divergence of a vector field is obtained. From that it follows once more that the divergence is independent of the coordinate system chosen (cf. p. 304).

If we choose $\phi = 0$, then the so-called *continuity equation* is obtained. It gives a necessary relation between the velocities and the densities for any fluid motion where mass is neither created nor annihilated.

Stokes's Theorem

Consider next a closed curve k in space provided with a positive direction. With this curve as a common boundary, two surfaces F_1 and F_2 are introduced having no other points in common. Let the region bounded by F_1 and F_2 be Ω. On the two surfaces, unit normal vectors $\mathbf{n}_1$ and $\mathbf{n}_2$ are introduced such that they together with the orientation of k essentially determine a right-handed screw. In this way the normal vectors of one of the surfaces is directed away from Ω, while the normal vectors of the other surface point into Ω (Fig. 4-47). Finally let $\mathbf{n}_0$ be the unit outer normal to the surface $F = F_1 + F_2$ which bounds Ω. By the use of Gauss's theorem on the rotation of a given vector field $\mathbf{V}$, the following is obtained:

$$\int_F (\mathbf{rot}\ \mathbf{V}) \cdot \mathbf{n}_0\, dF = \int_\Omega \mathrm{div}\ \mathbf{rot}\ \mathbf{V}\, d\Omega = \int_\Omega 0\, d\Omega = 0$$

or

$$\int_{F_1} (\mathbf{rot\ V}) \cdot \mathbf{n}_0\, dF + \int_{F_2} (\mathbf{rot\ V}) \cdot \mathbf{n}_0\, dF = 0$$

or

$$\int_{F_1} (\mathbf{rot\ V}) \cdot \mathbf{n}_1\, dF = \int_{F_2} (\mathbf{rot\ V}) \cdot \mathbf{n}_2\, dF.$$

We may thus conclude that the surface integral $\int_F (\mathbf{rot\ V}) \cdot \mathbf{n}\, dF$ is independent of the surface F (if only the unit normal $\mathbf{n}$ is defined as above): It depends only on (the rotation of) the given vector field $\mathbf{V}$ and on the given curve k (and its orientation).

Stokes's theorem now expresses the value of such a surface integral as

$$\int_F (\mathbf{rot\ V}) \cdot \mathbf{n}\, dF = \int_k \mathbf{V} \cdot d\mathbf{s}.$$

Here the line integral appearing on the right side is called the *circulation* of the given vector field $\mathbf{V}$ along the closed curve k.

Total Differentials in Three Variables

This is a convenient point to summarize the results obtained previously for total differentials in three variables. We shall now use the symbols of vector analysis.

To say that the expression $L(x,y,z)\, dx + M(x,y,z)\, dy + N(x,y,z)\, dz$ is a total differential with a primitive function $\phi(x,y,z)$ is equivalent to saying that the vector field $\mathbf{V}(x,y,z) = (L(x,y,z), M(x,y,z), N(x,y,z))$ is the gradient field belonging to the scalar field $\phi(x,y,z)$:

$$\mathbf{V}(x,y,z) = \mathbf{grad}\ \phi(x,y,z).$$

The cross-differentiation condition (p. 252) may be written $\mathbf{rot\ V} = \mathbf{0}$. The line integral condition (p. 262) states that the circulation of the vector field along an arbitrary closed curve is 0: $\int_k \mathbf{V} \cdot d\mathbf{s} = 0$. Under these conditions, Stokes's theorem simply gives $0 = 0$.

The previously mentioned condition for the existence of an integrating factor of a given differential expression in three variables (p. 252) may finally be expressed as $\mathbf{V} \cdot \mathbf{rot\ V} = 0$.

That this condition is necessary can be seen in the following way: Let a primitive function corresponding to the integrating factor $\mu(x,y,z)$ be $\phi(x,y,z)$. We then have $\mu\mathbf{V} = \mathbf{grad}\ \phi$ or $\mathbf{V} = (1/\mu)\ \mathbf{grad}\ \phi$.

From this we obtain by direct calculation **rot V** = **grad** $(1/\mu)$ × (**grad** ϕ), giving **V · rot V** = $(1/\mu)$ **grad** $\phi \cdot \{[\textbf{grad}\ (1/\mu)] \times \textbf{grad}\ \phi\}$ = 0.

Exercises

*1. Find the rotation of the velocity field belonging to a solid rotating with angular velocity ω around a fixed axis.

2. Consider a scalar field which in a given orthogonal system XYZ is represented by the function $F(x,y,z)$. Show that the scalar field which in the given system appears as the "product" of the so-called Laplace operator Δ (also written as ∇^2) and the function $F(x,y,z)$:

$$\Delta F = \frac{\partial^2 F}{\partial x^2} + \frac{\partial^2 F}{\partial y^2} + \frac{\partial^2 F}{\partial z^2}$$

in any other orthogonal system $X^1Y^1Z^1$ will appear correspondingly, i.e., as

$$\Delta^1 F^1 = \frac{\partial^2 F^1}{(\partial x^1)^2} + \frac{\partial^2 F^1}{(\partial y^1)^2} + \frac{\partial^2 F^1}{(\partial z^1)^2},$$

where $F^1(x^1,y^1,z^1) = F(x,y,z)$.

3. In a given orthogonal system $X\dot{Y}Z$ a scalar field is represented by the function $F(x,y,z)$. Spherical coordinates are now introduced with the usual position relative to the given coordinate system. The scalar field will then be represented by the function

$$G(r,\theta,\phi) = F(r \sin \theta \cos \phi, r \sin \theta \sin \phi, r \cos \theta).$$

Show, by direct calculation, that the scalar field ΔF (see Exercise 2) in spherical coordinates will be represented by the function

$$\frac{1}{r} \frac{\partial^2 (rG)}{\partial r^2} + \frac{1}{r^2 \sin \theta} \frac{\partial}{\partial \theta}\left(\sin \theta \frac{\partial G}{\partial \theta} \right) + \frac{1}{r^2 \sin^2 \theta} \frac{\partial^2 G}{\partial \phi^2}.$$

4. Show, by calculation in spherical as well as in orthogonal coordinates, that the function

$$G(r,\theta,\phi) = r^3 \cos 2\phi \ (\cos \theta - \cos 3\theta)$$

satisfies the Laplace equation $\Delta G = 0$ (see Exercise 3).

5. Show that Green's theorem (in the plane, see p. 279) may be looked upon as a special case of:

(a) Gauss's theorem.   (b) Stokes's theorem.

Answer

1. Introducing a coordinate system XYZ with the Z-axis as the axis of rotation, the velocity field is given by $\mathbf{V}(x,y,z) = (0,0,\omega) \times (x,y,z)$. From this **rot V** = $(0,0,2\omega)$.

4-10. VECTOR-VALUED FUNCTIONS OF TWO REAL VARIABLES

A *vector-valued function of two real variables* or, briefly, a *vector function of two variables*, has as its domain a set of ordered pairs of real numbers, while its range consists of (three-dimensional) vectors. To describe such a function we introduce a usual right-angled right-handed coordinate system XYZ. The function may then be represented by an equation of the form

$$\mathbf{r}(u,v) = f(u,v)\mathbf{i} + g(u,v)\mathbf{j} + h(u,v)\mathbf{k} = (f(u,v),g(u,v),h(u,v)).$$

Here the independent variables (the *parameters*) are u and v. The domain of the function, which is also the domain of the three real-valued *coordinate functions* f, g, and h, may be graphed as a set of points in a usual right-angled coordinate system UV. By the *graph* of the vector function we understand the set of all terminal points of the vectors $\mathbf{r}(u,v)$ drawn as position vectors in the coordinate system XYZ.

In the following we shall always use the same coordinate systems UV and XYZ. The vector function may then be looked upon as a mapping of a set of points in the UV-plane into the points in the XYZ-space (Figs. 4-48 and 4-49). Obviously the range of this mapping is also given by the parametric equations $x = f(u,v)$, $y = g(u,v)$, $z = h(u,v)$.

Continuous Vector Functions

A given vector function $\mathbf{r}(Q) = \mathbf{r}(u,v)$ is said to be *continuous* at the point $Q_0 = (u_0,v_0)$ if for every point sequence $Q_1,Q_2,. . .,Q_n,. . .$ belonging to the domain of the function and converging to Q_0 it is true that the corresponding vector sequence $\mathbf{r}(Q_1),\mathbf{r}(Q_2),. . .,\mathbf{r}(Q_n),. . .$

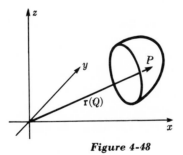

Figure 4-48

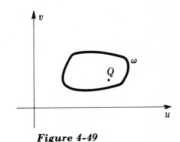

Figure 4-49

converges to $\mathbf{r}(Q_0) = \mathbf{r}(u_0,v_0)$. A necessary and sufficient condition for this is that the three coordinate functions are continuous at the point under consideration.

The graph of a vector function which is defined in some region ω and is continuous at every point of ω is called a *continuous surface*.

According to this definition the graph of a real-valued function $z = F(x,y)$ of two real variables (see p. 225) is a continuous surface if F is defined and continuous in some region of the XY-plane. The graph of F is identical with that of the vector function $\mathbf{r}(u,v) = (u,v,F(u,v))$, which satisfies the given conditions.

However, the use of vector functions in the definition of a continuous surface makes this notion very general, as it will also include point sets having more than one point with a given projection (x_0,y_0) in the XY-plane. The values of the parameters u and v corresponding to this are obtained as solutions to the two equations $f(u,v) = x_0$ and $g(u,v) = y_0$.

Example 4-27. $\mathbf{r}(u,v) = (v \cos u,\ v \sin u,\ bu)$, $-\infty < u < \infty$, $-\infty < v < \infty$ $(b \neq 0)$. The corresponding surface is a so-called *right helicoid*.

Corresponding respectively to $v = v_0$ and $u = u_0$ we obtain the so-called *parametric curves* on the surface:

$$\mathbf{r}(u,v_0) = (v_0 \cos u, v_0 \sin u, bu),$$

and

$$\mathbf{r}(u_0,v) = (v \cos u_0, v \sin u_0, bu_0).$$

These are seen to be circular helices (if $v_0 \neq 0$, see Example 3-40, p. 205) and straight lines intersecting the Z-axis at right angles, respectively.

The whole surface will be described by a straight line always intersecting the Z-axis at a right angle and at the same time moving along one of the helices considered.

An arbitrary point on the surface will, of course, be uniquely determined by the corresponding values of the two parameters u and v. These are here acting as *curvilinear coordinates* of the point considered.

Corresponding to an arbitrary point $(x_0,y_0) \neq (0,0)$ in the XY-plane there is an infinite number of points on the surface, namely, all points with curvilinear coordinates $(u,v) = (u_0 + p2\pi, v_0)$. For $(x_0,y_0) = (0,0)$, every point with this projection belongs to the surface $(v = 0)$. $\square$

From the above example it follows that in general it is not possible to represent a given surface by a function $z = z(x,y)$. This is, however, possible in case the equations $x = f(u,v)$ and $y = g(u,v)$ can be uniquely solved to give $u = \phi(x,y)$ and $v = \psi(x,y)$. An equation of the surface may then be obtained as $z = h(\phi(x,y),\psi(x,y))$.

Example 4-28. Restricting the domain of the above-considered vector function to $0 \le u \le \pi/2$, $0 < v \le 2$, the resulting surface (see Fig. 4-50) can be represented by a real-valued function $z = z(x,y)$ with the first quadrant of the circular disk $x^2 + y^2 \le 4$ ((0,0) not included) as its domain: $x = v \cos u$, $y = v \sin u$, giving uniquely

$$v = \sqrt{x^2 + y^2},$$

$$u = \arccos \frac{x}{\sqrt{x^2 + y^2}}.$$

From this we finally get

$$z = b \arccos \frac{x}{\sqrt{x^2 + y^2}}. \qquad \square$$

Differentiable Vector Functions

The notion of differentiability of a given vector function at a given point of its domain is now defined in close analogy with the corresponding definition for real functions of two variables (p. 231).

The vector function $\mathbf{r}(u,v)$ is said to be *differentiable* at the point (u_0, v_0) if the increment $\Delta\mathbf{r}$ of the function corresponding to increments Δu and Δv of the parameters can be written as follows:

$$\Delta\mathbf{r} = \mathbf{r}(u_0 + \Delta u, v_0 + \Delta v) - \mathbf{r}(u_0,v_0) = \mathbf{a}\,\Delta u + \mathbf{b}\,\Delta v + \mathbf{o}(\rho),$$

where $\mathbf{a}$ and $\mathbf{b}$ are constant vectors and $\rho = \sqrt{(\Delta u)^2 + (\Delta v)^2}$.

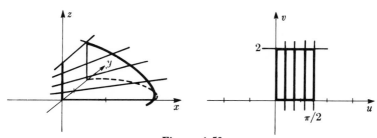

Figure 4-50

Written out in coordinates, the condition becomes

$$f(u_0 + \Delta u,\ v_0 + \Delta v) - f(u_0,v_0) = a_1\,\Delta u + b_1\,\Delta v + o_1(\rho),$$
$$g(u_0 + \Delta u,\ v_0 + \Delta v) - g(u_0,v_0) = a_2\,\Delta u + b_2\,\Delta v + o_2(\rho),$$
$$h(u_0 + \Delta u,\ v_0 + \Delta v) - h(u_0,v_0) = a_3\,\Delta u + b_3\,\Delta v + o_3(\rho).$$

From this it follows that the vector function is differentiable at (u_0,v_0) if and only if the three coordinate functions are differentiable at this point. Furthermore, it follows that

$$\mathbf{a} = (a_1,a_2,a_3) = \left(\frac{\partial f}{\partial u},\ \frac{\partial g}{\partial u},\ \frac{\partial h}{\partial u}\right)\left(= \frac{\partial \mathbf{r}}{\partial u} = \mathbf{r}'_u(u_0,v_0)\right),$$

and that

$$\mathbf{b} = (b_1,b_2,b_3) = \left(\frac{\partial f}{\partial v},\ \frac{\partial g}{\partial v},\ \frac{\partial h}{\partial v}\right)\left(= \frac{\partial \mathbf{r}}{\partial v} = \mathbf{r}'_v(u_0,v_0)\right).$$

If, as previously, we introduce the differentials du and dv of the two simple real functions u and v, respectively, corresponding to the above increments Δu and Δv of the parameters, then the increment of the differentiable vector function $\mathbf{r}(u,v)$ may be written

$$\Delta \mathbf{r} = \frac{\partial \mathbf{r}}{\partial u}\,du + \frac{\partial \mathbf{r}}{\partial v}\,dv + \mathbf{o}(\rho) = d\mathbf{r} + \mathbf{o}(\rho).$$

Here $d\mathbf{r} = (\partial \mathbf{r}/\partial u)\,du + (\partial \mathbf{r}/\partial v)\,dv$ is called the *differential* of the vector function at the point under consideration corresponding to the increments du and dv of the independent variables u and v, respectively.

Differentiable Surfaces

If $\partial \mathbf{r}/\partial u$ and $\partial \mathbf{r}/\partial v$ are proper vectors, then they give the directions of the tangents at the point P_0 of the parametric curves corresponding, respectively, to $v = v_0$ and $u = u_0$ (Fig. 4-51). If, furthermore, these two partial derivatives are not parallel, then they determine a plane.

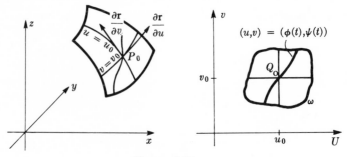

Figure 4-51

This plane is perpendicular to the (proper) vector $(\partial \mathbf{r}/\partial u) \times (\partial \mathbf{r}/\partial v)$:

$$\frac{\partial \mathbf{r}}{\partial u} \times \frac{\partial \mathbf{r}}{\partial v} = \left(\begin{vmatrix} \dfrac{\partial g}{\partial u} & \dfrac{\partial h}{\partial u} \\[2mm] \dfrac{\partial g}{\partial v} & \dfrac{\partial h}{\partial v} \end{vmatrix}, \begin{vmatrix} \dfrac{\partial h}{\partial u} & \dfrac{\partial f}{\partial u} \\[2mm] \dfrac{\partial h}{\partial v} & \dfrac{\partial f}{\partial v} \end{vmatrix}, \begin{vmatrix} \dfrac{\partial f}{\partial u} & \dfrac{\partial g}{\partial u} \\[2mm] \dfrac{\partial f}{\partial v} & \dfrac{\partial g}{\partial v} \end{vmatrix} \right)$$

$$= \left(\frac{\partial(y,z)}{\partial(u,v)}, \frac{\partial(z,x)}{\partial(u,v)}, \frac{\partial(x,y)}{\partial(u,v)} \right)$$

$$= (A(u_0,v_0), B(u_0,v_0), C(u_0,v_0)).$$

Consider now an arbitrary differentiable curve in the UV-plane, $(u,v) = (\phi(t),\psi(t))$, which for $t = t_0$ passes through the point Q_0. Corresponding to this we obtain a space curve $\mathbf{r}(t) = (f(\phi(t),\psi(t)), g(\phi(t), \psi(t)), h(\phi(t),\psi(t)))$, which is contained in the surface and which passes through the point P_0. On differentiation with respect to t we get

$$\mathbf{r}'(t_0) = \left(\frac{\partial f}{\partial u}\phi' + \frac{\partial f}{\partial v}\psi', \frac{\partial g}{\partial u}\phi' + \frac{\partial g}{\partial v}\psi', \frac{\partial h}{\partial u}\phi' + \frac{\partial h}{\partial v}\psi' \right)$$

$$= \frac{\partial \mathbf{r}}{\partial u}\phi'(t_0) + \frac{\partial \mathbf{r}}{\partial v}\psi'(t_0).$$

From this it follows that the space curve considered has a tangent vector at the point P_0 and that this vector lies in the plane just introduced. This is therefore called the *tangent plane* of the surface at the point P_0.

As a consequence of the above result the surface determined by a vector function $\mathbf{r}(u,v)$ defined in a region ω of the UV-plane is said to be a *differentiable surface* if the vector function at every point of ω is differentiable with (continuous and) linearly independent partial derivatives. Every differentiable surface then has a tangent plane at any of its points.

According to this definition the graph of a function $z = F(x,y)$ defined in a region ω of the XY-plane is a differentiable surface if only $\partial F/\partial x$ and $\partial F/\partial y$ exist and are continuous in the region. With the parametric representation previously used (p. 312) we obtain

$$(A,B,C) = \left(\begin{vmatrix} 0 & \dfrac{\partial F}{\partial u} \\[2mm] 1 & \dfrac{\partial F}{\partial v} \end{vmatrix}, \begin{vmatrix} \dfrac{\partial F}{\partial u} & 1 \\[2mm] \dfrac{\partial F}{\partial v} & 0 \end{vmatrix}, \begin{vmatrix} 1 & 0 \\[2mm] 0 & 1 \end{vmatrix} \right)$$

$$= \left(-\frac{\partial F}{\partial u}, -\frac{\partial F}{\partial v}, 1 \right) \neq \mathbf{0}$$

(cf. p. 234).

Example 4-29. For the right helicoid previously considered (Example 4-27) we have

$$\frac{\partial \mathbf{r}}{\partial u} = (-v \sin u, v \cos u, b), \quad \frac{\partial \mathbf{r}}{\partial v} = (\cos u, \sin u, 0),$$

and therefore

$$(A, B, C) = (-b \sin u, b \cos u, -v) \neq \mathbf{0}.$$

The equation of the tangent plane at the point $\mathbf{r}(u_0, v_0)$ is thus

$$-b \sin u_0 \ (x - v_0 \cos u_0) + b \cos u_0 \ (y - v_0 \sin u_0) - v_0(z - bu_0) = 0. \qquad \square$$

Area of a Differentiable Surface

Finally, we want briefly to derive a formula for the area of a differentiable surface determined by a vector function $\mathbf{r}(u,v)$ with a closed region ω of the UV-plane as its domain.

Corresponding to an infinitesimal rectangle in ω spanned by the vectors $(du,0)$ and $(0,dv)$ we obtain on the surface an infinitesimal parallelogram spanned by the vectors

$$d_u \mathbf{r} = \frac{\partial \mathbf{r}}{\partial u} du + \frac{\partial \mathbf{r}}{\partial v} 0 \quad \text{and} \quad d_v \mathbf{r} = \frac{\partial \mathbf{r}}{\partial u} 0 + \frac{\partial \mathbf{r}}{\partial v} dv.$$

The area of this parallelogram is

$$dS = |d_u \mathbf{r} \times d_v \mathbf{r}| = \left| \frac{\partial \mathbf{r}}{\partial u} \times \frac{\partial \mathbf{r}}{\partial v} \right| du \, dv$$
$$= \sqrt{A^2 + B^2 + C^2} \, du \, dv.$$

The total area of the surface is then obtained on integration as

$$S = \int_\omega \sqrt{A^2 + B^2 + C^2} \, du \, dv.$$

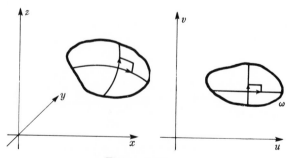

Figure 4-52

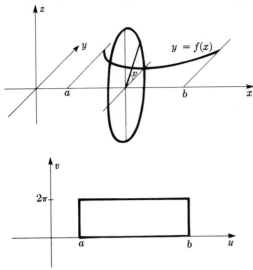

Figure 4-53

(Fig. 4-52).   If x and y are used as parameters, then for a differentiable surface $z = F(x,y)$ with a closed region ω as domain, we obtain

$$S = \int_\omega \sqrt{\left(\frac{\partial F}{\partial x}\right)^2 + \left(\frac{\partial F}{\partial y}\right)^2 + 1}\; dx\,dy,$$

which is in agreement with a previous result (p. 298).

Example 4-30.   Consider in the XY-plane a curve $y = f(x)$, $a \leq x \leq b$.   On rotation of 360° about the X-axis this describes a surface of revolution.   Using the abscissa and the angle of rotation as parameters, we obtain (Fig. 4-53)

$$\mathbf{r}(u,v) = (u,\, f(u)\cos v,\, f(u)\sin v) \qquad (a \leq u \leq b,\, 0 \leq v \leq 2\pi),$$

$$\frac{\partial \mathbf{r}}{\partial u} = (1,\, f'(u)\cos v,\, f'(u)\sin v),$$

$$\frac{\partial \mathbf{r}}{\partial v} = (0,\, -f(u)\sin v,\, f(u)\cos v),$$

$$(A,B,C) = (f(u)f'(u),\, -f(u)\cos v,\, -f(u)\sin v) \neq \mathbf{0},$$

$$S = \int_\omega |f(u)|\; \sqrt{1 + (f'(u))^2}\; du\,dv$$

$$= 2\pi \int_a^b |f(u)|\; \sqrt{1 + (f'(u))^2}\; du,$$

which is in agreement with the formula found previously (p. 203).   □

Exercises

1. Show that the surface

$$\mathbf{r}(u,v) = (a \cosh u \cosh v, \, a \cosh u \sinh v, \, a \sinh u)$$

can be obtained by a rotation of one branch of a hyperbola.

*2. Evaluate the surface integral of the function $G(x,y,z) = \sqrt{x^2 + y^2}$ over the surface $\mathbf{r}(u,v) = (v \cos u, \, v \sin u, \, u)$ $(0 \le u \le 4\pi, \, 1 \le v \le 2)$.

*3. Sketch the surface

$$\mathbf{r}(u,v) = (v \cos u, \, v \sin u, \, \tfrac{1}{2}u^2) \qquad (-\pi \le u \le \pi, \, 1 \le v \le 2)$$

and evaluate the integral of the function $G(x,y,z) = \sqrt{2(x^2 + y^2)z}$ over this surface.

Answers

2. $\dfrac{4\pi}{3} (5\sqrt{5} - 2\sqrt{2})$

3. $\frac{2}{15}[(\pi^2 + 4)^{5/2} - (\pi^2 + 1)^{5/2} - 31]$

Part III
Series,
Differential Equations,
and
Complex Functions

5

Infinite Series

5-1. SERIES WITH CONSTANT TERMS

The Notion of an Infinite Series

We have previously (p. 134) defined an infinite sequence of real numbers as a function from the set of positive integers to the set of real numbers. Consider now such a sequence u. In accordance with earlier conventions, its value at n (its nth element) is written u_n, while the sequence itself may be written $u_1, u_2, \ldots, u_n, \ldots$

Corresponding to the sequence u we now define a new sequence S, which is called the *(infinite) series* belonging to u. Its value at n is defined as

$$S_n = \sum_{k=1}^{n} u_k = u_1 + u_2 + \cdots + u_n.$$

S_n is often called the nth *partial sum* of the infinite series, while u_k is called the kth *term* of the infinite series.

S may be convergent, or it may be divergent. In the former case it has a limit σ, which is also called the *sum* of the infinite series and is written

$$\sigma = \sum_{k=1}^{\infty} u_k = u_1 + u_2 + \cdots + u_k + \cdots$$

From the equation $u_{n+1} = S_{n+1} - S_n$ which is valid for all n it follows directly that a necessary condition for the convergence of the infinite series S is that the original sequence u is convergent with the limit zero. We shall see below that this condition, however, is not sufficient (Example 5-3).

According to the above the sum of the infinite series S (in case it exists) is written

$$\sum_{k=1}^{\infty} u_k \qquad \text{or} \qquad u_1 + u_2 + \cdots + u_k + \cdots .$$

Very often, however, these two symbols are also used to denote the infinite series itself—whether it happens to be convergent or not. In practice this ambiguity will not lead to any confusion, and we shall also make use of it (see the examples below).

Example 5-1. The *geometric series* $a + aq + aq^2 + \cdots + aq^{k-1} + \cdots = \Sigma_{k=1}^{\infty} aq^{k-1}$ $(a \neq 0)$ is convergent with the sum $a/(1 - q)$ if $|q| < 1$ as the nth partial sum of the series,

$$S_n = a + aq + aq^2 + \cdots + aq^{n-1} = a\frac{1 - q^n}{1 - q}$$

converges to $a/(1 - q)$ as n tends to infinity. If $|q| \geq 1$ it follows from the above-mentioned necessary condition that the series is divergent.   □

Example 5-2. The series

$$\sum_{k=1}^{\infty} \frac{1}{k(k + 1)} = \frac{1}{1 \cdot 2} + \frac{1}{2 \cdot 3} + \cdots + \frac{1}{k(k + 1)} + \cdots$$

is convergent with the sum 1, as the nth partial sum is

$$S_n = \frac{1}{1 \cdot 2} + \frac{1}{2 \cdot 3} + \cdots + \frac{1}{n(n + 1)}$$

$$= \left(\frac{1}{1} - \frac{1}{2}\right) + \left(\frac{1}{2} - \frac{1}{3}\right) + \left(\frac{1}{3} - \frac{1}{4}\right) + \cdots + \left(\frac{1}{n} - \frac{1}{n + 1}\right)$$

$$= 1 - \frac{1}{n + 1}.$$

From this it is seen that $S_n \to 1$ as $n \to \infty$.   □

Example 5-3. The so-called *harmonic series* $\Sigma_{k=1}^{\infty} 1/k$ is not convergent, even though $1/k \to 0$ as $k \to \infty$. Considering the nth partial sum

$$S_n = \frac{1}{1} + \frac{1}{2} + \frac{1}{3} + \cdots + \frac{1}{n},$$

we see that it is larger than the integral $\int_1^{n+1}(1/x)\, dx = \ln(n+1)$, i.e., $S_n > \ln(n+1)$ and therefore $S_n \to \infty$ as $n \to \infty$. □

Convergence of Series with Positive Terms

It is immediately clear that if the series has positive terms only, then the sequence of partial sums will be monotone-increasing. Therefore a necessary and sufficient condition for convergence in this case simply is that the sequence considered has an upper limit.

The following simple test for convergence, the so-called *comparison test*, is valid for series with only positive terms: If for two series $\Sigma_{n=1}^{\infty} u_n$ and $\Sigma_{n=1}^{\infty} v_n$ it is true that $v_n \geq u_n$ for all n greater than some definite number N, then convergence of the v-series implies convergence of the u-series and divergence of the u-series implies divergence of the v-series. The validity of this follows at once from consideration of the nth partial sums of the series.

From the comparison test two other important tests for convergence follow immediately. These are often called the *Cauchy tests*. The first (*the root test*) states that a series with positive terms is convergent if there exists a positive number q less than 1 and an integer N, such that the nth root of the nth term in the series is less than or equal to q for all n greater than or equal to N. The other (*the ratio test*) states that a series with positive terms is convergent if $u_{n+1}/u_n \leq q$ for all $n \geq N$, where again q is some positive number less than 1 and N some integer.

In both cases the u-series has been compared with a geometric series with positive terms, i.e., a series of the form $\Sigma_{n=1}^{\infty} aq^n$ with $a > 0$ and $q > 0$. As already mentioned, such a series will be convergent in case $q < 1$. If it is valid that from a certain number N, $\sqrt[n]{u_n} \leq q < 1$, then evidently the terms in the u-series will be less than or equal to q^n for all $n \geq N$, and as a finite number of terms (from u_1 to u_{N-1}) cannot cause the series to diverge, it is certain that the u-series is convergent. In the same way it can be said that when $u_{n+1}/u_n \leq q$ for all $n \geq N$, then the following holds:

$$u_{N+1} \leq u_N q,$$
$$u_{N+2} \leq u_{N+1} q \leq u_N q^2$$
$$\cdot$$
$$\cdot$$
$$\cdot$$

Again, all terms in the u-series with $n \geq N$ are less than or equal to the corresponding terms in a convergent geometric series: $\Sigma_{n=1}^{\infty} u_N q^{-N} q^n$. It is also immediately obvious that a series diverges when for all $n \geq N$ either $\sqrt[n]{u_n} \geq 1$ or $u_{n+1}/u_n \geq 1$, as in this case not even the above-mentioned necessary condition for convergence ($u_n \to 0$ as $n \to \infty$) is satisfied.

It should be noted that the above remarks on the quantities $\sqrt[n]{u_n}$ and u_{n+1}/u_n are not exhaustive. If, for example, $\sqrt[n]{u_n} \to 1 - 0$ as $n \to \infty$, then the u-series may be convergent or it may be divergent. This agrees well with the fact that the Cauchy tests only give *sufficient* conditions for convergence.

As a last test for convergence of a series with positive terms, which are now also assumed to be decreasing in value, we shall mention the so-called *integral test*. Here the series is compared with an integral of a continuous function $f(x)$ which is positive and decreasing for $x \geq 1$, and which takes on the values u_n for $x = n$ ($n = 1,2,3,\ldots$). It is then true that the series $\Sigma_{n=1}^{\infty} u_n$ is convergent if the improper

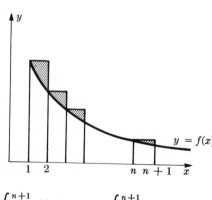

$$\int_1^{n+1} f(x) \, dx < S_n < \int_1^{n+1} f(x) \, dx + u_1$$

Figure 5-1

integral $\int_1^\infty f(x)\,dx$ is convergent, and divergent if the integral is divergent. A proof may be obtained by comparing the nth partial sum with the integral of $f(x)$ with upper limit $n + 1$ (Fig. 5-1).

The above considerations of series with positive terms are easily extended to series that contain only nonnegative terms, only negative terms, or only nonpositive terms.

Example 5-4

$\displaystyle\sum_{n=1}^{\infty} \frac{1}{n^2}$ is convergent $\left(\text{comparison test, Example 5-2,}\right.$

$$u_n < \frac{1}{(n-1)\cdot n}\bigg).$$

$\displaystyle\sum_{n=1}^{\infty} \frac{1}{3^n + 2}$ is convergent $\left(\text{ratio test, } \dfrac{u_{n+1}}{u_n} \to \dfrac{1}{3}\;(<1) \text{ as } n\to\infty\right).$

$\displaystyle\sum_{n=1}^{\infty} n2^{-n}$ is convergent $\left(\text{root test, } \sqrt[n]{u_n} \to \tfrac{1}{2}(<1) \text{ as } n\to\infty\right).$

$\displaystyle\sum_{n=1}^{\infty} \frac{1}{n^\alpha}\;(\alpha > 1)$ is convergent $\left(\text{integral test, } f(x) = \dfrac{1}{x^\alpha}\right).$

$\displaystyle\sum_{n=1}^{\infty} \frac{1}{n^\alpha}\;(0 < \alpha \leq 1)$ is divergent $\left(\text{integral test, } f(x) = \dfrac{1}{x^\alpha}\right).$ $\square$

Convergence of an Arbitrary Series

We shall now treat series $\Sigma_{n=1}^{\infty} u_n$, where no assumption is made regarding the signs of the terms. Together with such a series, we shall also consider the one that is formed by the absolute values of the terms in the given series, i.e., $\Sigma_{n=1}^{\infty} |u_n|$. It can be shown that if $\Sigma|u_n|$ is convergent, Σu_n will also be convergent. However, the converse statement is not valid; the convergence of Σu_n does not necessitate the convergence of $\Sigma|u_n|$ (see Example 5-5).

If for a series Σu_n it is true that both Σu_n and $\Sigma|u_n|$ are convergent, the series is said to be *absolutely convergent*. An examination of the absolute convergence of a series thus proceeds by the same methods as those used for series with only positive (nonnegative) terms.

A series which is convergent, but not absolutely convergent, is said to be *conditionally convergent*. It is easily seen that such a series must contain an infinite number of positive terms as well as an infinite number of negative terms.

It is true for absolutely convergent series that the sum is unaffected by a rearrangement of the terms, i.e., the order of the terms is immaterial. This can be proved for absolutely convergent series which contain an infinite number of positive terms and an infinite number of negative terms by using the fact that for these series both the sum of the positive terms taken by themselves, and the sum of the negative terms taken by themselves, converge.

For series which are conditionally convergent a theorem of Riemann is valid. This states that the order of the terms of the series can be changed in such a way that the new series produced will be convergent with an arbitrary number as its sum. Furthermore, the order of the terms of the series can be changed such that the series becomes divergent. The order of the terms is therefore important.

A special class of series, which have both positive and negative terms, is formed by the so-called *alternating series*, i.e., series of the form $\Sigma_{n=1}^{\infty} u_n(-1)^{n+1}$ (or $\Sigma_{n=1}^{\infty} u_n(-1)^n$), where $u_n > 0$ for all n. For these series *Leibniz's test* for convergence holds. It states that an alternating series is convergent if the absolute value of the nth term is decreasing and approaches zero as n tends to infinity or, in other words, if $u_1 > u_2 > u_3 > u_4 \cdots$ and $u_n \to 0$ as $n \to \infty$.

This is seen by considering the nth partial sum of the series $\Sigma_{n=1}^{\infty} u_n(-1)^{n+1}$:

$$S_n = u_1 - u_2 + u_3 \cdots \pm u_n.$$

Here, the sequence S_n (n even) is monotone-increasing ($S_2 < S_4 < S_6 < \cdots$), while the sequence S_n (n odd) is monotone-decreasing ($S_1 > S_3 > S_5 > \cdots$). This is an immediate consequence of the first assumption made regarding u_n. The sequence S_n ($n = 1,2,3, \ldots$) can thus be separated into a monotone-increasing and a monotone-decreasing sequence. Furthermore, as a consequence of the second assumption, the difference between the pth elements of the two sequences approaches zero as $p \to \infty$. Therefore the two monotone sequences considered have a common limit S. From this finally follows that the given alternating series is convergent—with the sum S (Fig. 5-2).

At the same time it is seen that the error made by considering only

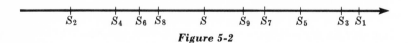

Figure 5-2

the first n terms of the series will be less than the absolute value of the next term: $|S_n - S| < u_{n+1}$.

Example 5-5. The series $\Sigma_{n=1}^{\infty}(1/n)(-1)^{n+1}$ is convergent (Leibniz's criterium). It is, however, not absolutely convergent, as the corresponding absolute series is not convergent (Example 5-3). As mentioned above, it is therefore possible to change the order of the terms to obtain a series which diverges. We shall now give an example of this.

With the order of the elements given above, the sequence of partial sums is

$$1; \tfrac{1}{2}; \tfrac{5}{6}; \tfrac{7}{12}; \tfrac{47}{60}; \tfrac{37}{60}; \cdots .$$

This shows that the sum of the series lies between, for example, $\tfrac{47}{60}$ and $\tfrac{37}{60}$. Now the order of the terms is changed in the following manner:

$$1 - \tfrac{1}{2} + \tfrac{1}{3} + \tfrac{1}{5} - \tfrac{1}{4} + \tfrac{1}{7} + \tfrac{1}{9} + \tfrac{1}{11} + \tfrac{1}{13} - \tfrac{1}{6} + \tfrac{1}{15} + \cdots + \tfrac{1}{29}$$
$$- \tfrac{1}{8} + \cdots ,$$

where two, four, eight, etc., consecutive positive terms are inserted between the negative terms. Let the corresponding sequence of partial sums be

$$S_1, S_2, S_3, \ldots, S_n, \ldots$$

From this, a divergent subsequence can easily be chosen; for example,

$$T_1, T_2, T_3, \ldots, T_n, \ldots ,$$

where $T_n = S_{n+2^n-1}$. Here the following is true:

$$T_{n+1} - T_n = S_{n+1+2^{n+1}-1} - S_{n+2^n-1}$$

$$= \frac{1}{2 \cdot 2^n - 1} + \frac{1}{2(2^n + 1) - 1} + \frac{1}{2(2^n + 2) - 1} + \cdots$$

$$+ \frac{1}{2(2^{n+1} - 1) - 1} - \frac{1}{2(n + 1)}$$

$$> 2^n \frac{1}{2(2^{n+1} - 1) - 1} - \frac{1}{2(n + 1)} = \frac{1}{4 - 3 \cdot 2^{-n}}$$

$$- \frac{1}{2(n + 1)} > \frac{1}{4} - \frac{1}{2(n + 1)},$$

and therefore also $T_{n+1} - T_n > \tfrac{1}{8}$ for all $n > 2$. The subsequence T_n thus diverges to ∞, and it follows that the sequence S_n cannot be convergent. $\square$

Operations with Convergent Series

Let the two series $\Sigma_{k=0}^{\infty} u_k$ and $\Sigma_{k=0}^{\infty} v_k$ be convergent with the sums U and V, respectively. Then the series $\Sigma_{k=0}^{\infty} a u_k$, where a is an arbitrary constant, is convergent with the sum aU. Also $\Sigma_{k=0}^{\infty}(u_k + v_k)$ is convergent with the sum $U + V$. Both of these results can be directly obtained by considering the appropriate partial sums, and are thus valid for any convergent series.

We have already mentioned that the order of the terms in an absolutely convergent series is immaterial, while this is not true for conditionally convergent series. If the two series considered are absolutely convergent and are multiplied formally in the manner

$$\left(\sum_{k=0}^{\infty} u_k \right) \left(\sum_{k=0}^{\infty} v_k \right) = (u_0 + u_1 + u_2 + \cdots)(v_0 + v_1 + v_2 + \cdots)$$

$$= u_0 v_0 + (u_0 v_1 + u_1 v_0) + (u_0 v_2 + u_1 v_1 + u_2 v_0)$$
$$+ \cdots$$

$$= \sum_{k=0}^{\infty} \left(\sum_{n=0}^{k} u_n v_{k-n} \right),$$

the resulting series will also be absolutely convergent, and with the sum UV.

The above can be more loosely formulated in the following way. It is permissible to carry out calculations with absolutely convergent series as if they were finite sums. In several cases this is not so for conditionally convergent series. In this connection, however, one warning should be given. While the insertion of an infinite number of parentheses always yields a (new) series with the same sum, the removal of an infinite number of parentheses, even in an absolutely convergent series, may yield a divergent series. As an example we mention the series

$$\sum_{k=0}^{\infty} (1 - 1) = (1 - 1) + (1 - 1) + (1 - 1) + \cdots.$$

In the special case of an absolutely convergent series of the form $S = a_0 + a_1 x + a_2 x^2 + \cdots + a_n x^n + \cdots$, where x is a fixed number, several simple formulas hold; for example,

$$S^2 = a_0^2 + 2a_0 a_1 x + (a_1^2 + 2a_0 a_2)x^2 + 2(a_0 a_3 + a_1 a_2)x^3 + \cdots.$$

This is a consequence of the above-mentioned multiplication rule. Furthermore,

$$S^{1/2} = a_0^{1/2} \left[1 + \frac{a_1}{2a_0} x + \left(\frac{1}{2} \frac{a_2}{a_0} - \frac{1}{8} \frac{a_1^2}{a_0^2} \right) x^2 \right.$$
$$\left. + \left(\frac{1}{2} \frac{a_3}{a_0} - \frac{1}{4} \frac{a_1 a_2}{a_0^2} + \frac{1}{16} \frac{a_1^3}{a_0^3} \right) x^3 + \cdots \right] \qquad (a_0 \neq 0),$$

$$S^{-1} = a_0^{-1} \left[1 - \frac{a_1}{a_0} x + \left(\frac{a_1^2}{a_0^2} - \frac{a_2}{a_0} \right) x^2 \right.$$
$$\left. + \left(\frac{2a_1 a_2}{a_0^2} - \frac{a_3}{a_0} - \frac{a_1^3}{a_0^3} \right) x^3 + \cdots \right] \qquad (a_0 \neq 0).$$

Infinite Products

The notion of infinite products will not be dealt with in detail. We shall only mention that the infinite product

$$\prod_{n=1}^{\infty} (1 + u_n) = (1 + u_1)(1 + u_2) \cdots (1 + u_n) \cdots ,$$

where none of the factors is zero, is said to be convergent with the value P if the sequence of *partial products*

$$P_1, P_2, P_3, \ldots, P_n, \ldots,$$

where

$$P_n = \prod_{k=1}^{n} (1 + u_k) = (1 + u_1) \cdots (1 + u_n),$$

is convergent with a limit P different from 0.

A necessary condition for convergence is apparently that $u_n \to 0$ as $n \to \infty$. It can be shown by consideration of the corresponding partial products that a necessary and sufficient condition for convergence of an infinite product with only positive factors is that the corresponding infinite series

$$\ln(1 + u_1) + \ln(1 + u_2) + \ln(1 + u_3) + \cdots$$

is convergent. Furthermore, as expected, the value P of the product and the sum S of the series is related by the equation $P = e^S$.

In analogy to the notion of absolute convergence for series, an infinite product is said to be *absolutely convergent* if the value of the product remains the same even if the order of the factors is changed in an arbitrary manner. It can be shown that a necessary and sufficient condition for absolute convergence of an infinite product $\prod_{n=1}^{\infty}(1 + u_n)$, where none of the factors is zero, is that the series $\Sigma_{n=1}^{\infty} u_n$ is absolutely convergent.

Exercises

*1. Find the sum of the convergent infinite series

$$\sum_{n=2}^{\infty} \left(\frac{1+(-1)^n}{2^n} + \frac{1-(-1)^n}{3^n} \right).$$

*2. Examine the following infinite series for convergence:

(a) $\displaystyle\sum_{n=2}^{\infty} \frac{1}{\ln n}.$ (d) $\displaystyle\sum_{n=1}^{\infty} \left(1-\frac{1}{n}\right).$ (g) $\displaystyle\sum_{n=1}^{\infty} \frac{1}{n!}.$

(b) $\displaystyle\sum_{n=2}^{\infty} \frac{1}{n \ln n}.$ (e) $\displaystyle\sum_{n=1}^{\infty} \left(1-\frac{1}{n}\right)^n.$ (h) $\displaystyle\sum_{n=1}^{\infty} \frac{2^n}{n!}.$

(c) $\displaystyle\sum_{n=2}^{\infty} \frac{1}{n^2 \ln n}.$ (f) $\displaystyle\sum_{n=1}^{\infty} \left(1-\frac{1}{n}\right)^{n^2}.$ (i) $\displaystyle\sum_{n=1}^{\infty} \frac{n^n}{n!}.$

3. Show that the infinite series $\Sigma_{n=1}^{\infty} (-1)^{n-1}/(2n-1)$ is conditionally convergent.

*4. Examine whether the following infinite series are absolutely convergent, conditionally convergent, or divergent:

(a) $\displaystyle\sum_{n=1}^{\infty} \frac{(-1)^{n-1}n}{3^{n-1}}.$ (c) $\displaystyle\sum_{n=1}^{\infty} \frac{(-1)^n \ln n}{2n}.$

(b) $\displaystyle\sum_{n=1}^{\infty} \frac{(-1)^{n-1}}{n^{1/3}}.$ (d) $\displaystyle\sum_{n=1}^{\infty} \frac{-3^{n+1}}{5^{n-1}n^2}.$

5. Investigate the infinite series

$$\frac{1}{\sqrt{2}-1} - \frac{1}{\sqrt{2}+1} + \frac{1}{\sqrt{3}-1} - \frac{1}{\sqrt{3}+1} + \cdots .$$

6. Calculate by the method given on page 326 the product of the two absolutely convergent series

$$\sum_{n=0}^{\infty} \frac{a^n}{n!} \quad \text{and} \quad \sum_{n=0}^{\infty} \frac{b^n}{n!}.$$

7. Find the sum of the finite series $\Sigma_{n=1}^{N} \sin nx$, where x is an arbitrary constant. Examine the corresponding infinite series for convergence.

8. An infinite series $a_1 + a_2 + a_3 + \cdots$ with partial sums $S_1, S_2, S_3, \ldots$ is said to be Cesàro-summable with the Cesàro sum S if

$$\lim_{n \to \infty} \frac{S_1 + S_2 + \cdots + S_n}{n} = S.$$

Show that the series $1 + \frac{1}{2} + \frac{1}{4} + \cdots + 1/2^n + \cdots$ has the Cesàro sum 2. Investigate correspondingly the series

$$1 - 1 + 1 - 1 + 1 - \cdots$$
$$1 - 2 + 3 - 4 + \cdots$$
$$1 + 0 - 1 + 1 + 0 - 1 + \cdots.$$

9. An infinite series $a_1 + a_2 + a_3 + \cdots$ is said to be Abel-summable with the Abel sum S if

$$\lim_{x \to 0+0} \sum_{n=1}^{\infty} a_n e^{-nx} = S,$$

or, equivalently,

$$\lim_{\xi \to 1-0} \sum_{n=1}^{\infty} a_n \xi^n = S.$$

Show that the series considered in Exercise 8 are Abel-summable. (It can be shown generally that Cesàro summability implies Abel summability with the same sum.)

10. By analogy with the above definitions of summability of infinite series (Exercises 8 and 9) the Cesàro value of an improper integral $\int_0^{\infty} f(x)\,dx$ is defined as

$$\lim_{\lambda \to \infty} \int_0^{\lambda} \left(1 - \frac{x}{\lambda}\right) f(x)\,dx$$

and the Abel value as

$$\lim_{\mu \to 0+0} \int_0^{\infty} f(x) e^{-\mu x}\,dx.$$

In both cases it is often said that a "convergence factor" has been used. Corresponding to these definitions, investigate the two improper integrals

$$\int_0^{\infty} \sin \beta x\, dx \quad \text{and} \quad \int_0^{\infty} \cos \beta x\, dx.$$

In contrast to the above it is not generally true that Cesàro convergence implies Abel convergence.

*11. Examine the following infinite products for convergence, and give the value of the product in case of convergence:

(a) $\displaystyle\prod_{n=1}^{\infty} \left(1 + \frac{1}{n}\right).$
(b) $\displaystyle\prod_{n=2}^{\infty} \left(1 - \frac{1}{n}\right).$
(c) $\displaystyle\prod_{n=2}^{\infty} \left(1 - \frac{1}{n^2}\right).$

Answers

1. $\frac{3}{4}$.
2. (a) div.   (d) div.   (g) conv.
   (b) div.   (e) div.   (h) conv.
   (c) conv.   (f) conv.   (i) div.
4. (a) abs. conv.   (c) cond. conv.
   (b) cond. conv. (d) abs. conv.
11. (a) div.   (b) div.   (c) conv. ($=\frac{1}{2}$).

5-2. SERIES WITH VARIABLE TERMS

Uniform Convergence

The terms in the series so far considered have been constant. It is now assumed that they contain a variable x. It then becomes of interest to investigate for which values of x the series converges. If the series is convergent for all x in some interval I, then the sum of the series $S(x)$ wil be a function of x in this interval. The series in question is said to *represent* this function or to be a *series expansion* of the function.

Example 5-6

$$\sum_{k=0}^{\infty} x^k \sin \alpha x = \sin \alpha x + x \sin \alpha x + x^2 \sin \alpha x + \cdots$$

is for every fixed x a geometric series. For $|x| < 1$ it is convergent and has the sum $(\sin \alpha x)/(1 - x)$. Thus the function $f(x) = (\sin \alpha x)/(1 - x)(|x| < 1)$ is represented by the given series. □

The notion of absolute convergence is carried over from series with constant terms, but now it also becomes necessary to be able to express whether the convergence is "equally good" everywhere inside the interval I in which the series is investigated: If it is valid for the series $S(x) = \Sigma_{n=1}^{\infty} u_n(x)$ that its partial sums $S_1(x); S_2(x); S_3(x); \ldots$ for an arbitrary positive ϵ satisfy the inequality $|S_n(x) - S(x)| < \epsilon$ for all n greater than some number N (where N is dependent only on ϵ, but not on x), then the series is said to be *uniformly convergent* in the interval I. The decisive fact is thus that corresponding to the given ϵ the same N can be used for all x in the interval I.

It can be shown for uniformly converging series that continuity of the terms of the series implies continuity of the sum and also that the definite integral of the sum function over such an interval can be obtained by term-by-term integration of the series. Furthermore, if all terms in the uniformly converging series have continuous derivatives and if the series obtained by formal differentiation is also uniformly convergent, then the sum function is differentiable and its derivative can be obtained by term-by-term differentiation. In brief, it is possible to calculate with uniformly convergent series as with finite sums of functions.

Example 5-7. $\zeta(x) = \Sigma_{n=1}^{\infty} 1/n^x$ is, as shown in Example 5-4, convergent for $1 < x < \infty$. For the difference between the nth partial sum and the sum of the series we have

$$\left| S_n(x) - S(x) \right| = \frac{1}{(n+1)^x} + \frac{1}{(n+2)^x} + \cdots$$

$$> \int_{n+1}^{\infty} \frac{dz}{z^x} = \frac{1}{(x-1)(n+1)^{x-1}}.$$

For any fixed value of n, this last expression will tend to infinity as $x \to 1 + 0$. The series is therefore not uniformly convergent in the interval $1 < x < \infty$. On the other hand, it can be shown to be so in every interval $\alpha \le x < \infty$, where $\alpha > 1$. The sum function here considered is called the *Riemann zeta function*. $\square$

Exercises

*1. Find the sum of the following convergent infinite series, $(x > 0)$:

(a) $\displaystyle\sum_{n=0}^{\infty} e^{-nx}$.

(b) $\displaystyle\sum_{n=0}^{\infty} ne^{-nx}$.

*2. Determine those values of x for which the following infinite series are convergent:

(a) $\dfrac{1}{x} + \dfrac{2!}{x^2} + \dfrac{3!}{x^3} + \dfrac{4!}{x^4} + \cdots$.

(b) $1 + \dfrac{3}{x} + \dfrac{3^2}{2!x^2} + \dfrac{3^3}{3!x^3} + \cdots$.

3. Determine the x-interval in which the infinite series $\Sigma_{n=1}^{\infty}(x/2)^n$ is convergent. Next, investigate whether the series is (a) absolutely convergent, and (b) uniformly convergent, in this interval.

Answers

1. (a) $1/(1 - e^{-x})$. (b) $e^{-x}/(1 - e^{-x})^2$.
2. (a) no values of x. (b) All values of $x \ne 0$.

5-3. POWER SERIES

Convergence of Power Series

A *power series* is a series of the following form:

$$\sum_{n=0}^{\infty} a_n x^n = a_0 + a_1 x + a_2 x^2 + \cdots,$$

where the coefficients a_n are constants and x is a variable.

Suppose that the interval of convergence is I (see below), and that the function represented by the series is f. Then it is sometimes convenient to consider the power series as a means of transforming one function, namely, the sequence $a_0, a_1, a_2, \ldots$, which is a function from the set of nonnegative integers to the set of real numbers (see p. 134), into another function, namely f, which is a function from I to the set of real numbers. We shall return to this point of view on page 336.

As power series with respect to the x-dependence remind one of geometric series, it seems reasonable to compare them with such series, i.e., to use the Cauchy tests to determine those values of x for which a given power series is absolutely convergent. In that way the following general result may be obtained: A power series $\sum_{n=0}^{\infty} a_n x^n$ is either only convergent for $x = 0$ ($\lambda = 0$) or absolutely convergent for $-\infty < x < \infty$ ($\lambda = \infty$) or absolutely convergent for $-\lambda < x < \lambda$ and divergent for $|x| > \lambda$, where λ is some positive number.

The interval $-\lambda < x < \lambda$ is called the *interval of convergence* of the power series, and λ is called the *radius of convergence*. Also from the Cauchy tests two frequently applicable methods for the determination of λ follow. These are

$$\sqrt[n]{|a_n|} \to L \quad \text{as } n \to \infty \qquad \text{gives } \lambda = \frac{1}{L}$$

and

$$\left| \frac{a_{n+1}}{a_n} \right| \to K \quad \text{as } n \to \infty \qquad \text{gives } \lambda = \frac{1}{K},$$

where it is understood that when L or $K = 0$, then $\lambda = \infty$, and when L or $K = \infty$, then $\lambda = 0$.

The above statement says nothing about what occurs at the end points of the interval of convergence, i.e., at $x = \pm \lambda$. Some series are convergent at both end points of the interval, other series are convergent at one and divergent at the other end point, still others are divergent at both end points. In all cases a closer investigation is needed before it can be ascertained which of these possibilities occurs in a given case.

As we saw above, it is true for power series that they are absolutely convergent (except possibly at two points) if they are convergent at all. Furthermore, it can be shown that they are uniformly convergent in every interval $a \leq x \leq b$ for which $-\lambda < a < b < \lambda$. Finally, as all terms in a power series have continuous derivatives and a formal differentiation of such a series turns out to give a power series with the same radius of convergence, it follows that it is possible to perform calculations with power series in much the same way as with finite polynomials.

Analytic Functions

It has been shown previously (p. 161) how an arbitrary function f with derivatives of every order can be expanded by means of Taylor's formula. When the function is expanded from the point $x_0 = 0$, the result is usually called *Maclaurin's formula:*

$$f(x) = f(0) + \frac{f'(0)}{1!} x + \frac{f''(0)}{2!} x^2 + \cdots + \frac{f^{(n-1)}(0)}{(n-1)!} x^{n-1} + R_n(x).$$

Except for the remainder $R_n(x)$, the function appears here as a polynomial in x of degree not more than $n - 1$ with coefficients determined by the value of the function and its first $(n - 1)$ derivatives at the point 0.

A function which can be represented by a power series is called an *analytic function.* We shall now show that such a power-series expansion for an analytic function is unique and that it arises from Maclaurin's formula in a very simple way.

Consider an analytic function $f(x) = \Sigma_{n=0}^{\infty} a_n x^n$. The differential quotients are then found by term-by-term differentiation:

$$
\begin{aligned}
f(x) &= a_0 + a_1 x + a_2 x^2 + a_3 x^3 + \cdots & f(0) &= a_0 & a_0 &= f(0) \\
f'(x) &= a_1 + 2a_2 x + 3a_3 x^2 + \cdots & f'(0) &= a_1 & a_1 &= f'(0)/1! \\
f''(x) &= 2a_2 + 3 \cdot 2a_3 x + \cdots & f''(0) &= 2a_2 & a_2 &= f''(0)/2! \\
& & f^{(n)}(0) &= n! a_n & a_n &= f^{(n)}(0)/n!
\end{aligned}
$$

The coefficients are thus completely determined by $f(x)$, which means that there exists only one power series representing $f(x)$. At the same time it is seen that this unique series is obtained from MacLaurin's formula as n tends to infinity.

It also follows that an analytic function is entirely determined when the value of the function and all its derivatives are known at the point 0. This implies that not all functions which are arbitrarily often differentiable are analytic. As an example we mention the function $y = e^{-1/x^2}$ for $x \neq 0$, $y = 0$ for $x = 0$, which is not analytic: It has derivatives of every order at the point 0, but they all have the value 0, and still the function is not a constant.

The condition that a function which is arbitrarily often differentiable in a certain interval is analytic is evidently that the remainder in Maclaurin's formula for every fixed value of x in the interval approaches zero as n tends to infinity.

Example 5-8. The functions e^x, $\sin x$, $\cos x$, expressed by Maclaurin's formula with the Lagrange remainder appear as follows:

$$e^x = 1 + x + \frac{x^2}{2!} + \frac{x^3}{3!} + \cdots + \frac{x^n}{n!} e^{\theta x} \qquad (0 < \theta < 1),$$

$$\sin x = \frac{x}{1!} - \frac{x^3}{3!} + \frac{x^5}{5!} - \frac{x^7}{7!} + \cdots + \frac{x^n}{n!} \sin\left(\theta x + n\frac{\pi}{2}\right)$$
$$(0 < \theta < 1),$$

$$\cos x = 1 - \frac{x^2}{2!} + \frac{x^4}{4!} - \frac{x^6}{6!} + \cdots + \frac{x^n}{n!} \cos\left(\theta x + n\frac{\pi}{2}\right)$$
$$(0 < \theta < 1).$$

On considering the remainder it is seen that in all three cases this approaches zero for any fixed value of $x(-\infty < x < \infty)$ as $n \to \infty$. The three functions are therefore analytic in the interval $-\infty < x < \infty$, and the infinite series which are obtained from the above as $n \to \infty$ are their (uniquely determined) power series expansions. $\quad\square$

Example 5-9. The *Mercator series*

$$\ln(1 + x) = \frac{x}{1} - \frac{x^2}{2} + \frac{x^3}{3} - \cdots,$$

and the *binomial series*

$$(1 + x)^\alpha = 1 + \frac{\alpha}{1} x + \frac{\alpha(\alpha - 1)}{1 \cdot 2} x^2 + \frac{\alpha(\alpha - 1)(\alpha - 2)}{1 \cdot 2 \cdot 3} x^3 + \cdots,$$

which are obtained from MacLaurin's formula, cannot be examined with the aid of the Lagrange remainder, as this does not give a sufficiently good estimate. With more refined methods it is, however, possible to show that both functions considered are analytic in the open interval $-1 < x < 1$. $\quad\square$

It can at times be of interest to find a series representing the inverse function of a monotone analytic function given its power series. Most often, a series such as the following is considered:

$$y = \sum_{n=1}^{\infty} a_n x^n = a_1 x + a_2 x^2 + \cdots$$

(note that $a_0 = 0$). It is then true that

$$x = \frac{1}{a_1}y - \frac{a_2}{a_1{}^3}y^2 + \frac{1}{a_1{}^5}(2a_2{}^2 - a_1a_3)y^3$$
$$+ \frac{1}{a_1{}^7}(5a_1a_2a_3 - a_1{}^2a_4 - 5a_2{}^3)y^4 + \cdots.$$

The coefficients in this inverse series are determined only with difficulty by elementary methods.

Exercises

*1. Determine the intervals of convergence of the following power series:

    (a) $2x + \frac{8}{3}x^3 + \frac{32}{5}x^5 + \frac{128}{7}x^7 + \cdots.$

    (b) $\dfrac{x}{1 \cdot 2} + \dfrac{x^2}{2 \cdot 3} + \dfrac{x^3}{2^2 \cdot 4} + \dfrac{x^4}{2^3 \cdot 5} + \cdots.$

    (c) $1 - \dfrac{x^2}{2^2} + \dfrac{x^4}{2^2 4^2} - \dfrac{x^6}{2^2 4^2 6^2} + \cdots.$

*2. Find the power series expansions of the functions $\cosh x$, $\sinh x$, $\cosh^2 x$, and arctan x, and determine the intervals of convergence.

*3. Find the interval of convergence and the sum of

    (a) $\displaystyle\sum_{n=2}^{\infty} \frac{1}{n(n-1)} x^n.$ (b) $\displaystyle\sum_{n=3}^{\infty} \frac{1}{n(n-1)(n-2)} x^n.$

4. Find those values of x for which the series

$$\sum_{n=1}^{\infty} \frac{(-1)^{n-1}}{n}(x^2 - 2x - 1)^n$$

is convergent, and find its sum.

5. Show that

$$\ln M = \ln N + 2\left(x + \frac{x^3}{3} + \frac{x^5}{5} + \cdots\right),$$

where $x = (M - N)/(M + N)$ $(M > 0, N > 0)$.

*6. Calculate, using expansion in a series, the following definite integrals to three decimal places:

    (a) $\displaystyle\int_0^{1/4} \ln(1 + \sqrt{x})\, dx.$ (b) $\displaystyle\int_0^1 \cos\sqrt{x}\, dx.$

7. Verify the following series expansions and give the intervals of convergence:

    (a) $\sin x \cos\sqrt{x} = x - \frac{1}{2}x^2 - \frac{1}{6}x^3 + \frac{59}{720}x^4 + \cdots.$

    (b) $\dfrac{1}{x} = \dfrac{1}{a} - \dfrac{1}{a^2}(x - a) + \dfrac{1}{a^3}(x - a)^2 - \dfrac{1}{a^4}(x - a)^3 + \cdots.$

8. Find a solution to the functional equation $F(x) + F(x^2) = x$ valid in a neighborhood of $x = 0$ by assuming a power expansion for $F(x)$. Determine the interval of convergence of the series obtained. In the same way investigate under which conditions the equation $F(x^a) + F(x^b) = x^c$ (a, b, c positive integers) has a nontrivial solution.

*9. Let $A = \{a_{ik}\}$ and $B = \{b_{ik}\}$ be matrices of infinite order. Evaluate the matrix product AB, when

(a) $\quad a_{ik} = \dfrac{i^k}{k!},$ $\qquad\qquad$ (b) $\quad a_{ik} = \dfrac{1}{(i+1)^k},$

$\quad\quad\ b_{ik} = k^i.$ $\qquad\qquad\qquad\ \ b_{ik} = \dfrac{1}{k^i}.$

($i = 1,2,3,\ldots;\ k = 1,2,3,\ldots$). Next, investigate whether the matrix product BA exists in each of the two cases.

10. Show that

$$\int_0^\pi \frac{dx}{1 - y\cos x} = \frac{\pi}{\sqrt{1 - y^2}} \qquad (|y| < 1).$$

Answers

1. (a) $|x| < \frac{1}{2}$. (b) $-2 \le x < 2$. (c) All x.

2. $\cosh x = 1 + \dfrac{x^2}{2!} + \dfrac{x^4}{4!} + \cdots$ (all x)

$\quad \sinh x = x + \dfrac{x^3}{3!} + \dfrac{x^5}{5!} + \cdots$ (all x)

$\quad \cosh^2 x = 1 + \dfrac{2^2 x^2}{2 \cdot 2!} + \dfrac{2^4 x^4}{2 \cdot 4!} + \cdots$ (all x)

$\quad \arctan x = x - \dfrac{x^3}{3} + \dfrac{x^5}{5} - \dfrac{x^7}{7} + \cdots$ ($-1 < x \le 1$)

3. (a) $(1 - x)\ln(1 - x) + x$ ($|x| \le 1$)

$\quad$ (b) $-\dfrac{(1 - x)^2}{2}\ln(1 - x) + \dfrac{(1 - x)^2}{4} + \dfrac{x^2}{2} - \dfrac{1}{4}$ ($|x| \le 1$)

6. (a) 0.071. (b) 0.764.

9. (a) $(AB)_{ik} = e^{ik} - 1$. (b) $(AB)_{ik} = 1/(k(i + 1) - 1)$.
$\quad$ The matrix product BA exists for case (b) but not for case (a).

5-4. THE LAPLACE TRANSFORMATION AND THE GAMMA FUNCTION

Laplace Transforms

It was mentioned above that power series could be considered as a means of transforming a given sequence a into a function f with an interval as its domain:

$$f(x) = \sum_{n=0}^{\infty} a_n x^n \quad \text{or} \quad f(x) = \sum_{n=0}^{\infty} a(n) x^n.$$

Now suppose that a is a function with the set of all nonnegative real numbers as its domain. In this case $\sum_{n=0}^{\infty} a(n) x^n$ is an average sum belonging to the improper integral $\int_0^{\infty} a(t) x^t \, dt$. It is convenient to substitute x by e^{-s} so that the integral can be written $\int_0^{\infty} a(t) e^{-st} \, dt$. This last expression determines a new function La, called the *Laplace transform* of a:

$$La(s) = \int_0^{\infty} a(t) e^{-st} \, dt.$$

La is defined at those values of s for which the corresponding improper integral is convergent; it can be shown that if the integral considered is convergent for $s = s_0$, then it will also be convergent for all $s > s_0$.

It is at once clear that the operator L which is called the *Laplace transformation*, is a linear operator, i.e.,

$$L(c_1 a_1 + c_2 a_2) = c_1 La_1 + c_2 La_2,$$

where c_1 and c_2 are arbitrary constants.

Example 5-10. The Laplace transform of the function $a(t) = \sin \omega t$ is defined for $s > 0$. Integrating by parts we find

$$L(\sin \omega t)(s) = \int_0^{\infty} \sin \omega t \, e^{-st} \, dt$$

$$= -\frac{1}{\omega} [e^{-st} \cos \omega t]_0^{\infty} - \frac{s}{\omega} \int_0^{\infty} \cos \omega t \, e^{-st} \, dt$$

$$= \frac{1}{\omega} - \frac{s}{\omega^2} [\sin \omega t \, e^{-st}]_0^{\infty} - \frac{s^2}{\omega^2} \int_0^{\infty} \sin \omega t \, e^{-st} \, dt$$

$$= \frac{1}{\omega} - \frac{s^2}{\omega^2} L(\sin \omega t)(s),$$

and therefore $L(\sin \omega t)(s) = \omega/(s^2 + \omega^2)$. Analogously, $L(\cos \omega t)(s) = s/(s^2 + \omega^2)$. $\square$

Example 5-11. The product of two absolutely convergent power series $\sum_{n=0}^{\infty} a_n x^n$ and $\sum_{n=0}^{\infty} b_n x^n$ is

$$\sum_{n=0}^{\infty} \left(\sum_{\nu=0}^{n} a_\nu b_{n-\nu} \right) x^n$$

(cf. p. 326). As an analogy to this, we shall now deduce a formula for the product of two Laplace transforms Lf and Lg. We have

$$Lf(s) \cdot Lg(s) = \int_0^\infty f(x)e^{-sx}\, dx \int_0^\infty g(y)e^{-sy}\, dy$$

$$= \int e^{-s(x+y)} f(x)g(y)\, dA.$$

The last integral is a double integral over the first quadrant of the XY-plane. When the linear transformation $x = v$, $y = u - v$, or

$$\begin{Bmatrix} u \\ v \end{Bmatrix} = \begin{Bmatrix} 1 & 1 \\ 1 & 0 \end{Bmatrix} \begin{Bmatrix} x \\ y \end{Bmatrix}$$

is introduced, the region of integration is mapped onto that section of the UV-plane which is determined by the inequalities $0 \le u < \infty$, $0 \le v \le u$. As the absolute value of the Jacobian for the corresponding transformation of the double integral is 1 (cf. p. 293), we have

$$Lf(s) \cdot Lg(s) = \iint e^{-su} f(v)g(u - v)\, du\, dv$$

$$= \int_0^\infty du \int_0^u e^{-su} f(v)g(u - v)\, dv$$

$$= \int_0^\infty \left[\int_0^u f(v)g(u - v)\, dv \right] e^{-su}\, du,$$

or, when the variable of integration u is replaced by t,

$$Lf(s) \cdot Lg(s) = \int_0^\infty \left[\int_0^t f(v)g(t - v)\, dv \right] e^{-st}\, dt$$

$$= L \left[\int_0^t f(v)g(t - v)\, dv \right] (s).$$

We have thus shown that the product of the Laplace transforms of two functions f and g is equal to the Laplace transform of the function $f * g$ defined by a so-called *convolution integral* in the following way:

$$[f * g](t) = \int_0^t f(v)g(t - v)\, dv.$$

The analogy with the above expression for the product of two power series is clearly seen. □

Applications of the Laplace Transforms

The most important application of the Laplace transforms arises from the fact that the operator L transforms the operation differentiation into the much simpler operation multiplication. This can be shown in the following way by using integration by parts on the expression for the Laplace transform of the derivative of a given function f:

$$Lf'(s) = \int_0^\infty f'(t)e^{-st} \, dt = [f(t)e^{-st}]_0^\infty + s \int_0^\infty f(t)e^{-st} \, dt$$
$$= -f(0) + sLf(s).$$

By continued use of this result, we get

$$Lf''(s) = -f'(0) - sf(0) + s^2Lf(s), \qquad \text{etc.}$$

Differential equations are equations which express a relation between a function and its derivatives. Where it is desired to find functions satisfying such an equation, Laplace transforms can be introduced with the consequence that the given differential equation is changed into an algebraic equation. This finds wide application, especially in the solution of partial differential equations. For this purpose, tables of Laplace transforms have been compiled. Of course these can also be used simply as tables of definite integrals of the form $\int_0^\infty f(x)e^{-\alpha x} \, dx$.

Example 5-12. It is required to find functions f such that $f''(t) + \omega^2 f(t) = 0$ for all t, and at the same time $f(0) = a$, $f'(0) = b$, where a and b are given numbers.

Application of the operator L on the given differential equation gives the following result:

$$-b - sa + s^2Lf(s) + \omega^2Lf(s) = 0,$$

where the linearity property of L and the fact that $L0 = 0$ has been used. From this algebraic equation in Lf we immediately obtain

$$Lf(s) = a\frac{s}{s^2 + \omega^2} + b\frac{1}{s^2 + \omega^2}.$$

It now remains to find functions f which have this Laplace transform; on comparison with Example 5-10, it is seen that one solution is

$$f(t) = a \cos \omega t + \frac{b}{\omega} \sin \omega t.$$

Furthermore this can be shown to be the only solution to the problem. We shall return to these questions in Chapter 6. □

The Gamma Function

The theory outlined above for Laplace transforms can be made fully rigorous. It is then one of the most powerful tools in applied mathematics. However, we shall leave this problem and confine ourselves to showing how the operator L relates the previously (p. 199) introduced function Γ with the power functions.

We have

$$\Gamma(x) = \int_0^\infty t^{x-1} e^{-t} \, dt.$$

Thus $\Gamma(x)$ is the value at $s = 1$ of the Laplace transform of the function $a(t) = t^{x-1}$, which contains x as a parameter. More generally the Laplace transform of a power function t^n is

$$L(t^n)(s) = \int_0^\infty t^n e^{-st} \, dt = \frac{\Gamma(n+1)}{s^{n+1}}.$$

This formula can be proved by elementary methods for $n = 0,1,2,\ldots$, and for an arbitrary $n(> -1)$ by using the definition of the Γ-function.

In applications of the Γ-function, it is often of interest to be able to give an approximate expression for $\Gamma(x)$ for very large values of x ($x \gg 1$). It is normally only necessary for this expression to have a small *relative error*, while the absolute error may be large. When the absolute error in the expression is denoted $\Delta\Gamma(x)$, it is only required that $\Delta\Gamma(x)/\Gamma(x)$ is small compared to 1, or in other words that $\ln \Gamma(x)$ has a small absolute error. An expression of that type is often called an *asymptotic expression*. We shall return to the exact meaning of this in Chapter 8.

The approximate expression for $\Gamma(x)$ is found by evaluating the integral in the following manner:

$$\int_0^\infty t^{x-1}e^{-t}\, dt = \int_0^\infty e^{(x-1)\ln t - t}\, dt$$

$$= \int_0^\infty \exp\left[(x-1)\ln(x-1) - (x-1) \right.$$

$$\left. - \frac{1}{2(x-1)}(t-(x-1))^2 + \cdots \right] dt.$$

We have expanded the exponent of the integrand in a Taylor series from the point $t = x - 1$, where the exponent assumes its greatest value. Therefore we have

$$\Gamma(x) \simeq \exp[(x-1)\ln(x-1) - (x-1)] \int_0^\infty \exp\left[-\frac{(t-(x-1))^2}{2(x-1)} \right] dt,$$

or, when $\tau = t - (x-1)$ is introduced,

$$\Gamma(x) \simeq \exp[(x-1)\ln(x-1) - (x-1)] \int_{-(x-1)}^\infty e^{-\tau^2/2(x-1)}\, d\tau.$$

As $x \gg 1$, and as the integrand $e^{-\tau^2/2(x-1)}$ is a function which takes on values substantially larger than 0 only in a small interval around $\tau = 0$, then the lower limit may approximately be replaced by $-\infty$, and thus (p. 277)

$$\Gamma(x) \simeq \{\exp[(x-1)\ln(x-1) - (x-1)]\}\sqrt{2\pi(x-1)}.$$

This is more conveniently written

$$x! = \Gamma(x+1) \approx x^x e^{-x}\sqrt{2\pi x}.$$

With more refined methods, it is possible to show that the so-called *Stirling's formula*,

$$x! = \Gamma(x+1) = x^x e^{-x}\sqrt{2\pi x}\left[1 + \frac{1}{12x} + \frac{1}{288x^2} + \cdots \right],$$

is valid as an asymptotic expression, i.e., as an expression which for a fixed number of terms in the parentheses becomes more and more accurate as x increases in value. Such an asymptotic expression gives rise to the introduction of a new symbol:

$$\Gamma(x + 1) = x^x e^{-x} \sqrt{2\pi x} \left[1 + O\left(\frac{1}{x}\right) \right] \quad \text{as } x \to \infty.$$

The meaning of this is that the parentheses for large values of x will be 1 except for a term, which at the most is a constant times x^{-1}. More generally, $f(x) = O(g(x))$, $x \to x_0$, signifies that there exists a neighborhood of x_0 and a number A such that $|f(x)| < A|g(x)|$ for all x in this neighborhood.

In many applications, where $N!$ is investigated for very large N, as, for example, in statistical mechanics, where $N \sim 10^{23}$, the approximation $\ln N! = N \ln N - N$, corresponding to the correct formula $\ln N! = N \ln N - N + O(\ln N)$, will be sufficient.

The method used above to obtain an asymptotic expression for an integral is applicable in cases where the integrand is very large in a small interval and tends rapidly to zero outside this interval. In the special case of an integrand of the form $\exp(xf(t))$, where x is a parameter which takes on a large value and $f(t)$ has a maximum value at $t = t_0$, the following is obtained as an asymptotic expression for the integral over an interval which contains t_0:

$$\int_a^b e^{xf(t)} \, dt \approx \int_{-\infty}^{+\infty} e^{xf(t)} \, dt \approx e^{xf(t_0)} \sqrt{\frac{-2\pi}{xf''(t_0)}}.$$

This is seen by methods completely analogous to those used above for the derivation of the first terms in Stirling's formula.

Exercises

*1. Find the Laplace transforms of the functions $\sqrt{x}$ and $x \sin \omega x$. In the last case it is easiest to start with the Laplace transform of $\sin \omega x$ or $\cos \omega x$.

*2. Show that if the two integrals

$$\int_0^\infty f(x) \, Lg(x) \, dx \quad \text{and} \quad \int_0^\infty g(y) \, Lf(y) \, dy$$

are convergent, they are equal. Use this to prove that

$$\int_0^\infty \frac{\sin x}{x} \, dx = \int_0^\infty \frac{dy}{1 + y^2} \left(= \frac{\pi}{2} \right).$$

3. Let g_1 and g_2 be polynomials of mth and nth degree, respectively, and let the n roots $a_1, a_2, \ldots, a_n$ of g_2 be real and different. Show that for $m < n$,

$$L^{-1}\left(\frac{g_1}{g_2}\right)(x) = \sum_{k=1}^{n} \frac{g_1(a_k)}{g_2'(a_k)} e^{a_k x}.$$

4. Show by a series expansion of the numerator in powers of e^{-x} followed by an integration that

$$\int_0^\infty \frac{x^{s-1}}{e^x - 1} dx = \Gamma(s)\zeta(s)$$

where $\zeta(s)$ is the Riemann zeta function.

Answers

1. $\dfrac{\sqrt{\pi}}{2s\sqrt{s}};\ \dfrac{2\omega s}{(s^2 + \omega^2)^2}$

2. The first two integrals mentioned are both equal to $\int_\omega f(x)g(y)e^{-xy}\, dA$, where ω is the first quadrant. By choosing $f(x) = \sin x$ and $g(y) = 1$ in these two integrals, the second result is easily obtained.

5-5. ORTHOGONAL SYSTEMS OF FUNCTIONS

Orthogonal Functions and Series Expansions

The power series expansions in x which have been considered above generally give rise to good approximations near the point $x = 0$, but the error which is introduced by taking only a finite number of terms in the series can increase rapidly with $|x|$. We shall now consider another type of series expansion, for which the approximation in a certain sense is "the best possible" in an interval rather than at a point.

Consider a set of functions of $\phi_n(x)$ $(n = 1,2,3,\ldots)$ which are all taken to be continuous in an interval $a \le x \le b$, and for which the following is true:

$$\int_a^b \phi_n(x)\phi_m(x)\, dx = \begin{cases} 1 & \text{if } n = m, \\ 0 & \text{if } n \ne m. \end{cases}$$

In what follows we shall write this

$$\int \phi_n(x)\phi_m(x)\, dx = \delta_{nm} \quad \text{or} \quad \int \phi_n\phi_m\, dx = \delta_{nm},$$

where the limits of integration (and the variable x) are understood, and where the Kronecker symbol δ_{nm} is used (p. 40).

It is useful to think of the above integral as a generalization of a *scalar product*. We have

$$\int \phi_n \phi_m \, dx = \lim_{\Delta_i x \to 0} \sum_i \phi_n(x_i) \phi_m(x_i) \, \Delta_i x,$$

which can be compared to the scalar product of two finite-dimensional vectors:

$$\mathbf{a} = (a_1, a_2, \ldots, a_N) \quad \text{and} \quad \mathbf{b} = (b_1, b_2, \ldots, b_N),$$

$$\mathbf{a} \cdot \mathbf{b} = \sum_{i=1}^{N} a_i b_i.$$

In agreement with this analogy, any two functions ϕ_n and ϕ_m with $n \neq m$ are said to be *orthogonal*, and the given set of functions is said to form an *orthogonal system of functions*. Furthermore, since the individual functions satisfy the relation $\int \phi_n^2 \, dx = 1$, i.e., are chosen so that the quantity which in the vector analogy corresponds to the square of the length is equal to 1, the system is also *orthonormal*. The functions ϕ_n $(n = 1,2,3,\ldots)$ are said to span a vector space of infinite dimension in which they correspond to the unit vectors. This space is called a *function space* or a *Hilbert space*.

We shall now examine how an arbitrary function f (with the same domain as the ϕ's) can be written as a linear combination of the ϕ's. We set

$$f(x) = \sum_{n=1}^{\infty} c_n \phi_n(x).$$

By multiplication by ϕ_k on both sides of the equals sign and integration with respect to x we have

$$\int f(x) \phi_k(x) \, dx = c_k.$$

This determines, at least formally, the expansion coefficients c_k.

We can here regard f as an arbitrary vector of infinite dimension and the quantity $\int f \phi_n \, dx$ as the "scalar product" of f with ϕ_n, or as the length of the "projection" on ϕ_n of f. The series expansion

$$f(x) = \sum_{n=1}^{\infty} \left(\int f \phi_n \, dx \right) \phi_n(x)$$

is thus completely analogous with the expansion of an N-dimensional vector $\mathbf{f}$ on the finite number of N-dimensional unit vectors $\mathbf{e}_1, \ldots, \mathbf{e}_N,$

which is

$$\mathbf{f} = \sum_{n=1}^{N} (\mathbf{f} \cdot \mathbf{e}_n)\mathbf{e}_n.$$

For further confirmation of this analogy we can examine how the generalized scalar product of two functions

$$h(x) = \Sigma a_n \phi_n(x) \qquad \text{and} \qquad g(x) = \Sigma b_m \phi_m(x)$$

can be expressed by the expansion coefficients a_n and b_m. The generalized scalar product, which we shall write (h,g) is

$$(h,g) = \int \left(\sum a_n \phi_n(x) \right) \left(\sum b_m \phi_m(x) \right) dx = \sum_{n=1}^{\infty} a_n b_n.$$

Here the last expression is the result of a formal calculation where the orthonormality properties of the ϕ's are used. The scalar product of two functions is thus a sum of products of the "coordinates" in the same way as the scalar product of two N-dimensional vectors $\mathbf{h} = (a_1, a_2, \ldots, a_N)$ and $\mathbf{g} = (b_1, b_2, \ldots, b_N)$ is

$$\mathbf{h} \cdot \mathbf{g} = \sum_{k=1}^{N} a_k b_k.$$

It is this last analogy between (h,g) and the usual scalar product which is interesting, rather than the immediate analogy previously mentioned, which is based on the integral as the limit of a sum. In the last analogy it is seen clearly how the coefficients in the series expansion play the same role as the coordinates in a finite-dimensional vector space.

Convergence of the Series

It is clear that the above formal considerations give no information as to whether the series considered are convergent, and, in case they are, whether they have the supposed sums. A closer examination shows that if the function $f(x)$ is *piecewise-differentiable* [i.e., if the interval $a \leq x \leq b$ can be divided into a finite number of intervals $\alpha \leq x \leq \beta$ such that $f(x)$ coincides in each open interval $\alpha < x < \beta$ with a function which is differentiable in the closed interval $\alpha \leq x \leq \beta$], then the above-considered expansion on an orthogonal system of functions is valid if at the possible points of discontinuity a value is given the function $f(x)$ which is the average value of its limits from the right and from the left. It is a necessary condition for the convergence, however, that the orthogonal system used is *complete* (see p. 347).

We shall not concern ourselves further with this problem of convergence, but instead examine which type of approximation we may obtain by expanding a function on an orthogonal system. To see this we consider the definite integral

$$\int_a^b \left[f(x) - \sum_{k=1}^{N_1} c_k' \phi_k(x) \right]^2 dx,$$

which shall be called the *square error*. For a given value of N_1 the square error appears as a function of the coefficients c_k' ($k = 1,2,\ldots,N_1$), and we now want to determine these such that the square error becomes as small as possible. The integral is therefore rewritten in the following way:

$$\int \left[f(x) - \sum_k c_k' \phi_k(x) \right]^2 dx = \int f(x)^2 \, dx + \sum c_k'^2 \int \phi_k(x)^2 \, dx$$
$$- 2 \sum c_k' \int f(x) \phi_k(x) \, dx$$
$$+ \sum_{k \neq l} \sum c_k' c_l' \int \phi_k(x) \phi_l(x) \, dx$$
$$= \int f(x)^2 \, dx + \sum c_k'^2 - 2 \sum c_k' c_k,$$

where we have used the orthonormality properties of the ϕ's. This is further rewritten as

$$\int \left[f(x) - \sum_k c_k' \phi_k(x) \right]^2 dx = \int f(x)^2 \, dx + \sum_k (c_k' - c_k)^2 - \sum_k c_k^2.$$

From this it is seen that the square error is least when each c_k' is equal to the previously determined expansion coefficient $c_k = \int f(x) \phi_k(x) \, dx$. As the square error is always positive or zero, then at the same time we obtain the *Bessel inequality* (valid for an arbitrary N_1):

$$\int [f(x)]^2 \, dx \geq \sum_{k=1}^{N_1} c_k^2.$$

A "geometric" interpretation of the Bessel inequality is easily obtained by considering its analogy in an N-dimensional vector space. Consider the vector $\mathbf{a} = (a_1, a_2, \ldots, a_N)$, and also the quantity $\sum_{k=1}^{N_1} a_k^2$, where $N_1 \leq N$. As the square of the length of the vector is $a^2 =$

$\Sigma_{k=1}^{N} a_k{}^2$ and as $\Sigma_{k=N_1+1}^{N} a_k{}^2 \geq 0$, we have

$$a^2 \geq \sum_{k=1}^{N_1} a_k{}^2 \qquad (N_1 \leq N).$$

The analogue of this in our vector space of infinite dimension ("$N = \infty$") is the Bessel inequality.

The orthogonal system of functions considered is said to be *complete* if it has the following property: When a sufficiently large number of terms N_1 are included in the sum $\Sigma_{k=1}^{N_1} c_k \phi_k(x)$, then the integral

$$\int_a^b \left[f(x) - \sum_{k=1}^{N_1} c_k \phi_k(x) \right]^2 dx$$

becomes less than ϵ, where ϵ is an arbitrarily small positive number. This must be true for any function $f(x)$ which is piecewise continuous in the interval $a \leq x \leq b$.

A large number of complete orthogonal systems have been introduced for use in applied mathematics. We shall now discuss a few of these.

5-6. FOURIER SERIES

Trigonometric Fourier Series

By direct evaluation it is easily seen that the set of functions

$$\frac{1}{\sqrt{2\pi}}, \frac{1}{\sqrt{\pi}} \cos x, \frac{1}{\sqrt{\pi}} \sin x, \frac{1}{\sqrt{\pi}} \cos 2x, \frac{1}{\sqrt{\pi}} \sin 2x, \ldots,$$

$$\frac{1}{\sqrt{\pi}} \cos nx, \frac{1}{\sqrt{\pi}} \sin nx, \ldots$$

form an orthonormal system in the interval $-\pi \leq x \leq \pi$. More generally, the functions

$$\frac{1}{\sqrt{2L}}, \ldots, \frac{1}{\sqrt{L}} \cos \frac{n\pi}{L} x, \frac{1}{\sqrt{L}} \sin \frac{n\pi}{L} x, \ldots$$

form an orthonormal system in the interval $-L \leq x \leq L$, where L is any positive number. All these systems can be shown to be complete.

Any function $f(x)$ piecewise-differentiable in an interval $-L \leq x \leq L$ can therefore be expanded in terms of these functions. The series obtained is called the (trigonometric) *Fourier expansion* or *Fourier series* for the function.

Example 5-13. As an example of a Fourier series we shall expand the function

$$f(x) = \begin{cases} -1 & \text{for } -\pi < x < 0, \\ 1 & \text{for } 0 < x < \pi. \end{cases}$$

We have

$$\frac{1}{\sqrt{\pi}} \int_{-\pi}^{\pi} \cos nx\, f(x)\, dx = 0$$

and

$$\frac{1}{\sqrt{\pi}} \int_{-\pi}^{\pi} \sin nx\, f(x)\, dx = \frac{2}{\sqrt{\pi}} \int_{0}^{\pi} \sin nx\, dx = \begin{cases} 0 & \text{for } n \text{ even,} \\ \dfrac{4}{\sqrt{\pi}\, n} & \text{for } n \text{ odd,} \end{cases}$$

where we have used the fact that f is an odd function $[f(-x) = -f(x)]$. The final result is then

$$f(x) = \frac{4}{\pi} \left[\frac{\sin x}{1} + \frac{\sin 3x}{3} + \frac{\sin 5x}{5} + \cdots \right].$$

In the corresponding way it is found, for example, that

$$f(x) = \begin{cases} -x & \text{for } -\pi < x < 0, \\ x & \text{for } 0 < x < \pi, \end{cases}$$

which is an even function $[f(x) = f(-x)]$ and can be written

$$f(x) = \frac{\pi}{2} - \frac{4}{\pi} \left[\frac{\cos x}{1^2} + \frac{\cos 3x}{3^2} + \frac{\cos 5x}{5^2} + \cdots \right]. \qquad \Box$$

Fourier series are very important in the solution of partial differential equations (see p. 415). In this connection, we mention that Fourier series (in the interval $-\pi \leq x \leq \pi$) usually are evaluated using the following formula:

$$f(x) = \tfrac{1}{2}\alpha_0 + \alpha_1 \cos x + \beta_1 \sin x + \cdots + \alpha_n \cos nx$$
$$+ \beta_n \sin nx + \cdots,$$

where $\alpha_n = (1/\pi)\int_{-\pi}^{\pi} f(x) \cos nx\, dx$ $(n = 0,1,2,\ldots)$ and $\beta_n = (1/\pi) \int_{-\pi}^{\pi} f(x) \sin nx\, dx$ $(n = 1,2,3,\ldots)$. This is easily seen to be in agreement with the above.

It is often possible to derive various interesting results from Fourier series by inserting special values of the variable. From the first of the above-considered series with $x = \pi/2$, and therefore $f(x) = 1$, we obtain

$$\frac{\pi}{4} = 1 - \tfrac{1}{3} + \tfrac{1}{5} - \tfrac{1}{7} + \cdots,$$

and from the second series (with $x = 0$),

$$\frac{\pi^2}{8} = \frac{1}{1^2} + \frac{1}{3^2} + \frac{1}{5^2} + \frac{1}{7^2} + \cdots.$$

From this last result we can easily find the sum S of the series

$$\sum_{n=1}^{\infty} \frac{1}{n^2} = \frac{1}{1^2} + \frac{1}{2^2} + \cdots + \frac{1}{n^2} + \cdots.$$

We have

$$\frac{1}{2^2} + \frac{1}{4^2} + \frac{1}{6^2} + \cdots = \frac{1}{4}\left(\frac{1}{1^2} + \frac{1}{2^2} + \frac{1}{3^2} + \cdots\right) = \frac{1}{4}S$$

and therefore $\pi^2/8 = S - \tfrac{1}{4}S$. Thus $S = \pi^2/6$.

Above we have only considered Fourier expansions of functions in some interval $-L \leq x \leq L$. As all terms in such series are periodic with the period $2L$, it follows that the series will be convergent for all x, and that the sum function will be periodic with this same period. This function is often referred to as the *periodic continuation* of the original function.

Exponential Fourier Series

The so-called *exponential Fourier series* are of even greater importance in the applications than the trigonometric series. They are based on the following system of functions, which are orthonormal in the interval $-\pi \leq x \leq \pi$.

$$\cdots, \frac{1}{\sqrt{2\pi}} e^{-inx}, \cdots, \frac{1}{\sqrt{2\pi}} e^{-ix}, \frac{1}{\sqrt{2\pi}}, \frac{1}{\sqrt{2\pi}} e^{ix}, \cdots,$$

$$\frac{1}{\sqrt{2\pi}} e^{inx}, \cdots \qquad (n = \ldots, 2, 3 \ldots).$$

These functions are complex and the definition of the generalized scalar product is analogous to that of vectors with complex components. This means that orthonormality now is expressed by $\int \phi_n^* \phi_m \, dx = \delta_{nm}$. The exponential Fourier series of a given function $f(x)$ may then be written

$$f(x) = C_0 \frac{1}{\sqrt{2\pi}} + \sum_{n=1}^{\infty} \left(C_{-n} \frac{1}{\sqrt{2\pi}} e^{-inx} + C_n \frac{1}{\sqrt{2\pi}} e^{inx} \right),$$

in which case the expansion coefficients are given by

$$C_n = \int \phi_n^*(x) f(x) \, dx = \frac{1}{\sqrt{2\pi}} \int_{-\pi}^{\pi} e^{-inx} f(x) \, dx \quad (n = 0, \pm 1, \pm 2, \ldots).$$

By comparison with the corresponding trigonometric Fourier series,

$$f(x) = a_0 \frac{1}{\sqrt{2\pi}} + \sum_{n=1}^{\infty} \left(a_n \frac{1}{\sqrt{\pi}} \cos nx + b_n \frac{1}{\sqrt{\pi}} \sin nx \right),$$

where

$$a_0 = \int_{-\pi}^{\pi} \frac{1}{\sqrt{2\pi}} f(x) \, dx, \qquad a_n = \int_{-\pi}^{\pi} \left(\frac{1}{\sqrt{\pi}} \cos nx \right) f(x) \, dx,$$

$$b_n = \int_{-\pi}^{\pi} \left(\frac{1}{\sqrt{\pi}} \sin nx \right) f(x) \, dx \qquad (n = 1,2,3, \ldots),$$

the following transformation formulas are obtained:

$$a_0 = C_0,$$
$$\left. \begin{aligned} a_n &= \frac{1}{\sqrt{2}} (C_n + C_{-n}) \\ b_n &= \frac{i}{\sqrt{2}} (C_n - C_{-n}) \end{aligned} \right\} \quad (n = 1,2,3, \ldots).$$

and

$$C_0 = a_0,$$
$$\left. \begin{aligned} C_n &= \frac{1}{\sqrt{2}} (a_n - ib_n) \\ C_{-n} &= \frac{1}{\sqrt{2}} (a_n + ib_n) \end{aligned} \right\} \quad (n = 1,2,3, \ldots).$$

Example 5-14. The function

$$f(x) = \begin{cases} -1 & \text{for } -\pi < x < 0, \\ 1 & \text{for } 0 < x < \pi, \end{cases}$$

has the exponential Fourier expansion

$$f(x) = -\sum_{\substack{n \text{ odd and} \\ \text{positive}}} \frac{2i}{\pi n} (e^{inx} - e^{-inx}).$$

This can be seen on comparison with Example 5-13, or by direct calculation of the expansion coefficients:

$$C_n = \frac{1}{\sqrt{2\pi}} \int_{-\pi}^{\pi} e^{-inx} f(x)\, dx = \begin{cases} -\dfrac{4i}{\sqrt{2\pi}n} & |n| \text{ odd,} \\ 0 & |n| \text{ even.} \end{cases} \quad \square$$

Exercises

*1. Find the Fourier series for the function $f(x) = x$ $(-\pi < x < \pi)$. Next, sketch the graph of the nth partial sum $(n = 1,2,3)$.

2. Expand the function

$$f(x) = \begin{cases} x & (0 \le x \le \pi/2), \\ \pi - x & (\pi/2 \le x < \pi), \end{cases} \qquad f(x) = f(-x)$$

in a Fourier series in the interval $-\pi < x < \pi$.

*3. Find the Fourier series for the periodic continuation of

(a) $f(x) = x^2$ $(-\pi < x < \pi)$.   (b) $f(x) = x^2$ $(-1 < x < 1)$.

4. With the help of the Fourier series for the function $f(x) = x^4$ $(-\pi < x < \pi)$, find the sum of the infinite series $\sum_{n=1}^{\infty} 1/n^4$. Could the same sum have been obtained from the results of Exercise 3?

5. Find the Fourier expansion for $\cos \lambda x$ $(-\pi < x < \pi)$, where λ is not an integer. Investigate the limiting process $\lambda \to$ integer.

Answers

1. $2[\sin x - \tfrac{1}{2} \sin 2x + \tfrac{1}{3} \sin 3x - \cdots]$

3. (a) $\dfrac{\pi^2}{3} - 4\left[\cos x - \dfrac{1}{2^2} \cos 2x + \dfrac{1}{3^2} \cos 3x - \cdots \right]$

   (b) $\dfrac{1}{3} - \dfrac{4}{\pi^2}\left[\cos \pi x - \dfrac{1}{2^2} \cos 2\pi x + \dfrac{1}{3^2} \cos 3\pi x - \cdots \right]$

5-7. LEGENDRE POLYNOMIALS

In the previous section we started with an orthonormal system of functions. In this section we shall now show how it may be possible from a given set of functions to construct an orthonormal system. As it has been shown that a large class of functions can be expanded in power series, it seems natural to examine whether it is possible from the functions 1, x, x^2, x^3, x^4, . . .,x^n,. . . to form linear combinations which are orthogonal in some interval such as $-1 \leq x \leq 1$.

This problem is analogous to the one of constructing ρ mutually perpendicular unit vectors as linear combinations of ρ linearly independent vectors, which we considered earlier (see p. 33). The method which was used then, the Schmidt orthogonalization method, can immediately be taken over, giving orthogonal functions $b_k(x)$ and orthonormal functions $n_k(x)$ in the following way:

$$b_0(x) = 1, \qquad\qquad n_0(x) = 1 \Big/ \sqrt{\int_{-1}^{1} 1^2 \, dx} = \frac{1}{\sqrt{2}},$$

$$b_1(x) = x - \frac{1}{\sqrt{2}} \int_{-1}^{1} \frac{1}{\sqrt{2}} x \, dx = x, \quad n_1(x) = x \Big/ \sqrt{\int_{-1}^{1} x^2 \, dx} = \sqrt{\frac{3}{2}}\, x,$$

$$b_2(x) = x^2 - \frac{1}{\sqrt{2}} \int_{-1}^{1} \frac{1}{\sqrt{2}} x^2 \, dx \qquad n_2(x) = \frac{x^2 - \dfrac{1}{3}}{\sqrt{\displaystyle\int_{-1}^{1} \left(x^2 - \frac{1}{3}\right)^2 dx}}$$

$$- \sqrt{\frac{3}{2}}\, x \int_{-1}^{1} x^2 \sqrt{\frac{3}{2}}\, x \, dx,$$

$$= x^2 - \frac{1}{3}, \qquad\qquad\qquad\qquad = \sqrt{\frac{5}{2}} \left(\frac{3}{2} x^2 - \frac{1}{2}\right),$$

etc.

The normalized functions are

$$\sqrt{\tfrac{1}{2}},\ \sqrt{\tfrac{3}{2}}x,\ \sqrt{\tfrac{5}{2}}\,(\tfrac{3}{2}x^2 - \tfrac{1}{2}),\ \sqrt{\tfrac{7}{2}}\,(\tfrac{5}{2}x^3 - \tfrac{3}{2}x),.\ .\ .,$$

or, as they are often written,

$$\sqrt{\frac{2n + 1}{2}}\ P_n(x) \qquad (n = 0,1,2,.\ .\ .).$$

Here $P_n(x)$ is called the *Legendre polynomial* of the nth degree, and we have

$$\int_{-1}^{1} P_n{}^2(x) \, dx = \frac{2}{2n + 1} \quad \text{and} \quad \int_{-1}^{1} P_n(x) P_m(x) \, dx = 0, \qquad (n \neq m).$$

The first Legendre polynomials are

$$P_0(x) = 1,$$
$$P_1(x) = x,$$
$$P_2(x) = \tfrac{1}{2}(3x^2 - 1),$$
$$P_3(x) = \tfrac{1}{2}(5x^3 - 3x),$$
$$P_4(x) = \tfrac{1}{8}(35x^4 - 30x^2 + 3),$$
$$P_5(x) = \tfrac{1}{8}(63x^5 - 70x^3 + 15x).$$

It can be shown generally that they can also be obtained from the following formula (*Rodrigues' formula*):

$$P_n(x) = \frac{1}{2^n n!} \frac{d^n}{dx^n} (x^2 - 1)^n,$$

and that they satisfy the following recursion formula:

$$nP_n(x) - (2n - 1)xP_{n-1}(x) + (n - 1)P_{n-2}(x) = 0.$$

This makes it possible to construct P_n from P_{n-1} and P_{n-2}. Other relations of this type which can be derived in a similar way are

$$nP_n(x) = xP'_n(x) - P'_{n-1}(x),$$
$$(2n + 1)P_n(x) = P'_{n+1}(x) - P'_{n-1}(x),$$

and

$$(x^2 - 1)P''_n(x) + 2xP'_n(x) - n(n + 1)P_n(x) = 0.$$

The last equation is called the *Legendre differential equation*.

The Legendre polynomials can be shown to form a complete orthogonal system for the interval $-1 \leq x \leq 1$. The evaluation of expansion coefficients can be much simplified by means of Rodrigues' formula, as will appear from the following example.

Example 5-15

$$\int_{-1}^{1} f(x)P_n(x)\, dx = \frac{1}{2^n n!} \left[f(x) \frac{d^{n-1}}{dx^{n-1}} (x^2 - 1)^n \right]_{-1}^{1}$$

$$- \frac{1}{2^n n!} \int_{-1}^{1} f'(x) \frac{d^{n-1}}{dx^{n-1}} (x^2 - 1)^n\, dx.$$

We have performed an integration by parts. The first term on the right side is seen to make no contribution. If this process is continued, the following is obtained:

$$\int_{-1}^{1} f(x)P_n(x)\,dx = \frac{(-1)^n}{2^n \cdot n!} \int_{-1}^{1} (x^2 - 1)^n f^{(n)}(x)\,dx. \qquad \square$$

Application of Legendre Polynomials to Curve Fitting

With the aid of these functions it is now possible to find that polynomial of a given degree which on the average best approximates a given function in the interval $-1 \le x \le 1$ in the following sense: The integral of the square of the difference between the function and the polynomial shall be the least possible.

Example 5-16. Find the second-degree polynomial which approximates $f(x) = x^4$ in the best possible manner in the interval $-1 \le x \le 1$. We set

$$x^4 \approx c_0 P_0(x) + c_1 P_1(x) + c_2 P_2(x),$$

as obviously every second-degree polynomial can be written as a linear combination of $P_0(x)$, $P_1(x)$, and $P_2(x)$. By considerations analogous to those on page 346 we obtain

$$c_0 = \tfrac{1}{2} \int_{-1}^{1} x^4 P_0(x)\,dx = \tfrac{1}{5},$$

$$c_1 = \tfrac{3}{2} \int_{-1}^{1} x^4 P_1(x)\,dx = 0,$$

$$c_2 = \tfrac{5}{2} \int_{-1}^{1} x^4 P_2(x)\,dx = \tfrac{4}{7}.$$

On substitution, the second-degree polynomial wanted is found to be $\tfrac{6}{7}x^2 - \tfrac{3}{35}$. In Fig. 5-3 it is seen how the parabola $y = \tfrac{6}{7}x^2 - \tfrac{3}{35}$

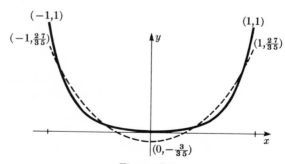

Figure 5-3

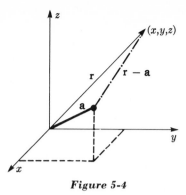

Figure 5-4

"winds itself" about the curve $y = x^4$, thus making the square error the least possible. □

Application of Legendre Polynomials in Describing Fields

The Legendre polynomials are of special importance, as they give a convenient description, among other things, of a number of important fields. We shall only consider one simple problem, that of describing the electric field generated by a unit charge located at a point determined by the position vector $\mathbf{a}$ (Fig. 5-4). The electric potential at a point determined by the position vector $\mathbf{r} = (x,y,z)$ is then (in suitable units)

$$V = \frac{1}{|\mathbf{r} - \mathbf{a}|} = \frac{1}{\sqrt{r^2 + a^2 - 2ar\cos\theta}},$$

where θ is the angle between $\mathbf{r}$ and $\mathbf{a}$. Into this expression $a/r = h$, $\cos\theta = z$, is introduced. The following expression for V is then valid for $h < 1$:

$$V = \frac{1}{r}\frac{1}{\sqrt{1 + h^2 - 2hz}} = \frac{1}{r}\sum_{n=0}^{\infty} h^n P_n(z) = \frac{1}{r}\sum_{n=0}^{\infty}\left(\frac{a}{r}\right)^n P_n(\cos\theta).$$

On using the binomial series on $(1 + h^2 - 2hz)^{-1/2}$, we obtain

$$1 + (-\tfrac{1}{2})(h^2 - 2hz) + \frac{(-\tfrac{1}{2})(-\tfrac{3}{2})}{2}(h^2 - 2hz)^2 + \cdots,$$

which on arranging in powers of h gives

$$1 + zh + \tfrac{1}{2}(3z^2 - 1)h^2 + \tfrac{1}{2}(5z^3 - 3z)h^3 + \cdots.$$

In this way it can be verified (for small n), that the P_n's just introduced are identical with the Legendre polynomials.

The functions $P_n(\cos\theta)$, with θ as the independent variable, are often named the *Legendre functions*. Obviously they satisfy the normalization condition

$$\int_0^\pi P_n(\cos\theta)P_m(\cos\theta)\sin\theta\, d\theta = \frac{2}{2n+1}\delta_{mn}.$$

These functions are, therefore, actually not orthogonal themselves, but only when multiplied by $\sqrt{\sin\theta}$. It is often said that $P_n(\cos\theta)$ ($n = 0,1,2,\ldots$) form an orthogonal set with $\sin\theta$ as the *weight factor*. This corresponds to a generalization of the scalar product where the lengths along the different axes are not measured in the same units, but where mutually perpendicular axes are still used (cf. p. 17). A number of functions (especially polynomials) which are orthogonal with weight factors, as, for example, e^{-x^2} (*Hermite polynomials*, $-\infty < x < \infty$) and e^{-x} (*Laguerre polynomials*, $0 \leq x < \infty$), are very important in pure and applied mathematics.

Exercises

1. Show, using Rodrigues' formula, that
   (a) $P_m(1) = 1$ and $P_m(-1) = (-1)^m$.
   (b) $\int_{-1}^1 x^n P_m(x)\, dx = 0$, if $m > n$, and therefore, that $\int_{-1}^1 f_n(x)P_m(x)\, dx = 0$, if $f_n(x)$ is a polynomial of degree $n < m$. Use these results to prove the formula

   $$\frac{dP_n(x)}{dx} = (2n-1)P_{n-1}(x) + (2n-5)P_{n-3}(x) + (2n-9)P_{n-5}(x) + \cdots,$$

   where the series ends with $3P_1(x)$ if n is even and with $P_0(x)$ if n is odd.
2. Use the results of Exercise 1 to show that:
   (a) $\dfrac{dP_{n+1}(x)}{dx} - \dfrac{dP_{n-1}(x)}{dx} = (2n+1)P_n(x)$.

   (b) $nP_n(x) = x\dfrac{dP_n(x)}{dx} - \dfrac{dP_{n-1}(x)}{dx}$.

*3. Find the first four polynomials of the nth degree, $H_n(x)$ ($n = 0,1,2,3,\ldots$), which are orthogonal in the interval $-\infty < x < \infty$ with the weight function e^{-x^2}, i.e., which satisfy the condition $\int_{-\infty}^\infty H_n(x)H_m(x)e^{-x^2}\, dx = 0$ when $n \neq m$. The polynomials are to be normalized so that $\int_{-\infty}^\infty [H_n(x)]^2 e^{-x^2}\, dx = 2^n n! \cdot \sqrt{\pi}$ (Hermite polynomials).

*4. Find the first four polynomials of the nth degree, $L_n(x)$ ($n = 0,1,2,3,\ldots$), which are orthogonal in the interval $0 \leq x < \infty$ with the weight function e^{-x}, i.e., which satisfy the condition $\int_0^\infty L_n(x)L_m(x)e^{-x}\, dx = 0$, when $n \neq m$. The polynomials are to be normalized so that $\int_0^\infty [L_n(x)]^2 e^{-x}\, dx = 1$ (Laguerre polynomials; the normalization $\int_0^\infty [L_n(x)]^2 e^{-x}\, dx = (n!)^2$ is also used).

Answers
3. $H_0(x) = 1$, $H_1(x) = 2x$, $H_2(x) = 4x^2 - 2$, $H_3(x) = 8x^3 - 12x$.
4. $L_0(x) = 1$, $L_1(x) = -x + 1$, $L_2(x) = \frac{1}{2}x^2 - 2x + 1$, $L_3(x) = -\frac{1}{6}x^3 + \frac{3}{2}x^2 - 3x + 1$.

5-8. FOURIER TRANSFORMATIONS

Exponential Fourier Transforms

We mentioned above that the set of trigonometric functions

$$\frac{1}{\sqrt{2L}}, \ldots, \frac{1}{\sqrt{L}} \cos \frac{n\pi}{L} x, \frac{1}{\sqrt{L}} \sin \frac{n\pi}{L} x, \ldots$$

made possible a series expansion of real functions $f(x)$ in the interval $-L \leq x \leq L$. The same is of course true (cf. p. 349) for the set of complex exponential functions

$$\frac{1}{\sqrt{2L}}, \ldots, \frac{1}{\sqrt{2L}} e^{in\pi x/L}, \frac{1}{\sqrt{2L}} e^{-in\pi x/L}, \ldots$$

As L is arbitrary, it is tempting to examine whether it can be made infinitely large, such that we obtain an expansion of $f(x)$ valid in the interval $-\infty < x < \infty$.

Qualitatively it might be said that as L tends to infinity, all the functions $(1/\sqrt{2L})e^{in\pi x/L}$ will approach 0 for all x, and thus become equal to zero in the limit. The resulting expansion, if existing, should therefore be of very little interest.

However, we have ignored the change which the Fourier coefficients undergo during this process. The change will, of course, be of such a type that the Fourier expansion, as L increases, will represent an increasingly large part of the given piecewise-differentiable function $f(x)$, namely, in the interval $-L \leq x \leq L$, while the expansion outside this interval will represent the periodic continuation of the function.

During the whole limiting process the changes therefore will "balance" each other in some way. The only question is that of what happens "at $L = \infty$."

For every (finite) L and every fixed value of x in the interval $-L \leq x \leq L$ we have

$$f(x) = \sum_{n=-\infty}^{\infty} C_n \frac{1}{\sqrt{2L}} e^{in\pi x/L} = \sum_{-\infty}^{\infty} \left[\int_{-L}^{L} e^{-in\pi x/L} f(x)\, dx \right] e^{in\pi x/L} \frac{1}{2L}.$$

We now introduce

$$h(y) = \left[\int_{-L}^{L} e^{-ixy} f(x) \, dx \right] e^{ixy},$$

which is defined for all y. Substituting y_n for $n\pi/L$ and Δy_n for $y_{n+1} - y_n = \pi/L$ we have

$$f(x) = \sum_{n=-\infty}^{\infty} h(y_n) \frac{1}{2L} = \frac{1}{2\pi} \sum_{n=-\infty}^{\infty} h(y_n) \, \Delta y_n.$$

This is an average sum of the improper integral

$$\frac{1}{2\pi} \int_{-\infty}^{\infty} h(y) \, dy = \frac{1}{2\pi} \int_{-\infty}^{\infty} \left[\int_{-L}^{L} e^{-ixy} f(x) \, dx \right] e^{ixy} \, dy,$$

corresponding to a division of the whole Y-axis into (equidistant) subintervals of lengths π/L.

Identifying these last expressions, and at the same time substituting L by ∞ in the improper integral, the following formula is obtained:

$$f(x) = \frac{1}{2\pi} \int_{-\infty}^{\infty} \left[\int_{-\infty}^{\infty} e^{-ixy} f(x) \, dx \right] e^{ixy} \, dy,$$

or

$$f(x) = \frac{1}{2\pi} \int_{-\infty}^{\infty} \left[e^{ixy} \int_{-\infty}^{\infty} e^{-iuy} f(u) \, du \right] dy.$$

This result, which is called the exponential form of the *Fourier integral theorem*, is valid if $f(x)$, besides being piecewise-differentiable, satisfies the condition that the integral $\int_{-\infty}^{\infty} |f(x)| \, dx$ is convergent.

We now introduce an operator F, called the *(exponential) Fourier transformation*, which by operating on the function f transforms it into a new function $Ff = g$, where

$$[Ff](y) = g(y) = \frac{1}{\sqrt{2\pi}} \int_{-\infty}^{\infty} e^{-ixy} f(x) \, dx.$$

Here Ff is called the *(exponential) Fourier transform* of f.

For the Fourier transform of g we then have

$$[Fg](x) = \frac{1}{\sqrt{2\pi}} \int_{-\infty}^{\infty} e^{-iyx} g(y)\, dy$$

$$= \frac{1}{2\pi} \int_{-\infty}^{\infty} \left[e^{i(-x)y} \int_{-\infty}^{\infty} e^{-iuy} f(u)\, du \right] dy.$$

According to the Fourier integral theorem this equals $f(-x)$. The Fourier integral theorem may therefore be formulated as follows:

$$[F(Ff)](x) = f(-x).$$

The operator G defined by the equation

$$[Gf](y) = \frac{1}{\sqrt{2\pi}} \int_{-\infty}^{\infty} e^{ixy} f(x)\, dx$$

may be looked upon as the inverse Fourier transformation, as we obviously have

$$[G(Ff)](x) = f(x) \qquad \text{and} \qquad [F(Gg)](y) = g(y).$$

As a consequence of this G is often written F^{-1}.

Other Fourier Transforms

In the previous section we have defined the (exponential) Fourier transform of a function $f(x)$. However, it must be noted that the designation "Fourier transform of $f(x)$" in the literature also may mean the functions given by

$$\int_{-\infty}^{\infty} e^{-ixy} f(x)\, dx, \qquad \int_{-\infty}^{\infty} e^{ixy} f(x)\, dx, \qquad \int_{-\infty}^{\infty} e^{2\pi ixy} f(x)\, dx,$$

or other combinations of 2π's and signs.

In analogy with the above, it is possible from the trigonometric Fourier series to obtain a real formulation of the Fourier integral theorem. In connection with this one also introduces the *Fourier cosine transform* a of the function f:

$$a(y) = \sqrt{\frac{2}{\pi}} \int_{0}^{\infty} f(x)\cos xy\, dx, \qquad f(x) = \sqrt{\frac{2}{\pi}} \int_{0}^{\infty} a(y)\cos xy\, dy,$$

and the *Fourier sine transform* b of the function f:

$$b(y) = \sqrt{\frac{2}{\pi}} \int_0^\infty f(x)\sin xy \, dx, \qquad f(x) = \sqrt{\frac{2}{\pi}} \int_0^\infty b(y)\sin xy \, dy.$$

Like the Laplace transformation, these three types of Fourier transformations are of great value in the solution of differential equations, as they all have the property of changing differentiation into multiplication. With special reference to this application of the Fourier transformations, tables of transforms have been compiled for large classes of functions. These can of course also be used as tables of definite integrals of the type

$$\int_{-\infty}^\infty e^{ixy}f(x) \, dx, \qquad \int_0^\infty f(x)\cos xy \, dx, \qquad \text{or} \qquad \int_0^\infty f(x)\sin xy \, dx.$$

Example 5-17. The exponential Fourier transform of the function

$$f(x) = \begin{cases} 0 & x < -1, \\ \frac{1}{2} & -1 < x < 1, \\ 0 & x > 1, \end{cases}$$

is (Fig. 5-5)

$$\frac{1}{2} \frac{1}{\sqrt{2\pi}} \int_{-1}^1 e^{-ixy} \, dx = -\frac{1}{2i\sqrt{2\pi}y}(e^{-iy} - e^{iy}) = \frac{1}{\sqrt{2\pi}} \frac{\sin y}{y}.$$

This illustrates how a "localized" function such as f discussed above becomes "delocalized" by the Fourier transformation. That the converse is not true can easily be seen. Let f be a localized function for which Ff is delocalized and let g be a delocalized function for which Fg is localized. (Such a function exists, for example, the above Ff.)

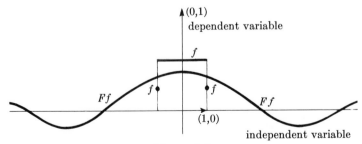

Figure 5-5

Then $f + g$ is a delocalized function whose Fourier transform is also delocalized.

The essential point is the following: If f is "smooth," then Ff is localized, and vice versa, i.e.,

$$f \text{ "smooth"} \qquad \text{if and only if} \qquad Ff \text{ "localized,"}$$
$$f \text{ "localized"} \qquad \text{if and only if} \qquad Ff \text{ "smooth."}$$

If a function is localized, it cannot be smooth itself, since it must vanish rapidly outside a narrow interval. Thus f "localized" implies f "nonsmooth," but obviously the converse will not hold in general. When f is nonsmooth, its Fourier transform will be delocalized. If in addition the transform is smooth, one can conclude that f is localized.

The function $(\sin y)/y$ is smooth besides being delocalized, and therefore its Fourier transform is localized.

It can now be conjectured that there exists a function which represents such a compromise between being "smooth" and being "localized," that it is unchanged by a Fourier transformation. This is actually the case, the function being $e^{-x^2/2}$, as can be verified by carrying out the integration. □

Exercises

*1. Find the exponential Fourier transform of

(a) $f(x) = \begin{cases} 1 & \text{for } |x| < a, \\ 0 & \text{for } |x| > a. \end{cases}$
(b) $f(x) = \begin{cases} x & \text{for } |x| < a, \\ 0 & \text{for } |x| > a. \end{cases}$

*2. Find the Fourier cosine transform of the function

$$f(x) = \begin{cases} 1 & \text{for } 0 < x < a, \\ 0 & \text{for } x > a. \end{cases}$$

3. Find the Fourier sine transform of the function

$$f(x) = \begin{cases} x & \text{for } 0 < x < a, \\ 0 & \text{for } x > a. \end{cases}$$

Answers

1. (a) $\sqrt{\dfrac{2}{\pi}} \dfrac{\sin ay}{y}$
(b) $i\sqrt{\dfrac{2}{\pi}} \left[\dfrac{a \cos ay}{y} - \dfrac{\sin ay}{y^2} \right]$

2. $\sqrt{\dfrac{2}{\pi}} \dfrac{\sin ay}{y}$

6

Differential Equations

6-1. ORDINARY DIFFERENTIAL EQUATIONS OF THE FIRST ORDER

Some Definitions

An equation which has a function as its unknown and which contains at least one derivative of this function is called a *differential equation*. Such an equation is said to be *ordinary* or *partial*, depending on whether the unknown is a function of one or more independent variables. It is said to be of the nth *order* in case the highest-order derivative of the unknown function occurring is of nth order.

An ordinary differential equation of the nth order can therefore always be written

$$F\left(x,y,\frac{dy}{dx}, \cdot \cdot \cdot,\frac{d^n y}{dx^n}\right) = 0,$$

where F is some function of $n + 2$ variables. Here y represents the value at x of the unknown function, dy/dx the value at x of the first derivative of the unknown function, etc. A real function ϕ with an interval I as its domain is then a *solution* to this equation in case the following is true for all x belonging to I:

$$F(x,\phi(x),\phi'(x), \cdot \cdot \cdot,\phi^{(n)}(x)) = 0.$$

The graph of a solution is often called an *integral curve* of the equation considered.

In this section we shall treat only ordinary differential equations of the first order, i.e., equations of the form $F(x,y, dy/dx) = 0$. Geometrically such an equation gives a relation between the abscissa, the ordinate, and the slope at the corresponding point which must be satisfied by every point of a curve in order that it be an integral curve.

Suppose that the given equation has only one solution for dy/dx, corresponding to every point (x,y) in some open region of the XY-plane. It is then possible to approximate the integral curve passing through a given point (x_0,y_0) of the region in the following way. The value α_0 of dy/dx at the point (x_0,y_0) is found from the equation, and the straight line having this slope and passing through (x_0,y_0) is taken as an approximation to the integral curve in some small interval $x_0 \le x \le x_0 + h$. The value α_1 of dy/dx at the point $(x_1,y_1) = (x_0 + h, y_0 + \alpha_0 h)$ is then determined from the equation, and the straight line having this slope and passing through (x_1,y_1) is taken as an approximation to the curve in the interval $x_1 \le x \le x_1 + h$, etc. (Fig. 6-1). It turns out that such a procedure may give usable results. We shall return to these problems in Chapter 8.

An Existence and Uniqueness Theorem

Consider an ordinary differential equation of the first order written in the form

$$\frac{dy}{dx} = f(x,y),$$

where $f(x,y)$ is a continuous function with a continuous partial derivative with respect to y in an open region ω of the XY-plane. It can then

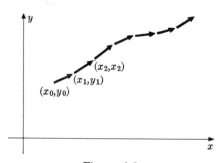

Figure 6-1

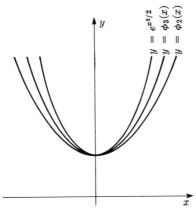

Figure 6-2

be proved that there exists one and only one integral curve passing through any given point of ω. This theorem is often called the *existence and uniqueness theorem* for first-order differential equations.

The theorem is usually proved by means of an *iterative process*. We shall not give any proof here, but confine ourselves to illustrate such a process by an example. We consider the differential equation $dy/dx = xy$. According to the above theorem there passes through every point of the plane exactly one integral curve. We want to find the integral curve $y = \phi(x)$ which passes through the point (0,1). Thus, from the beginning we have the following information: $\phi'(x) = x\phi(x)$ and $\phi(0) = 1$, and therefore also

$$\phi(x) = 1 + \int_0^x \phi'(t) \, dt = 1 + \int_0^x t\phi(t) \, dt.$$

As a first approximation we substitute $\phi_1(t) = 1$ for $\phi(t)$ on the right side of the equation. As a second approximation we then get

$$\phi_2(x) = 1 + \int_0^x t \, dt = 1 + \frac{x^2}{2},$$

which correspondingly gives (Fig. 6-2)

$$\phi_3(x) = 1 + \int_0^x t\left(1 + \frac{t^2}{2}\right) dt = 1 + \frac{x^2}{2} + \frac{x^4}{2 \cdot 4}, \qquad \text{etc.}$$

In the limit we obtain the infinite series

$$1 + \frac{x^2}{2} + \frac{x^4}{2 \cdot 4} + \cdots + \frac{x^{2n}}{2^n \cdot n!} + \cdots = \sum_{n=0}^{\infty} \frac{(x^2/2)^n}{n!} = e^{x^2/2}.$$

By inspection it is immediately seen that the function $\phi(x) = e^{x^2/2}$ is the solution wanted.

Correspondingly, we have in the general case of a differential equation written

$$\frac{dy}{dx} = a(x)y,$$

where $a(x)$ is a given function, that the solution $\phi(x)$ through a point (x_0, y_0) can be obtained by iteration. Introducing the operator S, which transforms any function $f(x)$ into the function $\int_{x_0}^{x} f(t) \, dt$, we get

$$\phi(x) = y_0(1 + [Sa](x) + [S(a(Sa))](x) + [S(a(S(a(Sa))))](x) + \cdots).$$

Further, introducing $A(x) = \int_{x_0}^{x} a(t) \, dt = Sa(x)$, we have

$$[S(a(Sa))](x) = \int_{x_0}^{x} a(t)A(t) \, dt = [\tfrac{1}{2}(A(t))^2]_{x_0}^{x} = \tfrac{1}{2}(A(x))^2$$

and

$$[S(a(S(a(Sa))))](x) = \int_{x_0}^{x} a(t)\tfrac{1}{2}(A(t))^2 \, dt = \left[\frac{1}{3!}(A(t))^3\right]_{x_0}^{x}$$

$$= \tfrac{1}{3}(A(x))^3, \qquad \text{etc.}$$

Hence

$$\phi(x) = y_0[1 + A(x) + \tfrac{1}{2}(A(x))^2 + \tfrac{1}{3}(A(x))^3 + \cdots],$$

or

$$\phi(x) = y_0 e^{A(x)} = y_0 \exp \int_{x_0}^{x} a(t) \, dt.$$

As we shall see below, this result can be obtained more easily by other methods. It is mentioned here because it permits a generalization applicable to the case of systems of differential equations (see p. 385).

Differential Equations on Differential Form

Consider an arbitrary integral curve of a differential equation

$$\frac{dy}{dx} + \frac{f(x,y)}{g(x,y)} = 0,$$

and let (x_0,y_0) be some point of this curve. As already mentioned, the slope of the curve at (x_0,y_0) is then $-f(x_0,y_0)/g(x_0,y_0)$. A vector on its tangent at (x_0,y_0) is therefore $(g(x_0,y_0),-f(x_0,y_0))$, while a vector perpendicular to this is $(f(x_0,y_0),g(x_0,y_0))$.

Now, suppose that the differentiable vector function $\mathbf{r}(t) = (\phi(t),\psi(t))$ has the curve considered as its graph, and that the point (x_0,y_0) corresponds to the parameter value $t = t_0$. The vector $\mathbf{r}'(t_0) = (\phi'(t_0),\psi'(t_0))$ will then lie on the tangent at the point considered, and we have

$$(f(x_0,y_0),g(x_0,y_0)) \cdot (\phi'(t_0),\psi'(t_0)) = 0,$$

or

$$f(\phi(t_0),\psi(t_0))\phi'(t_0) + g(\phi(t_0),\psi(t_0))\psi'(t_0) = 0.$$

We can formulate this result in the following way: If a differentiable curve given by a vector function $\mathbf{r}(t) = (x(t),y(t))$ is an integral curve of the differential equation $(dy/dx) + [f(x,y)/g(x,y)] = 0$, then the equation

$$f(x,y) \frac{dx}{dt} + g(x,y) \frac{dy}{dt} = 0$$

is satisfied by all t belonging to the domain of $\mathbf{r}(t)$.

The converse is also true. Thus it can be shown that any differentiable curve satisfying the equation $f(x,y)(dx/dt) + g(x,y)(dy/dt) = 0$, where $g(x,y) \neq 0$ everywhere, can also be represented by a function $y = \phi(x)$ which satisfies the equation $(dy/dx) + [f(x,y)/g(x,y)] = 0$. The two equations considered therefore have the same solution sets in every region of the plane where only $g(x,y) \neq 0$. Usually the former equation is written

$$f(x,y) \, dx + g(x,y) \, dy = 0,$$

where a "factor" $1/dt$ is understood. Formally it is obtained from the latter equation by multiplication with $g(x,y) \, dx$. The resulting equation is said to be on *differential form*.

For a differential equation $f(x,y) \, dx + g(x,y) \, dy = 0$ written on differential form, where $f(x,y)$ and $g(x,y)$ are given functions which have continuous partial derivatives in an open region ω, the following existence and uniqueness theorem is valid: Through every point of ω where $f(x,y)$ and $g(x,y)$ are not both zero, there passes one and only one integral curve of the equation.

A point where $f(x,y)$ and $g(x,y)$ are both zero is called a *singular point*. Nothing can be said beforehand about the number of integral curves passing through such a point.

Total Differentials and Integrating Factors

No method is known for solving an arbitrary first-order differential equation. However, in some very important special cases there do exist generally applicable methods. Consider the differential equation

$$f(x,y)\, dx + g(x,y)\, dy = 0,$$

and suppose that the left side of this equation is a total differential with the function $\Phi(x,y)$ as a primitive. For any differentiable curve $\mathbf{r}(t) = (x(t),y(t))$, we have

$$f(x(t),y(t))\, \frac{dx}{dt} + g(x(t),y(t))\, \frac{dy}{dt} = \frac{d}{dt}\, \Phi(x(t),y(t)),$$

by means of the chain rule (p. 236). Therefore the differentiable curve considered will be an integral curve if and only if

$$\frac{d}{dt}\, \Phi(x(t),y(t)) = 0 \qquad \text{or} \qquad \Phi(x(t),y(t)) = C,$$

where C is an arbitrary constant. The complete solution is thus represented by the equation $\Phi(x,y) = C$.

The particular solution containing a nonsingular point (x_0,y_0) will then be given by the equation $\Phi(x,y) = \Phi(x_0,y_0)$. Even if we have been able to determine the function Φ, this equation may give only little information, as the solution is only defined *implicitly*. In some cases it is easy to find a vector function $\mathbf{r}(t) = (x(t),y(t))$ satisfying the equation. It may also happen that the equation is easily solved with respect to y as $y = \phi(x)$, or with respect to x as $x = \psi(y)$; in such cases an *explicit* solution has been obtained.

If the left side of the given differential equation is not a total differential, the above method may still be used in case an integrating factor can be found. As a special example of this we consider the differential equation

$$f_1(x)g_1(y)\, dx + f_2(x)g_2(y)\, dy = 0$$

in a region where $f_2(x)g_1(y) \neq 0$. As an integrating factor we may then use $1/(f_2(x)g_1(y))$. The following equation, which obviously is equivalent to the original one, is then obtained:

$$\frac{f_1(x)}{f_2(x)}\, dx + \frac{g_2(y)}{g_1(y)}\, dy = 0.$$

Here the variables x and y have been *separated* (cf. p. 252). The left side is then a total differential, and the complete solution is given by

$$\int \frac{f_1(x)}{f_2(x)} \, dx + \int \frac{g_2(y)}{g_1(y)} \, dy = C.$$

Example 6-1. $yy' + x = 0$. For $y \neq 0$ this equation may be rewritten $y' = -x/y$. As the functions $-x/y$ and its derivative with respect to y, x/y^2, are both continuous in the half-planes $y > 0$ and $y < 0$, it follows that there is one and only one integral curve passing through every point with $y \neq 0$. As to the points on the X-axis [except possibly $(0,0)$], it follows directly from the given equation that there are no integral curves passing through them.

To solve the equation in the region $y > 0$ we rewrite it $(d/dx)(y^2) = -2x$, which immediately gives $y^2 = -x^2 + C$ or $y = \sqrt{C - x^2}$. The integral curves are thus half-circles with their center at $(0,0)$. In the same way we find $y = -\sqrt{C - x^2}$ in the region $y < 0$. The corresponding equation written on differential form is

$$x \, dx + y \, dy = 0.$$

Here the only singular point is $(0,0)$. Thus, through any other point there passes one and only one integral curve. The left side has the primitive $\Phi(x,y) = \frac{1}{2}(x^2 + y^2)$. The complete solution is therefore given by $x^2 + y^2 = 2C$, and the integral curves are seen to be circles with their center at $(0,0)$. From the fact that this is the complete solution we can conclude that any curve having the property that its tangent at an arbitrary point P is perpendicular to the position vector **OP** is (part of) a circle having its center at $(0,0)$.

A comparison between the two sets of solutions shows complete agreement with our general remarks above. The integral curves in the latter case may be considered to be fitted together of half-circles by means of points with vertical tangents. $\square$

Example 6-2. $y \, dx - x \, dy = 0$. In each of the open quadrants the variables can be separated, giving

$$\frac{1}{x} \, dx - \frac{1}{y} \, dy = 0 \qquad \text{or} \qquad d \ln \left| \frac{x}{y} \right| = 0.$$

Hence the complete solution (for $x \cdot y \neq 0$) is $\ln|x/y| = C$. In this case the solutions can also be given explicitly, for example, as $y = ax$, where a is an arbitrary constant different from zero (in the first and the third quadrant we have $a = e^{-C}$, in the two others $a = -e^{-C}$). The integral curves are thus open half-lines with $(0,0)$ as their common starting point. On direct substitution in the equation it is further seen that each of the four half-axes are integral curves [$\mathbf{r}(t) = (t,0)$, $0 \leq t < \infty$, etc.], and also that every pair of opposite half-lines may be put together to form one integral curve [including the point $(0,0)$]. $\square$

Example 6-3. The differential equation $dc/dt = -kc^2$ corresponding to a second-order chemical reaction may be rewritten $(dc/c^2) + k\,dt = 0$ and has the complete solution $-(1/c) + kt = \text{constant}$. If we require the solution which takes on the value c_0 at $t = 0$, the constant is $-1/c_0$ and the solution $c = c_0/(1 + kc_0 t)$ is obtained. $\square$

The Linear Differential Equation of the First Order

A differential equation which can be written in the form $(dy/dx) + f(x)y = g(x)$ is said to be *linear*, i.e., linear in dy/dx and y. In this very important case it is possible to give the complete solution explicitly.

Suppose $f(x)$ and $g(x)$ are continuous in some interval $a < x < b$. It follows that there will be exactly one integral curve through every point of the parallel strip given by $a < x < b$. To solve the equation we multiply by $e^{F(x)}$, where $F(x)$ is a primitive of $f(x)$:

$$\frac{dy}{dx} e^{F(x)} + ye^{F(x)}f(x) = g(x)e^{F(x)} \qquad \text{or} \qquad \frac{d}{dx}(ye^{F(x)}) = g(x)e^{F(x)}.$$

This can be integrated immediately, giving

$$ye^{F(x)} = \int g(x)e^{F(x)}\,dx + C.$$

From this the complete solution appears explicitly as

$$y = \exp[-\int f(x)\,dx]\{\int g(x)\exp[\int f(x)\,dx]\,dx + C\},$$

where C is an arbitrary constant that may assume any real value.

By the corresponding *homogeneous* equation we shall mean the equation $(dy/dx) + f(x)y = 0$. It follows from the above formula that the homogeneous equation has the complete solution $y = C\exp[-\int f(x)\,dx]$ (cf. p. 366), and also that the complete solution of the original equation can be obtained from the complete solution of the homogeneous equation by the addition of one solution of the original equation. This important result, which depends only on the linearity of the given equation, could also have been shown as follows.

Suppose that $\phi_0(x)$ $(a < x < b)$ is a solution of the given equation. Obviously, any function $\phi(x)$ with the same domain can be written $\phi(x) = \phi_0(x) + u(x)$. We now want to determine what condition must be satisfied by $u(x)$ in order that $\phi(x)$ is a solution of the given equation. Substitution gives

$$(\phi_0'(x) + u'(x)) + f(x)(\phi_0(x) + u(x)) = g(x),$$

or

$$(\phi_0'(x) + f(x)\phi_0(x)) + (u'(x) + f(x)u(x)) = g(x).$$

Here the first term on the left side equals the right side. Thus the condition on $u(x)$ is that $u(x)$ satisfies the homogeneous equation $u'(x) + f(x)u(x) = 0$.

Example 6-4. To solve the equation $xy' + y = 4x^3$ we rewrite the equation $y' + (1/x)y = 4x^2 (x \neq 0)$. Using the formula derived above we find

$$y = e^{-\ln|x|}[\int 4x^2 e^{\ln|x|}\, dx + C],$$

or

$$y = \begin{cases} x^3 + \dfrac{C}{x} & \text{for } x > 0, \\ x^3 - \dfrac{C}{x} & \text{for } x < 0. \end{cases}$$

It is seen that both solution sets can be given in one form, for example, as $y = x^3 + (C/x)$ $(-\infty < C < \infty)$. In general the solutions will diverge as $x \to 0$; only in the special case of $C = 0$ is this not so. The function $y = x^3$ satisfies the original equation for all x. □

Setting Up Differential Equations

Before leaving the first-order differential equations we shall consider a very simple physical problem giving rise to a differential equation. Suppose we have a cylindrical tank with a porous bottom of area A (cm^2). Water at a rate of a (cm^3/sec) runs into the tank from a tap. The outflow through the bottom is taken to be proportional to the instantaneous height of water with b (cm^3/sec-cm) as the constant of proportionality. At time 0 the tank is empty. It is required to find the height of water x (cm) as a function of time t (sec) (Fig. 6-3).

For this purpose we consider the situation during the interval of time from t to $t + dt$, where the height of water is changed from x to $x + dx$, and the volume of water in the tank is changed from V to $V + dV$. We have

$$dV = a \, dt - bx \, dt \quad \text{and} \quad dV = A \, dx,$$

so that

$$\frac{dx}{dt} + \frac{b}{A} x = \frac{a}{A}.$$

The complete solution of this linear differential equation is

$$x = e^{-(b/A)t} \left[\int \frac{a}{A} e^{(b/A)t} \, dt + C \right] = \frac{a}{b} + Ce^{-(b/A)t}.$$

The value of the arbitrary constant C can be determined from the fact that $x = 0$ at $t = 0$. We find $C = -a/b$, and the desired solution becomes

$$x = \frac{a}{b} (1 - e^{-(b/A)t}).$$

In this simple case it was possible to solve the resulting differential equation. However, some conclusions could have been drawn from the equation even if this had not been the case. The velocity of the surface (i.e., dx/dt) at $t = 0$ is a/A. This gives the slope of the tangent to the above curve at the point $(0,0)$. The height of the water increases with time and therefore the velocity decreases. The velocity becomes zero at a height of a/b. It seems reasonable that

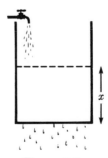

Figure 6-3

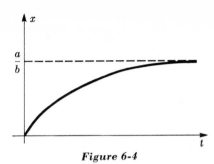

Figure 6-4

this height will never be attained, but that x will tend to a/b as t tends to infinity.

Exercises

*1. Solve the equation $(x + y)\, dx + (x - y)\, dy = 0$, and sketch the graphs of a few solutions.

*2. Solve the equation $(x + y)\, dx + (y - x)\, dy = 0$ by transforming to polar coordinates.

3. Solve the equation $y^2\, dx - 2xy\, dy = 0$.

*4. Solve the equation $y' + 2y = e^{ax}$.

5. Show that $I = \int_0^\infty \exp[-x^2 - y^2/x^2]\, dx$, considered as a function of y, satisfies the relation $dI/dy = -2I$, and thus evaluate the integral. For the determination of the constant of integration, the known value of $I(0)$ is used.

*6. Solve the equation $y' + y = y^2$ (see also Exercise 15).

*7. In Fig. 6-5, A designates a funnel with a valve which at first is completely filled with water, and B is an empty cylindrical container brought under A.

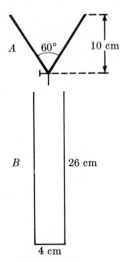

Figure 6-5

At time 0 the valve is opened and the water begins to flow down into B. When the flow from the funnel is assumed to be proportional to the height of water in the funnel (proportionality factor $\frac{1}{8}$ ml/sec-cm), find the time at which the valve must be closed so that B is exactly full.

8. Find all the differentiable curves in the XY-plane which have the property that the tangent at an arbitrary point P on the curve, except the origin O, is perpendicular to the mirror image of the vector $\mathbf{OP}$ in the X-axis.

9. Solve the equation $y(3x^2 - 1)dx - x(x^2 - 1)\,dy = 0$.

10. Solve the equation $y' + y = 3\cos x + \sin x$.

11. Solve the equations (a) $(x - 1)y' - 2y = 0$, and (b) $(x - 1)y' - 2y = x + 1$, and sketch the graphs of the solutions.

12. Solve the equations
    (a) $(\cos x + \sin x)y' - (\cos x - \sin x)y = 0$.
    (b) $(\cos x + \sin x)y' - (\cos x - \sin x)y = 2$.

13. Show that

$$I(y) = \int_0^\infty e^{-x^2} \cos 2xy \, dx = \tfrac{1}{2} \sqrt{\pi}\, e^{-y^2}$$

by expanding $\cos 2xy$ in a series of powers of x and integrating term by term.
Show also that $I(y)$ satisfies the equation $dI/dy = -2yI$, and in this way find the integral.

14. In Fig. 6-6, A designates a cylindrical container with height a(cm) and cross-sectional area 1 cm^2. Originally it is filled with a melt containing p grams of impurities. While the melted phase is stirred constantly, the material solidifies from the bottom up. This is assumed to occur without a change in volume. The solidification is stopped when $x = fa$ $(0 < f < 1)$.

When the concentration of impurities in a material which solidifies at an arbitrary time $[c_1(\text{g/cm}^3)]$ always is assumed to be a constant k times the concentration in the corresponding liquid phase $[c_2 \ (\text{g/cm}^3)]$, find the total content of impurity in the solid phase when the experiment is stopped. Also find the ratio between the average concentration of impurity in the resulting solid phase and the concentration in the original melt.

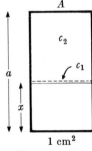

Figure 6-6

15. Show that the so-called *Bernoulli equation*

$$\frac{dy}{dx} + f(x)y = g(x)y^n \qquad (n \neq 1)$$

can be made linear by the substitution $y = z^{1/(1-n)}$, and then solve the equation

$$xy' + 2y = 8x^3 \sqrt{y}.$$

*16. Find all the curves in the first quadrant with the following property: When P designates an arbitrary point on the curve, T the intersection of the tangent to the curve with the Y-axis, N the intersection of the normal to the curve and the X-axis, and O the origin of the coordinate system, then TN is perpendicular to OP.

17. Solve the following problem, which was originally suggested and solved by l'Hôpital. Find all the curves through $(0,0)$ which have the property that the slope at every point $P(\neq(0,0))$ is a constant ($\neq 0$) divided by the distance between P and the line $y = x$ measured on the line through P perpendicular to the X-axis.

Answers

1. $x^2 + 2xy - y^2 = C.$
2. $re^{-\theta} = C.$
4. $y = \dfrac{e^{ax}}{a+2} + Ce^{-2x} \qquad (a \neq -2).$
   $y = xe^{-2x} + Ce^{-2x} \qquad (a = -2).$
6. $y = 1/(1 + Ce^x)$ and $y = 0.$
7. 112π sec.
16. $(x - (C/2))^2 + y^2 = C^2/4.$

6-2. ORDINARY DIFFERENTIAL EQUATIONS OF THE SECOND ORDER

The Homogeneous Linear Differential Equation of the Second Order

Above we have seen how the complete solution of a first-order differential equation in general contains one arbitrary constant. We shall now consider second-order differential equations, for which the complete solution generally contains two arbitrary constants.

Suppose we have a differential equation of the second order written

$$\frac{d^2y}{dx^2} = f\left(x, y, \frac{dy}{dx}\right),$$

where f is a continuous function of three variables having continuous partial derivatives with respect to the second and the third independent variables in an open region Ω of the three-dimensional space.

Suppose, furthermore, that (x_0, y_0, α_0) is a point of Ω. It can then be shown that there exists one and only one integral curve $y = \phi(x)$ of the given equation such that $\phi(x_0) = y_0$ and $\phi'(x_0) = \alpha_0$. This is *the existence and uniqueness theorem* for second-order differential equations.

The particular solution whose existence is guaranteed by this theorem can be determined approximately in the following way: From the equation the value β_0 of d^2y/dx^2 at the point (x_0, y_0) is found. As an approximation to the integral curve in an interval $x_0 \leq x \leq x_0 + h$, the parabola $y = y_0 + \alpha_0(x - x_0) + \frac{1}{2}\beta_0(x - x_0)^2$ is then used (cf. Taylor's formula, p. 161). From this equation the values y_1 and α_1 of y and dy/dx at $x_1 = x_0 + h$ are obtained, and using these the corresponding value β_1 of d^2y/dx^2 is found from the given differential equation. As an approximation to the integral curve in the interval $x_1 \leq x \leq x_1 + h$, the parabola $y = y_1 + \alpha_1(x - x_1) + \frac{1}{2}\beta_1(x - x_1)^2$ is used, etc.

A second-order differential equation that can be written in the form

$$\frac{d^2y}{dx^2} + f_1(x)\frac{dy}{dx} + f_0(x)y = g(x)$$

is said to be *linear*. Suppose that the three functions $f_1(x)$, $f_0(x)$, and $g(x)$ are all continuous in some interval $a < x < b$. It then follows from the existence and uniqueness theorem that there will be one and only one integral curve passing through a given point of the parallel strip $a < x < b$ with a given slope.

We shall only treat linear equations and start by considering the *homogeneous* linear equation

$$\frac{d^2y}{dx^2} + f_1(x)\frac{dy}{dx} + f_0(x)y = 0.$$

For this equation it is easily seen that if $\phi_1(x)$ and $\phi_2(x)$ are solutions, then every *linear combination* $C_1\phi_1(x) + C_2\phi_2(x)$, where C_1 and C_2 are arbitrary real constants, will also be a solution. Furthermore, it can be shown that if $\phi_1(x)$ and $\phi_2(x)$ are *linearly independent*, which simply means that they are not proportional, this will give the complete solution. Thus to solve a homogeneous linear differential equation of the second order it is only necessary to find two linearly independent solutions.

No general method is known for that. It is possible, however, by means of the so-called *method of variation of constants*, to find the complete solution in a parallel strip $a < x < b$ if only one solution $y_1 = \phi_1(x)$ $(a < x < b)$ is known, provided this solution is different from zero at every point. Obviously any function $\phi(x)$ with the domain $a < x < b$ can be written $\phi(x) = v(x)\phi_1(x)$. We now want to determine a necessary and sufficient condition that must be satisfied by $v(x)$ so that the corresponding $\phi(x)$ will be a solution of the differential equation. We have

$$\phi'(x) = v'(x)\phi_1(x) + v(x)\phi_1'(x)$$

and

$$\phi''(x) = v''(x)\phi_1(x) + 2v'(x)\phi_1'(x) + v(x)\phi_1''(x).$$

Substitution of this in the equation gives

$$\phi_1(x)v''(x) + (2\phi_1'(x) + f_1(x)\phi_1(x))v'(x)$$
$$+ (\phi_1''(x) + f_1(x)\phi_1'(x) + f_0(x)\phi_1(x))v(x) = 0.$$

The last term on the left side equals zero for all x, and we have therefore obtained a homogeneous linear first-order differential equation with $v'(x)$ as the unknown (cf. p. 370):

$$v'(x) = C_2 \exp\left[-\int \left(\frac{2\phi_1'(x)}{\phi_1(x)} + f_1(x)\right) dx \right]$$
$$= C_2 \frac{1}{(\phi_1(x))^2} \exp\left[-\int f_1(x)\, dx \right].$$

This immediately gives

$$v(x) = C_2 \int \frac{1}{(\phi_1(x))^2} \exp\left[-\int f_1(x)\, dx \right] dx + C_1,$$

and the complete solution of the given equation is thus

$$\phi(x) = v(x)\phi_1(x) = C_1\phi_1(x)$$
$$+ C_2\phi_1(x) \int \frac{1}{(\phi_1(x))^2} \exp\left[-\int f_1(x)dx \right] dx.$$

It follows that a solution $y_2 = \phi_2(x)$, which is linearly independent of the given solution $y_1 = \phi_1(x)$, is

$$y_2 = y_1 \int \frac{1}{y_1^2} \exp\left[-\int f_1(x)\, dx \right] dx.$$

In this way the problem of solving a homogeneous equation is reduced to that of finding just one nonzero solution. As already mentioned, no general method exists for this. In some cases it can be obtained by means of *"systematic guessing"*; a function which contains one or more parameters is substituted in the equation with the hope that the parameters can be determined such that the function becomes a solution. If the differential equation considered originates in a physical or chemical problem, previous knowledge of a nonmathematical nature may be of help in choosing a guess function.

The Inhomogeneous Linear Differential Equation of the Second Order

Next we turn to the inhomogeneous equation

$$\frac{d^2y}{dx^2} + f_1(x)\frac{dy}{dx} + f_0(x)y = g(x).$$

Suppose we know one solution $\phi_0(x)$ of this equation. As in the case of a first-order linear equation, it is easy to see that the complete solution can be obtained by adding $\phi_0(x)$ to the complete solution of the corresponding homogeneous equation:

$$\phi(x) = \phi_0(x) + C_1\phi_1(x) + C_2\phi_2(x).$$

In some cases a solution $\phi_0(x)$ can be found by systematic guessing. However, a solution can also be obtained from the following formula:

$$\phi_0(x) = \phi_2(x)\int \frac{\phi_1(x)g(x)}{W(x)}\,dx - \phi_1(x)\int \frac{\phi_2(x)g(x)}{W(x)}\,dx.$$

Here (as above) $\phi_1(x)$ and $\phi_2(x)$ are linearly independent solutions of the corresponding homogeneous equation, and $W(x)$ is the so-called *Wronskian*,

$$W(x) = \begin{vmatrix} \phi_1(x) & \phi_2(x) \\ \phi_1'(x) & \phi_2'(x) \end{vmatrix}.$$

It is obvious that $W(x)$ equals zero in case $\phi_1(x)$ and $\phi_2(x)$ are linearly dependent, and it can be shown that $W(x) \neq 0$ for all x if the two functions are linearly independent.

We shall not give any proof of the above formula but only mention that it can be obtained by means of the method of variation of constants. Two functions $v_1(x)$ and $v_2(x)$ are desired such that $\phi(x) = v_1(x)\phi_1(x) + v_2(x)\phi_2(x)$ becomes a solution of the given equation. As we have two unknown functions and only one equation, an additional condition may be imposed on the unknowns. It turns out to be convenient to require $v_1'(x)\phi_1(x) + v_2'(x)\phi_2(x) = 0$.

Example 6-5. $y'' - (6/x^2)y = x^2$ $(x > 0)$. We first consider the corresponding homogeneous equation $y'' - (6/x^2)y = 0$. A natural guess function here is $y = x^n$, where n is a parameter, since two differentiations have the same effect on the degree of x as a division by x^2. Substitution gives $n(n - 1)x^{n-2} - 6x^{n-2} = 0$. This will be satisfied for all $x > 0$ if $n^2 - n - 6 = 0$, i.e., if n is chosen to be -2 or 3. Hence in this case two linearly independent solutions are found at the same time, $\phi_1(x) = x^{-2}$ and $\phi_2(x) = x^3$. If only one had been obtained, another could have been expressed by means of the formula on page 377. The complete solution of the homogeneous equation is $y = C_1 x^{-2} + C_2 x^3$. To find a solution of the inhomogeneous equation we can use the formula given above. As $W(x) = x^{-2}3x^2 - (-2)x^{-3}x^3 = 5$ we get without any difficulty,

$$\phi_0(x) = x^3 \int \frac{x^{-2}x^2}{5}\, dx - x^{-2} \int \frac{x^3 x^2}{5}\, dx = \tfrac{1}{6}x^4.$$

Very often, however, this formula gives rise to complicated calculations; the guessing method, therefore, is preferred whenever possible. In this example a natural guess would be $y = ax^4$, with a as the parameter, as then both terms on the left side of the equation become of the same degree in x as on the right side. Substitution of $y = ax^4$ immediately gives $12ax^2 - 6ax^2 = x^2$, and thus $a = \tfrac{1}{6}$. The complete solution of the given equation is finally obtained as

$$y = \tfrac{1}{6}x^4 + C_1 x^{-2} + C_2 x^3. \qquad \square$$

Above we have seen how the complete solution of a second-order linear differential equation can be given explicitly if only one nonzero solution of the corresponding homogeneous equation is known. However, it should be emphasized that this may be only of limited value in case the integrals appearing in the complete solution cannot be further evaluated, i.e., cannot be expressed in terms of tabulated functions. If this is so, numerical methods have to be applied and this is also necessary when no nonzero solution of the homogeneous equation can be found.

Equations with Constant Coefficients

An important type of linear differential equations of the second order are the equations with constant coefficients to y and its derivatives.

We first consider the *homogeneous equation of the second order*

$$\frac{d^2y}{dx^2} + a_1 \frac{dy}{dx} + a_0y = 0,$$

which is written symbolically as $(D^2 + a_1D + a_0)y = 0$, where D denotes the differential operator d/dx and D^2 denotes

$$\frac{d}{dx}\left(\frac{d}{dx}\right) = \frac{d^2}{dx^2}.$$

A first-order homogeneous differential equation with a constant coefficient (i.e., $y' + a_0y = 0$) has an exponential function as solution. Thus we first guess that the second-order equation has a similar solution; i.e., we substitute $y = e^{\lambda x}$ into the equation to see if λ can be so chosen that the equation is satisfied. Thus

$$\lambda^2 e^{\lambda x} + a_1\lambda e^{\lambda x} + a_0 e^{\lambda x} = 0,$$

or

$$\lambda^2 + a_1\lambda + a_0 = 0,$$

and $y = e^{\lambda x}$ is thus a solution of the differential equation if and only if λ is a root in this quadratic equation. It is called the *characteristic equation* of the differential equation. It is obtained by replacing the operator D by the desired exponent λ. If the two roots λ_1 and λ_2 of the characteristic equation are different, the two solutions are independent, and the complete solution of the differential equation is

$$y = C_1 e^{\lambda_1 x} + C_2 e^{\lambda_2 x}.$$

If $\lambda_1 = \lambda_2 (= \lambda)$, then only one solution, $y = e^{\lambda x}$, is obtained. To find the form of a second solution we consider the case where the two roots in the characteristic equation are nearly equal. When we call one root λ and the other $\lambda + \epsilon$, we have the following two solutions to the differential equation:

$$y_1 = e^{\lambda x} \quad \text{and} \quad y_2 = e^{\lambda x + \epsilon x}.$$

As the differential equation is linear,

$$\frac{1}{\epsilon}(y_2 - y_1) = \frac{e^{\epsilon x} - 1}{\epsilon} e^{\lambda x}$$

is also a solution to the differential equation. This is the case however small ϵ is. In the limit $\epsilon \to 0$, y_1 and y_2 become identical, but the above linear combination becomes $y = xe^{\lambda x}$, as $\lim_{\epsilon \to 0} (e^{\epsilon x} - 1)/\epsilon = x$. This heuristic method of reasoning does not by itself guarantee that

$y = xe^{\lambda x}$ is a solution of the differential equation. However, substitution shows that when the characteristic equation has a double root, then $y = e^{\lambda x}$ and $y = xe^{\lambda x}$, which are independent of each other, are really both solutions of the differential equation. The complete solution is therefore $y = C_1 e^{\lambda x} + C_2 x e^{\lambda x}$.

The same result, of course, is obtainable by using the formula derived on page 377.

If λ_1 and λ_2 are complex numbers, then they must be complex-conjugated, as the coefficients in the second-degree equation which determines them are here assumed to be real (p. 89). Thus if $\lambda_1 = \alpha + i\beta$, then $\lambda_2 = \alpha - i\beta$. Therefore we obtain as solutions of the differential equation the complex functions

$$y = \exp[(\alpha \pm i\beta)x] = e^{\alpha x} e^{\pm i\beta x}.$$

The trigonometric functions $\sin \beta x$ and $\cos \beta x$ are linear combinations of $e^{i\beta x}$ and $e^{-i\beta x}$, namely (p. 223),

$$\sin \beta x = \frac{1}{2i}(e^{i\beta x} - e^{-i\beta x}),$$

$$\cos \beta x = \frac{1}{2}(e^{i\beta x} + e^{-i\beta x}).$$

Therefore it is clear that in this case the complete solution may be written

$$y = C_1 e^{\alpha x} \cos \beta x + C_2 e^{\alpha x} \sin \beta x,$$

where C_1 and C_2 are again arbitrary constants.

The inhomogeneous equation $(D^2 + a_1 D + a_0)y = f(x)$ may now be solved using the Wronskian, but usually it is easier to guess at a particular solution.

In applications, three special cases occur frequently, those where $f(x)$ is (1) a polynomial, (2) a trigonometric function ($A \sin \omega x$ or $A \cos \omega x$), or (3) an exponential function $Ae^{\omega x}$. In these cases the particular solutions are guessed to be (1) a polynomial of the same degree where the coefficients are chosen so that they satisfy the equation, and (2) $a \sin \omega x + b \cos \omega x$, where a and b are chosen so that the expression satisfies the inhomogeneous equation. If one of these terms satisfies the corresponding homogeneous equation, then the guess made is $x(a \sin \omega x + b \cos \omega x)$. In case (3) the particular solution is guessed to be an exponential function $ae^{\omega x}$, or, if this satisfies the homogeneous equation, the function $axe^{\omega x}$.

Example 6-6. $d^2y/dx^2 - 4y = \sin x$. The solution of the homogeneous equation is $y = C_1 e^{2x} + C_2 e^{-2x}$. To find a solution to the inhomogeneous equation, we guess at $y = a \sin x + b \cos x$. When this is substituted into the equation, we obtain

$$-a \sin x - b \cos x - 4(a \sin x + b \cos x) = \sin x,$$
$$(-5a - 1)\sin x + (-5b)\cos x = 0.$$

If this expression is to be valid for all x, we must have $b = 0$, $a = -\frac{1}{5}$. A particular solution is therefore $-\frac{1}{5} \sin x$, and the complete solution is $y = C_1 e^{2x} + C_2 e^{-2x} - \frac{1}{5} \sin x$, where C_1 and C_2 are arbitrary constants. □

These considerations can be immediately applied to linear differential equations with an order higher than two with constant coefficients to y and its derivatives.

Euler's Differential Equation

A more complicated type of second-order differential equation which may also be solved exactly by elementary methods is *Euler's differential equation*. At the same time this allows us an opportunity to illustrate the application of a change of variables in a differential equation. Euler's equation is

$$x^2 \frac{d^2y}{dx^2} + a_1 x \frac{dy}{dx} + a_0 y = 0.$$

For $x > 0$ the substitution $x = e^t$ can be made in the function y, after which it appears as $y(t)$ with $t = \ln x$. From this we obtain

$$\frac{dy}{dx} = \frac{dy}{dt}\frac{dt}{dx} = \frac{1}{x}\frac{dy}{dt},$$
$$\frac{d^2y}{dx^2} = \frac{d}{dx}\left(\frac{dy}{dx}\right) = -\frac{1}{x^2}\frac{dy}{dt} + \frac{1}{x}\frac{d}{dx}\left(\frac{dy}{dt}\right)$$
$$= -\frac{1}{x^2}\frac{dy}{dt} + \frac{1}{x}\frac{d^2y}{dt^2}\frac{dt}{dx} = \frac{1}{x^2}\left(\frac{d^2y}{dt^2} - \frac{dy}{dt}\right).$$

Substituting this in the differential equation we obtain

$$\frac{d^2y}{dt^2} + (a_1 - 1)\frac{dy}{dt} + a_0 y = 0.$$

This equation has constant coefficients and may be solved by the method given above. From this $y = y(t)$ is obtained, and in this expression the substitution $t = \ln x$ is made.

For $x < 0$ the analogous substitution $x = -e^t [t = \ln(-x)]$ is made, which leads to the same differential equation for the determination of $y = y(t)$ as above.

Exercises

*1. Solve the equation $y'' + 3y' + 2y = 10 \cos x$.

2. Solve the equation $y'' - y' - 2y = 6e^{-x}$. Sketch the curve of the special solution which at the point $(0,2)$ has a slope of -4.

*3. Solve the equation $y'' - 4y' + 4y = 4e^{2x}$.

*4. Solve the equation $x(x - 5)y'' + (20 - x^2)y' + (5x - 20)y = x(x - 5)^2$.

5. Find the complete solution to the equation $x^2 y'' - 2y = 0$.

6. Solve the equations (a) $y'' + 2y' = 0$ and (b) $y'' + 2y' = e^{-x}$.

7. Show that the Wronskian, $W(x)$, defined on page 378, is either equal to zero or else different from zero in all of its domain.

8. Show that a substitution $z = \phi(x)$ can always be introduced so that the differential equation $y'' + f(x)y' + g(x)y = h(x)$ is transformed into an equation which has a coefficient of dy/dz equal to zero. Then solve the equation

$$y'' - \frac{1}{x} y' + 4x^2 y = x^4 \qquad (x > 0).$$

*9. Solve the equation $y'' + 2y' + y = x + 2$. Sketch the curve of the solution which has a horizontal tangent at the point $(0,0)$.

10. Solve the equation $y'' + 2y' + 5y = 25x^3 - 11x$.

11. Solve the equation $y'' + y + 4 \cos x + 2 \sin x = 0$.

12. Show that

$$\phi(y) = \int_0^\infty \frac{\sin xy}{x(a^2 + x^2)} \, dx = \frac{\pi}{2a^2} (1 - e^{-ay}) \ (y \geq 0, \, a > 0).$$

[*Hint:* Show that $\phi''(y) - a^2 \phi(y)$ equals a constant.]

13. Solve the equation $xy'' + 2y' + xy = x \ (x > 0)$ when one solution to the corresponding homogeneous equation is given as the function $(\sin x)/x$.

*14. Solve the equation $x^2 y'' - 2xy' + 2y = 0$.

*15. Solve the equation $y''' - 6y'' + 13y' - 10y = 0$.

16. Solve the equation $y''' + 3y'' + 3y' + y = 0$.

17. A particle with mass 2 is acted on by an elastic force $\mathbf{K} = -8\mathbf{r}$, where $\mathbf{r}$ designates the position vector of the particle. When at time 0 the particle is at the point $(2\sqrt{3},0,0)$ and has the velocity $(8,4\sqrt{3},0)$, find the path the particle will follow. Determine the period of the particle. Give the initial velocity which must be chosen if the path is to be circular.

18. Find the curve in the first quadrant which is increasing, which passes through the point $(1,1)$ with a slope $\frac{1}{2}$, and which furthermore has the following property: When (x_p, y_p) designates an arbitrary point on the curve, then the area bounded by the curve, the coordinate axes, and the line $x = x_p$ is equal to $\frac{8}{3}$

of the triangle defined by the points (x_p, y_p), $(0, y_p)$ and the point where the tangent to the curve at (x_p, y_p) intersects the ordinate axis.

Answers

1. $y = \cos x + 3 \sin x + C_1 e^{-x} + C_2 e^{-2x}$.
3. $y = 2x^2 e^{2x} + C_1 e^{2x} + C_2 x e^{2x}$.
4. $y = \frac{1}{3} x^2 - x - 1 + C_1 x^5 + C_2 e^x$.
9. $y = x + C_1 e^{-x} + C_2 x e^{-x}$, $y = x - x e^{-x}$.
14. $y = C_1 x + C_2 x^2$.
15. $y = C_1 e^{2x} + C_2 e^{2x} \cos x + C_3 e^{2x} \sin x$.

6-3. COUPLED DIFFERENTIAL EQUATIONS

Solution by Iteration

Systems of *coupled first-order differential equations* often arise in connection with chemical kinetics. For example,

$$\dot{x}_1 = k_1 x_1 + k_2 x_2,$$
$$\dot{x}_2 = k_3 x_1 + k_4 x_2,$$

which are two homogeneous first-order differential equations with constant coefficients in the two unknown functions $x_1(t)$ and $x_2(t)$. Such equations can be made into one second-order differential equation in the following manner:

$$\ddot{x}_1 = k_1 \dot{x}_1 + k_2 \dot{x}_2$$
$$= k_1 \dot{x}_1 + k_2 k_3 x_1 + k_2 k_4 x_2$$
$$= k_1 \dot{x}_1 + k_2 k_3 x_1 + k_4 (\dot{x}_1 - k_1 x_1),$$

or

$$\ddot{x}_1 - (k_1 + k_4) \dot{x}_1 + (k_1 k_4 - k_2 k_3) x_1 = 0.$$

This can be solved with the aid of the method described above (p. 380), and x_2 can then be obtained without integration by substituting into the first of the two given equations.

This method can also be applied to certain differential equations with variable coefficients, since occasionally the resulting second-order differential equation is easier to solve than the original equations. More often, however, the reverse procedure is used; i.e., a second-order differential equation is rewritten as two coupled first-order differential equations (p. 409).

The following is a method for the solution of homogeneous first-order differential equations with variable coefficients. The equations

$$\dot{x}_1 = a_{11}(t) x_1 + a_{12}(t) x_2,$$
$$\dot{x}_2 = a_{21}(t) x_1 + a_{22}(t) x_2$$

are written $\dot{X} = AX$, where the two functions x_1 and x_2 are thought of as components of a vector X, and A is a matrix, the elements of which are functions of t. This equation is a first-order differential equation, and may be solved by an iteration method analogous to that used above (p. 366). If S designates an operator such that SA is the matrix which occurs when every element in A is integrated from t_0 to t, and X_0 designates the value of X at the time t_0, then $X = \Omega X_0$, where

$$\Omega = E + SA + S(ASA) + S(AS(ASA)) + \cdots$$

is a solution of the original differential equation. An analogous result is obtained when there are $N > 2$ homogeneous linear first-degree equations.

Equations with Constant Coefficients

The method of solution given above is of considerable importance from a theoretical point of view, because the series for X usually has a large domain of convergence. When A is a constant matrix, we can use the method to obtain the result $X(t) = [\exp At]X(0)$. For simplicity we have here set $t_0 = 0$, and by the exponential function of the matrix

$$At = \begin{Bmatrix} a_{11}t & a_{12}t & \cdots & a_{1N}t \\ a_{21}t & a_{22}t & \cdots & a_{2N}t \\ \cdot & \cdot & & \cdot \\ \cdot & \cdot & & \cdot \\ \cdot & \cdot & & \cdot \\ a_{N1}t & a_{N2}t & \cdots & a_{NN}t \end{Bmatrix}$$

we mean the limiting value for the sum

$$E + At + \frac{1}{2!}(At)^2 + \frac{1}{3!}(At)^3 + \cdots .$$

When A is not a constant matrix, it is in general not possible to write a solution to the equation $\dot{X} = AX$ as $X(t) = [\exp\{\int_0^t A\, dt\}]X(0)$, because SA and A do not commute now.

In the special case of a constant *diagonal* matrix D, we obtain

$$\exp(Dt) = \begin{Bmatrix} \exp(d_{11}t) & 0 & \cdots & 0 \\ 0 & \exp(d_{22}t) & \cdots & 0 \\ \cdot & \cdot & & \cdot \\ \cdot & \cdot & & \cdot \\ \cdot & \cdot & & \cdot \\ 0 & 0 & \cdots & \exp(d_{NN}t) \end{Bmatrix}.$$

This means that if there exists a linear transformation $X = QY$, where Q is a matrix with constant elements which diagonalizes the system of equations $\dot{X} = AX$, i.e., a transformation such that $\dot{Y} = Q^{-1}AQY$ and the matrix $Q^{-1}AQ$ is diagonal, then the solution of this equation for Y will be $y_k = y_k(0) \exp(\lambda_k t)$ $(k = 1,2\ .\ .\ .,N)$, where λ_k is the kth diagonal element of $Q^{-1}AQ$. Since the original variables x_k will be linear combinations of the y_k, we have

$$x_k = \sum_j b_{kj}e^{\lambda_j t}, \qquad b_{kj} = q_{kj}y_j(0),$$

and the λ's can now be determined in the usual way as the roots of the equation $|A - \lambda E| = 0$. The coefficients $y_j(0)$ may then be determined from the initial values, while q_{kj} has already been determined.

When A is a symmetric matrix, we know that there exists an orthogonal transformation which diagonalizes it (p. 73). A wider class of matrices which can be diagonalized by linear transformations does exist, but the diagonal elements will generally not be real. For all such matrices A which can be diagonalized by linear transformations, we see from the above that the solution to the equation $\dot{X} = AX$ must be $x_k = \Sigma_j b_{kj}e^{\lambda_j t}$.

The same result is obtained, of course, if it is simply assumed that $x_k = c_k e^{\lambda t}$ is a particular solution of the equation. We then have $X = Ce^{\lambda t}$, which on substitution into the equation gives $\lambda Ce^{\lambda t} = ACe^{\lambda t}$, or $AC = \lambda C$. It follows from this that λ is an eigenvalue of A corresponding to the eigenvector C. The possible values of λ are the eigenvalues of A, the coefficients q_{kj} $(k = 1,2,.\ .\ .,N)$ are obtained from the eigenvalue λ_j, and $y_j(0)$ $(j = 1,2,.\ .\ .,N)$ is determined from the N equations with N unknowns $\Sigma_j q_{kj}y_j(0) = x_k(0)$.

Example 6-7. The coupled differential equations

$$\dot{x} = x + 2y,$$
$$\dot{y} = 2x - 2y$$

have the solutions

$$x = k_1 e^{\lambda_1 t} + k_2 e^{\lambda_2 t},$$
$$y = k_3 e^{\lambda_1 t} + k_4 e^{\lambda_2 t},$$

where λ_1 and λ_2 are eigenvalues of the matrix

$$\begin{Bmatrix} 1 & 2 \\ 2 & -2 \end{Bmatrix};$$

i.e., we have

$$\begin{vmatrix} 1 - \lambda & 2 \\ 2 & -2 - \lambda \end{vmatrix} = 0 \quad \text{or} \quad \lambda = \begin{cases} 2 = \lambda_1, \, k_1/k_3 = 2, \\ -3 = \lambda_2, \, k_2/k_4 = -\tfrac{1}{2}. \end{cases}$$

If at time 0, $x = y = 1$, we have

$$k_1 = \tfrac{6}{5}, \qquad k_2 = -\tfrac{1}{5}, \qquad k_3 = \tfrac{3}{5}, \qquad k_4 = \tfrac{2}{5}.$$

In general when we solve for $e^{\lambda_1 t}$ and $e^{\lambda_2 t}$ we get

$$e^{\lambda_1 t} = \frac{k_4 x - k_2 y}{k_1 k_4 - k_2 k_3},$$
$$e^{\lambda_2 t} = \frac{-k_3 x + k_1 y}{k_1 k_4 - k_2 k_3};$$

hence

$$\left[\frac{k_4 x - k_2 y}{k_1 k_4 - k_2 k_3} \right]^{\lambda_2} = \left[\frac{k_1 y - k_3 x}{k_1 k_4 - k_2 k_3} \right]^{\lambda_1}.$$

It is sometimes convenient to draw the solution in an XY-plane with arrows to show in which direction the point moves on the curve when t increases.

In the special case discussed above we have for $t \to +\infty$, $x/y \to k_1/k_3 = 2$ and for $t \to -\infty$, $x/y \to k_2/k_4 = -\tfrac{1}{2}$ (Fig. 6-7). In the figure the solid line is the curve which passes through $(1,1)$ at time 0, the dotted lines are some solutions corresponding to other initial conditions.

The point $(0,0)$ is a so-called *stationary point*, as $\dot{x}$ and $\dot{y}$ are zero at this point. However, it is seen from the solution that arbitrarily near $(0,0)$ there are points with the property that a solution which

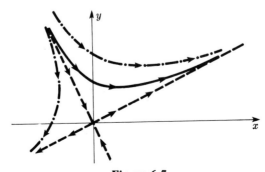

Figure 6-7

at time 0 passes through this point in time will move infinitely far away.   (0,0) is thus called an *unstable* stationary point.   □

An Example from Classical Mechanics

The above representation is especially important in classical statistical mechanics.   Here we consider a mechanical system described by the coordinates $(q_1, q_2, \ldots, q_N, p_1, p_2, \ldots, p_N)$, where the q's normally are the geometric coordinates of mass points and the p's are the momenta associated with them.   The total energy $H = H(p_1, p_2, \ldots, p_N, q_1, q_2, \ldots, q_N)$ is now given as a function of the p's and the q's. The evolution in time of the physical state of the system is then described by Hamilton's equations:

$$\dot{p}_k = -\frac{\partial H}{\partial q_k},$$

$$\dot{q}_k = \frac{\partial H}{\partial p_k},$$

i.e., there exists a set of coupled first-order differential equations for the p's and q's.   The $2N$-dimensional space which has as coordinates the geometrical coordinates and the momentum coordinates of the mechanical system is called the *phase space*, and it is often convenient to consider the path (or trajectory) in this space which corresponds to the evolution in time of the mechanical system.

As an example let us consider a simple *harmonic oscillator*, i.e., a system with energy $H = (1/2m)p^2 + \frac{1}{2}\gamma q^2$.   Partial differentiation of H with respect to p and q shows that the equations of motion are $\dot{p} = -\gamma q$, $\dot{q} = p/m$.   The equations are in this case solved most simply by converting them to a single second-order differential equation in q,

$$\ddot{q} = -\frac{\gamma}{m}q,$$

from which it follows that

$$q = a \sin \omega t + b \cos \omega t = A \sin(\omega t + \phi), \quad \omega = \sqrt{\frac{\gamma}{m}}.$$

Here a, b, A, and ϕ are arbitrary constants.   From the equation $p = m\dot{q}$ we then have

$$p = Am\omega \cos(\omega t + \phi).$$

The paths in phase space are ellipses with the equations

$$\frac{p^2}{(Am\omega)^2} + \frac{q^2}{(A)^2} = 1,$$

and $(q,p) = (0,0)$ is a stationary point, since at $(0,0)$ $\dot{p} = \dot{q} = 0$. In particular it is denoted a *stable* stationary point, since a trajectory which at time zero is in the neighborhood of this point will remain in the neighborhood at all later times.

Nonlinear Coupled First-Order Equations

Finally we shall consider some examples of nonlinear coupled first-order differential equations. For these we shall see that it is possible to have substantially more complicated curves in the phase space than those given above. The equations

$$\dot{x} = x - xy,$$
$$\dot{y} = xy - y$$

were used by Volterra for the description of a biological system of two species of animals, where the existence of one depends on the other. It is assumed that animal number 1, whose concentration is denoted by x, serves as food for animal number 2, whose concentration is denoted by y. Now x increases in proportion to x (as animal 1 is assumed to propagate itself faster than it naturally dies) and x also decreases in proportion to xy (as animal 2 eats animal 1 every time they meet). The propagation of animal 2 is assumed to be the faster the greater the availability of food, and, as it also dies, its concentration changes in proportion to y. Thus the above equations are obtained, in which for the sake of simplicity all proportionality factors are set equal to 1.

$(x^s,y^s) = (0,0)$ and $(1,1)$ are stationary points, since at these points the time derivatives of x and y are zero. To ascertain if they are stable or unstable points we set $x = x^s + x_1$ and $y = y^s + y_1$ and assume x_1 and y_1 to be so small that $x_1{}^2$, x_1y_1, and $y_1{}^2$ can be neglected compared to x_1 and y_1. The resulting equations are then said to be *linearized*. In the first case, we obtain

$$\dot{x}_1 = x_1,$$
$$\dot{y}_1 = -y_1,$$

and therefore

$$x_1 = x_1(0)e^t,$$
$$y_1 = y_1(0)e^{-t}.$$

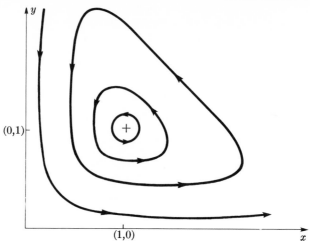

Figure 6-8

Thus $(0,0)$ is an unstable stationary point. For the second stationary point we get (analogously)

$$\dot{x}_1 = -y_1,$$
$$\dot{y}_1 = x_1,$$

and therefore

$$x_1 = x_1(0)\cos t - y_1(0)\sin t,$$
$$y_1 = y_1(0)\cos t + x_1(0)\sin t.$$

Thus the representative point (x,y), which represents the state of the system, moves in a circle around $(1,1)$. This point therefore is a stable stationary point.

On closer investigation it turns out that the paths in the XY-plane appear as shown in Fig. 6-8.

Generally it is not true for two coupled differential equations that the solutions are closed curves in the XY-plane. But it is generally true for the equations

$$\dot{x} = f(x,y),$$
$$\dot{y} = g(x,y)$$

that a solution which is limited for $t > t_0$, and which does not pass through any singular point for (f,g), i.e., a point where both $f(x,y)$ and $g(x,y)$ are zero, either is a closed curve or a spiral-shaped curve which asymptotically approaches a closed curve.

Consider, for example, the following system of equations:

$$\dot{x} = y + x(1 - x^2 - y^2),$$
$$\dot{y} = -x + y(1 - x^2 - y^2).$$

Near the stationary point (0,0) the corresponding linearized equations have the solution

$$x = x(0)e^t \cos t + y(0)e^t \sin t = e^t \sqrt{x(0)^2 + y(0)^2} \sin(t + \phi),$$
$$y = y(0)e^t \cos t - x(0)e^t \sin t = e^t \sqrt{x(0)^2 + y(0)^2} \cos(t + \phi).$$

The trajectory corresponding to this solution moves as a spiral away from (0,0), which is thus not a stable stationary point. However, the spiral does not cross the unit circle $(x,y) = (\sin t, \cos t)$, which is also a solution, but approaches it asymptotically. This appears to be contrary to the above-given solution of the linearized equations, but it is not, as the latter is approximately valid only in the neighborhood of (0,0). To see how the curve of the solution approaches the unit circle asymptotically, we shall change to polar coordinates in the original equation. Setting $x = r \cos \theta$ and $y = r \sin \theta$ and inserting this in the differential equations, we get

$$\dot{x} = \dot{r} \cos \theta - r\dot{\theta} \sin \theta = r \sin \theta + (r \cos \theta)(1 - r^2),$$
$$\dot{y} = \dot{r} \sin \theta + r\dot{\theta} \cos \theta = -r \cos \theta + (r \sin \theta)(1 - r^2),$$

where $x^2 + y^2 = r^2$. These equations are solved for $\dot{r}$ and $\dot{\theta}$, giving

$$\dot{r} = \frac{dr}{dt} = r(1 - r^2),$$

$$\dot{\theta} = \frac{d\theta}{dt} = -1,$$

with the solutions

$$r = \left[1 + \left(\frac{1}{r(0)^2} - 1\right)e^{-2t}\right]^{-1/2},$$
$$\theta = -t + \theta(0),$$

or

$$x = \left[1 + \left(\frac{1}{r(0)^2} - 1\right)e^{-2t}\right]^{-1/2} \cos(\theta(0) - t),$$

$$y = \left[1 + \left(\frac{1}{r(0)^2} - 1\right)e^{-2t}\right]^{-1/2} \sin(\theta(0) - t).$$

As $t \to \infty$, the trajectory therefore approaches arbitrarily close to the unit circle

$$x = \cos(\theta(0) - t) \left.\vphantom{\begin{matrix}a\\b\end{matrix}}\right\} \ \theta(0) = \arctan \frac{y(0)}{x(0)},$$
$$y = \sin(\theta(0) - t)$$

or $x^2 + y^2 = 1$, independent of whether $(x(0), y(0))$ lies inside or outside the unit circle.

Exercises

*1. Solve the two coupled differential equations

$$\dot{x} = y + t,$$
$$\dot{y} = -2x + 3y + 5t - 4.$$

*2. Solve the two coupled differential equations

$$\dot{x} = 3xt + yt,$$
$$\dot{y} = -6xt - 2yt.$$

Draw the curves of the solutions in an XY coordinate system.

3. A point moves in the XY-plane so that the angle from the position vector of the point to the velocity vector is at all times $45°$. Find the path that contains the point $(1,0)$.

*4. Solve the two coupled differential equations

$$\dot{x} = x^2 y - y^3,$$
$$\dot{y} = x^3 - xy^2.$$

As at first curves are sought in the XY-plane without regard to time relationships, a suitable differential equation on differential form is set up and solved.

*5. Solve the coupled differential equations

$$\dot{c}_1 = -3c_1 + c_2,$$
$$\dot{c}_2 = 3c_1 - 4c_2 + c_3,$$
$$\dot{c}_3 = 3c_2 - 3c_3,$$
$$\dot{c}_4 = 2c_3.$$

Find the set of solutions in the special case when $c_1(0) = c_3(0) = c_4(0) = 0$ and $c_2(0) = 5$.

6. Solve the three coupled differential equations

$$\dot{x} = -5x + 2z,$$
$$\dot{y} = -7y - 2z,$$
$$\dot{z} = 2x - 2y - 6z$$

by the method given on page 386. Give the solution in the case when

$$(x(0), y(0), z(0)) = (3, -1, -2).$$

7. Solve the two coupled differential equations

$$\dot{x} = x + 5y,$$
$$\dot{y} = -2x - y.$$

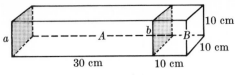

10 cm
10 cm
30 cm   10 cm

Figure 6-9

If the solutions are considered to be mapped as curves in a plane (with t as parameter) in a coordinate system XY, show that all these [except the solution $(x,y) = (0,0)$] are similar and similarly placed ellipses with centers at $(0,0)$.

8. Solve the two coupled differential equations

$$\dot{x} = 2x - y,$$
$$\dot{y} = x + 2y,$$

by transforming to polar coordinates.

In a coordinate system XY, sketch the curve of the solution for which $(x(0),y(0)) = (1,0)$.

9. The decay constant k for a radioactive material gives the probability that an arbitrary atom of the material under consideration which has not yet decayed disintegrates in the following unit of time.

The elements A, B, and C are considered to comprise a radioactive family as A decays to B ($k_A = a$), and B decays to C ($k_B = b$), while C is stable. At time 0, there are N_0 atoms of A, none of B, and none of C. Determine the future development of the system.

Numerical examples:

(a) $a = 0.2, b = 0.1.$ (c) $a = b = 0.2.$
(b) $a = 0.1, b = 0.2.$ (d) $a = b = 0.1.$

10. Determine all the pairs of functions $(y(x),z(x))$ which satisfy the differential equations

$$y' = -y + z, \qquad z' = -2y - 4z.$$

If the solutions are now considered to be mapped as curves in space $(x,y(x), z(x))$, show that through every point in space there passes exactly one solution curve.

*11. In Fig. 6-9, A and B designate two empty box-like containers. The dashed sides a and b are porous. Outside the containers a perfect vacuum is maintained. At time 0, 4 g of gas is injected into A and it is assumed that the gas instantaneously fills the volume A. When the transport of material through a porous side is assumed to be proportional to the difference between the concentrations on the two sides of the surface, determine the concentrations in A and B as functions of time. The proportionality factors for sides a and b are, respectively, $\frac{1}{2}$ liter/hour and $\frac{1}{8}$ liter/hour.

Answers

1. $x = C_1 e^t + C_2 e^{2t} + t$
$\quad y = C_1 e^t + 2C_2 e^{2t} + 1 - t$

2. $r = e^\theta$

4. $x = C_1 e^{-4C_1 C_2 t} + C_2 e^{4C_1 C_2 t}$

$y = -C_1 e^{-4C_1 C_2 t} + C_2 e^{4C_1 C_2 t}$

5. $c_1(t) = e^{-t} - e^{-6t}$

$c_2(t) = 2e^{-t} + 3e^{-6t}$

$c_3(t) = 3e^{-t} - 3e^{-6t}$

$c_4(t) = -6e^{-t} + e^{-6t} + 5$

11. $c_A = \frac{1}{3}e^{-t/12} + e^{-t/4}$

$c_B = e^{-t/12} - e^{-t/4}$

6-4. SOLUTION BY SERIES EXPANSION

Often it is impossible to solve a differential equation exactly. A solution in the form of a *power series* can then be attempted. We shall illustrate the method by solving the equation $y'' + y = 0$. A solution $y = \Sigma_{n=0}^{\infty} a_n x^{m+n}$ in the form of a series expansion is assumed and is substituted in the equation to give

$$(a_0 m(m-1)x^{m-2} + a_1(m+1)mx^{m-1} + a_2(m+2)(m+1)x^m + \cdots)$$
$$+ (a_0 x^m + a_1 x^{m+1} + a_2 x^{m+2} + \cdots) = 0.$$

When this is rearranged after powers of x we get

$$a_0 m(m-1)x^{m-2} + a_1(m+1)mx^{m-1} + (a_2(m+2)(m+1) + a_0)x^m$$
$$+ (a_3(m+3)(m+2) + a_1)x^{m+1} + \cdots = 0.$$

If this equation is to be valid for all x, then all the coefficients of x must be zero, or

$$a_0 m(m-1) = 0,$$
$$a_1(m+1)m = 0,$$
$$a_2(m+2)(m+1) + a_0 = 0, \text{ etc.}$$

It is now clear why the series $\Sigma_{n=0}^{\infty} a_n x^{m+n}$ was chosen instead of just $\Sigma_{n=0}^{\infty} a_n x^n$. At the outset we cannot be certain that the solution has a series expansion which begins with a constant term. That is, we cannot be sure that a_0 is different from zero unless we introduce an additional parameter in the exponent. In the series expansion we have used now it can always be assumed that $a_0 \neq 0$, and, as we shall see, it then becomes possible to determine the values of m for which the series can be a solution.

For the determination of the index m we have the indical equation $m(m-1) = 0$, with solutions $m = 0$ and $m = 1$. In the first case $a_2 = -[1/(1 \cdot 2)]a_0$ is obtained from the third equation, and then $a_4 = -[1/(3 \cdot 4)]a_2 = [1/(1 \cdot 2 \cdot 3 \cdot 4)]a_0$, etc., so that finally we have the series $a_0 [1 - (1/2!)x^2 + (1/4!)x^4 \cdot \cdot \cdot] = a_0 \cos x$. Independent of this we can also choose a_1 freely, by which a_3, a_5, etc., are determined. This gives the series $a_1(x - (1/3!)x^3 + \cdot \cdot \cdot) = a_1 \sin x$. Thus we have the well-known complete solution $y = a_1 \sin x + a_0 \cos x$, which contains the two linearly independent solutions $\sin x$ and $\cos x$. For the case $m = 1$ only one series is found, and this turns out to be $a_0 \sin x$.

As a rule it is possible to give *recursion formulas* for the coefficients a_n, i.e., formulas which express a_n by one or more of the previous coefficients. In the above example we saw that when $m = 0$ the coefficient of x^n is equal to $a_{n+2} (n + 2)(n + 1) + a_n$. As this must equal zero to satisfy the differential equation, we immediately have

$$a_{n+2} = - \frac{a_n}{(n + 1)(n + 2)}.$$

In this case the coefficient of x^{n+2} is expressed by a_n alone, but often the recursion formulas contain several coefficients with a lower index.

As the radius of convergence for the series given above is ∞, the solutions obtained in this way are valid in the interval $-\infty < x < \infty$. Conversely it also follows that it is possible to use a differential equation to determine the power series for a given function. The problem is then to find a simple differential equation which the function under consideration satisfies, and then to choose from the infinite series obtained the one which satisfies the same initial conditions as the given function.

Exercises

*1. Solve, using a series expansion, the differential equation

$$x^2(1 + x^2)y'' - 4xy' + 6y = 0.$$

Sum the series which arise.

*2. Find a solution to the so-called *confluent hypergeometric equation*

$$xy'' + (c - x)y' - ay = 0$$

for the case $c > 0$ in the form of a power series. Show that when $c = 1$ and $a = -n$, the Laguerre polynomial considered in Exercise 4 on page 356 ($n = 0,1,2,3$) is a solution.

3. The function

$$J_n(x) = \frac{1}{\pi} \int_0^\pi \cos(nt - x \sin t) \, dt \qquad (n \text{ an integer}),$$

which is analytic for all x, is called the Bessel function of order n. Show that it satisfies the equation

$$x^2y'' + xy' + (x^2 - n^2)y = 0$$

(Bessel's differential equation). Use this to find a power series for $J_0(x)$.

Answers

1. $y = C_1x^2/(1 + x^2) + C_2x^3/(1 + x^2)$.

2. $y = 1 + \dfrac{a}{c}x + \dfrac{a(a + 1)}{c(c + 1)2!}x^2 + \dfrac{a(a + 1)(a + 2)}{c(c + 1)(c + 2)3!}x^3 + \cdots$

6-5. EIGENVALUE PROBLEMS

Boundary Value Problems

Up to now only second-order differential equations with a given set of initial values (x,y,y') have been considered. Quite often, however, situations are encountered in which the values of the required function are given at two points and no conditions are imposed on the derivative. Such a problem is called a *boundary value problem*. Problems for which the value of the derivative is given at two points or in which the value of the function is given at one point and the value of the derivative is given at another point are also called boundary value problems. Here we shall only consider the first of these cases.

While an *initial value problem* always has a solution (except possibly at "singular points"), this is not generally true for a boundary value problem.

For example, consider the equation $-(d^2/dx^2)\phi(x) = \lambda\phi(x)$, where $\phi(x)$ is the unknown function and λ is a positive number. The boundary conditions are assumed to be $\phi(0) = 0$ and $\phi(L) = 0$. The general solution to the equation is

$$\phi(x) = a \sin \sqrt{\lambda}\, x + b \cos \sqrt{\lambda}\, x.$$

As $\phi(0)$ is zero, $b = 0$. The other boundary condition then gives $a \sin \sqrt{\lambda}\, L = 0$, but this cannot be used to determine a, as when $a = 0$ only the *trivial solution* that ϕ is identical to zero is obtained. The condition at $x = L$, on the other hand, expresses that only when λ satisfies the relations $\sqrt{\lambda}\, L = n\pi$, i.e., $\lambda = (\pi^2/L^2)n^2$, does the equation have nontrivial solutions which satisfy the boundary conditions. The combination of the differential equation and the boundary conditions can thus result in the fact that a *nontrivial solution* only exists for certain *discrete values* of a parameter.

When we designate the operator $-(d^2/dx^2)$ by $\mathcal{H}$ we can write the above equation $\mathcal{H}\phi = \lambda\phi$, and the analogy with the eigenvalue problems discussed in Chapter 1 is at once evident. The possible values of λ are called the *eigenvalues* of the operator, and the functions corresponding to these values of λ are called the *eigenfunctions*. Just as an eigenvector belonging to a given eigenvalue of a matrix is determined except for a constant factor, when the possibility that two independent vectors can correspond to the same eigenvalue is neglected, we see that the function ϕ is determined except for a factor a. This also immediately follows from the fact that the differential equation which we consider is homogeneous.

In the diagonalization of matrices the arbitrary factor in the eigenvector was used to normalize the vector, so that it became a unit vector. Correspondingly, an eigenfunction is now normalized so that the integral of its square is 1 (p. 343). In the example we consider we set

$$\int_0^L [\phi(x)]^2 \, dx = a^2 \int_0^L \sin^2 \frac{\pi n}{L} x \, dx = \frac{a^2 L}{2} = 1,$$

and thus get $a = \sqrt{2/L}$ and $\phi_n(x) = \sqrt{2/L} \sin(\pi n/L)x$. Thus the operator $\mathcal{H} = -d^2/dx^2$, with the boundary conditions $\phi(0) = \phi(L) = 0$, has the eigenvalues

$$\lambda_n = \frac{\pi^2 n^2}{L^2},$$

and the normalized eigenfunctions belonging to these are

$$\phi_n(x) = \sqrt{\frac{2}{L}} \sin \frac{\pi n}{L} x.$$

It is now easy to verify that

$$\int_0^L \phi_i(x)\phi_k(x) \, dx = \delta_{ik}.$$

Thus the eigenfunctions belonging to the different eigenvalues are mutually orthogonal in the sense defined previously (p. 344). This corresponds precisely to what was found for eigenvectors.

Hermitian Operators

The result derived here for a special case can be shown to be valid for all operators $\mathcal{H}$ which satisfy the relation

$$\int_a^b \phi_1 \mathcal{H} \phi_2 \, dx = \int_a^b \phi_2 \mathcal{H} \phi_1 \, dx,$$

where ϕ_1 and ϕ_2 are arbitrary functions which satisfy the boundary conditions at $x = a$ and $x = b$.

An operator which satisfies this condition is called *Hermitian*. The condition that an operator is Hermitian is thus that the generalized scalar product of ϕ_1 and $\mathcal{H}\phi_2$ is equal to the generalized scalar product of ϕ_2 and $\mathcal{H}\phi_1$. As we shall see below, a Hermitian operator is analogous to a *symmetric matrix*, and it has real eigenvalues, just as is the case for symmetric matrices (p. 75).

Most of the differential operators which are encountered in applications have the form

$$-\frac{d}{dx}\left[p(x)\frac{d}{dx}\right] + q(x).$$

The boundary value conditions usually have such a form that either $p(x)$, or the solutions to the equation $\mathcal{H}\phi = \lambda\phi$ or their derivatives, are zero on the boundary of the interval, i.e., at $x = a$ and $x = b$. Under these conditions it is easy to show that $\mathcal{H}$ is Hermitian. By partial integration we have, since $p\phi\phi'$ is zero at the boundaries,

$$\int_a^b \phi_1 \mathcal{H} \phi_2 \, dx = \int_a^b \phi_1 \left[-\frac{d}{dx}\{p(x)\phi_2'(x)\} + q(x)\phi_2(x) \right] dx$$

$$= [-\phi_1 p(x)\phi_2']_a^b + \int_a^b p(x)\phi_2'\phi_1' \, dx + \int_a^b \phi_1 q \phi_2 \, dx$$

$$= \int_a^b p(x)\phi_2'\phi_1' \, dx + \int_a^b \phi_1 q \phi_2 \, dx.$$

One more partial integration finally converts this to

$$\int_a^b \phi_2 \left[-\frac{d}{dx}\{p(x)\phi_1'(x)\} + q(x)\phi_1(x) \right] dx = \int_a^b \phi_2 \mathcal{H} \phi_1 \, dx,$$

which proves the assertion that $\mathcal{H}$ is Hermitian.

The solutions to the equations $\mathcal{H}\phi_n = \lambda_n\phi_n$ $(n = 1,2,\ldots)$, where $\mathcal{H}$ is a Hermitian operator, can be imagined to be expanded on a complete system of functions $\psi_1,\psi_2,\ldots$, which are orthonormal over the interval $a \le x \le b$, and which also satisfy the boundary conditions. In this way each solution is represented by a sequence of numbers—the coefficients in its expansion. Thus each function ϕ_n corresponds to a *vector in a space of infinite dimensions* (p. 344). In the same way, the numbers

$$H_{ik} = \int_a^b \psi_i \mathcal{H} \psi_k \, dx$$

can be considered as the elements of a *matrix of an infinitely high order* which represents the operator $\mathcal{H}$. The orthonormal solutions to the equation $\mathcal{H}\phi_n = \lambda_n\phi_n$ span the coordinate system in which the representation of the operator $\mathcal{H}$ is diagonal.

We shall now show that if an arbitrary normalized function ϕ is substituted in place of ϕ_n in the expression $\int \phi_n \mathcal{H} \phi_n \, dx$, and $\mathcal{H}$ is Hermitian, the integral will always be greater than or equal to the smallest eigenvalue λ_1 of the operator. Since the (unknown) solutions ϕ_n of the equation $\mathcal{H}\phi_n = \lambda_n\phi_n$ $(n = 1,2,\ldots)$ form an orthonormal set, the function ϕ can be expanded on them as

$$\phi = \Sigma c_n \phi_n,$$

and since ϕ is normalized, we have that $\Sigma c_n{}^2 = 1$. Then

$$\int_a^b \phi\mathcal{H}\phi \, dx = \int_a^b \left(\sum c_n\phi_n\right) \mathcal{H} \left(\sum c_n\phi_n\right) dx$$

$$= \int_a^b \left(\sum_n c_n\phi_n\right)\left(\sum_n c_n\lambda_n\phi_n\right) dx$$

$$= \sum_n \lambda_n c_n{}^2 \ge \lambda_1 \sum_n c_n{}^2 = \lambda_1.$$

This inequality may be used to find an approximate value for λ_1 if a normalized function ϕ which satisfies the boundary conditions and which contains one or more parameters is used.

The integral $\int \phi\mathcal{H}\phi \, dx$ then becomes a function of these parameters, and, by finding the least value of the integral considered as a function of these parameters, an estimate is obtained for the least eigenvalue. This method of estimating the smallest eigenvalue is called the *variational method*.

Example 6-8. The differential equation

$$\left(-\frac{d^2}{dx^2} + x^2\right)\phi = \lambda\phi \quad (-\infty < x < \infty,\ \phi(-\infty) = \phi(\infty) = 0)$$

has 1 as the least eigenvalue and the corresponding normalized eigenfunction is $(1/\sqrt[4]{\pi})e^{-x^2/2}$. (The following eigenvalues are 3,5,7,. . . .) We shall determine an approximate value of the smallest eigenvalue by using the trial function

$$\phi = \begin{cases} a(b^2 - x^2) & -b < x < b, \\ 0 & |x| > b. \end{cases}$$

The function is first normalized

$$\int_{-\infty}^{\infty} \phi^2\,dx = \int_{-b}^{b} a^2(b^2 - x^2)^2\,dx = \tfrac{16}{15}a^2b^5 = 1.$$

Thus $a^2 = \tfrac{15}{16}b^{-5}$. This is used to eliminate a from the following expressions. Then $\int \phi \mathcal{H}\phi\,dx$ is found to be

$$-\int_{-b}^{b} a(b^2 - x^2)\frac{d^2}{dx^2} a(b^2 - x^2)\,dx + \int_{-b}^{b} x^2 a^2(b^2 - x^2)^2\,dx$$
$$= \tfrac{8}{3}a^2b^3 + \tfrac{16}{105}a^2b^7 = \tfrac{5}{2}b^{-2} + \tfrac{1}{7}b^2.$$

We shall now find the minimum for the function $f(b) = (5/2b^2) + (b^2/7)$. Differentiating we see that the minimum occurs for $b^2 = \sqrt{\tfrac{35}{2}}$, and the lowest eigenvalue is therefore approximated by $f(\sqrt[4]{\tfrac{35}{2}}) = \tfrac{2}{7}\sqrt{\tfrac{35}{2}} \approx 1.20$. Despite the fact that the function $\phi = a(b^2 - x^2)$ is only a very crude approximation to the correct eigenfunction, the estimate for the lowest eigenvalue is not so poor.   □

Ritz' Variational Method

A special form of the above method is the so-called *Ritz method*, in which the trial function is taken to be a *linear combination* of functions which separately satisfy the boundary conditions:

$$\phi = c_1 f_1(x) + c_2 f_2(x) + \cdots + c_N f_N(x) = \sum_{n=1}^{N} c_n f_n(x).$$

The functions $f_n(x)$ $(n = 1,2,. . .,N)$ contain no parameters, so that $\int \phi \mathcal{H}\phi\,dx / \int \phi^2\,dx$ now is a function, $F(c_1,. . .,c_N)$, only of the coefficients c_n $(n = 1,2,. . .,N)$. On substitution of the expression for ϕ in the integral we obtain

$$F(c_1, c_2, \ldots, c_N) = \frac{\int (\Sigma c_n f_n(x)) \mathcal{H}(\Sigma c_n f_n(x)) \, dx}{\int (\Sigma c_n f_n(x))(\Sigma c_n f_n(x)) \, dx} = \frac{\Sigma\Sigma c_n c_m H_{nm}}{\Sigma\Sigma c_n c_m S_{nm}}.$$

We have used the abbreviations $H_{nm} = \int f_n \mathcal{H} f_m \, dx$ and $S_{nm} = \int f_n f_m \, dx$, and it follows that $H_{mn} = H_{nm}$ and $S_{nm} = S_{mn}$. We now have

$$F\Sigma\Sigma c_n c_m S_{nm} = \Sigma\Sigma c_n c_m H_{nm},$$

and on differentiating this expression with respect to c_m we get

$$\left(\frac{\partial F}{\partial c_m}\right) \sum_{n=1}^{N} \sum_{m=1}^{N} c_n c_m S_{nm} + 2F \sum_{n=1}^{N} c_n S_{nm} = 2 \sum_{n=1}^{N} c_n H_{nm}.$$

A necessary condition for F to be a minimum is that $\partial F/\partial c_m = 0$ $(m = 1, 2, \ldots, N)$. Therefore for the determination of the c's we have

$$\Sigma c_n H_{nm} - F\Sigma c_n S_{nm} = 0 \qquad (m = 1, 2, \ldots, N).$$

This is a system of homogeneous linear equations, and thus it has a nontrivial solution only if the determinant vanishes:

$$\begin{vmatrix} H_{11} - FS_{11} & H_{12} - FS_{12} & \cdots \\ H_{21} - FS_{21} & H_{22} - FS_{22} & \cdots \\ \cdot & \cdot & \\ \cdot & \cdot & \\ \cdot & \cdot & \end{vmatrix} = 0.$$

This is an Nth-degree equation in F, the lowest root of which gives an approximate value for the least eigenvalue of the operator $\mathcal{H}$. If this value for F is inserted into the system of equations, the coefficients c_n $(n = 1, 2, \ldots, N)$ can be determined for the linear combination $\phi = \Sigma c_n f_n(x)$. This then gives the approximation to that solution of the differential equation $\mathcal{H}\phi = \lambda\phi$ which corresponds to the smallest eigenvalue.

Whenever possible a set of functions $f_1, f_2, \ldots, f_N$ are chosen which are mutually orthonormal. The integrals S_{nm} then become δ_{nm} and the determinant becomes

$$\begin{vmatrix} H_{11} - \lambda & H_{12} & \cdots \\ H_{21} & H_{22} - \lambda & \cdots \\ \cdot & \cdot & \\ \cdot & \cdot & \\ \cdot & \cdot & \end{vmatrix} = 0 \qquad \text{or} \qquad |H - \lambda E| = 0.$$

Here we have written λ for $F(c_1, \ldots, c_N)$ to show the analogy to the *characteristic equation* for a matrix. It must be remembered, however, that it is only the smallest root of the equation in λ in which we are interested.

When the determination of the least eigenvalue of the equation $\mathcal{H}\phi = \lambda\phi$ is carried out by the use of a so-called linear variational function $\Sigma c_n f_n(x)$, the individual terms of which are orthonormal, then the determination is formally identical to finding the smallest eigenvalue of a matrix of order N. The matrix which must be diagonalized is formed by the so-called *matrix elements* of the operator, $H_{nm} = \int f_n \mathcal{H} f_m \, dx$. If a linear combination of the eigenfunctions of the operator had been used, then, as mentioned on page 399, we should have found that the matrix which represents the operator would have been diagonal with the eigenvalues as the diagonal elements. It is therefore said that *the operator is diagonal* in the "coordinate system" in function space which is spanned by its own eigenfunctions.

The problem of the determination of eigenfunctions and eigenvectors is therefore formally the same as that of finding the coordinate system in which a symmetric tensor is in a diagonal form, but now the "coordinate system" which we consider here (and formally "rotate") has an infinite number of dimensions. Solving a differential-equation eigenvalue problem exactly is equivalent to diagonalizing a matrix of infinitely high order. The approximate methods used above are based on replacing the $\infty \times \infty$ matrix by an $N \times N$ matrix, which is then diagonalized. If the system of orthogonal functions from which the N functions in the trial function have been taken is complete, then an arbitrarily good approximation to the least eigenvalue can be obtained by increasing N. If it is not a complete orthogonal system, then it is not certain that this holds true.

Exercises

1. Show that the nth Hermite polynomial

$$H_n(x) = (-1)^n e^{x^2} \frac{d^n}{dx^n} (e^{-x^2})$$

satisfies the differential equation

$$y'' - 2xy' + 2ny = 0.$$

Show next that the function $\phi_n(x) = H_n(x)e^{-x^2/2}$ is an eigenfunction for the operator $(-(d^2/dx^2) + x^2)$ corresponding to the eigenvalue $(2n + 1)$, and the boundary condition $\phi_n(x) \to 0$ for $x \to \pm \infty$.

*2. Find the solution to the differential equation $-y'' = f(x)$, where

$$f(x) = \begin{cases} 0 & \text{for } 0 \leq x \leq 1, \\ 1 & \text{for } x > 1, \end{cases}$$

for which $y(0) = 0$ and $y'(0) = 1$. (Make use of the condition that the solution must be (continuous and) differentiable also for $x = 1$.)

Outline a method for solving the eigenvalue problem

$$-y'' + \phi(x)y = \lambda y, \qquad \phi(x) = \begin{cases} 0 & \text{for } 0 \leq x \leq \pi/2, \\ a & \text{for } \pi/2 < x \leq \pi, \end{cases}$$

and where the boundary conditions are $y(0) = y(\pi) = 0$.

3. Show that every differential operator of second order of the form $f(x)(d^2/dx^2) + g(x)(d/dx) + h(x)$ can on multiplication by a function of x be brought into the form

$$-\frac{d}{dx}\left[p(x)\frac{d}{dx} \right] + q(x),$$

and express the function used by an indefinite integral. Show next that every linear differential equation of the form

$$-\frac{d}{dx}\left[p(x)\frac{dy}{dx} \right] + q(x)y = \lambda\omega(x)y$$

can be rewritten

$$-\frac{d^2z}{dt^2} + \phi(t)z = \lambda z$$

by the change of variables

$$z = y \sqrt[4]{p(x)\omega(x)}, \qquad t = \int \sqrt{\frac{\omega(x)}{p(x)}}\, dx.$$

*4. Find the approximate value of the lowest eigenvalue for the equation $\mathcal{JC}y = \lambda y$, where $\mathcal{JC} = -(d/dx)(x(d/dx))$ and the boundary conditions are $y(0) = y(1) = 0$. Use a linear combination of $\phi_n(x) = x^n(1 - x)$ $(n = 1,2)$ as a trial function.

5. Show that Legendre's differential equation

$$(x^2 - 1)P_n''(x) + 2xP_n'(x) - n(n + 1)P_n(x) = 0$$

is of the form discussed in this section (i.e., contains a Hermitian operator).

Answers

2. $y = \begin{cases} x & \text{for } 0 \leq x \leq 1 \\ -\frac{1}{2}x^2 + 2x - \frac{1}{2} & \text{for } x > 1 \end{cases}$

The function

$$y = \begin{cases} A_1 \sin \sqrt{\lambda}\, x & 0 \leq x < \dfrac{\pi}{2} \\ A_2 \sin [\sqrt{\lambda - a}\, (\pi - x)] & \dfrac{\pi}{2} < x \leq \pi \end{cases}$$

satisfies the boundary conditions. When we require it to be (defined, continuous, and) differentiable also at $\pi/2$ we get, for $\sin \sqrt{\lambda} \, (\pi/2) \neq 0$,

$$\sqrt{\lambda - a} \cot \left(\sqrt{\lambda - a} \, \frac{\pi}{2} \right) + \sqrt{\lambda} \cot \left(\sqrt{\lambda} \, \frac{\pi}{2} \right) = 0,$$

which determines the eigenvalues λ.

4. $H_{nm} = (2mn + m + n)/(m + n)(m + n + 1)(m + n + 2)$
$S_{nm} = 2/(m + n + 1)(m + n + 2)(m + n + 3)$
Using ϕ_1 only: $\lambda_1 \approx 5$. Using ϕ_1 and ϕ_2: $\lambda_1 \approx 13 - \sqrt{92} = 3.41$.

6-6. CALCULUS OF VARIATIONS

Euler's Equation

In certain physical applications problems of extrema occur, where the independent variable is not a number but a function. A class of such problems can be treated with the aid of differential equations, in that a necessary condition for the extremum is that the desired function satisfies a definite differential equation.

Let y designate a function which can vary freely inside a given domain of continuous, piecewise-differentiable functions. If to every function y in the domain there is associated a number I, then we say that I is a *functional* of y and write it $I[y]$.

We shall only consider functionals where I is given by a definite integral such as

$$I[y] = \int_{x_1}^{x_2} F(x,y,y') \, dx,$$

in which F is a known function of three variables.

It shall now be shown how a function can be found for which the functional takes on an extreme value. This will be restricted to finding only a necessary condition and considering only the case where the points (x_1,y_1) and (x_2,y_2) are fixed. As we only seek a necessary condition which the solution must satisfy, we can assume in the reasoning that a solution exists.

The solution is designated $y = y(x)$, and $y(x) + \alpha\beta(x)$ is substituted for y in the integral. Here $\beta(x)$ is an arbitrary function of x which satisfies only the condition that it is zero on the boundaries, and α is a number. As $y(x_1) = y_1$ and $y(x_2) = y_2$, then $y + \alpha\beta$ also satisfies this condition. We shall now assume that when $y + \alpha\beta$ is substituted for y, there is an extreme value at $\alpha = 0$ independent of β.

By this trick we have succeeded in making I a function of the number α when $\beta(x)$ is fixed.

$$\left[\frac{dI}{d\alpha}\right]_{\alpha=0} = \left[\frac{d}{d\alpha}\int_{x_1}^{x_2} F(x, y + \alpha\beta, y' + \alpha\beta')\, dx\right]_{\alpha=0}$$

$$= \left[\int_{x_1}^{x_2}\left(\frac{\partial F}{\partial y}\beta + \frac{\partial F}{\partial y'}\beta'\right) dx\right]_{\alpha=0}.$$

The order of the two operations—differentiation with respect to the parameter α and integration with respect to x—can be interchanged because the limits of integration are not dependent on α. On partial integration, the following is obtained:

$$\left[\frac{dI}{d\alpha}\right]_{\alpha=0} = \left[\beta\frac{\partial F}{\partial y'}\right]_{x_1}^{x_2} + \int_{x_1}^{x_2}\left(\frac{\partial F}{\partial y} - \frac{d}{dx}\frac{\partial F}{\partial y'}\right)\beta\, dx.$$

The first term is zero, as $\beta(x_1) = \beta(x_2) = 0$, and as $\beta(x)$ is an arbitrary function, then $[dI/d\alpha]_{\alpha=0} = 0$ gives

$$\frac{\partial F}{\partial y} - \frac{d}{dx}\frac{\partial F}{\partial y'} = 0.$$

This is then the desired necessary condition which y must satisfy if $I[y]$ is to be stationary. It is usually called *Euler's equation*.

The reasoning behind the above argument is that using $\beta(x)$ and α, a function $y + \alpha\beta$ can be constructed so that by a suitable choice of α and β, it can be any desired continuous, piecewise-differentiable function which passes through (x_1,y_1) and (x_2,y_2), and for $\alpha = 0$ becomes the solution $y(x)$ the existence of which we assumed. As we assumed that the problem has a solution, then the condition we have found for y is only a necessary condition, and not a sufficient condition for $I[y]$ to have an extreme value.

Calculation of the partial derivatives $\partial F/\partial y$ and $\partial F/\partial y'$ [which is immediate, as $F = F(x,y,y')$ is a known function of three variables] shows that Euler's equation is a second-order differential equation for $y(x)$. When y' is different from zero it can also be written

$$\frac{\partial F}{\partial x} - \frac{d}{dx}\left[F - y'\frac{\partial F}{\partial y'}\right] = 0.$$

This formulation is especially convenient when F does not explicitly depend on x, as then

$$\frac{d}{dx}\left[F - y'\frac{\partial F}{\partial y'}\right] = 0 \quad \text{or} \quad F - y'\frac{\partial F}{\partial y'} = C$$

is obtained, where C is a constant.

If instead we had considered an integrand F which was dependent on several functions of the same independent variable x, $y_1(x),y_2(x), \ldots, y_N(x)$ and their derivatives $y_1'(x),y_2'(x), \ldots, y_N'(x)$, then we would have obtained a Euler equation for every function $y_n(x)$,

$$\frac{\partial F}{\partial y_n} - \frac{d}{dx}\frac{\partial F}{\partial y_n'} = 0 \quad (n = 1,2,\ldots,N).$$

Example 6-9. To clarify the result obtained above, we can determine the necessary condition which a curve must satisfy in order that the distance measured between two fixed points on the curve is the shortest possible. The distance between (x_1,y_1) and (x_2,y_2) measured along $y = y(x)$ is

$$I[y] = \int_{x_1}^{x_2} \sqrt{1 + y'^2}\, dx.$$

Thus in this case $F(x,y,y') = \sqrt{1 + y'^2}$ is a function of y' only. We therefore have $\partial F/\partial y = 0$, and Euler's equation is

$$-\frac{d}{dx}\frac{\partial}{\partial y'}[1 + y'^2]^{1/2} = 0, \quad \text{or} \quad \frac{d}{dx}\left[\frac{y'}{\sqrt{1 + y'^2}}\right] = 0.$$

This means that $y'/(1 + y'^2)^{1/2}$ is constant, which implies that y' is a constant. The necessary condition that a curve is the shortest path between two points is therefore that the slope of the curve is constant, or, in other words, that the curve is a straight line. $\square$

A weakness in the above argument was that we began by assuming that there existed a function $y(x)$ which made $I[y]$ stationary. This is an important point, as there exist quite simple variational problems which have no solution—for example, that of finding the continuous, piecewise-differentiable function which passes through $(-1,-1)$ and $(1,1)$, and which makes the integral

$$\int_{-1}^{1} x^2 y'^2\, dx$$

as small as possible. It can be shown directly that there is no continuous curve which minimizes the integral. The integral is at once seen to be greater than or equal to zero, since the integrand is positive or zero at every point. But the integral cannot be zero, as this assumes that the integrand is zero at every point $x \neq 0$, which is impossible for a curve of the desired type. The function

$$y(x) = \begin{cases} -1 & \text{for } -1 \leq x \leq -\epsilon, \\ x/\epsilon & \text{for } -\epsilon \leq x \leq \epsilon, \\ 1 & \text{for } \epsilon \leq x \leq 1 \end{cases}$$

will for $0 < \epsilon \leq 1$ be a continuous, piecewise-differentiable function which passes through $(-1, -1)$, and $(1,1)$; i.e., it satisfies the conditions we impose on the function which will give the functional a minimum value. For a fixed value of ϵ, we now have

$$\int_{-1}^{1} x^2 y'^2 \, dx = \int_{-\epsilon}^{\epsilon} \frac{x^2}{\epsilon^2} \, dx = \frac{2\epsilon}{3}.$$

If in this expression we let $\epsilon \to 0$, the functional, which for this special choice of y is a function of ϵ, will also approach zero as its lower limit. The functional can thus take on an arbitrary small positive value; but, as seen from above, it cannot be zero. Thus it does not have a minimum value for any continuous, piecewise-differentiable function.

It has been possible for certain classes of problems to find both necessary and sufficient conditions for variational problems. As this requires more advanced methods, and as it is usually also of minor importance in applications where the existence of a solution generally

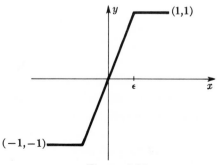

Figure 6-10

is assured by information of a non mathematical nature, it shall not be treated here.

An Application in Classical Mechanics

The so-called *Lagrangian formulation* of classical mechanics gives an important application of the calculus of variations. Consider the one-dimensional motion of a point with mass m in a conservative field of force. Let $x = x(t)$ be the coordinate of the point at time t, and let $V(x)$ be the potential energy of the point mass at x. From *Newton's second law* we have $m\ddot{x} = -\partial V/\partial x$, as the force which acts on the particle is the negative derivative of the potential V (p. 263). The kinetic energy of the particle is $T = \frac{1}{2}m\dot{x}^2$. We now construct a function, the *Lagrangian L*,

$$L = T - V = \tfrac{1}{2}m\dot{x}^2 - V(x).$$

It is then easily verified that the above equation of motion is equivalent to

$$\frac{\partial L}{\partial x} - \frac{d}{dt}\frac{\partial L}{\partial \dot{x}} = 0,$$

which is often called the *Lagrange equation*. Instead of using Newton's second law as the basic law for mechanics, it can therefore be said that the motion of the mechanical system takes place in such a way that the path of the particle between points $x_1 = x(t_1)$ and $x_2 = x(t_2)$ satisfies Lagrange's equation, or, that the integral $\int_{t_1}^{t_2} L\, dt$ is stationary (*Hamilton's principle*).

It is possible from Lagrange's equation to derive yet another formulation of Newton's second law by introducing the so-called *Hamilton function*, or *Hamiltonian*,

$$H = \dot{x}\frac{\partial L}{\partial \dot{x}} - L = H(x,p),$$

where p is $\partial L/\partial \dot{x}$. The Hamiltonian should be considered as a function of x and p only, and this is achieved by eliminating $\dot{x}$ by using the equation defining p. In the simple case which we consider here, we have $p = m\dot{x}$, i.e., p is the momentum, and $H = \dot{x}m\dot{x} - \frac{1}{2}m\dot{x}^2 + V = (p^2/2m) + V(x)$. The Hamiltonian therefore equals the total energy of the system.

We now have $H = \dot{x}p - L$, and therefore also

$$dH = \left(\frac{\partial H}{\partial p}\right) dp + \left(\frac{\partial H}{\partial x}\right) dx$$

$$= \dot{x}\, dp + p\, d\dot{x} - \frac{\partial L}{\partial x} dx - \frac{\partial L}{\partial \dot{x}} d\dot{x} = \dot{x}\, dp - \frac{\partial L}{\partial x} dx = \dot{x}\, dp - \dot{p}\, dx,$$

as by definition $p = \partial L/\partial \dot{x}$ and by Lagrange's equation $\partial L/\partial x = \dot{p}$. Therefore $(\partial H/\partial p - \dot{x})\, dp + (\partial H/\partial x + \dot{p})\, dx$ is equal to zero. As dp and dx are arbitrary changes of p and x, it must be true that

$$\frac{\partial H}{\partial p} = \dot{x},$$

$$\frac{\partial H}{\partial x} = -\dot{p}.$$

These equations are called *Hamilton's equations* and were mentioned previously in connection with coupled differential equations (p. 388). What we have done here is to rewrite a differential equation of the second order in the form of two coupled differential equations of the first order (p. 384). The transformation from the Lagrange equation to the Hamilton equations, which has been illustrated here by an example from physics, is actually a purely mathematical statement independent of Newton's second law. To see this clearly, we shall finally give a general formulation of the result obtained above for $N = 1$.

Let $L(x_1, x_2, \ldots, x_N, \dot{x}_1, \dot{x}_2, \ldots, \dot{x}_N)$ be a function of the N variables $x_1(t), x_2(t), \ldots, x_N(t)$, which all depend on the same parameter t, and their derivatives with respect to this parameter. The necessary conditions for the integral $\int_{t_1}^{t_2} L\, dt$ to be stationary are that

$$\frac{\partial L}{\partial x_n} - \frac{d}{dt}\frac{\partial L}{\partial \dot{x}_n} = 0 \qquad (n = 1, 2, \ldots, N).$$

When these equations are satisfied, it is also true that

$$\frac{\partial H}{\partial x_n} = -\dot{p}_n,$$

$$\frac{\partial H}{\partial p_n} = \dot{x}_n,$$

where $p_n = \partial L/\partial \dot{x}_n$, and $H = H(x_1, \ldots, x_N, p_1, \ldots, p_N)$ is defined by

$$H = \sum_{n=1}^{N} \dot{x}_n p_n - L.$$

Isoperimetric Problems

An important application of the calculus of variations occurs in connection with the so-called *isoperimetric problems*. Here a function is sought which gives a functional an extreme value, and at the same time satisfies another condition which usually has the form that another functional must have a constant value. A classical problem from which the name for this type of problem has arisen is to find the closed curve which for a given perimeter bounds the greatest area.

We wish to find a function $y(x)$ which gives the functional

$$I_1[y] = \int_{x_1}^{x_2} F(x,y,y') \, dx$$

an extreme value, and at the same time satisfies the condition that the functional

$$I_2[y] = \int_{x_1}^{x_2} K(x,y,y') \, dx$$

must have a fixed value.

As an introduction we shall consider the simpler problem of finding the extremum for a function of three variables $u = f(x,y,z)$, given that between the three variables x, y, and z there exists a relation $\phi(x,y,z) = 0$. This problem can be solved by eliminating one of the variables, for example z, in $f(x,y,z)$ with the help of the relation $\phi = 0$. We then obtain $u = g(x,y)$ and its stationary points are obtained by solving the equations

$$(1) \qquad \frac{\partial g}{\partial x} = \frac{\partial f}{\partial x} + \frac{\partial f}{\partial z}\frac{\partial z}{\partial x} = 0,$$

$$(2) \qquad \frac{\partial g}{\partial y} = \frac{\partial f}{\partial y} + \frac{\partial f}{\partial z}\frac{\partial z}{\partial y} = 0,$$

in which $\partial z/\partial x$ and $\partial z/\partial y$ are determined from

$$(3) \qquad \frac{\partial \phi}{\partial x} + \frac{\partial \phi}{\partial z}\frac{\partial z}{\partial x} = 0,$$

$$(4) \qquad \frac{\partial \phi}{\partial y} + \frac{\partial \phi}{\partial z}\frac{\partial z}{\partial y} = 0.$$

On elimination of $\partial z/\partial x$ and $\partial z/\partial y$, it follows from these equations that

$$\begin{vmatrix} \dfrac{\partial f}{\partial x} & \dfrac{\partial f}{\partial z} \\[2mm] \dfrac{\partial \phi}{\partial x} & \dfrac{\partial \phi}{\partial z} \end{vmatrix} = 0 \; [(1) \text{ and } (3)], \qquad \begin{vmatrix} \dfrac{\partial f}{\partial y} & \dfrac{\partial f}{\partial z} \\[2mm] \dfrac{\partial \phi}{\partial y} & \dfrac{\partial \phi}{\partial z} \end{vmatrix} = 0 \; [(2) \text{ and } (4)].$$

It is of course at the same time true that $\phi(x,y,z) = 0$. As $f(x,y,z)$ and $\phi(x,y,z)$ are given functions, it is possible from these last three equations to determine the values of (x,y,z) for which $u = f(x,y,z)$ has a stationary value, while at the same time $\phi(x,y,z) = 0$.

When the equations for the determination of stationary points are written in this form, their solution is identical with the solution to the problem of finding a stationary point for the function $f(x,y,z) - \lambda\phi(x,y,z)$, where λ is an arbitrary number. A necessary condition for this is the following:

$$\frac{\partial f}{\partial x} - \lambda \frac{\partial \phi}{\partial x} = 0, \qquad \frac{\partial f}{\partial y} - \lambda \frac{\partial \phi}{\partial y} = 0, \qquad \frac{\partial f}{\partial z} - \lambda \frac{\partial \phi}{\partial z} = 0.$$

From the last equation we obtain $\lambda = (\partial f/\partial z)/(\partial \phi/\partial z)$. When this is inserted into the first two equations, the equations derived above are obtained.

Hence, if it is desired to find stationary values for $f(x,y,z)$, given that (x,y,z) satisfy $\phi(x,y,z) = 0$, then instead of eliminating z it is only necessary to find the stationary values for the function $f - \lambda\phi$, when $f - \lambda\phi$ is treated as a function of three independent variables. The previously undetermined number λ is called a *Lagrange multiplier;* its values can be determined when the values of x, y, and z are found, for which $f - \lambda\phi$ is stationary.

In an analogous manner, it can now be shown that a necessary condition that $I_1[y]$ has a stationary value, given that $I_2[y]$ has a fixed value, is that $F - \lambda K$ satisfies the Euler equation.

Example 6-10. As an example, we can consider a simplified version of one of the classical isoperimetric problems. We seek the solid of revolution which has the greatest volume for a given area. We imagine that the function $y(x)$ passes through $(0,0)$ and $(a,0)$, $(a > 0)$.

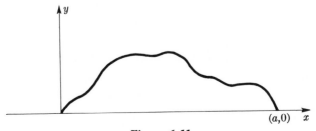

Figure 6-11

The volume of the body obtained on rotating $y(x)$ about the x-axis is

$$I_1[y] = \pi \int_0^a y^2 \, dx,$$

and the surface area is

$$I_2[y] = 2\pi \int_0^a y \sqrt{1 + y'^2} \, dx = A.$$

The function of x, y, and y', which must satisfy the Euler equation, is then

$$G = \pi y^2 - 2\pi \lambda y \sqrt{1 + y'^2}.$$

As this function does not depend on x, we have $G - y'(\partial G/\partial y') = C_1$, where C_1 is a constant (p. 406). This gives

$$y^2 - 2\lambda y \sqrt{1 + y'^2} + 2\lambda y'^2 y \frac{1}{\sqrt{1 + y'^2}} = C,$$

or

$$y^2 - \frac{2\lambda y}{\sqrt{1 + y'^2}} = C.$$

As $y(0) = 0$, C must be zero.

If we now solve for y', we have

$$y' = \pm \frac{\sqrt{4\lambda^2 - y^2}}{y},$$

or

$$\frac{1}{2} \frac{d(y^2)}{dx} = \pm \sqrt{4\lambda^2 - y^2},$$

which on integration gives

$$\mp \sqrt{4\lambda^2 - y^2} = x + C_2.$$

The condition that $y(0)$ must be zero thus necessitates that $C_2 = \pm 2\lambda$, and since λ is undetermined until later, we can choose to set $C_2 = -2\lambda$ and thus $(x - 2\lambda)^2 + y^2 = 4\lambda^2$. Therefore $y = y(x)$ is a circle with center at $(2\lambda,0)$ and radius 2λ. As we began by assuming that the curve passes through $(a,0)$, then $\lambda = a/4$, and the value of a can be expressed in terms of the surface area A by means of the equation $A = 4\pi(a/2)^2 = \pi a^2$.

It must finally be noted that we have only shown that it is a *necessary* condition for a maximum volume that $y = y(x)$ is a semicircle. $\square$

The Inverse Problem

The inverse problem in the calculus of variations will now be treated briefly. We ask if a given differential equation is the Euler equation for a variational problem. Let us specifically study the case where the differential equation is the eigenvalue equation.

$$\mathcal{H}\phi(x) = \lambda\phi(x) \qquad (a \leq x \leq b),$$

where $\mathcal{H}$ is an Hermitian operator, which for simplicity we assume has the form (p. 398)

$$\mathcal{H} = -\frac{d}{dx}\left[p(x)\frac{d}{dx}\right] + q(x),$$

where we use the same boundary conditions as previously, i.e., $p\phi\phi' = 0$ on the boundaries.

We shall now see that this differential equation is the Euler equation corresponding to the variational problem of finding the minimum for the integral

$$\int_a^b \left[p(x)\left(\frac{d\phi}{dx}\right)^2 + q(x)\phi^2\right] dx,$$

given that

$$\int_a^b \phi^2 \, dx = 1.$$

This follows immediately, since the Euler equation is

$$\frac{\partial}{\partial\phi}[p\phi'^2 + q\phi^2 - \lambda\phi^2] - \frac{d}{dx}\frac{\partial}{\partial\phi'}[p\phi'^2 + q\phi^2 - \lambda\phi^2] = 0$$

or

$$\left\{-\frac{d}{dx}\left[p\frac{d}{dx}\right] + q\right\}\phi = \lambda\phi,$$

i.e., $\mathcal{H}\phi = \lambda\phi$.

As we have previously made use of the fact that one of the solutions to $\mathcal{H}\phi = \lambda\phi$ minimizes $\int \phi\mathcal{H}\phi \, dx$ when at the same time $\int \phi^2 \, dx = 1$, it is of interest to see if a relationship exists between these two variational principles. On partial integration we have that

$$\int_a^b \phi \mathcal{H} \phi \, dx = \int_a^b \phi \left\{ -\frac{d}{dx}\left[p(x) \frac{d\phi}{dx} \right] + q\phi \right\} dx$$

$$= -[\phi p(x)\phi']_a^b + \int_a^b [p\phi'^2 + q\phi^2] \, dx,$$

and as previously (p. 398) mentioned, the parentheses vanish at both boundaries, so that

$$\int_a^b \phi \mathcal{H} \phi \, dx = \int_a^b [p\phi'^2 + q\phi^2] \, dx.$$

Thus the two methods of formulating the variational problem are equivalent.

Exercises

*1. Show that the solution to the differential equation

$$\frac{d}{dx}\left(p(x) \frac{dy}{dx} \right) - g(x)y - f(x) = 0,$$

which takes on definite values for $x = a$ and $x = b$, can be found as the function which (for the same fixed boundary conditions) gives an extremum for the integral

$$\int_a^b [py'^2 + gy^2 + 2fy] \, dx.$$

Use this method to solve the equation $y'' + y + x = 0$, $y(0) = y(1) = 0$, approximately by guessing a solution that satisfies the boundary conditions and contains one or more parameters that can be varied; for example,

$$y = x(1 - x)(a_0 + a_1 x + \cdots + a_n x^n) \qquad (n = 1, 2).$$

Compare this with the exact solution.

2. In polar coordinates the distance between two points A and B measured along a curve is

$$I = \int_{(A)}^{(B)} \sqrt{1 + r^2 \left(\frac{d\theta}{dr} \right)^2} \, dr.$$

Show, using this expression, that the shortest distance is along the straight line AB.

*3. Find the Euler equation of the following isoperimetric problem:

$$\int_0^1 xy'^2\, dx \text{ minimum}, \qquad \int_0^1 xy^2\, dx = 1, \qquad y(0) \text{ and } y'(0) \text{ finite}, \; y(1) = 0.$$

Answers

1. The exact solution is $y = (\sin x/\sin 1) - x$. Using $y = a_0 x(1 - x)$: $a_0 = 5/18$. Using $y = x(1 - x)(a_0 + a_1 x)$: $a_0 = 71/369$ and $a_1 = 7/41$.
3. $(d/dx)(x(dy/dx)) + \lambda xy = 0$.

6-7. PARTIAL DIFFERENTIAL EQUATIONS

By a *partial differential equation* we mean an equation between a function of several variables, one or more of its partial derivatives, and the independent variable. In practice, partial differential equations of the second order, often with constant coefficients, are the most important. Without delving into a complete treatment of such equations, we shall now give a few characteristic examples of solutions of partial differential equations with two independent variables. The complete solution to these equations is usually so flexible that not only is it possible to specify that a solution (*an integral surface*) pass through one or more given points, but it may also be made to pass through one or more given curves. Instead of arbitrary constants, the complete solution of a partial differential equation will usually contain *arbitrary functions*.

Example 6-11. $x(\partial z/\partial x) + y(\partial z/\partial y) = 0$ has as a solution $z = \Phi(x/y)$, where Φ is an arbitrary function of one variable. This is shown by differentiation:

$$x\frac{\partial z}{\partial x} + y\frac{\partial z}{\partial y} = x\frac{1}{y}\Phi' - y\frac{x}{y^2}\Phi' = 0.$$

As the normal vector to the surface $z = z(x,y)$ at the point $(x,y,z(x,y))$ is $(\partial z/\partial x,\, \partial z/\partial y,\, -1)$, the geometrical condition imposed on the function z by the differential equation is that the vector $(x,y,0)$ at every point on the surface is perpendicular to the local normal vector, and thus is contained in the tangent plane of the surface at the point. In Fig. 6-12 it is shown geometrically how a solution is found which contains the curve k.

An example of a surface of this type has been previously considered (p. 312). □

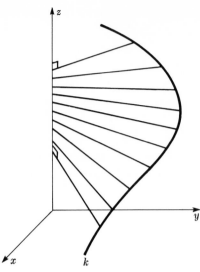

Figure 6-12

Example 6-12. The differential equation for a string which is stretched along the x-axis and in time carries out vibrations in an XU-plane is

$$\frac{\partial^2 u}{\partial x^2} = \frac{1}{c^2}\frac{\partial^2 u}{\partial t^2}.$$

Here $u(x,t)$ designates the deviation of the string from the equilibrium position at the point with coordinate x at time t. The wave velocity c is $\sqrt{s/m}$, where s is the tension of the string and m the mass per unit length.

When we consider a solution in the interval $-\infty < x < \infty$, $0 < t < \infty$, it is seen by differentiation that an arbitrary function with the argument $(x - ct)$ or $(x + ct)$ is a solution. The complete solution is

$$u = \phi_1(x - ct) + \phi_2(x + ct),$$

where ϕ_1 and ϕ_2 are arbitrary functions of one variable corresponding to waves of arbitrary shape which move with velocity c in the same and opposite directions as the positive direction of the X-axis, respectively.

In the more interesting case, where the string is fixed at both ends, i.e., $u(0,t) = u(L,t) = 0$ for all t, the so-called *separation of variables* is used. We attempt to solve the equation by setting $u = X(x)T(t)$, where X is a function of x only and T is a function of t only. Inserting in the equation we obtain

$$TX'' = \frac{1}{c^2} X\ddot{T} \qquad \text{or} \qquad \frac{\ddot{T}}{c^2 T} = \frac{X''}{X}.$$

As the left side now depends only on t and the right side only on x, they can be equal for all t and x only if they are both equal to a constant, which must be negative because of the boundary conditions. We shall denote this constant by $-\lambda$, so that λ is positive. We then have $X'' = -\lambda X$. From the boundary conditions, $X(0) = X(L) = 0$, we have (p. 396)

$$\lambda = \frac{n^2\pi^2}{L^2} \qquad \text{and} \qquad X = C_n \sin \frac{n\pi}{L} x.$$

Thus λ is determined from the boundary conditions.

The value for λ found in this manner is used in the equation for T, which is solved to give

$$T = A_n \cos \frac{n\pi}{L} ct + B_n \sin \frac{n\pi}{L} ct.$$

Any expression of the form

$$\left(a_n \cos \frac{n\pi}{L} ct + b_n \sin \frac{n\pi}{L} ct \right) \sin \frac{n\pi}{L} x$$

is therefore a solution. By using the fact that the trigonometric functions form a complete orthogonal system, it can be shown that the complete solution is

$$\sum_{n=1}^{\infty} \left(a_n \cos \frac{n\pi}{L} ct + b_n \sin \frac{n\pi}{L} ct \right) \sin \frac{n\pi}{L} x.$$

The individual solutions represent standing waves with the period τ, where

$$\frac{\pi nc}{L} \tau = 2\pi \qquad \text{or} \qquad \tau = \frac{2L}{nc}.$$

The coefficients a_n and b_n can be determined if the initial conditions for the string are known, i.e., if $u(x,0)$ and $(\partial u/\partial t)_{t=0}$ are known functions of x. It follows from the solution given above that their Fourier expansions (which are uniquely determined) will be

$$\sum_{n=1}^{\infty} a_n \sin \frac{n\pi}{L} x \quad \text{and} \quad \sum_{n=1}^{\infty} \frac{n\pi}{L} cb_n \sin \frac{n\pi}{L} x,$$

respectively.

If for example the string at time 0 is stretched as shown in Fig. 6-13 and is not in motion, then $b_n = 0$ (for all n) and a_n is determined from the fact that the above function (continued as an odd function in the interval $[-L, 0]$) has the Fourier expansion

$$\frac{8h}{\pi^2} \left\{ \sin \frac{\pi x}{L} - \frac{1}{9} \sin \frac{3\pi x}{L} + \frac{1}{25} \sin \frac{5\pi x}{L} + \cdots \right\}.$$

The solution to the differential equation thus becomes

$$u = \frac{8h}{\pi^2} \left\{ \cos \frac{\pi ct}{L} \sin \frac{\pi}{L} x - \frac{1}{9} \cos \frac{3\pi ct}{L} \sin \frac{3\pi x}{L} \right.$$
$$\left. + \frac{1}{25} \cos \frac{5\pi ct}{L} \sin \frac{5\pi x}{L} \cdots \right\}. \qquad \Box$$

Example 6-13. $\partial c / \partial t = D(\partial^2 c / \partial x^2)$ is the equation for one-dimensional diffusion, when $c(x,t)$ is the concentration at the point x at the time t and D is a positive constant. The solution for diffusion in a region $0 \leq x \leq L$, $t > 0$ can be found in the same way as shown above, giving when $c(0,t) = c(L,t) = 0$,

$$c = \sum_{n=1}^{\infty} k_n \sin \left(\frac{n\pi}{L} x \right) \exp \left(- \frac{n^2 \pi^2}{L^2} Dt \right).$$

More often one is interested in the solution in the interval $-\infty < x < \infty$, $t > 0$, which has the property that for $t = 0$ the total amount

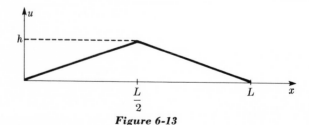

Figure 6-13

of material P is gathered at a point $x = 0$. This solution is

$$\frac{c}{P} = \frac{1}{\sqrt{4\pi Dt}} e^{-x^2/4Dt} = f(x,t),$$

which on substitution is seen to satisfy the differential equation. Furthermore, $\int_{-\infty}^{\infty} c(x,t)\, dx = P$ at every time $t > 0$.

For $t \to 0$, the function on the right side will approach zero when $x \neq 0$, and infinity when $x = 0$. The limiting function corresponding to this is the so-called δ-*function*, $\delta(x)$. It is not a function in the usual sense, but a so-called *"generalized function"* and in the present case the meaning of this statement can be made particularly clear. Even though $\delta(x)$ is not a function, we see that its integral, given by

$$\int_{-\infty}^{\infty} \delta(x)\, dx = \lim_{t \to 0} \int_{-\infty}^{\infty} \frac{1}{\sqrt{4\pi Dt}} e^{-x^2/4Dt}\, dx = 1,$$

is a well-defined quantity. When $t \to 0$, the integrand will become very large at $x = 0$ and simultaneously very small at all other places. For a fixed value $t = t_0$, for every $\epsilon > 0$, an $\eta(>0)$ can be chosen such that

$$\int_{-\eta}^{\eta} f(x,t_0)\, dx > 1 - \epsilon.$$

When $t_0 \to 0$, for a fixed ϵ the necessary value for η will become smaller and smaller. It is thus intuitively reasonable to say that for $t = 0$, the integrand will be a function which is equal to zero for $x \neq 0$, and that the integral $\int \delta(x)\, dx$ over an arbitrary interval around 0 is 1. However, it must be remembered that this function is only a shorthand notation for an exchange of a limiting process and an integration, and that the δ-function really has no meaning unless an integration over its argument is finally carried out.

By identifying the δ-function with the above limiting value, it can be shown that the δ-function satisfies the following equations:

$$\int_{-\infty}^{\infty} F(x)\delta(x - a)\, dx = F(a), \qquad \int_{-\infty}^{\infty} F(x)\delta(cx)\, dx = \frac{1}{|c|} F(0).$$

Here $F(x)$ is an arbitrary function which must be integrable from $-\infty$ to $+\infty$, and c is a constant. $\quad\square$

Exercises

1. Show by a geometrical argument that every differentiable function of the form $z = f(x^2 + y^2)$ satisfies the differential equation

$$y \frac{\partial z}{\partial x} - x \frac{\partial z}{\partial y} = 0.$$

2. Let a space be filled with a homogeneous material in which the temperature T at an arbitrary point is dependent only on its abscissa x and the time t. In Fig. 6-14 (1) and (2) mark a pair of plane surfaces (with area A) perpendicular to the X-axis and separated by a distance l. When these are permanently held at temperatures T_1 and T_2, respectively, then the amount of heat transported from (1) to (2) during a time Δt will be

$$\Delta Q = k \frac{T_1 - T_2}{l} A \, \Delta t,$$

where the constant k is the thermal conductivity of the material considered.

When a designates the density of the material and c its heat capacity, show that the temperature function $T = T(x,t)$ will satisfy the differential equation

$$\frac{\partial T}{\partial t} = \frac{k}{ac} \frac{\partial^2 T}{\partial x^2}.$$

*3. Find the Laplace transform of

$$f(x) = \begin{cases} 0 & 0 \le x < x_1, \\ h & x_1 \le x \le x_2, \\ 0 & x_2 < x, \end{cases}$$

and then consider the limiting process x_1 fixed, $x_2 - x_1 \to 0$, $h \to \infty$, $(x_2 - x_1)h = 1$. Thus $f(x)$ becomes the function $\delta(x - x_1)$ discussed above.

*4. Show that the δ-function $\delta(x)$ can be considered as the derivative with respect to x of the function

$$U(x) = \begin{cases} 0 & \text{for } x < 0, \\ 1 & \text{for } x > 0. \end{cases}$$

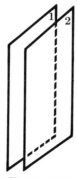

Figure 6-14

5. Show the following:

(a) $x\delta'(x) = -\delta(x)$.

(b) $\delta(x^2 - a^2) = \dfrac{1}{2a}\,(\delta(x - a) + \delta(x + a))$ $(a > 0)$.

*6. Solve the following differential equations both directly and by using the Laplace transformation:

(a) $\dfrac{dx}{dt} + x = 0,$

(b) $\dfrac{dx}{dt} + x = e^{-t},$ $x(0) = 1.$

(c) $\dfrac{dx}{dt} + x = \delta(t - 1)$

Answers

3. $Lf(y) = h[\exp(-yx_1) - \exp(-yx_2)]/y$

     $[L\delta(x - x_1)](y) = \lim_{x_2 \to x_1} Lf(y) = \exp(-yx_1)$

4. $[LU(x - x_1)](y) = (1/y)\exp(-x_1 y) = y^{-1}[L\delta(x - x_1)](y).$ (See Exercise 3.)

6. (a) $x = e^{-t}$.   (b) $x = e^{-t}(1 + t)$.   (c) $x = e^{-t}(1 + e^{-1}U(t - 1))$. (See Exercise 4.)

7

Complex Functions

7-1. COMPLEX-VALUED FUNCTIONS OF ONE COMPLEX VARIABLE

Complex Numbers

In previous chapters we have several times had occasion to use complex numbers. For instance, in connection with matrices (p. 90), the exponential function (p. 223), Fourier series (p. 349), and second-order differential equations (p. 381). On page 221 the concept of a complex-valued function of one complex variable was introduced. It is the theory of such functions which we shall now consider, and it is this application of complex numbers which shows, even more than those mentioned above, that complex numbers are indeed very useful.

As an introduction we state some basic facts about complex numbers. Any complex number z can be written in a unique way as $x + iy$, where x and y are real numbers; x is called *the real part* of z [$\text{Re}(z)$], y *the imaginary part* of z [$\text{Im}(z)$]. In a usual right-angled coordinate system z is represented by the point (x,y). If (r,θ) are polar coordinates of this point, then r is the absolute value or the modulus of z ($r = |z| = \text{mod } z$), while θ is an argument of z (Fig. 7-1):

$$z = x + iy = r(\cos \theta + i \sin \theta) = re^{i\theta}.$$

Even if $r > 0$, the argument of z is only determined to a multiple of 2π.

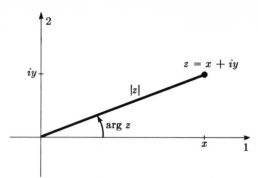

Figure 7-1

For *the principal argument* of z we shall write arg z $(-\pi < \arg z \leq \pi)$. The complex conjugate of z is

$$z^* = x - iy = r(\cos \theta - i \sin \theta) = re^{-i\theta}.$$

For any two complex numbers z_1 and z_2 we have

$$z_1 + z_2 = (x_1 + iy_1) + (x_2 + iy_2) = (x_1 + x_2) + i(y_1 + y_2),$$
$$z_1 z_2 = (x_1 + iy_1)(x_2 + iy_2) = (x_1 x_2 - y_1 y_2) + i(x_1 y_2 + x_2 y_1)$$
$$= r_1 e^{i\theta_1} r_2 e^{i\theta_2} = r_1 r_2 e^{i(\theta_1 + \theta_2)},$$
$$|z_1 z_2| = |z_1| \, |z_2|,$$

arg $(z_1 z_2)$ = arg z_1 + arg z_2 (except possibly for multiples of 2π).

For the n nth roots of $z = re^{i\theta}$, we have

$$\sqrt[n]{z} = z^{1/n} = r^{1/n} e^{i(\theta + 2k\pi)/n} \qquad (k = 0,1,2,\ldots,n-1).$$

It should be noted that any nth root of z is written $\sqrt[n]{z}$ (or $z^{1/n}$). Finally, we mention that the absolute value of z may be obtained as the nonnegative real number $\sqrt{zz^*}$.

Sequences and Series

The notion of an (infinite) sequence was introduced on page 134. A *sequence of complex numbers* $z_1, z_2, \ldots, z_n, \ldots$ is (of course) said to be convergent with the limit z_0 ($z_n \to z_0$ as $n \to \infty$ or $\lim_{n \to \infty} z_n = z_0$) in case it is possible corresponding to any positive real number ϵ to determine a number N such that $|z_n - z_0| < \epsilon$ for every $n > N$. From this definition it follows that a sequence z_n converges to z_0 if and only if $\text{Re}(z_n)$ converges to $\text{Re}(z_0)$ and $\text{Im}(z_n)$ converges to $\text{Im}(z_0)$. It also follows that when two sequences z_n and w_n are convergent with limits z_0 and w_0, so are the sequences $z_n \pm w_n$, $z_n w_n$, and z_n/w_n, with limits $z_0 \pm w_0$, $z_0 w_0$, and z_0/w_0, respectively—in the last case with the obvious provision that the elements and the limit of the latter sequence must be different from zero.

What was said on page 319 regarding infinite series of real numbers is immediately carried over to the more general case of infinite *series of complex numbers*. Thus a series $z_1 + z_2 + \cdots + z_k + \cdots$ or $\Sigma_{k=1}^{\infty} z_k$ is said to be convergent with the sum S_0 if the sequence of partial sums $S_n \ (= \Sigma_{k=1}^{n} z_k)$ converges to S_0. From this it follows that the series $\Sigma_{k=1}^{\infty} z_k$ converges to S_0 if and only if $\Sigma_{k=1}^{\infty} \mathrm{Re}(z_k)$ converges to $\mathrm{Re}(S_0)$ and $\Sigma_{k=1}^{\infty} \mathrm{Im}(z_k)$ converges to $\mathrm{Im}(S_0)$.

The (complex) series $\Sigma_{k=1}^{\infty} z_k$ is said to be absolutely convergent if the corresponding (real) series of absolute values $\Sigma_{k=1}^{\infty} |z_k|$ is convergent. It can be shown that absolute convergence of a series implies convergence. As the absolute convergence of a complex series depends solely on the convergence of a real series with positive (nonnegative) terms, it follows that the comparison test, the root test, and the ratio test (p. 321) may be applied also here. Finally we mention that the rules about multiplication and inversion of series can be taken over in the form in which they were stated for real series.

Example 7-1. Consider the geometric series

$$\sum_{k=1}^{\infty} aq^{k-1} = a + aq + aq^2 + \cdots ,$$

where $a(\neq 0)$ and q are given complex numbers (cf. Example 5-1, p. 320). For $|q| \geq 1$ the series is divergent, as the nth term then does not tend to zero as n tends to infinity. For $|q| < 1$ the series is convergent with the sum $a/(1 - q)$. This follows immediately from the formula

$$S_n = \sum_{k=1}^{n} aq^{k-1} = a \frac{1 - q^n}{1 - q}$$

valid for any a and for any $q \neq 1$. Obviously, the series is also absolutely convergent when $|q| < 1$.

Let us consider more closely the case $a = 1$, $q = -\frac{1}{4} + i(\sqrt{3}/4)$:

$$\sum_{k=1}^{\infty} \left(-\frac{1}{4} + i\frac{\sqrt{3}}{4}\right)^{k-1} = 1 + \left(-\frac{1}{4} + i\frac{\sqrt{3}}{4}\right) + \left(-\frac{1}{4} + i\frac{\sqrt{3}}{4}\right)^2$$

$$+ \cdots = \frac{5}{7} + i\frac{\sqrt{3}}{7}.$$

From $|q| = \frac{1}{2}$ and arg $q = 2\pi/3$ we get $q^n = (1/2^n)[\cos(2n\pi/3) + i\sin(2n\pi/3)]$. For the "real part" of the series we therefore obtain

$$1 - \tfrac{1}{4} - \tfrac{1}{8} + \tfrac{1}{8} - \tfrac{1}{32} - \tfrac{1}{64} - \tfrac{1}{64} - \cdots$$

$$= 1 - \tfrac{1}{4}(1 + \tfrac{1}{8} + \cdots) = 1 - \tfrac{1}{4}\frac{1}{1-\frac{1}{8}} = \tfrac{5}{7},$$

and for the "imaginary part" of the series,

$$0 + \frac{\sqrt{3}}{4} - \frac{\sqrt{3}}{8} + 0 + \frac{\sqrt{3}}{32} - \frac{\sqrt{3}}{64} + 0 + \cdots$$

$$= \frac{\sqrt{3}}{8}\left(1 + \frac{1}{8} + \cdots\right) = \frac{\sqrt{3}}{8}\frac{1}{1-\frac{1}{8}} = \frac{\sqrt{3}}{7}.$$

In agreement with the above theory we have thus found—by direct calculation—that the sum of the real (imaginary) part of the original series equals the real (imaginary) part of its sum.   □

Limits and Continuity

Consider now a complex-valued function f of one complex variable, which we shall denote briefly as a *complex function*. Using z as the independent variable and w as the dependent variable, we have $w = f(z)$. Furthermore, introducing $x = \mathrm{Re}(z)$, $y = \mathrm{Im}(z)$, $u = \mathrm{Re}(w)$, and $v = \mathrm{Im}(w)$, we also have $u + iv = f(x + iy)$. It follows that u as well as v are real-valued functions of two real variables:

$$u = \mathrm{Re}(f(x + iy)), \qquad v = \mathrm{Im}(f(x + iy)).$$

Conversely, given two such functions $u = u(x,y)$ and $v = v(x,y)$ with a common domain, they determine a complex function

$$f(x + iy) = u(x,y) + iv(x,y).$$

We shall often use this correspondence between complex functions of one variable and pairs of real functions of two variables. It will then become an important task to find those special conditions which must be satisfied by a pair of real functions in order that the corresponding complex function has certain properties (to be defined below) such as that of being continuous or differentiable.

Graphically a complex function may be looked upon as a mapping of points in one complex plane (the XY-plane) onto points in another complex plane (the UV-plane). In view of this a geometric terminology is generally used in describing the domain as well as the range of a complex function (see p. 226).

The concepts of limit and continuity of complex functions are introduced in close analogy to the corresponding concepts for other types of functions (see, for example, p. 136 and p. 227). Consider the complex function $w = f(z)$ defined in a deleted neighborhood of the point z_0. The function f is then said to have the *limit* c at the point $z_0 (f(z) \to c$ as $z \to z_0$ or $\lim_{z \to z_0} f(z) = c$) when for any (complex) sequence, which is within the domain of f and does not contain z_0, but converges to z_0, it is true that the corresponding (complex) sequence of f-values converges to c. Equivalent to this definition is the following, which does not make use of the notion of a sequence: $f(z) \to c$ as $z \to z_0$ when for any real $\epsilon > 0$ there exists a real $\delta > 0$ such that $|f(z) - c| < \epsilon$ whenever $0 < |z - z_0| < \delta$. Geometrically this latter definition says that the set of points in the domain of f which are mapped into any given neighborhood of c always has to contain a deleted neighborhood of z_0 (Fig. 7-2).

The function f is furthermore said to be *continuous* at the point z_0 if it is also defined at z_0 and its limit at z_0 is $f(z_0)$, i.e., if $f(z) \to f(z_0)$ as $z \to z_0$. If f is continuous at every point of some region, f is said to be continuous in that region. Simple calculations show that sums, differences, products, and quotients (except for division by zero) of continuous functions are continuous themselves, as are functions obtained by composition of continuous functions. Finally we mention the important fact that the function $f(x + iy) = u(x,y) + iv(x,y)$ is continuous at the point $x_0 + iy_0$ if and only if the two real functions $u(x,y)$ and $v(x,y)$ are continuous at the point (x_0,y_0).

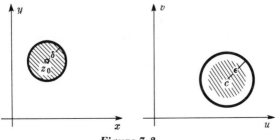

Figure 7-2

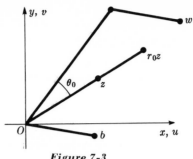

Figure 7-3

Example 7-2. As a simple example of a continuous function we consider the linear function $w = az + b$ with the set of all complex numbers as its domain. Here $a(= r_0 e^{i\theta_0})$ and b are given complex numbers. Graphing z and w in the same complex plane, we can give a simple geometric interpretation of the function. The image of z is obtained from z by a geometric multiplication about O followed by a rotation around O and a translation (Fig. 7-3). ☐

Exercises

1. Show that for any complex number $z = x + iy$ it holds that

$$\frac{1}{\sqrt{2}}(|x| + |y|) \le |x + iy| \le |x| + |y|.$$

*2. Show that the function

$$w = (x^2 - y^2 - 2xy - y) + i(x^2 - y^2 + 2xy + x)$$

can be written as a polynomial in z.

*3. Determine the convergence radius for the following series:

$$\sum_{n=1}^{\infty} \frac{z^n}{n^3}; \quad \sum_{n=0}^{\infty} \frac{z^{n^2}}{n!}; \quad \sum_{n=0}^{\infty} n!z^n.$$

4. Show that the function $w = (z + 2)/(z - 1)$ in general maps a circle in the XY-plane into a circle in the UV-plane. Are there any exceptions?
5. Two complex variables $z = x + iy$ and $w = u + iv$ are related by $z^2 = w$. Determine the curve in the complex plane described by the point w when the point z follows the curves (a) $x = c$. (b) $y = c$. (c) $x - y = 0$. (d) $x^2 + y^2 = 1$.

Answers
2. $w = (1 + i)z^2 + iz$.
3. $\lambda = 1; \lambda = 1; \lambda = 0$.

7-2. *DIFFERENTIATION AND INTEGRATION*

Derivatives and Differentials

The complex function $w = f(z)$ defined in a neighborhood of the point z_0 is said to be *differentiable* at z_0 if the difference quotient

$$\frac{\Delta w}{\Delta z} = \frac{f(z_0 + \Delta z) - f(z_0)}{\Delta z}$$

has a limit as Δz approaches 0. The limit is called the *differential quotient* or the *derivative* of f at the point z_0, and is written $f'(z_0)$. If f has a continuous derivative at every point of some open region, f is said to be *analytic* in that region.

The above is seen to correspond rather closely to what was said about differentiability in connection with real functions of one variable (see p. 145). Corresponding to what was obtained then we immediately get the following results valid for any complex z_0: $f(z) = $ constant gives $f'(z_0) = 0$, $f(z) = z$ gives $f'(z_0) = 1$, $f(z) = z^n$ gives $f'(z_0) = nz_0^{n-1}$. Furthermore, it is easily seen that a complex function f is differentiable at the point z_0 with the derivative $f'(z_0)$, if and only if

$$\Delta w = f'(z_0) \, \Delta z + o(\Delta z),$$

where $o(\Delta z)/\Delta z \to 0$ as $\Delta z \to 0$. As before, this gives rise to the introduction of a *differential: dw* $= f'(z_0) \, \Delta z$, and another way of writing the derivative: $f'(z_0) = dw/dz$. Also the rules for differentiation of sums, differences, products, and quotients, as well as the law for differentiation of composite functions, will hold in the form stated previously. It is also clear, however, that for a function of a complex variable, differentiability is a much more stringent requirement than for a function of a real variable, since z in the complex plane (so to speak) can approach z_0 from all directions, and it is required that the derivative be independent of this direction of approach. We shall now explore the consequences of this in more detail.

Suppose f is analytic in an open region w, and let z_0 be an arbitrary point of w. Rewriting the function considered as $f(x + iy) = u(x,y) + iv(x,y)$, we have the following expression for the difference quotient of f at the point $z_0 = x_0 + iy_0$:

$$\frac{\Delta w}{\Delta z} =$$

$$\frac{u(x_0 + \Delta x, y_0 + \Delta y) + iv(x_0 + \Delta x, y_0 + \Delta y) - u(x_0,y_0) - iv(x_0,y_0)}{\Delta x + i \, \Delta y}.$$

Choosing $\Delta y = 0$, we have

$$\frac{dw}{dz} = \lim_{\Delta x \to 0} \frac{(u(x_0 + \Delta x, y_0) - u(x_0,y_0)) + i(v(x_0 + \Delta x, y_0) - v(x_0,y_0))}{\Delta x}$$

$$= \frac{\partial u}{\partial x} + i\frac{\partial v}{\partial x}.$$

We can say that the derivative has been obtained by letting Δz approach zero through real values. Correspondingly, if we let Δz approach zero through purely imaginary values, we obtain

$$\frac{dw}{dz} = \lim_{\Delta y \to 0} \frac{(u(x_0, y_0 + \Delta y) - u(x_0,y_0)) + i(v(x_0, y_0 + \Delta y) - v(x_0,y_0))}{i\,\Delta y}$$

$$= \frac{\partial v}{\partial y} - i\frac{\partial u}{\partial y}.$$

Equating the two final expressions for dw/dz we find

$$\frac{\partial u}{\partial x} = \frac{\partial v}{\partial y} \quad \text{and} \quad \frac{\partial u}{\partial y} = -\frac{\partial v}{\partial x}.$$

These two equations, which are usually called the *Cauchy-Riemann equations*, are therefore necessary conditions for $w = f(z)$ to be analytic. By a slightly more elaborate, but perfectly straightforward argument, one can show that a sufficient condition for a complex function $w = f(z)$ to be analytic in an open region is that the above four partial derivatives are continuous and satisfy the Cauchy-Riemann equations in that region. The Cauchy-Riemann equations may be replaced by other equations. A more general condition is that the directional derivatives of the real part of w in directions specified by the unit vectors $\mathbf{n}_1$ and $\mathbf{n}_2 = \hat{\mathbf{n}}_1$ in the XY-plane are equal to the directional derivatives of the imaginary part of w in the directions specified by $\hat{\mathbf{n}}_1$ and $\hat{\mathbf{n}}_2$, respectively. The Cauchy-Riemann equations stated above then correspond to the particular choices $\mathbf{n}_1 = (1,0)$ and $\mathbf{n}_2 = (0,1)$ in the more general condition.

To prove the more general assertion we shall temporarily introduce ϕ'_θ as a short way of writing the directional derivative of a function $\phi(x,y)$ in the direction given by the unit vector $(\cos \theta, \sin \theta)$. We then have for any θ (see p. 238)

$$u'_\theta = \frac{\partial u}{\partial x}\cos \theta + \frac{\partial u}{\partial y}\sin \theta \quad \text{and} \quad v'_{\theta+(\pi/2)} = -\frac{\partial v}{\partial x}\sin \theta + \frac{\partial v}{\partial y}\cos \theta.$$

It follows immediately from the Cauchy-Riemann equations that if the function we consider is analytic, then $u'_\theta = v'_{\theta+(\pi/2)}$ for any θ, in particular for two values θ_0 and $\theta_0 + (\pi/2)$. Conversely, suppose we have

$$u'_{\theta_0} = v'_{\theta_0+(\pi/2)} \qquad \text{and} \qquad u'_{\theta_0+(\pi/2)} = v'_{\theta_0+\pi}$$

for some θ_0, i.e.,

$$\frac{\partial u}{\partial x} \cos \theta_0 + \frac{\partial u}{\partial y} \sin \theta_0 = -\frac{\partial v}{\partial x} \sin \theta_0 + \frac{\partial v}{\partial y} \cos \theta_0$$

and

$$-\frac{\partial u}{\partial x} \sin \theta_0 + \frac{\partial u}{\partial y} \cos \theta_0 = -\frac{\partial v}{\partial x} \cos \theta_0 - \frac{\partial v}{\partial y} \sin \theta_0.$$

Eliminating $\cos \theta_0$ and $\sin \theta_0$ we obtain

$$\frac{\partial u}{\partial x} = \frac{\partial v}{\partial y} \qquad \text{and} \qquad \frac{\partial u}{\partial y} = -\frac{\partial v}{\partial x},$$

which shows that the function is analytic.

A real function $\phi(x,y)$ of two real variables is said to be *harmonic* if it satisfies the following partial differential equation:

$$\frac{\partial^2 \phi}{\partial x^2} + \frac{\partial^2 \phi}{\partial y^2} = 0.$$

It follows immediately from the Cauchy-Riemann equations that the real part $u(x,y)$ as well as the imaginary part $v(x,y)$ of an analytic function is harmonic:

$$\frac{\partial^2 u}{\partial x^2} + \frac{\partial^2 u}{\partial y^2} = \frac{\partial^2 v}{\partial y\,\partial x} - \frac{\partial^2 v}{\partial x\,\partial y} = 0,$$

$$\frac{\partial^2 v}{\partial x^2} + \frac{\partial^2 v}{\partial y^2} = -\frac{\partial^2 u}{\partial y\,\partial x} + \frac{\partial^2 u}{\partial x\,\partial y} = 0.$$

So far we have written the independent variable as $z = x + iy$ and corresponding to this we have been working with the real and the imaginary parts of $f(z)$ as functions of x and y: $f(z) = u(x,y) + iv(x,y)$. Suppose now that we introduce polar coordinates in the plane of the independent variable, writing z as $re^{i\theta}$. The real and the imaginary parts of $f(z)$ will then appear as functions of r and θ. Explicit expressions for these new functions may be obtained from the former ones by replacing x by $r \cos \theta$ and y by $r \sin \theta$. As a result we then get $f(z) = u(r,\theta) + iv(r,\theta)$.

Now suppose that $w = f(z)$ is differentiable at the point $z = re^{i\theta}$. As a general expression for the difference quotient we then have

$$\frac{\Delta w}{\Delta z} = \frac{u(r + \Delta r, \theta + \Delta\theta) + iv(r + \Delta r, \theta + \Delta\theta) - u(r,\theta) - iv(r,\theta)}{(r + \Delta r)e^{i(\theta + \Delta\theta)} - re^{i\theta}}.$$

Here choosing $\Delta\theta = 0$ we get

$$\frac{dw}{dz} = \lim_{\Delta r \to 0} \frac{u(r + \Delta r, \theta) - u(r,\theta) + i(v(r + \Delta r, \theta) - v(r,\theta))}{\Delta r\, e^{i\theta}}$$

$$= e^{-i\theta}\left(\frac{\partial u}{\partial r} + i\frac{\partial v}{\partial r}\right).$$

To obtain a suitable version of the (generalized) Cauchy-Riemann equations we choose $\mathbf{n}_1 = (\cos\theta, \sin\theta)$ and consequently $\mathbf{n}_2 = (-\sin\theta, \cos\theta)$, giving

$$\frac{\partial u}{\partial r} = \frac{1}{r}\frac{\partial v}{\partial \theta} \quad \text{and} \quad \frac{1}{r}\frac{\partial u}{\partial \theta} = -\frac{\partial v}{\partial r}.$$

It follows from this that dw/dz just as well might have been written

$$\frac{dw}{dz} = e^{-i\theta}\frac{1}{r}\left(\frac{\partial v}{\partial \theta} - i\frac{\partial u}{\partial \theta}\right),$$

which of course also would result from the above general expression for $\Delta w/\Delta z$ by choosing $\Delta r = 0$.

Example 7-3. For the very simple analytic function $w = z^2$ we have, as already mentioned, $dw/dz = 2z$. Introducing $z = x + iy$ we find $u(x,y) = x^2 - y^2$ and $v(x,y) = 2xy$, giving $\partial u/\partial x = 2x$, $\partial u/\partial y = -2y$, $\partial v/\partial x = 2y$, and $\partial v/\partial y = 2x$. In agreement with the theory, these partial derivatives satisfy the Cauchy-Riemann equations. Also, the above two formulas for dw/dz in terms of partial derivatives are seen to be valid. Introducing $z = re^{i\theta}$ we find $u(r,\theta) = r^2 \cos 2\theta$ and $v(r,\theta) = r^2 \sin 2\theta$, giving $\partial u/\partial r = 2r \cos 2\theta$, $\partial u/\partial\theta = -2r^2 \sin 2\theta$, $\partial v/\partial r = 2r \sin 2\theta$, and $\partial v/\partial\theta = 2r^2 \cos 2\theta$, in agreement with the theory. A general view of the function considered may be obtained by graphing a number of curves $u(x,y) = $ constant and $v(x,y) = $ constant in the XY-plane (Fig. 7-4). □

Integrals

Let $w = f(z)$ be a complex function continuous in an open region ω, and let k be a differentiable curve belonging to ω and given by a com-

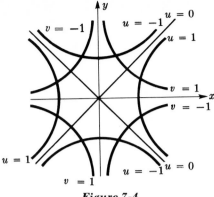

Figure 7-4

plex-valued function of one real variable $z = x(t) + iy(t)$, $\alpha \le t \le \beta$. $A = (x(\alpha),y(\alpha))$ is the initial point of k; $B = (x(\beta),y(\beta))$ is the terminal point of k. The parametric interval $[\alpha,\beta]$ is now divided into n subintervals of lengths $\Delta_j t$ $(j = 1,2,\ldots,n)$ and in each of these a point t_j is chosen. In this way k becomes divided into n smaller curve segments, each of these containing one point $Q_j = (x(t_j),y(t_j))$. Introducing $\Delta_j z = \Delta_j x + i\,\Delta_j y$ as the difference between the complex numbers corresponding to the terminal point and the initial point of the jth segment of k and furthermore $z_j = x_j + iy_j$ as the complex number corresponding to the point Q_j, we then consider the following average sum (Fig. 7-5):

$$\sum_{j=1}^{n} f(z_j)\,\Delta_j z = \sum_{j=1}^{n} (u(x_j,y_j) + iv(x_j,y_j))(\Delta_j x + i\,\Delta_j y)$$

$$= \sum_{j=1}^{n} (u(x_j,y_j)\,\Delta_j x - v(x_j,y_j)\,\Delta_j y)$$

$$+ i\sum_{j=1}^{n} (v(x_j,y_j)\,\Delta_j x + u(x_j,y_j)\,\Delta_j y).$$

A comparison with page 255 immediately shows that the average sum considered will have a certain limit as n tends to infinity if only the length of the greatest t-subinterval approaches zero at the same time, and also that this limit may be expressed by means of line integrals as

$$\int_k u(x,y)\,dx - v(x,y)\,dy + i\int_k v(x,y)\,dx + u(x,y)\,dy.$$

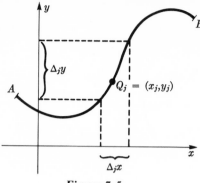

Figure 7-5

This limit is called *the (complex) integral of f along k* and is usually written

$$\int_k f(z)\, dz \qquad \text{or} \qquad \int_k (u(x,y) + iv(x,y))(dx + i\, dy).$$

The problem of evaluating such an integral is thus reduced to that of evaluating two definite integrals of real functions:

$$\int_k f(z)\, dz = \int_\alpha^\beta \left(u(x(t),y(t))\, \frac{dx}{dt} - v(x(t),y(t))\, \frac{dy}{dt} \right) dt$$

$$+ i \int_\alpha^\beta \left(v(x(t),y(t))\, \frac{dx}{dt} + u(x(t),y(t))\, \frac{dy}{dt} \right) dt,$$

or to one definite integral of a complex function of one real variable (cf. p. 222):

$$\int_k f(z)\, dz = \int_\alpha^\beta f(x(t) + iy(t)) \left(\frac{dx}{dt} + i \frac{dy}{dt} \right) dt$$

$$= \int_\alpha^\beta f(z(t))\, \frac{dz}{dt}\, dt.$$

If the path of integration is only piecewise-differentiable, the integral is defined as the sum of the integrals along the differentiable parts.

Introducing G such that $|f(z)| \le G$ for all z on k, we obtain

$$\left| \sum_{j=1}^{n} f(z_j)\, \Delta_j z \right| \le \sum_{j=1}^{n} |f(z_j)|\, |\Delta_j z| \le G \sum_{j=1}^{n} |\Delta_j z|,$$

which in the limit gives

$$\left| \int_k f(z)\, dz \right| \le Gs,$$

where $s = \lim \Sigma |\Delta z|$ is the length of the curve k.

Suppose that f, ω, A, and B are given. In general, $\int_k f(z)\, dz$ will then depend on the path of integration joining A and B. This will not be so, however, if f is analytic in ω and if ω is simply connected. In this case the Cauchy-Riemann equations directly show that the sufficient condition of cross differentiation (see p. 249) is fulfilled for the real as well as the imaginary part of the complex integral. This important result, called the *Cauchy integral theorem*, is often stated in the following way: The integral of an analytic function along any closed curve in a simply connected region is zero. We shall later see more in detail what may happen if the path of integration encloses one or several *singularities*, i.e., points not belonging to the domain of the analytic integrand.

Example 7-4. Consider the function $w = 1/z$, which is analytic for all values of z except $z = 0$. The integral along the circle with center at $(2,0)$ and radius 1 traversed in the counterclockwise sense can conveniently be written

$$\oint_{|z-2|=1} \frac{1}{z}\, dz.$$

It follows immediately from the above that its value is 0, as the path does not enclose the singularity at $(0,0)$. For the integral

$$\oint_{|z|=1} \frac{1}{z}\, dz$$

this argument does not apply (Fig. 7-6). To find its value we introduce

$$z = x + iy, \qquad \frac{1}{z} = \frac{x}{x^2 + y^2} - i\frac{y}{x^2 + y^2},$$

$$x(t) = \cos t, \qquad y(t) = \sin t, \qquad 0 \le t \le 2\pi,$$

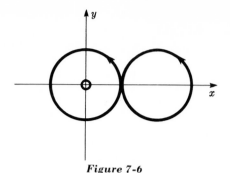

Figure 7-6

giving

$$\oint_{|z|=1} \frac{1}{z}\,dz = \int_0^{2\pi}\left[\frac{\cos t}{\cos^2 t + \sin^2 t}(-\sin t) + \frac{\sin t}{\cos^2 t + \sin^2 t}(\cos t)\right]dt$$

$$+ i\int_0^{2\pi}\left[-\frac{\sin t}{\cos^2 t + \sin^2 t}(-\sin t) + \frac{\cos t}{\cos^2 t + \sin^2 t}(\cos t)\right]dt = 2\pi i.$$

A simpler way of evaluating the integral is obtained by representing the path of integration by the function $z = e^{it}$, $0 \le t \le 2\pi$:

$$\oint_{|z|=1} \frac{1}{z}\,dz = \int_0^{2\pi}\frac{1}{e^{it}}\frac{de^{it}}{dt}\,dt = \int_0^{2\pi} i\,dt = 2\pi i. \qquad \square$$

Analytic Functions

From what has been said about continuity and differentiability of complex functions it follows that the sum, the difference, and the product, as well as the quotient of any two complex functions analytic in a common open region, is again analytic in this region (except at points where the denominator function is zero). This implies that every polynomial and every rational function in z is analytic in the whole of its domain, since this is the case for the two simple functions $f(z) = $ constant and $f(z) = z$.

Also the complex exponential function

$$f(z) = e^z = e^x(\cos y + i \sin y)$$

is analytic in the whole complex plane as the Cauchy-Riemann equations are satisfied for every z:

$$\frac{\partial}{\partial x}(e^x \cos y) = \frac{\partial}{\partial y}(e^x \sin y), \qquad \frac{\partial}{\partial y}(e^x \cos x) = -\frac{\partial}{\partial x}(e^x \sin y).$$

For the derivative of this function we have

$$f'(z) = \frac{\partial}{\partial x}(e^x \cos y) + i\frac{\partial}{\partial x}(e^x \sin y) = e^z.$$

Using the above, combined with the fact that composition of analytic functions gives an analytic function with the "expected" derivative, we find that the complex trigonometric and hyperbolic functions defined below (cf. p. 223) are analytic for all z with the derivatives stated:

$$\cos z = \frac{e^{iz} + e^{-iz}}{2} \qquad \frac{d}{dz}\cos z = -\sin z,$$

$$\sin z = \frac{e^{iz} - e^{-iz}}{2i} \qquad \frac{d}{dz}\sin z = \cos z,$$

$$\cosh z = \frac{e^z + e^{-z}}{2} \qquad \frac{d}{dz}\cosh z = \sinh z,$$

$$\sinh z = \frac{e^z - e^{-z}}{2} \qquad \frac{d}{dz}\sinh z = \cosh z.$$

It is possible to prove that if a number of analytic functions are defined in an open region which contains an interval on the real axis, any identity involving only addition and multiplication which holds between these functions when z is real will hold also when z is not real. This means, for instance, that all the familiar theorems about the real trigonometric functions also hold if the arguments of the trigonometric functions are complex.

The above implies that given a real function $\phi(x)$ of a real variable x ($a \leq x \leq b$) there is at most one complex analytic function $f(z)$ which reduces to $\phi(x)$ when z is real. It follows that all our generalizations from real functions to analytic functions of a complex variable are unique. The operative word in this connection is "analytic": it is possible to construct several such functions of a complex variable which reduce to $\phi(x)$ for z real if they are not required to be analytic.

Power Series

We are now in a position to consider the concept of a complex *power series*, i.e., a series of the form

$$\sum_{n=0}^{\infty} a_n z^n = a_0 + a_1 z + a_2 z^2 + \cdots,$$

where the a's are complex constants and z is a complex variable. Most of the results found for real power series can be carried over to this more general case with only one important change: the radius of convergence (p. 332) now really becomes a radius. Corresponding to every complex power series there exists a nonnegative real number λ (possibly $\lambda = \infty$) such that the power series is absolutely convergent for all z for which $|z| < \lambda$, and divergent for all z for which $|z| > \lambda$. No general statement can be made about the convergence on the boundary of the circular region of convergence. The value of λ may be found precisely as before, for example, as

$$\lim_{n \to \infty} \left| \frac{a_n}{a_{n+1}} \right| \quad \text{or} \quad \lim_{n \to \infty} \frac{1}{\sqrt[n]{|a_n|}},$$

in case these exist.

Any function f represented by a power series,

$$f(z) = a_0 + a_1 z + a_2 z^2 + \cdots \qquad (|z| < \lambda),$$

is continuous in the whole of its domain. Furthermore, it is differentiable, and its derivative can be obtained by term-by-term differentiation, which gives a series with the same radius of convergence:

$$f'(z) = a_1 + 2a_2 z + 3a_3 z^2 + \cdots \qquad |z| < \lambda.$$

This new series thus also represents a continuous function. It follows that f is analytic, and (also) that f has derivatives of any order. Finally, we mention that the integral of f along any (piecewise) differentiable curve belonging to the domain of f may be obtained by term-by-term integration.

By continued differentiation of the above power series it follows that we have $f^{(n)}(0) = n! a_n$ ($n = 1, 2, \ldots$), and therefore also

$$f(z) = f(0) + \frac{f'(0)}{1} z + \frac{f''(0)}{2} z^2 + \cdots \qquad (|z| < \lambda).$$

As in the real case we thus have that a function which can be expanded in a power series is completely determined by the value of the function itself and its derivatives at the one point 0. For the case of real functions it was mentioned (p. 333) that there exist functions $f(x)$ which have derivatives of any order (for all x), but which cannot be represented by power series. This result, however, is not carried over to the theory of complex functions: As we shall show later, any complex function which has a continuous derivative (is analytic) inside a circle with its center at (0,0) can also be represented by a power series inside the circle. This rather surprising result perhaps explains why the notion of an analytic function was defined differently in the real and in the complex case (cf. p. 333 and p. 429).

Example 7-5. As important examples of power series expansions valid for all z we mention the following:

$$e^z = 1 + \frac{z}{1!} + \frac{z^2}{2!} + \cdots,$$

$$\cos z = 1 - \frac{z^2}{2!} + \frac{z^4}{4!} - \cdots,$$

$$\sin z = z - \frac{z^3}{3!} + \frac{z^5}{5!} - \cdots,$$

all carried over directly from the real case (p. 334). □

Inverse Functions

Consider the analytic function $w = f(z)$, with the open region ω as its domain and with M as its range. Suppose that the derivative of f is different from zero at every point of ω and also that the function considered is one-to-one. It follows immediately (from the latter assumption) that $w = f(z)$ has an inverse function $z = \phi(w)$ with M as its domain and with ω as its range. Moreover, it can be shown that M is an open region, that the inverse function is analytic, and that its derivative at the arbitrary point $w_0 [= f(z_0)]$ is $\phi'(w_0) = 1/f'(z_0)$.

As an illustration of this general theorem we shall consider one important example, the function $f(z) = e^z$, which is analytic in the whole complex plane with a derivative different from zero. However, it is not one-to-one, as, for instance, $f(0) = f(2\pi i)$. To examine the situation more closely we consider the equation $e^z = w_0$, where w_0 is an arbitrary complex number and z is the unknown. Introducing $z = x + iy$ we have

$$e^x(\cos y + i \sin y) = w_0,$$

which is satisfied if and only if

$$e^x = |w_0| \quad \text{and} \quad y = \arg w_0 + 2p\pi$$

for some integer p. This shows that the equation has no solution for $w_0 = 0$ and an infinity of solutions for $w_0 \neq 0$, namely, $z = \ln|w_0| + i(\arg w_0 + 2p\pi)$. It follows that the exponential function $w = e^z$ assumes every possible value (i.e., $w \neq 0$) exactly once in an arbitrary region given by an inequality of the form $\alpha < \text{Im}(z) \leq \alpha + 2\pi$. Any of the above solutions is called a *logarithm* of w_0 and written log w_0, while the one corresponding to $p = 0$ is called the *principal logarithm* of w_0 and written Log w_0.

To apply the above general theorem we now consider the exponential function $w = e^z$ with the restricted domain ω given by the inequality $-\pi < \text{Im}(z) < \pi$. It is obvious that ω is an open region; furthermore, our considerations show that this function is one-to-one and that its range M is the set of all complex numbers w except the nonpositive real ones (Fig. 7-7). For the inverse function we have

$$z = \ln|w| + i \arg w$$

or

$$z = \text{Log } w.$$

We can conclude that this new function is analytic and that its derivative at the point w is

$$\frac{dz}{dw} = \frac{1}{dw/dz} = \frac{1}{e^z} = \frac{1}{w}.$$

Of course these conclusions can also be drawn by direct calculations. Below this is done, and at the same time, the names of the two variables

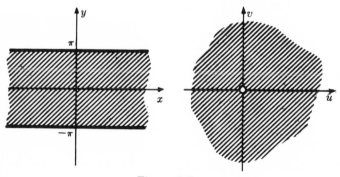

Figure 7-7

are interchanged and polar coordinates are introduced in the plane of the independent variable. Thus we consider the function

$$w = \text{Log } z = \ln r + i\theta \qquad (r > 0, -\pi < \theta < \pi).$$

As the Cauchy-Riemann equations (in their polar form) are satisfied,

$$\frac{\partial}{\partial r} \ln r = \frac{1}{r} \frac{\partial \theta}{\partial \theta} \qquad \text{and} \qquad \frac{1}{r} \frac{\partial}{\partial \theta} \ln r = -\frac{\partial \theta}{\partial r},$$

we conclude that the function considered is analytic. For the derivative of the function we obtain

$$\frac{dw}{dz} = e^{-i\theta} \left(\frac{\partial}{\partial r} \ln r + i \frac{\partial \theta}{\partial r} \right) = e^{-i\theta} \frac{1}{r} = \frac{1}{z}.$$

Exercises

*1. Find the conditions one must impose on two functions of one variable $g_1(x)$ and $g_2(y)$ in order that $w = u(x,y) + iv(x,y)$, where $u(x,y) = g_1(x) + g_2(y)$, be analytic.

2. Find all analytic functions $f(z) = u(x,y) + iv(x,y)$ for which u is a function of x only and v is a function of y only.

*3. Evaluate the following integrals

(a) $\displaystyle\int_1^{2+i} (1 + 3z^2 + z^3)\, dz$ (b) $\displaystyle\int_i^3 (z^2 + z^4)\, dz$

4. Using the results on page 434, prove the following formula:

$$\int_k f'(z)\,dz = f(z_1) - f(z_0),$$

where z_0 is the initial point of k, and z_1 the terminal point of k.

Answers

1. $g_1(x) = ax^2 + b_1x + c_1$; $g_2(y) = -ay^2 + b_2y + c_2$.
3. (a) $18i$.   (b) $288/5 + 2i/15$.

7-3. INTEGRATION AND SERIES EXPANSIONS

Cauchy's Integral Formula

Above we have seen that for an analytic function the integral along a closed path is zero if the function is also analytic in the whole of the region bounded by the path, whereas the integral along a path which encloses a singularity of the function may be different from zero. We shall now investigate the latter case more closely. Consider a function $f(z)$ which is analytic in an open region ω except at z_0. We will

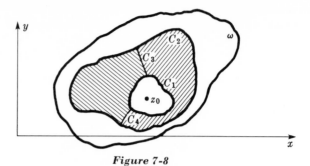

Figure 7-8

prove that the integral along C_1 in the positive direction is equal to the integral along C_2 in the same direction (Fig. 7-8). To do this we introduce two curves C_3 and C_4 connecting C_1 and C_2. In this way we obtain two regions (shaded in Fig. 7-8) bounded by two closed curves which we shall call C' and C''. As the singularity lies outside each of these, we have

$$\oint_{C'} f(z)\, dz = 0 \qquad \text{and} \qquad \oint_{C''} f(z)\, dz = 0.$$

Adding these two equations, the contributions from C_3 and C_4 cancel and we get

$$\oint_{C_1} f(z)\, dz + \oint_{C_2} f(z)\, dz = 0.$$

From this we conclude that the integral $\oint f(z)\, dz$ is independent of the path as long as the path encloses the singularity.

We shall use this result on a particular example. Let the function $\phi(z)$ be analytic in ω (without any singularity) and let us consider

$$\oint_{C} \frac{\phi(z)}{z - z_0}\, dz,$$

where C encloses the point z_0.

The integrand obviously has a singularity at z_0 and we now want to determine the value of the integral. Since it is independent of the path, we can choose this to be a circle with radius ϵ and center z_0. If ϵ is very small, we expect that $\phi(z)$ on the path will be approximately constant and equal to $\phi(z_0)$. This suggests the validity of the following, which is in fact true:

$$\oint \frac{\phi(z)}{z - z_0}\, dz = \phi(z_0) \oint \frac{dz}{z - z_0}.$$

It is not necessary to specify that the integral on the right side should be calculated for a vanishingly small radius in the circle, since this integral also is independent of the path. A direct calculation gives $2\pi i$ (cf. Example 7-4, where the case $z_0 = 0$ was considered), and we therefore have

$$\phi(z_0) = \frac{1}{2\pi i} \oint \frac{\phi(z)}{z - z_0}\, dz,$$

which is *Cauchy's integral formula*. It shows that the values of $\phi(z)$ on a closed curve in the complex plane completely determine its value at any point inside the curve. If in particular we consider a circular path with z_0 as its center and r_0 as its radius such that $\phi(z)$ is equal to $\phi(z_0 + re^{i\theta})$ on the path and $dz = ire^{i\theta}\, d\theta$, we have

$$\phi(z_0) = \frac{1}{2\pi i} \oint \frac{\phi(z_0 + re^{i\theta})}{re^{i\theta}}\, ire^{i\theta}\, d\theta = \frac{1}{2\pi} \int_0^{2\pi} \phi(z_0 + re^{i\theta})\, d\theta;$$

that is, the value of an analytic function at a point is the average of its values on a circle with this point as its center.

The Taylor Expansion

Using Cauchy's integral formula on the analytic function f,

$$f(z_0) = \frac{1}{2\pi i} \oint \frac{f(z)}{z - z_0}\, dz,$$

the following result can be derived:

$$f^{(n)}(z_0) = \frac{n!}{2\pi i} \oint \frac{f(z)}{(z - z_0)^{n+1}}\, dz.$$

Formally, this appears from n differentiations with respect to z_0, when the differentiations on the right side are performed under the integral sign.

Suppose now that f is analytic inside a circle C with radius R and center z_0 and let z_1 be an arbitrary point belonging to this region (Fig. 7-9). We then have

$$f(z_1) = \frac{1}{2\pi i} \oint_C \frac{f(z)}{z - z_1}\, dz = \frac{1}{2\pi i} \oint_C \frac{f(z)}{z - z_0} \frac{1}{1 - [(z_1 - z_0)/(z - z_0)]}\, dz$$

As $\left| (z_1 - z_0)/(z - z_0) \right| < 1$ we also have (cf. Example 7-1)

$$f(z_1) = \frac{1}{2\pi i} \oint_C \frac{f(z)}{z - z_0} \left[1 + \frac{z_1 - z_0}{z - z_0} + \left(\frac{z_1 - z_0}{z - z_0} \right)^2 + \cdots \right] dz.$$

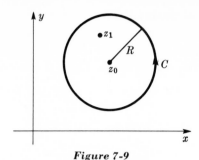

Figure 7-9

By a term-by-term integration (which can be shown to be permissible) we then obtain

$$f(z_1) = \frac{1}{2\pi i} \oint_C \frac{f(z)}{z - z_0} \, dz + \frac{1}{2\pi i} \oint_C \frac{f(z)}{(z - z_0)^2} \, dz \, (z_1 - z_0) + \cdots$$

or—using the above—

$$f(z_1) = f(z_0) + \frac{f'(z_0)}{1!} (z_1 - z_0) + \frac{f''(z_0)}{2!} (z_1 - z_0)^2 + \cdots .$$

This means that the *Taylor series expansion* is valid for f inside the circle considered. In the special case of $z_0 = 0$, we obtain the power series in z considered on page 438.

The Laurent Expansion

Above we have assumed that $f(z)$ is analytic inside a circle with center at z_0 and we have seen that the function can then be expanded in a power series in $z - z_0$. For various reasons this sometimes appears as a rather narrow point of view. For one thing it may be necessary to work with an analytic function which is singular at the point around which one is interested in studying it. It may also be that one would prefer a domain of convergence which is not circular. The way out of these difficulties is to consider the expansion $\sum_{n=0}^{\infty} a_n (z - z_0)^n$ together with an expansion such as

$$\sum_{n=0}^{\infty} b_n [\rho(z - z_0)]^n,$$

where $\rho(z - z_0)$ is some simple function of $z - z_0$. The function $\rho(z - z_0)$, which is of primary importance, is $(z - z_0)^{-1}$; i.e., one considers expansions of the type

$$\sum_{n=0}^{\infty} a_n(z - z_0)^n + \sum_{n=0}^{\infty} b_n(z - z_0)^{-n},$$

usually called *Laurent expansions*. Here the first sum will have a circular region of convergence such as $|z - z_0| < R_2$, while the second sum will converge when $|(z - z_0)^{-1}|$ is less than some positive number r_1 (if it is convergent at all), i.e., when $|z - z_0| > 1/r_1 = R_1$. In case $R_1 < R_2$, we can conclude that the total expression converges inside an annular region, namely, the region given by $R_1 < |z - z_0| < R_2$ (Fig. 7-10). If the series expansion is formulated as

$$f(z) = \sum_{n=-\infty}^{\infty} a_n(z - z_0)^n,$$

one can prove that the coefficients a_n for all integer values of n are given by

$$a_n = \frac{1}{2\pi i} \oint_C \frac{f(z)}{(z - z_0)^{n+1}} dz,$$

where C is any circle belonging to the region and with its center at z_0. It turns out that any function $f(z)$ analytic in a region $R_1 < |z - z_0| < R_2$ can be expanded in a Laurent expansion as above.

In such a Laurent expansion it may happen that all the b_n's are zero, in which case we have an ordinary Taylor expansion. This is the case for functions such as e^z, sin z, and cos z, which have already been considered corresponding to $z_0 = 0$. Even if a function has a singularity at z_0, it may be that all b_n's are zero. This is true, for instance, for

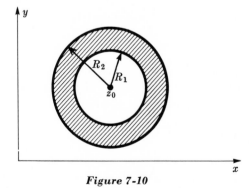

Figure 7-10

$f(z) = \sin z/z$ at $z = z_0$, and it implies that the singularity at 0 can be removed by introducing $f(0) = a_0 \ (= 1)$. It may also happen that there is (only) a finite number of b_n's which are different from zero. This is the case, for instance, for the function $\cot z (= \cos z/\sin z)$ and $\coth z (= \cosh z/\sinh z)$ with $z_0 = 0$:

$$\cot z = \frac{1}{z} - \frac{z}{3} - \frac{z^3}{45} - \frac{2z^5}{945} - \cdots \,,$$

$$\coth z = \frac{1}{z} + \frac{z}{3} - \frac{z^3}{45} + \frac{2z^5}{945} - \cdots .$$

When the expansion of $f(z)$ around z_0 contains a finite number of terms $b_n(z - z_0)^{-n}$ ($b_n \neq 0$) and the largest value of n which occurs is N, the function is said to have *a pole of order N at z_0*. Functions of this type actually give rise to only small difficulties in handling, since one can always reduce the expansion to one of the Taylor type by considering the function $(z - z_0)^N f(z)$ instead of $f(z)$ itself.

Finally, it is possible to have expansions where infinitely many terms with negative powers of $(z - z_0)$ occur. In these cases the singularity at z_0 is said to be *essential*, and one also speaks about a pole at z_0 of infinite order. An example of this is

$$\exp\left(\frac{1}{z}\right) = 1 + z^{-1} + \frac{1}{2!} z^{-2} + \frac{1}{3!} z^{-3} + \cdots .$$

Here the essential singularity is said to be *isolated*, since there exists a neighborhood of the point $z_0 = 0$ containing no other singularities. It may also happen, however, that every neighborhood of the singularity z_0 contains other singularities. This is the case, for instance, with $z_0 = 0$ and $f(z) = \exp[1/\sin (1/z)]$, where $f(z)$ is singular for $z = 1/n\pi (n = \pm 1, \pm 2, \pm 3, \ldots)$. In the following we shall exclusively be concerned with isolated singularities.

Residues

Suppose $f(z)$ has an isolated singularity at the point z_0. In the Laurent expansion $\Sigma_{n=-\infty}^{\infty} a_n(z - z_0)^n$ of $f(z)$ around z_0, the coefficient a_{-1} is called the *residue* of $f(z)$ at z_0, often written $\text{Res}[f(z), z_0]$. If $f(z)$ has a pole of order n at z_0, i.e., if we have

$$f(z) = \frac{a_{-n}}{(z - z_0)^n} + \frac{a_{-n+1}}{(z - z_0)^{n-1}} + \cdots + \frac{a_{-1}}{z - z_0} + \sum_{n=0}^{\infty} a_n(z - z_0)^n,$$

then

$$\text{Res}[f(z),z_0] = \lim_{z \to z_0} \frac{1}{(n-1)!} \frac{d^{n-1}}{dz^{n-1}} ((z - z_0)^n f(z)),$$

which, in the special case of $n = 1$, reduces to

$$\text{Res}[f(z),z_0] = \lim_{z \to z_0} (z - z_0)f(z).$$

Whether or not the pole at z_0 is of finite order, however, the following formula is valid:

$$\oint_C f(z)\, dz = 2\pi i\, \text{Res}[f(z),z_0].$$

Here C is any closed curve which belongs to the region of convergence of the above Laurent expansion and which encloses the point z_0. The formula can be obtained by a term-by-term integration of the Laurent expansion using the fact that $\oint_C (z - z_0)^n\, dz$ is equal to zero for $n \neq -1$ and equal to $2\pi i$ for $n = -1$. Obviously, the same procedure may be used to demonstrate the validity of the general expression for a_n given on page 445. Inserting -1 for n in that formula we then immediately get the above.

Example 7-6. For the function $f(z) = 1/z^4(1 - z^2)$ we have

$$f(z) = \frac{1}{z^4} + \frac{1}{z^2} + 1 + z^2 + z^4 + \cdots \qquad (0 < |z| < 1).$$

Hence, it has an isolated pole of order 4 at the point 0, its residue at this point is zero, and we have, for instance,

$$\oint_{|z|=1/2} \frac{1}{z^4(1 - z^2)}\, dz = 0. \qquad \square$$

Example 7-7. To evaluate the integral

$$\oint_C \frac{ze^z}{z^2 - 1}\, dz$$

(Fig. 7-11), where C is the curve indicated in the figure, we note that the integrand $f(z) = ze^z/(z^2 - 1)$ has only one singularity inside C,

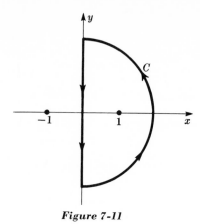

Figure 7-11

the point $z = 1$, which is a pole of order 1:

$$\text{Res}[ze^z/(z^2 - 1),1] = \lim_{z \to 1} (z - 1)\frac{ze^z}{z^2 - 1} = \frac{e}{2}.$$

The integral considered therefore equals $2\pi i(e/2) = \pi ei$.   □

If the curve along which the integration is carried out encloses more than one isolated singularity, the value of the integral becomes equal to the product of $2\pi i$ and the sum of the corresponding residues. This can be seen by cutting up the region into several regions which contain one singularity each and use an argument akin to the one which we used on page 442. We thus obtain the *Cauchy residue theorem:*

$$\oint_C f(z)\, dz = 2\pi i \sum_k \text{Res}[f(z),z_k],$$

where the summation goes over all enclosed singularities. This theorem is often of great help in the evaluation of real integrals, as will be shown in an example below.

Example 7-8. If in Example 7-7 we change the path to the complete circle $|z| = 2$, we enclose two singularities, one at $z = 1$ and one at $z = -1$. Both are first-order poles and the residues are $e/2$ and $1/2e$. Accordingly, the integral is $\pi i[e + (1/e)]$.   □

Example 7-9. To evaluate the real integral $\int_{-\infty}^{\infty} dx/(1 + x^4)$, we consider the complex integral $\oint_C dz/(1 + z^4)$. The path C consists of a half-circle with radius R larger than 1 and a part of the real axis

(Fig. 7-12). $1/(1 + z^4)$ has two poles of order 1 in the region enclosed, at $e^{i\pi/4}$ and at $e^{3i\pi/4}$, shown as dots on Fig. 7-12. The residue at $e^{i\pi/4}$ is obtained as

$$\lim_{z \to e^{i\pi/4}} \frac{z - e^{i\pi/4}}{z^4 + 1} = \lim_{z \to e^{i\pi/4}} \frac{1}{4z^3} = -\frac{e^{i\pi/4}}{4},$$

where we have used l'Hôspital's rule, and the residue at $e^{3i\pi/4}$ is found in the same way to be $-\frac{1}{4}e^{3i\pi/4}$. We therefore have

$$\oint \frac{dz}{1 + z^4} = -2\pi i \frac{e^{i\pi/4} + e^{3i\pi/4}}{4}$$

$$= -i\pi e^{i\pi/2} \cos(\pi/4) = \frac{\pi\sqrt{2}}{2}.$$

This result is independent of the radius R of the circle considered. As to the contribution to the integral from the circular part C_1 of the path of integration we have (cf. p. 435)

$$\left| \oint_{C_1} \frac{1}{1 + z^4} \, dz \right| \le \frac{1}{R^4 - 1} \pi R,$$

which shows that $\int_{C_1} [1/(1 + z^4)] \, dz$ tends to zero as R tends to infinity. Hence, in the limit we obtain

$$\int_{-\infty}^{\infty} \frac{1}{1 + z^4} \, dz = \frac{\pi\sqrt{2}}{2},$$

i.e., an evaluation of a real integral. This result could of course also have been found using the standard procedure for the integration of rational functions discussed on page 193. The calculations would, however, then become rather lengthy. □

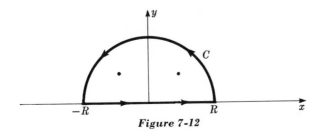

Figure 7-12

Exercises

1. Prove that if $f(z)$ is analytic in a domain which includes the region $|z - z_0| \le R$ and G is the maximum value of $|f(z)|$ on the circle $|z - z_0| = R$, then for all n it holds that $|f^{(n)}(z_0)| \le Gn!/R^n$.

2. Show, using the result of Exercise 1, that a function which is analytic and bounded for all values of z is a constant (Liouville's theorem).

*3. Find the value of the integral

$$\oint_C \frac{dz}{1 + z^2 + z^4 + z^6},$$

where C is a contour which encloses all the singularities.

4. Integrate the function e^{iz}/z along a contour consisting of two half-circles with center at $z = 0$, with radii R and r, which lie above the real axis and the parts of the real axis lying between the two half-circles. Show by letting $R \to \infty$ and $r \to 0$ that

$$\int_0^\infty \frac{\sin x}{x} \, dx = \frac{\pi}{2}.$$

5. Show by means of contour integration that

$$\int_{-\infty}^\infty \frac{e^{x/2}}{1 + e^x} \, dx = \pi.$$

*6. Evaluate

$$\int_0^\infty \frac{\cos x}{(1 + x^2)} \, dx$$

by means of contour integration.

7. The function $f(x) = 1/(1 + x^2)$ can be Taylor-expanded around $x = 0$ to give $f(x) = 1 - x^2 + x^4 - \cdots$ with convergence interval $|x| < 1$. The obvious reason for the length of this interval is that the corresponding function of a complex variable has singularities at $z = i$ and $z = -i$. Show that $f(x)$ also can be expanded, for instance as $\Sigma c_n (x - 1)^n$, and that the interval of convergence then is $1 - \sqrt{2} < x < 1 + \sqrt{2}$.

Answers
3. 0.   6. $\pi/2e$.

8

Numerical Analysis

8-1. INTERPOLATION

Problems in Numerical Analysis

So far we have only briefly considered the problem of how we can obtain the numerical values for solutions of mathematical problems. Furthermore, in many cases functions have been defined by integrals (which could not be expressed by other functional expressions) or by infinite series, without showing how from these it is possible to obtain tabulated values of the functions introduced.

The problem of the numerical evaluation of a definite integral or of the sum of an infinite series is solved in principle by referring to the definition of a definite integral of a function or of the sum of a series. However, in most applications, the elementary methods immediately derived from these are time-consuming.

In addition to the numerical problem described above, the question also arises of how equations may be solved when they have roots which cannot be expressed with the aid of the functions previously introduced. An even more complicated problem is how differential equations may be approximately solved. We shall treat the first of these problems rather thoroughly, but we shall only outline some methods for the numerical solution of simple differential equations.

As nearly all the methods we shall use are based on the application of interpolation formulas, we shall begin by discussing these.

Interpolation is the common name for methods of finding values of a function $y = f(x)$ for an arbitrary argument if a priori values are known only for a series of discrete x-values. Thus a table is given $(x_0,y_0),(x_1,y_1),\ldots,(x_n,y_n)(x_0 < x_1 < \cdots < x_n)$, and we have to determine $y = f(x)$ for a value of x between x_0 and x_n. If the value of x lies outside the interval $x_0 \leq x \leq x_n$, the method is usually called *extrapolation*, even if in principle it is the same process.

As the function $f(x)$ is not known in the entire interval $x_0 < x < x_n$, it is not possible simply to substitute x in a functional expression $y = f(x)$ and find y. The best that can be achieved is therefore to find some function the graph of which passes through the points $(x_0,y_0),\ldots,(x_n,y_n)$ and then use this function to determine y.

In principle there is complete freedom in the choice of such a function, but for the sake of convenience a polynomial is usually chosen, since this is easy to construct with the desired properties, and also is free of singularities. Unless the properties of the function suggest the choice of a specific interpolation function, a polynomial is always chosen.

Lagrange's Interpolation Formula

We shall now show that there exists one and only one polynomial of a degree smaller than or equal to n the graph of which passes through the points $(x_0,y_0),(x_1,y_1),\ldots,(x_n,y_n)$.

It is clear that there cannot be more than one polynomial of this type. If there were two different polynomials $P(x)$ and $P^*(x)$ which both satisfied the conditions, then $P(x) - P^*(x)$ would also be a polynomial of a degree which is at most n, which is zero for $(n + 1)$ values of the variable x. Such a polynomial, however, is identically zero, i.e., $P(x)$ is identical to $P^*(x)$.

On the other hand, there does exist one polynomial $P_n(x)$ which for $x = x_0,x_1,\ldots,x_n$ takes on the values $y_0,y_1,\ldots,y_n$. This follows from the fact that it can be constructed in the following way:

$$P_n(x) = y_0L_0^n(x) + y_1L_1^n(x) + \cdots + y_nL_n^n(x)$$

with

$$L_j^n(x) = \frac{(x - x_0) \cdots (x - x_{j-1})(x - x_{j+1}) \cdots (x - x_n)}{(x_j - x_0) \cdots (x_j - x_{j-1})(x_j - x_{j+1}) \cdots (x_j - x_n)}.$$

On substitution it is seen directly that this polynomial takes on the given values at $x_0, x_1, \ldots, x_n$.

This expression is called *Lagrange's interpolation formula.* We shall now see how it is possible to estimate the error which is made on applying this to an otherwise arbitrary function.

To do this we introduce the difference quotients, which are also called the "divided differences," DD:

$$[x_i x_j] = \frac{y_i - y_j}{x_i - x_j},$$

$$[x_i x_j x_k] = \frac{[x_i x_j] - [x_j x_k]}{x_i - x_k},$$

$$[x_i x_j x_k x_l] = \frac{[x_i x_j x_k] - [x_j x_k x_l]}{x_i - x_l}, \qquad \text{etc.}$$

It is seen that $[x_i x_j] = [x_j x_i]$, and that

$$[x_i x_j] = \frac{y_i}{x_i - x_j} + \frac{y_j}{x_j - x_i};$$

thus we have

$$[x_i x_j x_k] = \frac{y_i}{(x_i - x_j)(x_i - x_k)} + \frac{y_j}{(x_j - x_i)(x_j - x_k)}$$
$$+ \frac{y_k}{(x_k - x_i)(x_k - x_j)},$$

and, more generally,

$$[x_0 x_1 x_2 \cdots x_n] = \frac{y_0}{(x_0 - x_1)(x_0 - x_2) \cdots (x_0 - x_n)}$$
$$+ \frac{y_1}{(x_1 - x_0)(x_1 - x_2) \cdots (x_1 - x_n)}$$
$$+ \cdots + \frac{y_n}{(x_n - x_0) \cdots (x_n - x_{n-1})}.$$

Thus $[x_0 \cdots x_n]$ is equal to a sum of $(n + 1)$ fractions. The numerator in each of these is equal to one of the functional values, and the denominator is the product of the n differences which arise when the other arguments are subtracted from the argument corresponding to the numerator. From this it follows at once that every difference quotient is a symmetric function of the arguments; i.e., its value is unchanged if some of the arguments are interchanged.

To find the error which is made on interpolation with a polynomial of degree at most equal to n, we use the above expression, but now we include the coordinates of the point (x,y):

$$[xx_0x_1 \cdots x_n] = \frac{y}{(x - x_0) \cdots (x - x_n)}$$
$$+ \frac{y_0}{(x_0 - x) \cdots (x_0 - x_n)} + \cdots + \frac{y_n}{(x_n - x) \cdots (x_n - x_{n-1})}.$$

Solving for y we get

$$y = y_0 L_0^n(x) + y_1 L_1^n(x) + \cdots + y_n L_n^n(x) + R_{n+1}(x)$$

with

$$R_{n+1}(x) = (x - x_0)(x - x_1) \cdots (x - x_n)[xx_0x_1 \cdots x_n].$$

Just as in the analogous derivation for the error which was given for a Taylor series expansion (p. 160), we know that the largest error which can be made on interpolating with a polynomial of degree at most equal to n in the interval $x_0 \leq x \leq x_n$ is the largest absolute value which the so-called *remainder* R_{n+1} takes on in the interval.

However, this does not immediately help us, as the remainder is zero for $x = x_0, x_1, \ldots, x_n$ and is unknown for other values of x. If $f(x)$ is known analytically (and thus interpolation is used only because it is easier to calculate the functional values with the aid of this expression), it is possible to make use of the fact that there exists a value $x = \xi$ in the interval considered such that

$$[xx_0x_1 \cdots x_n] = \frac{f^{(n+1)}(\xi)}{(n + 1)!}.$$

This can be seen on repeated use of the mean value theorem.

For the special case of $n = 1$, we have

$$y = y_0 L_0^1(x) + y_1 L_1^1(x) + R_2(x)$$
$$= y_0 \frac{x - x_1}{x_0 - x_1} + y_1 \frac{x - x_0}{x_1 - x_0} + (x - x_0)(x - x_1) \frac{f''(\xi)}{2!}$$
$$= y_0 + \frac{x - x_0}{x_1 - x_0}(y_1 - y_0) + (x - x_0)(x - x_1) \frac{f''(\xi)}{2!},$$

which is the well-known expression for *linear interpolation*.

Newton's Formula

While Lagrange's interpolation formula is useful for many theoretical investigations, it is often more convenient for practical applica-

Table 8-1

x	y	DD_1	DD_2	DD_3	DD_4
x_0	y_0				
		$[x_0x_1]$			
x_1	y_1		$[x_0x_1x_2]$		
		$[x_1x_2]$		$[x_0x_1x_2x_3]$	
x_2	y_2		$[x_1x_2x_3]$		$[x_0x_1x_2x_3x_4]$
		$[x_2x_3]$		$[x_1x_2x_3x_4]$	
x_3	y_3		$[x_2x_3x_4]$		
		$[x_3x_4]$			
x_4	y_4				

tions to use a formula where the approximating polynomial is expressed directly with the aid of the finite divided differences. Such an expression was given by Newton:

$$P_n(x) = y_0 + (x - x_0)[x_0x_1] + (x - x_0)(x - x_1)[x_0x_1x_2] + \cdots$$
$$+ (x - x_0)(x - x_1) \cdots (x - x_{n-1})[x_0x_1 \cdots x_n].$$

If the above remainder is used, the following is valid. When $y = f(x)$ is differentiable $(n + 1)$ times in the interval $a \leq x \leq b$ and $x_0, x_1, \ldots, x_n$ are $(n + 1)$ different values in this interval, then

$$f(x) = y_0 + (x - x_0)[x_0x_1] + (x - x_0)(x - x_1)[x_0x_1x_2] + \cdots$$
$$+ (x - x_0)(x - x_1) \cdots (x - x_{n-1})[x_0x_1 \cdots x_n]$$
$$+ (x - x_0)(x - x_1) \cdots (x - x_n)\frac{f^{(n+1)}(\xi)}{(n + 1)!},$$

where ξ lies between a and b.

In practical calculations a table of the difference quotients is usually made, Table 8-1 $(n = 4)$.

Example 8-1. Find the approximating polynomial of degree at most equal to 3 which takes on the values of Table 8-2.

The table of difference quotients is shown as Table 8-3, and the polynomial is therefore

Table 8-2

x	2	3	5	6
y	5	2	3	4

Table 8-3

x	y	DD_1	DD_2	DD_3
2	5			
		-3		
3	2		$\frac{7}{6}$	
		$\frac{1}{2}$		$-\frac{1}{4}$
5	3		$\frac{1}{6}$	
		1		
6	4			

$$P(x) = 5 - 3(x - 2) + \tfrac{7}{6}(x - 2)(x - 3) - \tfrac{1}{4}(x - 2)(x - 3)(x - 5)$$

or

$$P(x) = -\tfrac{1}{4}x^3 + \tfrac{11}{3}x^2 - \tfrac{199}{12}x + \tfrac{51}{2}.$$

In most numerical calculations it is just as convenient to use the polynomial in the form given first as in the second form.   □

Example 8-2. Find a polynomial which is equal to $\sin x$ for $x = 21°, 22°, 24°$, and $25°$, and calculate from this $\sin 23°$ (Table 8-4).

$$P(x) = 0.35837 + 0.01624(x - 21) - 0.00006(x - 21)(x - 22).$$

As a polynomial of the second degree is used here, the remainder is, for $x = 23°$,

$$\frac{2 \cdot 1 \cdot (-1)}{3!} \left[\frac{d^3}{dx^3} \sin x\right]_{x=\xi} \approx 2 \cdot 10^{-6}.$$

x gives the angle measured in degrees, $21° \le \xi \le 24°$, and $(d/dx) \sin x =$

Table 8-4

$x°$	$\sin x°$	DD_1	DD_2	DD_3
21	0.35837			
		0.01624		
22	0.37461		-0.00006	
		0.01606		0.00000
24	0.40674		-0.00006	
		0.01588		
25	0.42262			

$(2\pi/360) \cos x$. We can only hope to find $\sin 23°$ with five decimal places, and the approximation used is therefore sufficient. On substitution we get $\sin 23° = 0.39073$, which is in agreement with the tabulated value to five decimal places. However, possible rounding-off errors could have resulted in an error in the fifth decimal place. □

In the special case where the values of the argument are equidistant, i.e., where $x_k = x_0 + kh$, and h is a constant, the differences $\Delta y_0 = y_1 - y_0$, $\Delta y_1 = y_2 - y_1$, $\Delta^2 y_0 = \Delta y_1 - \Delta y_0$, etc., are tabulated as in Table 8-5.

The difference quotients are obtained from the differences Δ^k by dividing by $k!h^k$. *Newton's interpolation formula* then takes the form

$$f(x) = y_0 + \frac{\Delta y_0}{1!h}(x - x_0) + \frac{\Delta^2 y_0}{2!h^2}(x - x_0)(x - x_0 - h) + \cdots$$

$$+ \frac{\Delta^n y_0}{n!h^n}(x - x_0) \cdots (x - x_0 - (n-1)h)$$

$$+ \frac{f^{(n+1)}(\xi)}{(n+1)!}(x - x_0) \cdots (x - x_0 - nh),$$

which strongly resembles Taylor's formula and indeed passes over into it in the limit $h \to 0$.

If we set $x = x_0 + hz$ and therefore $(x - x_0 - kh)/h = z - k$, Newton's formula can be written

$$f(x_0 + hz) = y_0 + \frac{z}{1!}\Delta y_0 + \frac{z(z-1)}{2!}\Delta^2 y_0 + \cdots$$

$$+ \frac{z(z-1) \cdots (z-n+1)}{n!}\Delta^n y_0$$

$$+ \frac{z(z-1) \cdots (z-n)}{(n+1)!}h^{n+1}f^{(n+1)}(\xi).$$

Table 8-5

x_0	y_0				
		Δy_0			
$x_0 + h$	y_1		$\Delta^2 y_0$		
		Δy_1		$\Delta^3 y_0$	
$x_0 + 2h$	y_2		$\Delta^2 y_1$		$\Delta^4 y_0$
		Δy_2		$\Delta^3 y_1$	
$x_0 + 3h$	y_3		$\Delta^2 y_2$		
		Δy_3			
$x_0 + 4h$	y_4				

In this expression, only differences from the upper diagonal line in the table are used (the "descending differences"). This is therefore used for interpolation close to x_0. The analogous expression for interpolation near x_n is

$$f(x_n + hz) = y_n + \frac{z}{1!} \Delta y_{n-1} + \frac{z(z+1)}{2!} \Delta^2 y_{n-2} + \cdots$$

$$+ \frac{z(z+1) \cdots (z+n-1)}{n!} \Delta^n y_0$$

$$+ \frac{z(z+1) \cdots (z+n)}{(n+1)!} h^{n+1} f^{(n+1)}(\xi).$$

Example 8-3. From a table of $y = e^x$, the following values are obtained: exp 1.6 = 4.953, exp 1.7 = 5.474, exp 1.8 = 6.050. Calculate exp 1.65 with the help of Newton's method.

As 1.65 is close to 1.6, we use the formula with descending differences.

$$f(x_0 + hz) = y_0 + z \Delta y_0 + \frac{z(z-1)}{2!} \Delta^2 y_0 + R_3.$$

As $x_0 = 1.6$, $h = 0.1$, and $z = 0.5$, $y_0 = 4.953$, $\Delta y_0 = 0.521$, and $\Delta^2 y_0 = 0.055$, we have

$$\exp 1.65 = 4.953 + 0.5 \cdot 0.521 - \frac{0.5 \cdot 0.5}{2} 0.055 + R_3$$

$$= 5.207 + R_3.$$

As $y''' = e^x$, we have

$$R_3 \approx \frac{0.5 \cdot 0.5 \cdot 1.5}{6} (0.1)^3 \cdot 6 \approx 4.10^{-4},$$

and the three decimal places given above are therefore correct. In this case, a significant error will be made if one uses ordinary linear interpolation, since then one gets exp 1.65 $\sim$ 5.214. Because $y = \exp x$ has the simple functional equation $\exp(x + y) = (\exp x)(\exp y)$, it is actually much easier to use $\exp(1.65) = (\exp 1.6)(\exp 0.05)$, when a table of the exponential function for arguments 0.01 − 0.09 (0.01) is available. For further interpolation, tables with values of the argument 0.001 − 0.009(0.001), etc., may be used. These tables must, however, contain sufficient decimal places such that exp 0.05 is known, at least with the same relative accuracy as exp 1.6. Using this method we find that exp 1.65 = 4.953 × 1.0513 = 5.207.   □

Aitken's Method

Another method of interpolation, which however still uses the polynomial $P_n(x)$, has been given by Aitken. It is an iterative method in which we start by interpolating linearly,

$$I_{0,1}(x) = \frac{1}{x_1 - x_0} \begin{vmatrix} y_0 & x_0 - x \\ y_1 & x_1 - x \end{vmatrix}.$$

$I_{0,1}(x)$ is the desired value of y for the value of the argument x lying between x_0 and x_1. The index 0,1 on I refers to the fact that in the interpolation, the two points with abscissas x_0 and x_1 were used, or, in other words, that linear interpolations were used.

In an analogous manner we now calculate $I_{1,2}(x)$ as

$$I_{1,2}(x) = \frac{1}{x_2 - x_1} \begin{vmatrix} y_1 & x_1 - x \\ y_2 & x_2 - x \end{vmatrix},$$

and then proceed to the next approximation, which is

$$y = I_{0,1,2} = \frac{1}{x_2 - x_0} \begin{vmatrix} I_{0,1}(x) & x_0 - x \\ I_{1,2}(x) & x_2 - x \end{vmatrix}.$$

By evaluating the determinants one can verify that the second-degree polynomial $I_{0,1,2}(x)$ derived in this way is identical with that derived using the Lagrange method on the same three points. Aitken's method, however, possesses two advantages. First, the y-values are easier to calculate (using, for instance, a desk calculator), and, second, it is seen directly how large the difference is between linear interpolation and the next approximation (quadratic interpolation). On continuing the interpolation with a third-degree polynomial formed in the analogous manner, it is again seen directly how much this improves the approximation, etc.

It should be noted that as a result of the above rules for the formation of the I's, the following is true:

$$I_{0,1,2} = \frac{1}{x_2 - x_0} \begin{vmatrix} I_{0,1}(x) & x_0 - x \\ I_{1,2}(x) & x_2 - x \end{vmatrix} = \frac{1}{x_2 - x_1} \begin{vmatrix} I_{0,1}(x) & x_1 - x \\ I_{0,2}(x) & x_2 - x \end{vmatrix}$$

$$= \frac{1}{x_1 - x_0} \begin{vmatrix} I_{0,2}(x) & x_0 - x \\ I_{1,2}(x) & x_1 - x \end{vmatrix}.$$

As an example of the next approximation we mention

$$I_{0,1,2,3} = \frac{1}{x_3 - x_2} \begin{vmatrix} I_{0,1,2}(x) & x_2 - x \\ I_{0,1,3}(x) & x_3 - x \end{vmatrix}.$$

All the interpolation formulas given here have been based on the use of polynomials as interpolation functions. If one interpolates in a table of a function such as $y = \sqrt{x}$, which has a vertical tangent at (0,0), it will be found that, no matter where in the table the interpolation is carried out, if tabulated points from the region around (0,0) are used, the results are very uncertain. This is because on obtaining the remainder it is necessary to use the greatest absolute value of some derivative inside the interval from which the tabulated points have been taken.

Exercises

*1. Find the approximating polynomial of at most third degree for the function 2^x by using the points $(x,2^x)$ $(x = -1,0,1,2)$, and use this to calculate $\sqrt{2}$. Estimate the maximum error. Finally, compare the polynomial with the first four terms of the Taylor series expansion of 2^x from the point 0.

*2. From Table 8-6 find log 2.01 to the greatest possible accuracy and give an upper limit for the error.

Table 8-6

x	$\log x$
2.00	0.3010 3000
2.02	0.3053 5137
2.04	0.3096 3017
2.06	0.3138 6722

3. Find the second-degree polynomial which has the same values as $\Gamma(x)$ for $x = 1, 2,$ and 3, and the third-degree polynomial which has the same values as $\Gamma(x)$ for $x = 1, 2, 3,$ and 4.

   Find an approximate value for $\Gamma(\frac{3}{2})$ using both expressions, and compare it with the exact value $\sqrt{\pi}/2$.

Answers

1. $\frac{1}{12}x^3 + \frac{1}{4}x^2 + \frac{2}{3}x + 1$; $2^{1/2} \approx \frac{45}{32} = 1.406$. $\left|R_4(\frac{1}{2})\right| < 0.023$. Taylor expansion gives $0.0555x^3 + 0.2402x^2 + 0.6931x + 1$.

2. 0.30319606. Except possibly for rounding-off errors, this result is of the same accuracy as the given table.

8-2. DIFFERENTIATION AND INTEGRATION

Numerical Differentiation

The above interpolation functions can be used to obtain formulas for *numerical differentiation*. These are formulas which give the differential quotient of a function for a series of discrete values of the argument for which a table of the function exists. If the table is not equidistant, then as a rule it is best to calculate the approximating polynomial first, and then differentiate that. For equidistant points, however, convenient formulas can be constructed which give the differential quotiénts directly from the functional values.

In the following, y_n designates the value of the function for the argument $x_n = x_0 + nh$, y'_n the derivative at this point, and $y^{(n)}$ the nth derivative of y corresponding to a value of x which lies between the least and the greatest of the tabulated values of x used in the equation at hand.

If a second-degree polynomial is used as an interpolation function, i.e., if three tabulated values are used, then it can be shown that

$$y'_0 = \frac{1}{2h}\,(-3y_0 + 4y_1 - y_2) + \frac{h^2}{3}\,y'''$$

$$y'_1 = \frac{1}{2h}\,(- y_0 + y_2) - \frac{h^2}{6}\,y'''$$

$$y'_2 = \frac{1}{2h}\,(y_0 - 4y_1 + 3y_2) + \frac{h^2}{3}\,y'''.$$

These expressions demonstrate very characteristically that the second form is both easier to use (only two terms) and more accurate (the remainder is least). This should therefore always be used when possible.

It is also true that formulas which correspond to interpolation with a polynomial of odd degree are not significantly more accurate than those which correspond to interpolation with a polynomial one degree lower; thus they are seldom used. The next set of differentiation formulas which are of interest is, therefore,

$$y'_0 = \frac{1}{12h}\,(-25y_0 + 48y_1 - 36y_2 + 16y_3 - 3y_4) + \frac{h^4}{5}\,y^{(5)},$$

$$y'_1 = \frac{1}{12h}\,(- 3y_0 - 10y_1 + 18y_2 - 6y_3 + y_4) - \frac{h^4}{20}\,y^{(5)},$$

$$y'_2 = \frac{1}{12h}\,(y_0 - 8y_1 + 8y_3 - y_4) + \frac{h^4}{30}\,y^{(5)},$$

$$y'_3 = \frac{1}{12h}\,(- y_0 + 6y_1 - 18y_2 + 10y_3 + 3y_4) - \frac{h^4}{20}\,y^{(5)},$$

$$y'_4 = \frac{1}{12h}\,(3y_0 - 16y_1 + 36y_2 - 48y_3 + 25y_4) + \frac{h^4}{5}\,y^{(5)}.$$

Here, as above, we see that the central formula is of the greatest practical value.

Example 8-4. Using the numbers from Example 8-2, we want to find $y' = (d/dx) \sin x$ for $x = 23\pi/180$, where x now is measured in radians. A second-degree polynomial is used as the interpolation function, giving

$$\frac{180}{2\pi} (0.40674 - 0.37461) = 0.92045.$$

The correct value (with five decimal places) is 0.92050.

The only inaccuracy in the formula for y' arises because y''' must be taken at an unknown point, and since in this case $(h^2/6)y'''$ is nearly constant ($\simeq 4.7 \cdot 10^{-5}$) inside the interval considered, $22\pi/180 < x < 24\pi/180$, the approximation can be improved here by including the remainder. When this is done we get agreement with the correct value to five decimal places. An improvement of this kind is only possible when the higher derivatives of the function which is under consideration are known to be approximately constant over the interval considered.

Here again a rounding-off error could have given rise to inaccuracy in the last figure. □

Numerical Integration

Numerical evaluation of integrals is also based on the interpolating polynomials, but in this case two different situations can arise. The simplest case arises when one wants to calculate the integral of a function which is tabulated. In this case the integrand is interpolated between the known functional values, giving rise to a so-called *closed integration formula*. A more complicated situation arises in connection with the numerical integration of differential equations, where it is of interest to extrapolate functions and then integrate them. Formulas used for this are often called *open formulas*.

Below we list the most important of these two types of integration formulas. They can all be derived from an interpolating polynomial. In all cases the values of the argument are equidistant, $x_k = x_0 + kh$.

Closed formulas:

$$\int_{x_0}^{x_1} y \, dx = \frac{h}{2} (y_0 + y_1) - \frac{y''h^3}{12} \qquad \text{(Trapezoid rule)},$$

$$\int_{x_0}^{x_2} y \, dx = \frac{h}{3} (y_0 + 4y_1 + y_2) - \frac{y^{(4)} h^5}{90} \qquad \text{(Simpson's rule)},$$

$$\int_{x_0}^{x_3} y \, dx = \frac{3h}{8} (y_0 + 3y_1 + 3y_2 + y_3) - \frac{3y^{(4)} h^5}{80},$$

$$\int_{x_0}^{x_4} y \, dx = \frac{4h}{90} (7y_0 + 32y_1 + 12y_2 + 32y_3 + 7y_4) - \frac{8y^{(6)} h^7}{945}.$$

Open formulas:

$$\int_{x_0}^{x_3} y \, dx = \frac{3h}{2} (y_1 + y_2) + \frac{h^3}{4} y''$$

$$\int_{x_0}^{x_4} y \, dx = \frac{4h}{3} (2y_1 - y_2 + 2y_3) + \frac{28h^5}{90} y^{(4)}.$$

The error in the closed interpolation formula, which uses four points, is of the same order of magnitude as that of the formula which uses one point less. This has to do with the fact that *Simpson's rule*, which does not use more than three points, actually corresponds to an interpolating third-degree polynomial. A similar relationship is valid for all integration formulas with an even number of points. Thus, in general, the integration interval should be divided into an even number of subintervals, after which one of the formulas with an even number of intervals (i.e., with an odd number of points of division) can be used as many times as necessary. Only if this is inconvenient due to other reasons should a combination of formulas with even and odd numbers of points of division be used.

Example 8-5. Calculate the integral of $1/x$ from 1 to 3. We choose $h = 0.5$ and use Simpson's rule twice:

$$\int_{1}^{3} \frac{dx}{x} \approx \frac{0.5}{3} \left(\frac{1}{1} + \frac{4}{1.5} + \frac{1}{2} \right) + \frac{0.5}{3} \left(\frac{1}{2} + \frac{4}{2.5} + \frac{1}{3} \right) = \frac{11}{10}.$$

The maximal error is

$$\frac{24 \cdot (0.5)^5}{1^5 \cdot 90} + \frac{24 \cdot (0.5)^5}{2^5 \cdot 90} \approx 0.009.$$

Table 8-7

	Multiplier	*Result*
1.0000	1	1.0000
0.6667	4	2.6668
0.5000	2	1.0000
0.4000	4	1.6000
0.3333	1	0.3333
		6.6001

We therefore have $\ln 3 \approx 1.10$, as compared to the value correct to four decimal places, 1.0986.

In more extensive calculations of this type, a table of the type shown in Table 8-7 can conveniently be constructed. After this the sum is multiplied by $0.5/3 = 0.16667$, and we obtain 1.100.

If the numerical integration is carried out with a formula which has five points of division, then in an analogous manner the result $\ln 3 \approx 1.0993$ is obtained. This is not a considerable improvement, and, furthermore, the error term is larger. If the result is to be improved, it is more useful to make a finer division in the interval $1 \le x \le 2$, which contributes with a greater error than does the interval $2 \le x \le 3$. In practice this is of course done by introducing more points of division, but it is interesting to note for this simple example that if only the five points of division used when Simpson's rule was applied twice had been distributed differently we would have obtained an improvement. As points of division we can, for instance, use $1, \frac{4}{3}, \frac{5}{3}, \frac{7}{3}$, and 3, in which case we get $\ln 3 \approx 1.0995$. Although the value of the integral has not been improved very much, the maximal error is now only 0.004. $\square$

Exercises

*1. Use $\int_0^1 [1/(1 + x^2)] \, dx$ to calculate π with the aid of Simpson's rule. Give the maximum error.

*2. Calculate $\ln 1.02$ to 10 decimal places using Simpson's rule.

3. Calculate $\int_0^\infty dx/(1 + x^2)$ numerically by subdividing the region of integration, making the region finite by a suitable substitution, and then using Simpson's rule.

4. The integral $I(y) = \int_0^y x^3/(e^x - 1) \, dx$, which appears in the Debye theory for heat capacity, cannot be expressed by means of functions introduced so far. Calculate $I(1)$ numerically.

Answers
1. Using $h = \frac{1}{2}$ we get $\frac{47}{15} = 3.133$ (max. error $\frac{1}{30}$).
2. 0.0198026273.

8-3. *ASYMPTOTIC FORMULAS FOR INTEGRALS*

Asymptotic Methods

When it is desired to integrate numerically a function $f(x)$ which increases very rapidly with x, the above formulas will prove unsuitable. To circumvent this, a guess can be made as to how the integral behaves *asymptotically* for large x. Let the supposed asymptotic behavior be given by the function $g(x)$. Then we set

$$\int_0^x f(t)\, dt = g(x)\phi(x),$$

which on differentiation gives

$$g(x)\phi'(x) + g'(x)\phi(x) = f(x).$$

This is a differential equation for the determination of the unknown function $\phi(x)$. This (often very simple) first-order differential equation is then solved numerically. When one attempts an exact solution of the differential equation, the original integral is of course obtained.

This trick is useful, especially with integrals of the form $\exp(f(x))$, where $f(x)$ increases with x. It is then found by setting $g(x) = e^{f(x)}$ that $\phi(x)$ is determined from $\phi'(x) + f'(x)\phi(x) = 1$. As an example we consider $\int_0^x e^{t^2}\, dt = \phi(x)e^{x^2}$, from which the differential equation $\phi'(x) + 2x\phi(x) = 1$ is obtained. This can be solved numerically with the aid of the method given on page 482.

Quite often, however, one only wants to know how the integral behaves for very large x with an accuracy which is relatively good, even though the absolute error may be very large. Then a so-called *asymptotic series* is constructed, most often with the aid of partial integrations.

In the example mentioned above, when integration is carried out from 1 to x we get

$$\int_1^x e^{t^2}\, dt = \int_1^x \frac{1}{2t} e^{t^2} 2t\, dt = \left[\frac{1}{2t} e^{t^2}\right]_1^x + \int_1^x \frac{1}{2t^2} e^{t^2}\, dt,$$

and

$$\int_1^x \frac{1}{2t^2} e^{t^2} dt = \int_1^x \frac{1}{4t^3} e^{t^2} 2t \, dt = \left[\frac{1}{4t^3} e^{t^2} \right]_1^x + \int_1^x \frac{3}{4t^4} e^{t^2} dt,$$

etc., so that we have

$$\int_1^x e^{t^2} dt = e^{x^2} \left[\frac{1}{2x} + \frac{1}{4x^3} + \frac{3}{8x^5} + \cdots + \frac{1 \cdot 3 \cdot 5 \cdot \ldots \cdot (2n-1)}{2^{n+1} x^{2n+1}} + O\left(\frac{1}{x^{2n+2}} \right) \right].$$

The error which is introduced by leaving out an integral $\int_1^x t^{-n} e^{t^2} dt$ is $O(x^{-n})e^{x^2}$, and all contributions from the lower limit in the integrals are negligible, as they are $O(1)$. For the same reason it can also be said that the series is just as well an asymptotic series for $\int_0^x e^{t^2} dt$, as this differs from $\int_1^x e^{t^2} dt$ only by a number independent of x, i.e., a quantity which is $O(1)$.

If the criteria for convergence developed previously are used on the series which is shown in brackets, the series is seen to diverge for all x. Without delving more deeply into the theory for such diverging series, we only mention that they can be used with advantage in numerical calculations when the series are cut off, usually before or at the term which is least for a fixed value of x. The previously mentioned (p. 341) Stirling series for $\Gamma(x)$ is an expansion of this same type. However, in spite of this application, their meaning is quite different from that of power series because they are constructed so that for a fixed number of terms in the series they give an increasingly better (relative) approximation when x increases. On the other hand, power series for a fixed x give a better and better approximation when an increasing number of terms are included in the series.

Exercises

1. Let the function $h(x)$ be monotone-decreasing for $0 \le x < \infty$, and let $h'(0) < 0$, so that the function does not have its maximum value at a point with a horizontal tangent.

   Show by expanding the exponent (from $x = 0$) by a Taylor series that for $t \to \infty$, $\int_0^\infty e^{th(x)} dx$ will be asymptotically equal to $[-th'(0)]^{-1} e^{th(0)}$.

2. Show by a Taylor expansion of the exponent that $\int_a^b g(x) e^{th(x)} dx$, where $h(x)$ has its maximum at x_0, $a < x_0 < b$, $h''(x_0) < 0$, and $g(x_0) \ne 0$, is asymptotically equal to

$$g(x_0) \sqrt{\frac{-2\pi}{th''(x_0)}} e^{th(x_0)} \qquad \text{for } t \to \infty.$$

*3. Find an asymptotic expression for $\int_0^\pi \sin^n x \, dx$ for $n \to \infty$, using the method discussed on page 342.

4. Find an asymptotic expression for the B-function

$$B(n,m) = \int_0^1 x^{n-1}(1-x)^{m-1} \, dx \qquad \text{for } n,m \to \infty.$$

It can be shown that

$$B(n,m) = \frac{\Gamma(n)\Gamma(m)}{\Gamma(n+m)}.$$

Compare the result obtained with Stirling's formula.

*5. Find the values of the following integrals:

$$\int_0^1 \frac{\sqrt{x}}{1+e^x} \, dx, \qquad \int_0^a \frac{\sqrt{x}}{1+e^x} \, dx \ (a \ll 1), \qquad \int_0^\infty \frac{\sqrt{x}}{1+e^x} \, dx,$$

$$\int_A^\infty \frac{\sqrt{x}}{1+e^x} \, dx \quad (A \gg 1),$$

using numerical integration, series expansion, or asymptotic expressions.

Answers

3. $\displaystyle \int_0^\pi \sin^n x \, dx = \int_0^\pi \exp[n \ln \sin x] \, dx \approx \int_{-\infty}^\infty \exp\left[-n\left(x - \frac{\pi}{2}\right)^2 \Big/ 2\right] dx = \sqrt{\frac{2\pi}{n}}.$

The exact result is $\displaystyle \sqrt{\pi}\, \Gamma\left(\frac{n+1}{2}\right)\Big/ \Gamma\left(\frac{n}{2}+1\right).$

5. $\displaystyle \int_0^1 \frac{\sqrt{x}}{1+e^x} \, dx \approx 0.23, \qquad$ by numerical integration

$$\int_0^a \frac{\sqrt{x}}{1+e^x} \, dx = \frac{1}{2}\int_0^a \sqrt{x}\,[1 - \tfrac{1}{2}x + \cdots] \, dx = \tfrac{1}{3}a^{3/2} - \tfrac{1}{10}a^{5/2} + \cdots$$

$$\int_0^\infty \frac{\sqrt{x}}{1+e^x} \, dx = \int_0^\infty \sqrt{x}\, e^{-x}[1 - e^{-x} + e^{-2x} - \cdots] \, dx$$

$$= \frac{\sqrt{\pi}}{2}\left(\frac{1}{1^{3/2}} - \frac{1}{2^{3/2}} + \frac{1}{3^{3/2}} - \cdots\right)$$

$$\int_A^\infty \frac{\sqrt{x}}{1+e^x} \, dx \approx \sqrt{A}\, e^{-A} \qquad \text{(see Exercise 1)}$$

8-4.   SYMBOLIC CALCULUS WITH DIFFERENCES

The Difference Operators

Above we have used the symbol Δ with the meaning

$$\Delta f(x_n) = f(x_n + h) - f(x_n) = y_{n+1} - y_n$$

and further

$$\Delta^2 y_n = \Delta^2 f(x_n) = \Delta(\Delta f_n) = \Delta f_{n+1} - \Delta f_n = f_{n+2} - 2f_{n+1} + f_n, \text{ etc.}$$

where, as we shall do often in the following, we use the designations y_n and f_n for $f(x_n)$. We shall now see how this "operator" Δ is related to the differential operator $D = d/dx$ used in previous chapters. Thus we shall be able to derive relationships between differential quotients and finite differences.

Let us first give a list of the operators we shall use:

$$\Delta f(x) = f(x + h) - f(x) \qquad \text{(the difference operator)}$$
$$Ef(x) = f(x + h) \qquad \text{(the shift operator)}$$
$$\delta f(x) = f(x + \tfrac{1}{2}h) - f(x - \tfrac{1}{2}h) \quad \text{(the symmetric difference operator)}$$
$$Df(x) = \frac{d}{dx}f(x) \qquad \text{(the differential operator)}$$

It should be noted that $ED = DE$, etc.; i.e., all the operators introduced here *commute*, and thus calculations with the operators can be carried out as if they were numbers.

We immediately have $\Delta f(x) = Ef(x) - f(x)$ or $\Delta = E - 1$. Furthermore, we can formally write, on using the Taylor expansion for an exponential function,

$$e^{hD}f(x) = f(x) + hDf(x) + \frac{h^2 D^2}{2!} f(x) + \cdots$$

$$= f(x) + f'(x)h + f''(x)\frac{h^2}{2} + \cdots$$

$$= f(x + h) = Ef(x).$$

Thus we have, formally, $E = e^{hD}$. δ can also be expressed by D as $\delta = 2 \sinh \tfrac{1}{2}hD$. If the operator $U = hD$ is now introduced, the above relation may be written $\delta = 2 \sinh \tfrac{1}{2}U$.

Using the above formulas some previously used expressions can be readily derived. Newton's formula, for instance, may be derived by writing

$$f(x_0 + zh) = E^z f_0 = (1 + \Delta)^z f_0.$$

The correctness of this is verified immediately when z is a positive integer, since, for instance,

$$E^2 f_0 = E(Ef_0) = Ef(x_0 + h) = f(x_0 + 2h) = f_2.$$

We now proceed purely formally, accepting the expression for any value of z. Using the binomial theorem we have

$$f(x_0 + zh) = \left(1 + z\Delta + \frac{1}{2!}z(z-1)\Delta^2 + \cdots\right)f_0$$

$$= f_0 + z\,\Delta f_0 + \frac{1}{2!}z(z-1)\Delta^2 f_0 + \cdots,$$

which is Newtons formula.

A relationship between δ^2 and D^2 which is required later (p. 484) may be obtained in the following manner: As a first approximation we have $\delta^2 f \approx h^2 D^2 f = U^2 f$. We then set $\delta^2 f = \phi(\delta)U^2 f$, where $\phi(\delta)$ is an operator which "corrects" the error made in the first approximation. Thus, formally,

$$\phi(\delta) = \left(\frac{U}{\delta}\right)^{-2} = \left[\frac{\sinh^{-1}(\frac{1}{2}\delta)}{\frac{1}{2}\delta}\right]^{-2},$$

which, when expanded in a Taylor series in powers of δ, gives

$$\phi(\delta) = 1 + \tfrac{1}{12}\delta^2 - \tfrac{1}{240}\delta^4 + \cdots.$$

We therefore have

$$\delta^2 f = h^2[f'' + \tfrac{1}{12}\delta^2 f'' - \tfrac{1}{240}\delta^4 f'' + \cdots]$$

$$= h^2 f''(x) + \frac{h^2}{12}[f''(x+h) - 2f''(x) + f''(x-h)] - \cdots.$$

As the last example of this method, we derive the relationship between a definite integral and the δ-operator. As a first approximation we have the trapezoidal rule

$$\int_{x_0}^{x_1} f\,dx = \tfrac{1}{2}h(f_0 + f_1) = \tfrac{1}{2}h(E + 1)f_0.$$

This is improved by inserting a correction term C into the formula:

$$\int_{x_0}^{x_1} f\,dx = \tfrac{1}{2}h(f_0 + f_1 + C) = \tfrac{1}{2}h(E + 1)f_0 + \tfrac{1}{2}hC.$$

The integral on the left side can be written as $(E - 1)D^{-1}f_0$, because D^{-1}, the inverse operator of D, must be interpreted as an integration with respect to x such that $D^{-1}f_0$ is a primitive function belonging to

$f(x)$ at the point x_0.   Then we have

$$C = \left[\frac{2(E - 1)}{U} - (E + 1) \right] f_0.$$

All the integration formulas that were considered on page 463 can be viewed as different expansions of this expression for C.

The Euler-Maclaurin Formula

The expression for a definite integral derived above may be used to derive the Euler-Maclaurin formula by expanding C in powers of $U = hD$.   The expression for C is first rewritten

$$C = \frac{1}{D} \left[\frac{2}{U} - \frac{E + 1}{E - 1} \right] (E - 1)Df_0,$$

by multiplying from the front by $1/D$ and from behind by D.   We then have

$$C = \frac{h}{U} \left[\frac{2}{U} - \frac{e^U + 1}{e^U - 1} \right] \{f'(x_0 + h) - f'(x_0)\}$$

$$= -\frac{2h}{U^2} \left[\frac{1}{2} U \coth \frac{1}{2} U - 1 \right] \{f'(x_0 + h) - f'(x_0)\}.$$

The function $\frac{1}{2}U \coth \frac{1}{2}U$ can be expanded in a Taylor series in the following manner:

$$\frac{1}{2} U \coth \frac{1}{2} U = 1 + \frac{1}{2!} B_1 U^2 - \frac{1}{4!} B_2 U^4 + \frac{1}{6!} B_3 U^6 \cdots,$$

where the B_n's are called the *Bernoulli numbers* and have the values $B_1 = \frac{1}{6}$, $B_2 = \frac{1}{30}$, $B_3 = \frac{1}{42}$, $B_4 = \frac{1}{30}$, $B_5 = \frac{5}{66}$, $B_6 = \frac{691}{2730}, \ldots$

It must be noted that this definition of the Bernoulli numbers is not the only one used, even if it is the most usual.   If a formula is applied which contains Bernoulli numbers, then one should always check to see how they are defined.

We now have

$$\frac{2}{U^2} \left(\frac{1}{2} U \coth \frac{1}{2} U - 1 \right) = B_1 - \frac{2}{4!} B_2 U^2 + \frac{2}{6!} B_3 U^4 \cdots$$

$$= \frac{1}{6} \left[1 - \frac{1}{60} U^2 + \frac{1}{2520} U^4 \right.$$

$$\left. - \frac{1}{100,800} U^6 \cdots \right].$$

Inserting this into the expression for the integral, we obtain

$$\int_{x_0}^{x_1} f(x)\, dx = \frac{1}{2} h \left\{ (f_0 + f_1) - \frac{1}{6} h \left[(f_1' - f_0') - \frac{1}{60} h^2 (f_1''' - f_0''') \right. \right.$$
$$\left. \left. + \frac{1}{2520} h^4 (f_1^{(5)} - f_0^{(5)}) - \frac{1}{100,800} h^6 (f_1^{(7)} - f_0^{(7)}) \right] \right\} + O(h^9).$$

This formula as it stands does not have a wide range of application, since the higher derivatives of an integrand are seldom known. If the integral from x_0 to x_n is divided into n intervals of length h, however, and if the above formula is used on each of them, then on summation the so-called *Euler-Maclaurin formula* is obtained.

$$\int_{x_0}^{x_n} f(x)\, dx = h(f_0 + f_1 + \cdots + f_n) - \frac{h}{2} (f_0 + f_n)$$
$$- \frac{h^2}{12} (f_n' - f_0') + \frac{h^4}{720} (f_n''' - f_0''') - \cdots .$$

For the special case of $h = 1$ and $x_0 = 0$, this formula may be used to find an approximate value for a sum of terms f_k $(k = 0,1,2,\ldots,n)$:

$$\sum_{k=0}^{n} f_k = \int_{0}^{n} f(x)\, dx + \frac{1}{2} (f_0 + f_n) + \frac{1}{12} (f_n' - f_0')$$
$$- \frac{1}{720} (f_n''' - f_0''') + \cdots .$$

This expression is of major importance in the calculation of infinite sums $\Sigma_{k=0}^{\infty} f_k$. If the function $f(x)$ which has the values f_k for $x = k$ $(k = 0,1,2,\ldots)$ and all its derivatives approach zero when x approaches infinity, and if the integral $\int_0^\infty f(x)\, dx$ and the sum $\Sigma_0^\infty f_k$ both converge, then it is true that

$$\sum_{n=0}^{\infty} f_k = \int_{0}^{\infty} f(x)\, dx + \frac{1}{2} f_0 - \frac{1}{12} f_0' + \frac{1}{720} f_0'''$$
$$- \frac{1}{30,240} f_0^{(5)} + \frac{1}{1,209,600} f_0^{(7)} - \cdots .$$

In this way the original infinite series has been converted to a new infinite series which, however, often converges considerably more rapidly, so that it is only necessary to include a few terms.

Example 8-6. We have previously shown (p. 349) that

$$\sum_{n=1}^{\infty} \frac{1}{n^2} = \sum_{n=0}^{\infty} \frac{1}{(1+n)^2} = \frac{\pi^2}{6}.$$

We shall now use this to calculate π^2. We obtain

$$\pi^2 = 6 \int_0^{\infty} \frac{dx}{(1+x)^2} + \frac{6}{2} \cdot 1 - \frac{6}{12}(-2!) + \frac{6}{720}(-4!)$$

$$- \frac{6}{30,240}(-6!) + \frac{6}{1,209,600}(-8!) - \cdots$$

$$= 6 + 3 + 1 - \frac{1}{5} + \frac{1}{7} - \frac{1}{5} + \cdots.$$

This is a series of terms which apparently decrease more slowly than the original. It is therefore possible that the error one obtains using a finite number of terms from this expression may be large, even though it probably is smaller than that obtained using the original series, as the new series is an alternating one. That this is actually the case can be seen by adding the terms shown on the right side, whereby we obtain 9.743, while π^2 is 9.870. However, if five terms are taken in the original series, the result is

$$\pi^2 \approx 6[\tfrac{1}{1} + \tfrac{1}{4} + \tfrac{1}{9} + \tfrac{1}{16} + \tfrac{1}{25}] = 8.782.$$

There is thus an obvious advantage in using the Euler-Maclaurin formula. This can be shown with greater clarity when the sum is written

$$\sum_{1}^{\infty} \frac{1}{n^2} = \sum_{1}^{9} \frac{1}{n^2} + \sum_{0}^{\infty} \frac{1}{(10+n)^2}$$

and we only use the Euler-Maclaurin formula on the last term, while the first sum is calculated in the usual manner. This gives

$$\sum_1^9 \frac{1}{n^2} = \frac{1}{1} + \frac{1}{4} + \cdots + \frac{1}{81} = 1.5397677312$$

$$\sum_{n=0}^{\infty} \frac{1}{(10+n)^2} = \frac{1}{10} + \frac{1}{2}\frac{1}{100} + \frac{1}{12}\frac{2}{10^3} - \frac{1}{720}\frac{24}{10^5}$$

$$= \frac{0.1051663333}{1.6449340645},$$

and thus $\pi^2 = 6 \cdot 1.6449340645 = 9.869604387$.

By this trick the function used in the Euler-Maclaurin formula is reduced by a factor of one-hundredth at the initial point ($x = 0$), and its derivative is even many times smaller, so that the accuracy is increased enormously. The true value for π^2 is only 0.000000014 higher than the above result. □

Example 8-7. In the statistical mechanical theory for the diatomic molecule, the following sum arises:

$$f(\theta) = \sum_{n=0}^{\infty} (2n+1)e^{-n(n+1)\theta} \qquad (\theta > 0).$$

As a result of the above, we have that since

$$\int_0^{\infty} (2x+1)e^{-x(x+1)\theta}\, dx = \int_0^{\infty} e^{-x(x+1)\theta}\, d(x(x+1)) = \frac{1}{\theta},$$

we get

$$f(\theta) = \frac{1}{\theta} + \frac{1}{2} - \frac{1}{12}(2-\theta) + \frac{1}{720}(-12\theta + 12\theta^2 - \theta^3)$$

$$- \frac{1}{30{,}240}(120\theta^2 - 180\theta^3 + 30\theta^4 - \theta^5) + \cdots$$

$$= \frac{1}{\theta} + \frac{1}{3} + \frac{\theta}{15} + \frac{40\theta^2}{315} + \cdots. \qquad \square$$

Example 8-8. As a simple example of an application of the summation formula, we finally consider the infinite series

$$\sum_{n=0}^{\infty} e^{-nx} = 1 + \frac{1}{e^x} + \frac{1}{e^{2x}} + \cdots \qquad (x > 0).$$

Here we obtain

$$\sum_{n=0}^{\infty} e^{-nx} = \frac{1}{x} + \frac{1}{2} + \frac{1}{12} x - \frac{1}{720} x^3 + \cdots .$$

The original sum may be calculated exactly, as it is an infinite geometric series. Therefore we have

$$\sum_{n=0}^{\infty} (e^{-x})^n = \frac{1}{1 - e^{-x}}.$$

In order to see that this and the above expression are in agreement, the difference between the exact sum and $1/x$ is expanded in a Taylor series from $x = 0$, giving

$$\frac{1}{1 - e^{-x}} - \frac{1}{x} = \frac{1}{2} + \frac{1}{12} x - \frac{1}{720} x^3 \cdots . \qquad \square$$

Euler's Method

In the summation of slowly converging infinite series with alternating signs, a method attributed to Euler is sometimes useful. With this method, a new series, which in general converges more rapidly, is formed from the original.

Let the series be

$$S = \sum_{n=0}^{\infty} (-1)^n u_n = u_0 - u_1 + u_2 - u_3 + u_4 \cdots ,$$

and consider u_n as a function of n. We then have

$$S = (1 - E + E^2 - E^3 \cdots)u_0 \qquad (h = 1)$$
$$= \frac{1}{1 + E} u_0 = \frac{1}{2 + \Delta} u_0$$
$$= \tfrac{1}{2}(u_0 - \tfrac{1}{2} \Delta u_0 + \tfrac{1}{4}\Delta^2 u_0 - \tfrac{1}{8}\Delta^3 u_0 \cdots).$$

Table 8-8

u	Δu	$\Delta^2 u$	$\Delta^3 u$
0.00800			
	-0.00508		
0.00292		0.00353	
	-0.00155		-0.00260
0.00137		0.00093	
	-0.00062		
0.00075			

$$\frac{\pi^3}{32} \approx 1 - \frac{1}{3^3} + \frac{1}{2} \cdot 0.0080 + \frac{1}{4} \cdot 0.00508 + \frac{1}{8} \cdot 0.00353$$
$$+ \frac{1}{16} \cdot 0.00260 = 0.9688.$$

Example 8-9. A simple example of the above method is

$$\sum_{n=0}^{\infty} \frac{(-1)^n}{(2n+1)^3} = 1 - \frac{1}{3^3} + \frac{1}{5^3} - \frac{1}{7^3} \cdots ,$$

which has the sum $\pi^3/32$. The sum is written

$$1 - \frac{1}{3^3} + \left(\frac{1}{5^3} - \frac{1}{7^3} \cdots \right)$$

and the summation formula is applied to the part in parentheses. It is convenient to construct a table such as Table 8-8. The correct result to four decimal places is 0.9689.

In this example the accuracy could of course have been considerably increased by summing more than the two first terms without use of the summation formula. It is seen also that in this case Euler's method does not substantially reduce the labor involved in the calculation. □

Exercises

*1. Tabulate *Riemann's zeta function* $\zeta(x) = \sum_{n=1}^{\infty} n^{-x}$ for $x = 3, 4, 5,$ and 6 with the help of the Euler-Maclaurin formula. On page 349 it is shown that $\zeta(2) = \pi^2/6$. Do the calculated values give reason to expect that generally there is a similarly simple relationship between $\zeta(n)$ and π^n?

*2. Find, using Euler's method, the value of the infinite series

$$\sum_{n=0}^{\infty} (-1)^n \frac{1}{\sqrt{n+1}}.$$

Answers

1. $\zeta(3) = 1.20206; \zeta(4) = 1.08232; \zeta(5) = 1.03693; \zeta(6) = 1.01734.$ No, only for n even. For instance, $\pi^3/\zeta(3) \approx 25.8$.

2. 0.6049.

8-5. SOLUTION OF EQUATIONS

Exact Solution of Quadratic and Cubic Equations

The *quadratic equation* $ax^2 + bx + c = 0$ can be solved exactly, giving

$$x = \frac{-b \pm \sqrt{b^2 - 4ac}}{2a}.$$

When $4ac$ is small compared to b^2 ($4ac \ll b^2$), one root will be very much larger than the other, and the former root will be determined with a greater relative accuracy than the latter. Using the fact that the above expression for the roots is identical with

$$x = \frac{-2c}{b \pm \sqrt{b^2 - 4ac}},$$

the latter root can be determined with greater accuracy.

Example 8-10. $x^2 - 18x + 1 = 0.$ The standard method gives $9 \pm \sqrt{80}$, which using a standard table of square roots gives $\lambda_1 = 17.9443$, $\lambda_2 = 0.0557$. The second root is determined fairly inaccurately. This can be improved by setting $\lambda_2 = (17.9443)^{-1} = 0.055728$, or by initially using

$$\lambda_2 = \frac{-2 \cdot 1}{-18 - \sqrt{320}}. \qquad \square$$

The *cubic equation* $ax^3 + bx^2 + cx + d = 0$ can be reduced in many different ways. A new cubic equation in y which contains no quadratic term is obtained if we set $y = \beta[x + (b/3a)]$. Furthermore, β can be chosen so that the coefficient of y in the *reduced equation* becomes 0, 1 or -1. Thus every cubic equation can be converted to one of the three standard forms: $y^3 + K = 0$, $y^3 + y + K = 0$, or $y^3 - y + K = 0$. The solutions to these equations are tabulated as a function of K, in the case of the first simply in cube-root tables.

Another possibility is to choose β so that the equation for y is of the form $4y^3 \pm 3y - K = 0$ $(K \geq 0)$, and after this to substitute $y = \sinh u$ (if the sign for y is $+$), $y = \cosh u$ (if the sign for y is $-$ and $K > 1$), or $y = \cos u$ (if the sign for y is $-$ and $K \leq 1$). The equations then reduce to $\sinh 3u = K$, $\cosh 3u = K$, and $\cos 3u = K$, and the solutions to these can be found in tables of hyperbolic or trigonometric functions.

As soon as one (real) root $x = \alpha$ to the equation has been found, then division by $(x - \alpha)$ will give a quadratic equation which can be solved in an elementary way. This will often be the simplest procedure, especially when the other two roots are complex.

A fourth-degree equation may also be solved exactly, but the method of solution is of even less practical interest than the one for cubic equations.

Estimation of the Roots of Equations

The solutions of more complicated equations can often be found by approximation methods. Of these, the most useful type is the *iteration method* described in the next section. To be able to use these methods, it is necessary to know approximate values for the desired roots. If the equation is of the form $F(x) = 0$, they can be estimated by drawing the curve $y = F(x)$ and examining the positions of its zero points.

For polynomials it can be used to advantage in the tabulation of the function that for an nth-degree polynomial Δ^n is constant; i.e., if a sufficient number of values of the function are known to give $\Delta^n y$ at one point, then by adding this to $\Delta^{n-1}y$ at a point, $\Delta^{n-1}y$ at its neighboring point can be found, etc. In this way the polynomial can be built up from the nth difference known only at one point. This method will often be considerably faster than direct calculation. The method is especially useful for the equation $|A - \lambda E| = 0$, which is of the nth degree in λ if A and E are matrices of order n (see p. 75).

Example 8-11. $y = x^2 - 5x + 6$ passes through the points $(-1,12)$, $(0,6)$, $(1,2)$. From this we form a table (Fig. 8-1), where $- - -$ indicates how $\Delta^2 y(-1) = 2$ is found from the tabulated values, and $\rightarrow$ indicates how the table is built up from them. $\square$

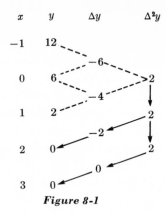

Figure 8-1

Example 8-12. In some equations it is simplest to estimate the position of the roots when the equation is written $F(x) = G(x)$. As an example we consider the equation $kx = \tanh x$, which occurs in the statistical mechanical theory for phase transitions.

A solution x_0 to this equation is desired as a function of the parameter k, or more correctly, $\tanh x_0$ is desired as a function of k.

If the two curves $y = kx$ and $y = \tanh x$ are graphed in the same coordinate system for different values of k, it is easy to estimate for which x-values the relationship $kx = \tanh x$ is valid, and in this way $\tanh x_0$ can be found as a function of k (Fig. 8-2). □

Iterative Processes. The Newton-Raphson Method

When for some equation $F(x) = 0$ an approximate value x_0 to the root x^* is known, then a better approximation x_1 can be found if the equation can be converted into the form $x = f(x)$ where $|f'(x)| \leq c < 1$ in the vicinity of $x = x^*$.

As an improved value of x we take $x_1 = f(x_0)$, and this value is again improved to $x_2 = f(x_1)$, etc.; thus

$$\left|x_n - x^*\right| = \left|f(x_{n-1}) - f(x^*)\right| = \left|f'(\xi)\right| \left|x_{n-1} - x^*\right|,$$

where the mean value theorem assures us that the last equality is satisfied for a value of ξ which lies between x_{n-1} and x^*. Furthermore, as a result of the assumption about $f'(x)$ in the vicinity of x^*, if x_0 belongs to this region, all the following approximations to x^* will also belong to the region, since

$$\left|x_n - x^*\right| \leq c\left|x_{n-1} - x^*\right| \leq c^n\left|x_0 - x^*\right|.$$

As the last expression approaches zero for $n \to \infty$, then the iterative process will converge.

Example 8-13. In pH calculations, equations arise such as

$$F(x) = 1.03x^4 + 0.78 \cdot 10^{-2} x^3 - 8.95 \cdot 10^{-5} = 0,$$

where x designates the hydrogen ion concentration. The equation is written

$$x = \left(\frac{8.95 \cdot 10^{-5}}{1.03x + 0.78 \cdot 10^{-2}} \right)^{1/3},$$

and a root is sought near $x_0 = 0.1$ $(|f'(x_0)| \sim \frac{1}{3})$. A few iterations give $x = 0.0949$. The calculations can easily be carried out using a slide rule. □

Iterative processes are often classified in the following way. Consider the equation $x_{n+1} = f(x_n)$, and assume that $x_n = x^* + \epsilon_n$. By a Taylor expansion we obtain

$$x^* + \epsilon_{n+1} = x_{n+1} = f(x_n) = f(x^* + \epsilon_n)$$
$$= f(x^*) + f'(x^*)\epsilon_n + \frac{1}{2!} f''(x^*)\epsilon_n^2 + \cdots,$$

or

$$\epsilon_{n+1} = f'(x^*)\epsilon_n + \frac{1}{2!} f''(x^*)\epsilon_n^2 + \cdots,$$

as $x^* = f(x^*)$, since x^* is the exact solution.

When $f'(x^*) \neq 0$, the iteration method is said to be of *first order*, and in this case it is seen that ϵ_{n+1} is of the same order of magnitude as ϵ_n. If $f'(x^*) = 0$, but $f''(x^*) \neq 0$, the process is said to be of the *second order*, etc. Unless it is possible to choose $f(x)$ so that $|f'(x^*)| \ll 1$, then generally an attempt should be made to find a second-order process. In principle, of course, a *third-order* process would be even

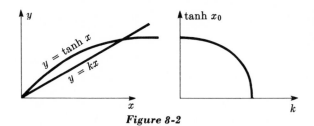

Figure 8-2

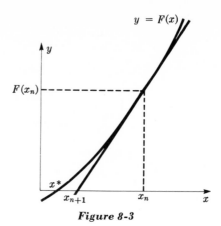

Figure 8-3

better, but as a rule it is only possible to achieve this with a very complicated expression for $f(x)$, and it is therefore of less interest in practical calculations.

An especially convenient rewriting of the equation $F(x) = 0$ to the form $x = f(x)$ is $x = x - F(x)/F'(x)$, which is used in the so-called *Newton-Raphson method*. When this is used in an iterative process, one sets

$$x_{n+1} = x_n - \frac{F(x_n)}{F'(x_n)}.$$

x_{n+1} is seen to be the abscissa to the intersection between the x-axis and the tangent to $y = F(x)$ at the point $(x_n, F(x_n))$ (Fig. 8-3).

The differential quotient of $f(x) = x - F(x)/F'(x)$ taken at the point x^* is

$$f'(x^*) = 1 - \frac{(F'(x^*))^2 - F(x^*)F''(x^*)}{(F'(x^*))^2} = \frac{F(x^*)F''(x^*)}{(F'(x^*))^2} = 0,$$

since $F(x^*) = 0$. The second derivative at $x = x^*$ is, however, generally $\neq 0$. Thus the process is of the second order.

A special case of this iteration process is Newton's method for finding square roots. This corresponds to solving the equation $F(x) = x^2 - a = 0$. We set

$$x_{n+1} = \tfrac{1}{2}\left(x_n + \frac{a}{x_n}\right).$$

x_n will then converge to $\sqrt{a}$ when $n \to \infty$, assuming that x_0 was chosen as a positive number.

Example 8-14. We want to determine $\sqrt{5}$ and choose $x_0 = 2$.

$$x_1 = \tfrac{1}{2}(2 + \tfrac{5}{2}) = 2.25,$$

$$x_2 = \tfrac{1}{2}\left(2.25 + \frac{5}{2.25}\right) = 2.2361, \text{ etc.} \qquad \square$$

Example 8-15. Systems of equations with several unknowns can also be solved by iteration. As an example we take

$$x^2 + y^2 - 2 = 0,$$
$$3xy - y^3 - 1 = 0.$$

When the two curves $x^2 + y^2 = 2$ and $x = (1 + y^3)/3y$ are graphed in the same coordinate system, they are seen to intersect at four points, which have coordinates (solution sets) which easily can be estimated.

Of the four possible solution sets we require the one for which $x \sim 0.8$ and $y \sim 1$. We set

$$x = \frac{y^2}{3} + \frac{1}{3y},$$
$$y = \sqrt{2 - x^2},$$
or generally
$$\begin{cases} x = f(x,y), \\ y = g(x,y), \end{cases}$$

and use $x_0 = 0.8$ and $y_0 = 1$. Then y_1 is obtained from x_0, x_1 from y_0, etc. A few iterations give $x = 0.755$ and $y = 1.196$. $\qquad \square$

Example 8-16. Even if a set of values satisfies the equations to a good approximation, it can still be well removed from the true values. The linear equations

$$6.9x - 4.7y = 9.1,$$
$$4.7x - 3.2y = 6.2,$$

for example, will be satisfied approximately by $x = -1.2$ and $y = -3.7$ (the left sides being 9.11 and 6.20). This is, however, far from the true solution $x = 2$, $y = 1$.

If one iteration is carried out starting from the values $x = -1.2$ and $y = -3.7$, then a considerable variation is obtained in (x,y). This shows that to control the validity of a solution which has been obtained by iteration, it is better to iterate once more rather than to substitute into the equations.

Geometrically the two linear equations correspond to nearly parallel lines, and it is therefore easy to understand that even a very poor approximation to the true solution still roughly satisfies the equations. $\qquad \square$

Exercises

*1. Find all the roots of the equation $x^3 - 3x + 1 = 0$ to three decimal places.

*2. Determine to four decimal places the area of the greatest rectangle that can be inscribed between the x-axis and the curve $y = \sin x$ $(0 \leq x \leq \pi)$.

*3. Show that the equation $e^x + \ln x = a$ has exactly one root for every a. Find an approximate value for this in the cases $a = 2$, $a = 3$, and $a \gg 1$.

4. Draw the graph of the equation $\ln(x + y) = xy$.

Answers

1. $-1.879; 0.347; 1.532$.
2. 1.1222.
3. $0.799; 1.074; \approx \ln a$.

8-6. NUMERICAL SOLUTION OF DIFFERENTIAL EQUATIONS

First-Order Equations

We have seen on page 394 how it is possible to find an approximate solution to a differential equation as a series expansion, and on page 400 we have seen that some boundary value problems can be solved by direct variation. These could be called *analytical approximation methods*, as the solutions are expressed by functions, not by a table of functional values.

We shall now consider the *numerical solution* of differential equations, i.e., methods where a table is constructed in a step-wise fashion for the desired function. However, only two methods will be illustrated by examples, and no estimate will be made of the error.

Let us consider a first-order differential equation (which does not need to be linear), e.g., $y' = f(x,y)$. Using the previously derived formula for the numerical calculation of y' (p. 461), we have

$$y_{n+1} = y_{n-1} + 2hy'_n.$$

This gives us a rough, but very simple, method for numerical solution of the equation. To use the method we must choose an h and know two values of y from which y' can be calculated with the help of the given differential equation. These values, as a rule, are obtained by an expansion of $y(x)$ in a Taylor series from the given initial point (x_0, y_0).

Example 8-17. We want to solve the equation $y' = x - y$ when it is given that the solution must pass through $(0,0)$. The exact solution is easily seen to be $y = x - 1 + e^{-x}$. We shall now solve the equation numerically with $h = 0.1$, using the above-mentioned method.

$y(0.1)$ is found with the help of a Taylor series,

$$y(0.1) = y(0) + y'(0) \cdot 0.1 + \tfrac{1}{2}y''(0) \cdot (0.1)^2.$$

The series expansion is cut off after the term with $(0.1)^2$, as the formula that we shall use has an error term proportional to h^3. Since $y(0) = 0$, we have, from the differential equation,

$$y'(0) = 0 - y(0) = 0,$$
$$y''(0) = 1 - y'(0) = 1,$$

and therefore

$$y(0.1) = 0 + 0 + \tfrac{1}{2} \cdot 1 \cdot (0.1)^2 = 0.005.$$

We now have

$$y'(0.1) = 0.1 - 0.005 = 0.095,$$

and therefore

$$y(0.2) = y(0) + 2 \cdot 0.1 \cdot 0.095 = 0.019.$$

For further calculation, it is most convenient to construct a table, Table 8-9. The exact value of y (0.5) can be calculated from the above exact expression for y, and to four decimal places is equal to 0.1065. □

The method used above to solve first-order equations is not very accurate, and if great accuracy is required, h must be made very small; i.e., a large number of steps must be used to reach, for example, $x = 0.5$ starting from $x = 0$. Rather than do this, other formulas are used. A commonly applied technique is to use one formula to calculate an approximate value for y_{n+1}, for example, the open integration formula (p. 463) used on y':

$$y_{n+1} \approx y_{n-3} + \frac{4h}{3}(2y'_n - y'_{n-1} + 2y'_{n-2}).$$

Table 8-9

x	y	y'
0	0.000	0.000
0.1	0.005	0.095
0.2	0.019	0.181
0.3	0.041	0.259
0.4	0.071	0.329
0.5	0.107	

To correct the values obtained, Simpson's rule is used, again on y':

$$y_{n+1} \approx y_{n-1} + \frac{h}{3}(y'_{n+1} + 4y'_n + y'_{n-1}).$$

With the help of the first formula, an approximate value for y_{n+1} is obtained, which on substitution into the differential equation gives an approximate value for y'_{n+1}. This is then used in the second formula to give a better value for y_{n+1}, which on substitution into the differential equation results in an improved value for y'_{n+1}. The last formula is used iteratively as many times as is necessary, until (y_{n+1}, y'_{n+1}) satisfies the second expression with the given (or previously calculated) values of y_n, y_{n-1}, and y'_{n-1}.

Second-Order Equations

In the case of linear second-order differential equations, it is in principle sufficient to consider the equations without y', as this term can always be eliminated if it originally is in the equation. Consider the equation

$$y'' + f(x)y' + g(x)y = h(x),$$

and set $y = z \exp\left[-\frac{1}{2}\int f(x)\, dx\right]$. Then for the determination of $z = z(x)$ we have

$$z'' + [g(x) - \tfrac{1}{2}f'(x) - \tfrac{1}{4}\{f(x)\}^2]z = h(x)\,\exp[\tfrac{1}{2}\int f(x)\, dx].$$

This is a convenient reduction, especially if $h(x) = 0$. In the cases where $h(x) \neq 0$, the right side may become numerically so large that it is difficult to carry out subsequent calculations.

For a second-order differential equation without first-order terms, where the equation now does not need to be linear, $y'' = f(x,y)$, we may now use the formula derived on page 469 for the relationship between D^2 and δ^2

$$\delta^2 y_n \cong h^2(y''_n + \tfrac{1}{12}\delta^2 y''_n).$$

Example 8-18. Solve numerically the differential equation $y'' = (x^2 - 1)y$ with initial conditions $y(0) = 1$ and $y'(0) = 0$. First we calculate a few values of y by expanding in a series as in the previous example. We have

$$y \cong 1 - \tfrac{1}{2}x^2 + \tfrac{1}{8}x^4$$

and therefore

$$y(0) \ \ = 1.00000, \qquad y''(0) \ \ = -1.00000,$$
$$y(0.1) = 0.99501, \qquad y''(0.1) = -0.98506,$$
$$y(0.2) = 0.98020, \qquad y''(0.2) = -0.94099.$$

Then, using the equation given above, the table of Fig. 8-4 is constructed. The numbers which are above the dashes are those which were determined by the Taylor series expansion and substitution into the differential equation. The procedure is now to estimate a trial value of $\delta^2 y''$ corresponding to an x-value which is larger by h than the largest x-value for which $\delta^2 y''$ is known. For this x-value, y'' is known and from this and the trial value for $\delta^2 y''$, $\delta^2 y$ is calculated from

$$\delta^2 y = h^2(y'' + \tfrac{1}{12}\delta^2 y'').$$

From $\delta^2 y$, we now calculate δy and y for x-values which are h larger than the values before them. From y and x, the value of y'' is calculated by substitution into the differential equation. Finally, from the y''-value a value is calculated for $\delta^2 y''$, and the original estimate of $\delta^2 y''$ can then be improved. If h is chosen to be reasonably small, then the term $\tfrac{1}{12}\delta^2 y''$ will be small compared to y'', so that it will seldom be necessary to recalculate. Even though the estimate for $\delta^2 y''$ was not estimated correctly it is sufficient to use the improved value of $\delta^2 y''$ in further calculations.

In Fig. 8-4 the arrows show how the calculations proceed and the arrow $-o\rightarrow$ shows that the calculation involved in this step uses an

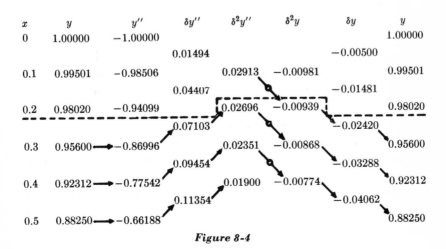

Figure 8-4

estimated value of $\delta^2 y''$. The values of $\delta^2 y''$ in the figure are not estimated values, but those obtained by calculating through once with the estimated values.

Comparison with the exact solution, which is $y = \exp(-x^2/2)$, shows the numerical solution to be correct to five figures. $\quad\square$

The method used above for the numerical solution of second-order differential equations which do not contain first-order derivatives is, in spite of its simplicity, a rather exact method, as the error in the formula used can be shown to be $O(h^6)$. It is thus in marked contrast to the method used for first-order equations, which primarily had an illustrative purpose.

Exercises

1. Integrate numerically the differential equation $dy/dx = -xy$, $y(0) = 1$, from $x = 0$ to $x = 1$ and compare with the exact solution.
2. The differential equation $xy'' + y' + xy = 0$ with initial values $y(0) = 1$, $y'(0) = 0$, has as a solution the Bessel function $J_0(x)$ discussed in Exercise 3, page 395. Integrate the differential equation numerically from $x = 0$ to $x = 1$, and compare with the tabulated values $J_0(0.5) = 0.9385$, $J_0(1) = 0.7652$.

8-7. NUMERICAL ANALYSIS OF EXPERIMENTAL DATA

Until now we have assumed that the initial numbers in the numerical analysis were *exact* (aside from rounding-off errors), but in practice numbers are quite often used which are the results of measurements and which therefore have *random errors*.

When a theory exists which gives the functional relationship between the measured values, then most often the best values are first determined—with the help of statistical methods—for the parameters in the expressions used to describe the experimental results. Further calculations are then made with these parameters. When there is no knowledge beforehand of what type of functional relationship there should be, it is possible in many ways to smooth the experimental results before calculations are carried out. Such a procedure is imperative when numerical differentiation is to be used.

The simplest smoothing which can be made (with equidistant measurements) is to replace the measured functional value with the average value of itself and the two or four closest measurements. The last method ("*smoothing by five*") has become especially popular. Although this method, without any doubt, gives a series of experimental results which are "smoother" than the original, and thus can be of practical help in certain cases, it must be said that its theoretical basis is exceedingly unsatisfactory. Moreover, it can be directly harmful in the case when the "true" relationship is not very "smooth," since the method then will tend to falsify the results.

Another method for smoothing the experimental data y_n ($n = 1, 2, . . .$) is to fit, for example, a polynomial $P(x)$ of third degree to seven points in a manner such that the sum

$$\sum_{n=1}^{7} (P(x_n) - y_n)^2$$

is as small as possible (*method of least squares*). This polynomial is used subsequently to calculate the corrected value of the central point of the original points.

The essential feature of the method, which we shall not describe more closely, is that the number of points used is greater than $n + 1$, where n is the degree of the polynomial. It is, therefore, generally not possible to have the polynomial go through all the points used.

With seven points and a third-degree polynomial, the smoothing formula can be shown to be

$$y_0^{(j)} = \tfrac{1}{21}(-2y_{-3} + 3y_{-2} + 6y_{-1} + 7y_0 + 6y_1 + 3y_2 - 2y_3),$$

where (j) stands for the index of the smoothed value. Formulas of this type have probably more justification than the above-mentioned smoothing method, but they are also considerably more time-consuming to work with.

In conclusion it must be said that for every smoothing process it is necessary to start by making an assumption about what is meant by a "smooth" curve, and normally this cannot be verified before the investigation has been concluded. Since no universal criterion for "smoothness" can be given, most smoothing processes should be taken with a grain of salt and should be accepted only if they give reasonable results in the situation under consideration.

Index